P9-CQX-262

SAMPLED-DATA CONTROL SYSTEMS

NEW YORK · JOHN WILEY & SONS, INC.

London · Chapman & Hall, Limited

SAMPLED-DATA CONTROL SYSTEMS

ELIAHU I. JURY

Associate Professor of Electrical Engineering

University of California, Berkeley

Library of Congress Catalog Card Number: 58-13462

Printed in the United States of America

In memory of my father Abraham

PREFACE

Interest in and vigorous analytical investigations of sampled-data control systems began in the early forties when, during the war, problems connected with radar control units were encountered. With the rapid advancements made in the field of digital computers during the last few years, more interest, attention, and activity were directed toward the incorporation of digital computers into control systems. The basic operation of such computers in the systems by necessity tends to reduce them to sampled-data control systems.

My work and activity with sampled-data control systems started in the late forties and early fifties when I was in residence at Columbia University in New York, engaged in writing a doctoral thesis in this field. My activity in this field has been intensified and extended considerably since moving to the University of California at Berkeley where I am presently associated.

The main objective of writing this manuscript was to develop a basic theory that can be applied to sampled-data systems, to other allied fields such as circuits, networks, and computers, and to the general field of system engineering. The theory developed and derived is extensively augmented with examples throughout the main body of the text. Although not many practical systems are investigated in detail, the material presented will undoubtedly help the practicing engineer solve problems that face him in the course of his work. The research engineer and the instructor who use this manuscript should find that the formulations of the various methods of analysis and synthesis presented in this text, together with problems composed for each chapter, stimulate an interest in applying the various techniques to fields other than sampled-data systems.

The main bulk of the material of this manuscript has been taught for the last two years as a two-semester graduate course in the field of control systems. The prerequisites for this course are undergraduate courses in feedback system theory and theory of complex functions or operational circuit analysis. At Berkeley this course may be taken simultaneously with a graduate course in feedback control systems or a graduate course in transform methods.

The material of the first semester in the sampled-data control systems course taught at Berkeley is oriented toward the analysis problem, and the first four chapters and Chapter 8 stress this objective. The second semester of this course is directed toward synthesis and Chapters 5, 6, and 7 are written mainly for this purpose. The material of Chapter 9, when time permits, is taught in either part of the course.

The theory discussed in the first chapter illustrates the various applications of the z-transform method, in particular, to sampled-data control systems. The theory is developed to such an extent that the reader will be able to pursue an investigation of sampled-data control systems in his work.

The modified z-transform method discussed in Chapter 2 is for the most part an extension of the z-transform to obtain the system behavior at all times. The use of digital computers in control systems requires obtaining information about the system behavior at all times, both for analysis and design purposes. To this end, this chapter covers the investigation of the mathematical model of such systems.

The third chapter continues the analysis in the z-plane through the use of the root-locus method.

The frequency response methods discussed in Chapter 4 will supplement the z-transform approach of the first three chapters. It gives another point of view of analysis with which the control engineer is very familiar.

Chapter 5 deals with the synthesis problem and, in particular, with the discrete-compensation method in which the discrete and digital processing units are synthesized to yield an acceptable performance.

The continuous-compensation method discussed in Chapter 6 is a useful procedure in the continuous network compensation of sampled-data control systems. Both frequency response and time domain methods are presented in this chapter.

Physical implementation and the various methods available for realizing the discrete compensators discussed in Chapter 5 are presented in detail in Chapter 7; this supplements the design procedures discussed in the preceding chapters.

Chapter 8 deals mainly with some applications of both the z-transform and the modified z-transform in the approximate analysis of continuous systems and in the operational solution of difference equations. This chapter can be studied and discussed after the material of the first two chapters has been digested.

Finally, the exact analysis and stability study of sampled-data systems with finite pulse width and the limitations of the z-transform are extensively studied in Chapter 9. The p-transform method is introduced and its applications to pulse-modulated feedback systems are discussed.

The development of this manuscript was aided considerably by the efforts of the students and research workers in this field at the University of California. To mention but a few of those whose efforts are gratefully appreciated, let me thank Messrs. G. Farmanfarma, F. W. Mullin, F. Semelka, W. Schroeder, and G. Lendaris. I also appreciate the generous support and interest of the Office of Scientific Research (Air Force) which at present maintains an active research program in this field at the University of California at Berkeley.

I am indebted to Professor A. M. Hopkin for his comments and suggestions after he taught this course at Berkeley and to Professor P. L. Morton and Professor John R. Whinnery (Chairman of the Department) for their stimulating interest and aid in making possible the writing of this manuscript. The work of Mrs. L. Gilmore in typing the manuscript is gratefully acknowledged.

It is evident that the material of this manuscript is based on the studies and research efforts of many workers in the field. In quoting other authors I have referred to their articles. Undoubtedly there are other authors who have contributed to some of the theory of the present material. I wish to offer my apology to those who have contributed to this field and whose names and publications are omitted either by ignorance or inadvertence.

In conclusion, it is hoped that this manuscript will assist the practicing engineer in industry in solving some of his problems, the research worker in a scientific institution in pursuing further research in the field, and the university professor in increasing his knowledge of the material in this field and in pursuing further studies and applications of some of the ideas presented.

ELIAHU I. JURY

September 1958
Berkeley, California

CONTENTS

CHAPTER 1

z-Transform Method of Analysis

1.0 Introduction

Sampled-data control systems are systems in which signals are applied at *equally spaced* intervals of time at one or more points; no information is received between two consecutive signals. This definition of sampled-data control systems can be extended to include systems in which signals are applied at random intervals of time; these can be classified as aperiodic sampled-data control systems.

At present, the features of sampled-data systems are playing an important role in the field of automatic control and communication systems. Economical use of equipment, rigid performance, and lightness of weight are important factors with which engineers must cope. Rapid advancements made in recent years in the development of digital computers and their use as components in feedback systems have increased the interest and importance of sampled-data systems. The advantages of the use of such digital feedback systems lies in their ability to handle a wide variety of compensation procedures; and if a high-speed computer is used, it can compute for a number of channels in a single equipment. In fact, we may consider continuous control systems as a special case of the general field of sampled-data control systems, that is, where T, the sampling period, approaches zero.

The applications of sampled-data control systems are wide and diversified and can be, on the whole, divided into two main categories:

A. Those systems in which information is available only in samples. These include the following:

1. Radar-tracking systems.
2. Data transmission link which is shared among several control systems.
3. Digital computers in control systems.

B. Those systems in which the sampling information is purposely introduced, although it is available at all times. This is one of the recent trends, the guiding principle being the maximum use of equipment combined with the minimum cost. Sampling information is purposely introduced:

1. When the error sampling system can be made extremely sensitive by not requiring it to drive a load continuously, for example, the galvanometer and chopper bar.
2. When the error computing system can be time-shared among several control problems, which makes for efficient use of the computer.
3. In the field of process control where more economical use of measuring devices of temperature, pressure, and flow can be realized.
4. In communication systems (time division networks) in which transmission plays an important role in modern devices and a high signal to noise ratio is a prime factor in their efficient use.
5. In control system design when, under certain conditions, a sampled-data control system with variable pulse width and variable sampling intervals behaves better than continuous systems. This is particularly true in compensations of systems having plants with transportation lag.
6. In a telemetering system, with which it is often preferable to use a single communication channel to transmit information about several independent variables. Under these conditions, it becomes necessary to assign the communication link to each variable for a duration of time in rotation. This can be achieved at the sending end by a sampler with pulse width h and period T. A similar synchronized sampler at the receiving end can then feed the received information to the correct data reducing devices.

To illustrate briefly the various applications of sampled-data systems, the following three examples are indicated.

Example 1. A Multichannel System for a Drift Stabilization System †

In this system, shown in Fig. 1.1, one stabilization amplifier is used to stabilize a group of d-c amplifiers with the aid of a sampler (commutator) which samples the error point voltage of each amplifier in turn.

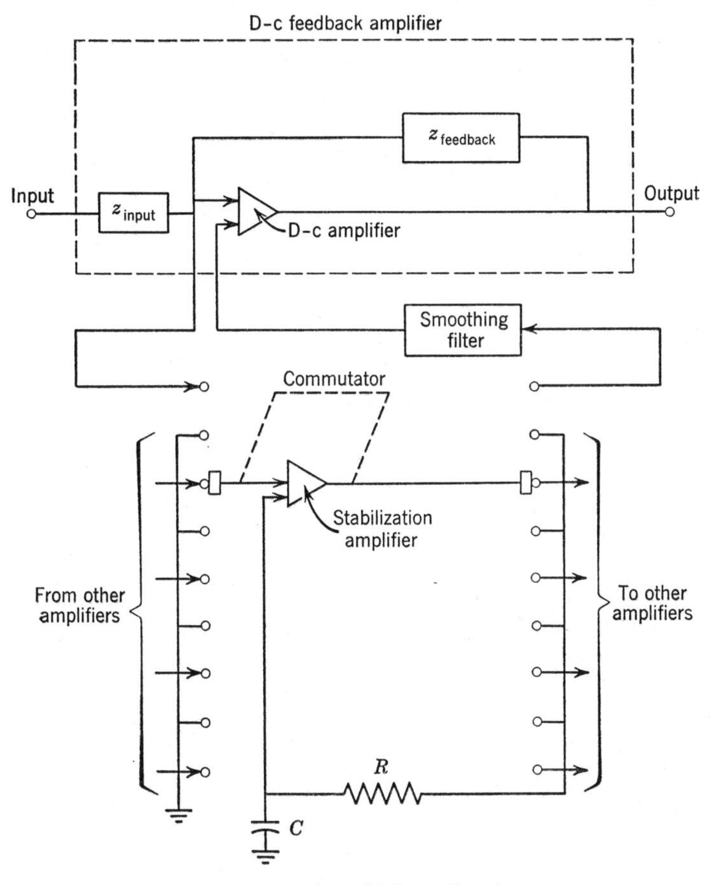

Figure 1.1 A multichannel system

Any voltage present at the error point of a particular amplifier is applied to the stabilization amplifier as a series of pulses occurring at the repetition rate of the commutator. These pulses are amplified and inverted in the stabilization amplifier, demodulated at the output section of the

† P. G. Pantazelos, "Sampled-Data Analysis of a Drift-Stabilization System," A.I.E.E. Conference Paper No. CP 56-961, presented in Chicago, Ill., October 1956.

commutator, and applied to the same amplifier through a smoothing filter. Thus, several d-c amplifiers can time-share one stabilization amplifier, a feature which reduces the cost, size, and maintenance of equipment.

EXAMPLE 2. RADAR TRACKING SYSTEM †

In this system the tracking of targets which appear on the screen through the use of a search radar is done automatically. This system, which is also called the "track-while-scan" system, must make estimates

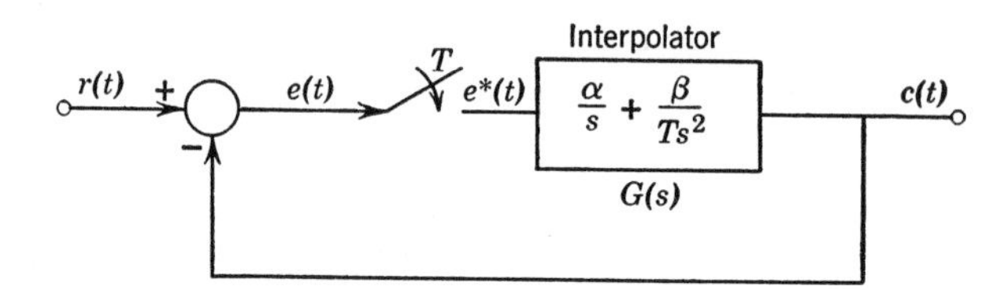

Figure 1.2 Sampled-data feedback system equivalent to track-while-scan system (Courtesy R.C.A. Laboratories, Princeton, N. J.)

of the present value of the signal from the past sampled values of the signal, the sampling being done at regular intervals.

A particular system is shown in Fig. 1.2. In this system, the target motion is a sequence of straight-line constant-velocity paths. The successive corrections in the computed position and velocity of the target are made proportional to the deviations of the computed from the measured positions at sampling instants. The constants of proportionality α and β, used in correcting the position and velocity of the estimated target course, completely characterize the performance of the indicated system.

EXAMPLE 3. TIME-SHARING SYSTEM

Time sharing of the transmission medium among as many messages as possible is an important economic factor in the cost of information transmission. One such method is Time Multiplexing, whereby each message is assigned a time duration h to a particular medium of transmission. For instance, a periodically sampled network, shown in Fig. 1.3, with finite pulse width is of special interest in the economic transmission of information.

The mathematical techniques and the theory developed in the work of sampled-data systems are widely used in the fields of mathematics,

† J. Sklansky, "Optimizing the Dynamic Parameters of a Track-While-Scan System," *R.C.A. Review*, Vol. 18, No. 2, 1957, pp. 163–185.

network theory, numerical analysis, computer analysis, in the synthesis of continuous control systems, and in the operational research field. For instance, the z-transform theory developed in recent years is extensively used in the solution of difference and differential equations, both linear and non-linear, in the solution of boundary problems, in time domain synthesis, in economic control systems, and in approximation problems of various subjects of engineering sciences. In the following chapters,

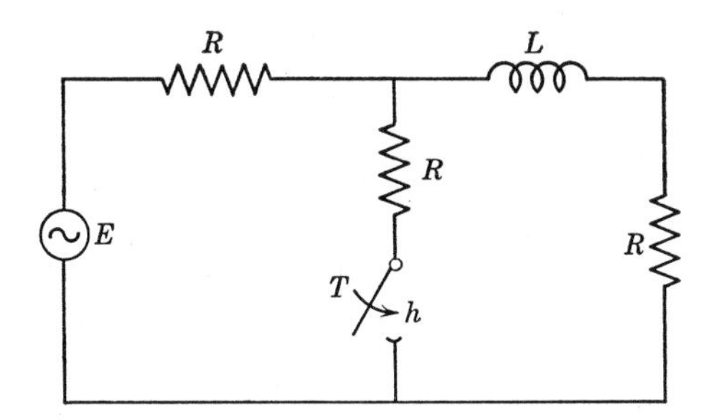

Figure 1.3 Periodically sampled network

the z-transform, the modified z-transform, and the p-transform theories are developed, extended, and studied with the main emphasis on sampled-data systems. However, their applications to other fields should not be overlooked.

1.1 Sampling Process Representation

From the definition of sampled-data systems, it is evident that the information received by the system is discrete and is admitted at equal intervals of time; thus mathematically this can be represented by a sampler that periodically samples the continuous information and delivers a set of pulses to the system. Figure 1.4 represents a linear sampled-data system, with the sampler assumed to be ideal (can break or make instantly with no sparking).

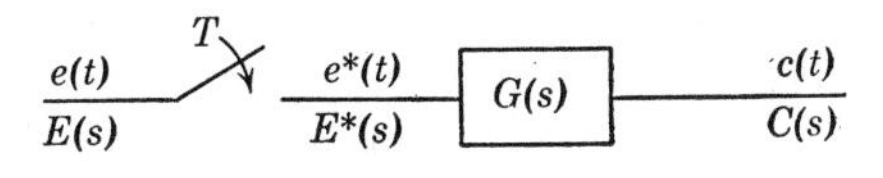

Figure 1.4 Sampled-data system

If the continuous input $e(t)$ is represented in Fig. 1.5*a*, then the sampler output $e_p(t)$ can be physically illustrated in Fig. 1.5*b*.

In some cases the time closure of the sampler h (or the information duration) is very small compared to the dominant time constant of the continuous system; then we can replace the set of finite pulses of Fig.

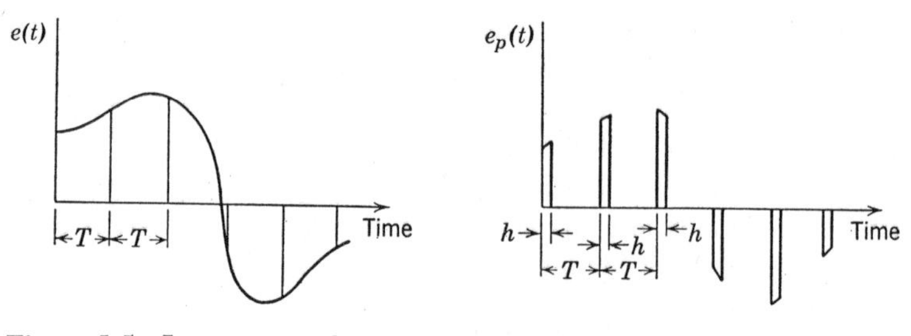

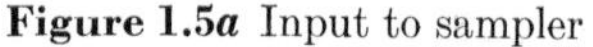

Figure 1.5*a* Input to sampler

Figure 1.5*b* Actual sampler output

1.5*b* by impulses of areas equal to the corresponding input function provided the gain of the system following the sampler is replaced by $K \times h$, where K is the gain of the continuous system.† It is evident that unless this condition is satisfied, the mathematical description of the sampler as producing a train of impulses, as shown in Fig. 1.6, is not an exact description. Also, for any finite value of h this description is approximate, as will be discussed in Chapter 9.

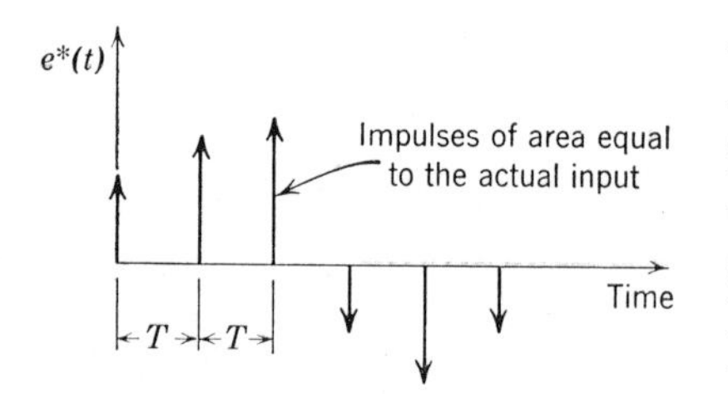

Figure 1.6 Mathematical sampler output

For the analysis the following assumptions are made.

1. The sampler is ideal (can break and make contact instantly).
2. The pulse duration h is very small compared to the dominant linear system time constants.
3. The sampler operation is periodic.
4. The sampled information is fed to a linear relaxed system.

These assumptions will be discussed in detail in later chapters, as well as the error involved in the system response based on these assumptions.

1.2 Mathematical Description of the Sampler

The basic equation which describes the sampler output as indicated in Fig. 1.4 is

$$e^*(t) = e(t) \times \delta_T(t) \tag{1.1}$$

† See Chapter 9 for an exact analysis of a system with finite pulse widths and for a discussion of the validity of this approximation.

where $\delta_T(t)$ represents a series of unit impulses (area equal to unity) equally spaced in time and extends from minus infinity to plus infinity, as shown in Fig. 1.7 and represented in the following expression:

$$\delta_T(t) = \sum_{n=-\infty}^{n=\infty} \delta(t - nT) \tag{1.1a}$$

Equation (1.1) can be visualized as amplitude modulation of the unit impulses by the input signal.

For inputs that have zero value for negative time, that is,

$$e(t) = 0, \qquad t < 0 \tag{1.2}$$

the unit impulses are described for positive values of time only; these values extend from zero to infinity.

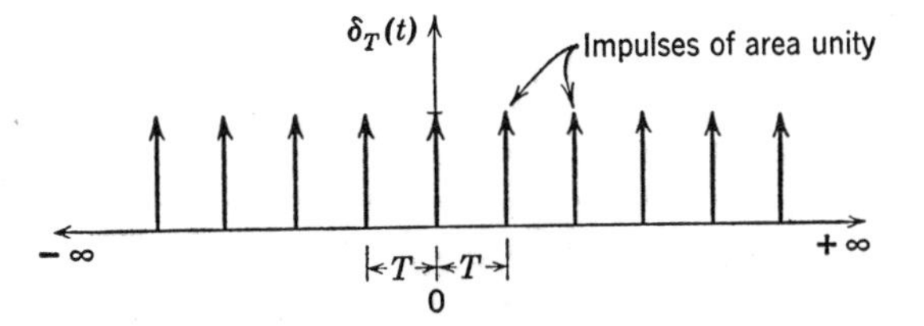

Figure 1.7 String of unit impulses

Since equation (1.1) is described as the multiplication of two time functions, starting from $t \geq 0$, the theory of real multiplication † can be applied to obtain the Laplace transform of $e^*(t)$. Thus,

$$\mathcal{L}[e^*(t)] = \mathcal{L}[e(t) \times \delta_T(t)] = \frac{1}{2\pi j}\int_{c-j\infty}^{c+j\infty} E(p)\frac{1}{1 - e^{-T(s-p)}}\,dp \tag{1.3}$$

where

$$E(s) = \mathcal{L}[e(t)] \tag{1.4}$$

$$\mathcal{L}[\delta_T(t)] = 1 + e^{-Ts} + e^{-2Ts} + e^{-3Ts} + \cdots = \frac{1}{1 - e^{-Ts}} \qquad \text{for } \left|e^{Ts}\right| < 1 \tag{1.5}$$

The contour of integration of equation (1.3) in the complex p-plane is along a path $c - j\infty$ to $c + j\infty$, which satisfies the following condition:

$$\sigma_{a2} < c < \sigma - \sigma_{a1}, \qquad \max(\sigma_{a1}, \sigma_{a2}, \sigma_{a1} + \sigma_{a2}) < \sigma \tag{1.6 ‡}$$

† M. F. Gardner and J. L. Barnes, *Transients in Linear Systems*, Vol. 1, John Wiley & Sons, New York, 1942.

‡ M. F. Gardner and J. L. Barnes, *Transients in Linear Systems*, Vol. 1, John Wiley & Sons, New York, 1942, pp. 275–278, where c = real part of p, σ_{a1} = abscissa of absolute convergence of $\delta_T(t)$, σ = real part of s, σ_{a2} = abscissa of absolute convergence of $e(t)$. In this case $\sigma_{a1} = 0$.

These conditions restrict the path of integration to an analytic strip which does not enclose or pass through the poles of the integrand in equation (1.3), as shown in Fig. 1.8.

In effecting the contour integration, we can enclose the poles of $1/(1 - e^{-Ts})$ in the right half of the p-plane, or alternately, we may enclose the left half-plane provided the integral is zero along the infinite semi-circle in both the right and left half-planes. This is assured, since

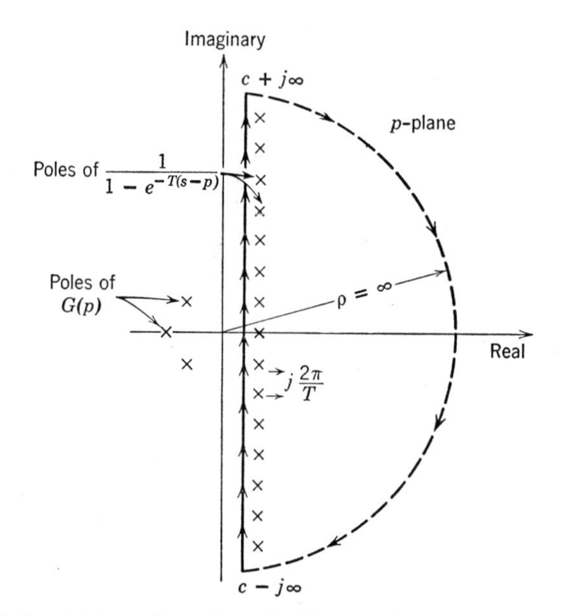

Figure 1.8 Paths of integrations along the line $c - j\infty$ to $c + j\infty$ and in the right half of the p-plane

it is assumed that the degree of the denominator of $E(s)$ in s is higher than that of the numerator by at least two.

From the above it follows that equation (1.3) can be written

$$E^*(s) = \mathcal{L}\,[e^*(t)] = \frac{1}{2\pi j}\int_{c-j\infty}^{c+j\infty} E(p)\,\frac{1}{1 - e^{-T(s-p)}}\,dp$$

$$= \frac{1}{2\pi j}\oint E(p)\,\frac{1}{1 - e^{-T(s-p)}}\,dp \tag{1.7}$$

It is noticed that the line integral is equivalent to integration in the negative sense along the closed integral in the right half of the plane, since the integral is zero along the infinite semi-circle. Thus we can apply Cauchy's integral formula which gives the value of the integral as follows:

$$\frac{1}{2\pi j}\oint E(p)\frac{1}{1-e^{-T(s-p)}}\,dp = -\text{ (Sum of the residues of the integrand at the poles enclosed)}$$

The poles of the integrand in the right half-plane are the zeros of the following function,

$$1 - e^{-T(s-p)} = 0 \tag{1.8}$$

which yields

$$-T(s-p) = 2\pi kj, \qquad -\infty < k < \infty,\ k = \text{integer} \tag{1.9}$$

or

$$p = s + \frac{2\pi kj}{T} \tag{1.10}$$

Thus,

$$E^*(s) = -\sum_{k=-\infty}^{k=\infty} \frac{E(p)}{\dfrac{d}{dp}[1-e^{-T(s-p)}]}\Bigg|_{p=s+\frac{2\pi kj}{T}} \tag{1.11}$$

Since

$$\frac{d}{dp}[1-e^{-T(s-p)}]_{p=s+\frac{2\pi kj}{T}} = -Te^{j2\pi k} \tag{1.12}$$

then

$$E^*(s) = \frac{1}{T}\sum_{k=-\infty}^{k=\infty} E\left(s + j\frac{2\pi k}{T}\right) \tag{1.13}$$

but $2\pi/T = \omega_r$ = sampling frequency; hence

$$E^*(s) = \frac{1}{T}\sum_{k=-\infty}^{k=\infty} E(s + jk\omega_r) \tag{1.14 †}$$

Equation (1.14) is of infinite series form, which indicates that the sampler produces high-frequency components.

† For the case $E(s)$ has a denominator one degree higher in s than the numerator or $e(0^+) \neq 0$, equation (1.14) should be modified to read

$$E^*(s) = \frac{1}{T}\sum_{k=-\infty}^{k=\infty} E(s + jk\omega_r) + \tfrac{1}{2}e(0^+) \tag{1.14a}$$

The addition of the term $\frac{1}{2}e(0^+)$ is brought about in view of the definition of the sampling process which assumes that at $t = 0$, $e = e(0^+)$. In the following discussions it is assumed that the error $e(0^+) = 0$ usually holds in sampled-data control systems. Equation (1.14) is further studied and utilized in Chapter 4.

Assume that the input signal has a frequency spectrum as shown in Fig. 1.9; then the sampler output contains the frequency spectrum of the input plus other frequencies † as shown in Fig. 1.10.

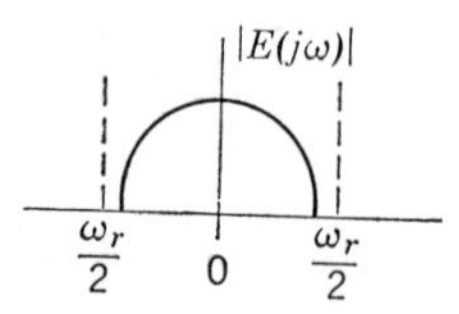

Figure 1.9 Frequency spectrum of sampler input

This case illustrates the sampler output when the highest-frequency component of the input is less than half the sampling frequency, that is,

$$\omega \leq \omega_r/2 \tag{1.15}$$

It is evident that for such a choice of the sampling frequency we can recover the input signal without any distortion, as shown in Fig. 1.10. In contrast, if the sampling frequency is less than twice the highest frequency of the input, the sampler output signal is a distorted picture of its input signal as shown in Figs. 1.11

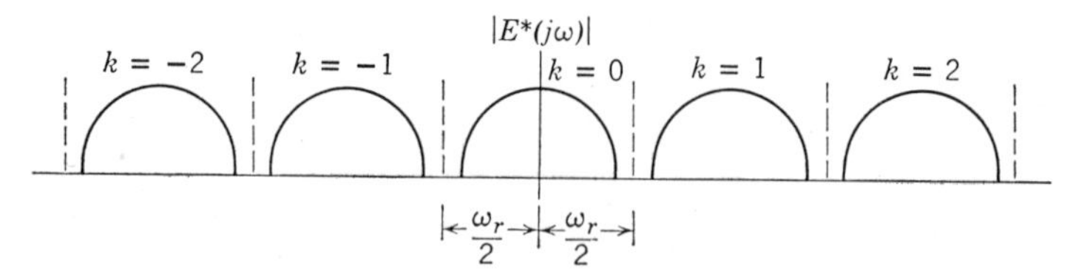

Figure 1.10 Frequency spectrum of sampler output

and 1.12. The corresponding sampler input-output relationships in time are shown in Figs. 1.13*a* through 1.14*b*.

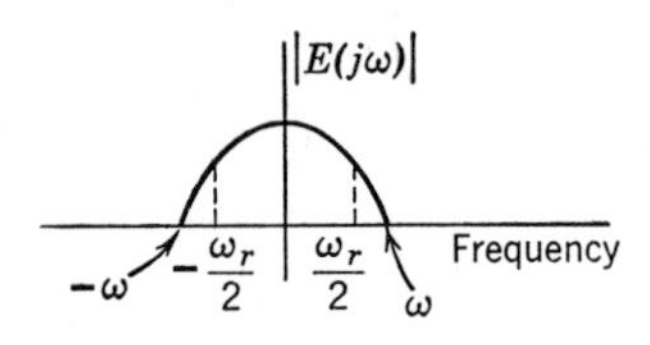

Figure 1.11 Frequency spectrum of sampler input for $\omega > \omega_r/2$

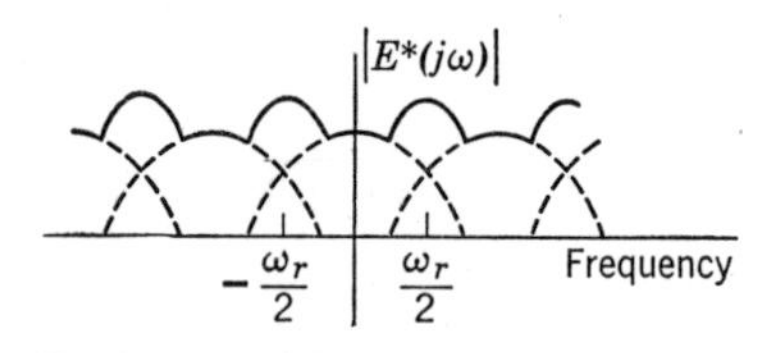

Figure 1.12 Frequency spectrum of sampler output for $\omega > \omega_r/2$

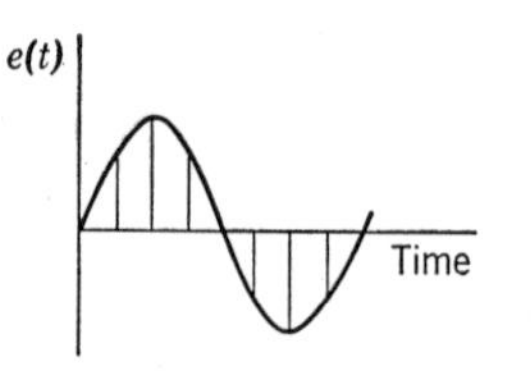

Figure 1.13*a* Input to sampler

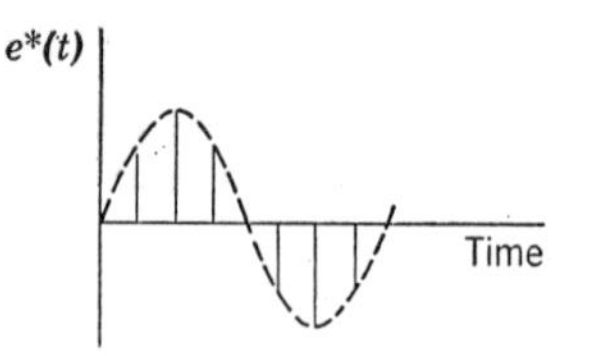

Figure 1.13*b* Output of sampler

† W. K. Linvill, "Sampled-Data Control Systems Studied through Comparison of Sampling with Amplitude Modulation," *Trans. A.I.E.E.*, Vol. 70, Pt. II, 1951, pp. 1779–1788.

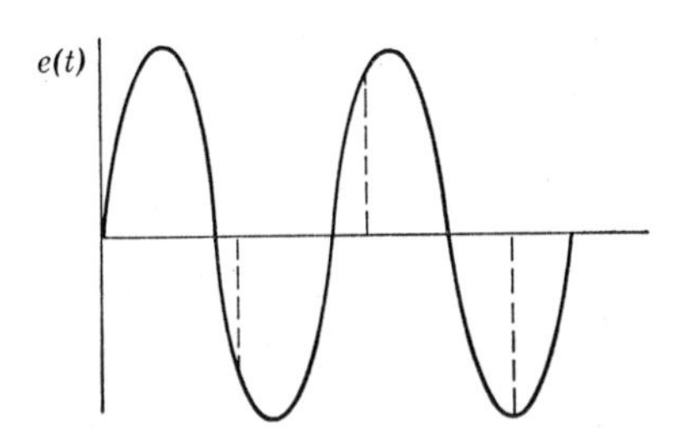

Figure 1.14a Input to sampler for $\omega > \omega_r/2$

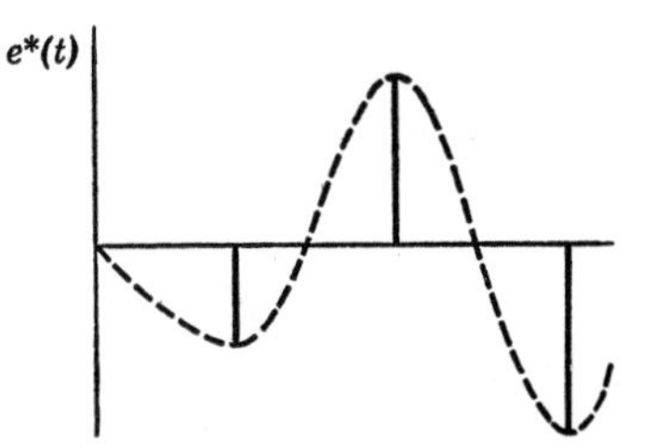

Figure 1.14b Output of sampler for $\omega > \omega_r/2$

1.3 Sampling Theorem

In order to recover the input signal, the sampling frequency should be larger than or equal to twice the highest-frequency component of the input signal.†

$$\omega_r \geq 2\omega \tag{1.16}$$

1.4 z-Transform Method

An alternate closed form of $E^*(s)$ can be derived by evaluating the integral of equation (1.3) differently. The integration along the line $c - j\infty$ to $c + j\infty$ is also equivalent to integration in a positive sense along the closed contour formed by that line and the infinite semi-circle in the left half-plane of complex frequency, p, as shown in Fig. 1.15. This is true because the integral vanishes along the infinite semi-circle, owing to the fact that the denominator of $E(s)$ is of a higher degree in s than the numerator.

$$\mathfrak{L}\,[e^*(t)] = \frac{1}{2\pi j}\int_{c-j\infty}^{c+j\infty} E(p)\,\frac{1}{1 - e^{-T(s-p)}}\,dp$$

$$= \frac{1}{2\pi j}\oint E(p)\,\frac{1}{1 - e^{-T(s-p)}}\,dp \tag{1.17}$$

The integral equals the sum of the residues of the function in the closed path. If $E(s) = A(s)/B(s)$, then $E^*(s)$ can be expressed in the following

† C. E. Shannon, "Communication in the Presence of Noise," *Proc. I.R.E.*, Vol. 37, No. 1, 1949, pp. 10–21.

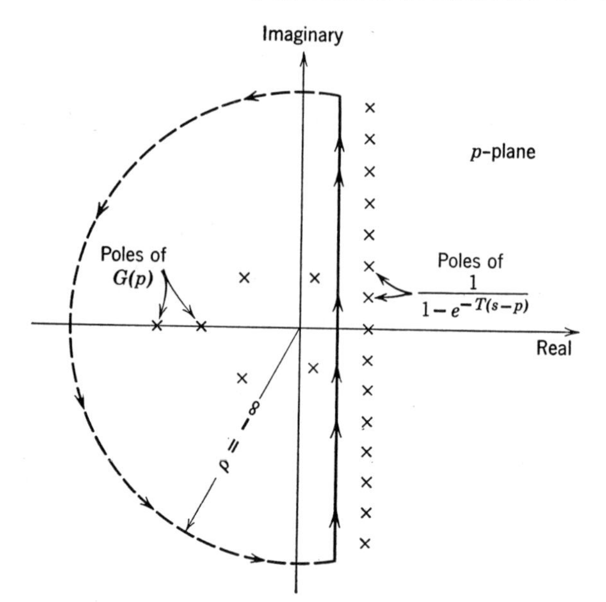

Figure 1.15 Path of integration in the left half of the p-plane

general form:

$$\mathcal{L}\,[e^*(t)] = \sum_{\text{Roots of } B(p)} \text{Residue of } \frac{A(p)}{B(p)} \frac{1}{1 - e^{Tp}e^{-Ts}} \tag{1.18}$$

where $B(p) = B(s)\,|_{s=p}$.

A special case arises when $B(s)$ has simple roots only. Then equation (1.18) can be expressed as follows:

$$E^*(s) = \sum_{n=1}^{N} \frac{A(s_n)}{B'(s_n)} \frac{1}{1 - e^{-T(s-s_n)}} \qquad (1.19)\dagger$$

where $s_1, s_2, s_3, \cdots, s_n$ are the simple roots of $B(s)$ and

$$B'(s_n) = \left.\frac{dB}{ds}\right|_{s=s_n} \tag{1.20}$$

Thus, it is noticed from equations (1.18) and (1.19) that the Laplace transform of the sampled input is a function of the variable e^{Ts} only, and that the other terms are constants. Therefore for notational convenience e^{Ts} is replaced ‡ by z, and the transform of the sampled input becomes a

† For the case $E(s)$ has a denominator only one degree higher in s than the numerator, or $e(0^+) \neq 0$, equation (1.19) can still be applied. This is justified in view of the definition of the sampling process which stipulates that at $t = 0$, $e = e(0^+)$.

‡ John M. Salzer, in his article entitled "Frequency Analysis of Digital Computers," *Proc. I.R.E.*, Vol. 42, No. 2, 1954, defines z as e^{-Ts}.

rational function of z, denoted as $E^*(z)$, † and is called the z-transform ‡ of $e(t)$ or $E(s)$ alternately; but strictly speaking, it is the Laplace transform of the sampled input $e^*(t)$.

Equation (1.1) can be differently written in terms of the input signal if we apply the Laplace transform to the following relation:

$$e^*(t) = e(t)\,\delta_T(t) = \sum_{n=0}^{\infty} e(nT)\,\delta(t - nT) \tag{1.21}$$

Effecting the $\mathfrak{L}$-transforms of these equations, we obtain the following relation:

$$\mathfrak{L}\,[e^*(t)] = \sum_{n=0}^{\infty} e(nT)\,e^{-nTs} = \left[\sum_{n=0}^{\infty} e(nT)\,z^{-n}\right]_{z=e^{Ts}} = E^*(z) \tag{1.22}$$

Thus equation (1.22) is another form of writing the z-transform of the input.

EXAMPLE 1

To illustrate the various relations derived previously assume

$$E(s) = \frac{1}{s(s+a)} \tag{1.23}$$

The z-transform of equation (1.23) can be obtained from relation (1.19) as follows:

$$A(s) = 1, \qquad B(s) = s(s+a), \qquad s_1 = 0, \qquad s_2 = -a \tag{1.24}$$

$$E^*(s) = \sum_{n=1}^{2} \frac{A(s_n)}{B'(s_n)} \frac{1}{1 - e^{-T(s-s_n)}}$$

$$= \left.\frac{1}{\dfrac{d}{ds}[s(s+a)]}\right|_{s_1=0} \frac{1}{1 - e^{-Ts}} + \left.\frac{1}{\dfrac{d}{ds}[s(s+a)]}\right|_{s_2=-a} \frac{1}{1 - e^{-T(s+a)}}$$

$$= \frac{1}{a}\left(\frac{z}{z-1} - \frac{z}{z - e^{-aT}}\right) = \left[\frac{1}{a}\,z\,\frac{(1 - e^{-aT})}{(z - e^{-aT})} \times \frac{1}{z-1}\right]_{z=e^{Ts}} \tag{1.25}$$

† It is to be noted that $E^*(z)$ is $E^*(s)$ with e^{sT} replaced by z. Or, strictly, the notation should be $E^*(s) = E^*(1/T \ln z)$. In some publications $E^*(z)$ appears as $E(z)$; however, to associate the star with the sampling process, the former is used throughout the text.

‡ J. R. Ragazzini and L. A. Zadeh, "Analysis of Sampled-Data Systems," *Trans. A.I.E.E.*, Vol. 71, Pt. II, 1952, pp. 225–234.

It is noticed that the above equation is a function of z and can be denoted as $E^*(z)$. Similarly from equation (1.22) we can write,

$$\mathcal{L}\,[e^*(t)] = \sum_{n=0}^{\infty} e(nT)\, e^{-nTs} \tag{1.26}$$

In this example,

$$e(nT) = \mathcal{L}^{-1}\,[E(s)]\big|_{t=nT} = \frac{1}{a}\,(1 - e^{-at})\big|_{t=nT} = \frac{1}{a} - \frac{e^{-anT}}{a} \tag{1.27}$$

Thus,

$$E^*(z) = \sum_{n=0}^{\infty}\left(\frac{1}{a} - \frac{e^{-anT}}{a}\right) z^{-n} = \frac{1}{a}\,\frac{z}{z-1} - \frac{1}{a}\,\frac{z}{z - e^{-aT}}$$

$$= \frac{1}{a}\,z\left(\frac{1 - e^{-aT}}{z - e^{-aT}}\right) \times \frac{1}{z-1} \tag{1.28}$$

To show the equivalence to the form of $E^*(s)$ given in equation (1.14), expand the following function in partial fractions as follows:

$$\frac{1}{a}\,\frac{1}{1 - e^{-Ts}} - \frac{1}{a}\,\frac{1}{1 - e^{-T(s+a)}} = \frac{k_1}{s} + \frac{k_2}{s + j\omega_r} + \frac{k'_2}{s - j\omega_r} + \cdots + \frac{1}{2a}$$

$$- \left[\frac{k_a}{s+a} + \frac{k_b}{(s+a) + j\omega_r} + \frac{k'_b}{(s+a) - j\omega_r}\right.$$

$$\left. + \frac{k_c}{(s+a) + 2j\omega_r} + \frac{k'_c}{(s+a) - 2j\omega_r} + \cdots + \frac{1}{2a}\right] \tag{1.29}$$

where $\omega_r = 2\pi/T$. The coefficients $k_1, k_2 \cdots k_a, k_b \cdots$ can be obtained in the following manner:

$$k_1 = \frac{1}{a}\,\frac{1}{\dfrac{d}{ds}(1 - e^{-Ts})}\Bigg|_{s=0} = \frac{-1}{aT} \tag{1.30}$$

$$k_2 = \frac{1}{a}\,\frac{1}{\dfrac{d}{ds}(1 - e^{-Ts})}\Bigg|_{s=0+j\omega_r} = \frac{-1}{a}\,\frac{1}{T} \tag{1.31}$$

$\vdots$

Similarly,

$$k_a = \frac{1}{a}\,\frac{1}{\dfrac{d}{ds}[1 - e^{-T(s+a)}]}\Bigg|_{s=-a} = \frac{-1}{aT} \tag{1.32}$$

$$k_b = \frac{1}{a} \frac{1}{\frac{d}{ds}[1 - e^{-T(s+a)}]}\Bigg|_{s=-a+j\omega r} = \frac{-1}{aT} \tag{1.33}$$

$\vdots$

Therefore equation (1.29) can be written as

$$\frac{1}{a}\left(\frac{z}{z-1} - \frac{z}{z-e^{-aT}}\right) = \frac{1}{aT}\left[\left(\frac{1}{s} - \frac{1}{s+a}\right) + \left(\frac{1}{s+j\omega_r} - \frac{1}{s+a+j\omega_r}\right)\right.$$

$$\left. + \left(\frac{1}{s-j\omega_r} - \frac{1}{s+a-j\omega_r}\right) + \cdots\right.$$

$$= \frac{1}{aT}\left[\frac{a}{s(s+a)} + \frac{a}{(s+j\omega_r)(s+a+j\omega_r)}\right.$$

$$\left. + \frac{a}{(s-j\omega_r)(s+a-j\omega_r)} + \cdots\right]$$

$$= \frac{1}{T}\sum_{k=-\infty}^{k=\infty} E(s+jk\omega_r) \tag{1.34}$$

Thus it is shown that the relations derived in equations (1.25), (1.28), and (1.34) are identical and yield the same result for the z-transform of $E(s)$.

Example 2

In some cases $B(s)$ in equation (1.18) has multiple roots of order k; to obtain the corresponding $E^*(z)$, find first the z-transform of this function:

$$E_1(s) = \frac{1}{(s+a)^2} = -\frac{\partial}{\partial a}\frac{1}{s+a} \tag{1.35}$$

which yields

$$E_1{}^*(z) = \mathfrak{z}\left[\frac{1}{(s+a)^2}\right] = -\frac{\partial}{\partial a}\mathfrak{z}\left(\frac{1}{s+a}\right) \tag{1.36}$$

The notation $\mathfrak{z}$ indicates the z-transform of the function which it prefixes. Similarly, if

$$E(s) = \frac{1}{(s+a)^k} \tag{1.37}$$

then

$$\mathfrak{z}\,[E(s)] = E^*(z) = (-1)^{k-1}\frac{1}{k-1!}\frac{\partial^{k-1}}{\partial_a^{k-1}}\frac{z}{z-e^{-aT}} \tag{1.38}$$

and if

$$E(s) = \frac{1}{s^k}, \qquad k = \text{positive integer} \tag{1.39}$$

$$E^*(z) = (-1)^{k-1}\frac{1}{k-1!}\lim_{a\to 0}\frac{\partial^{k-1}}{\partial_a^{k-1}}\frac{z}{z-e^{-aT}}$$

Thus, in general, the following theorem holds:

$$\text{If} \quad E_1(s) = \frac{\partial}{\partial a}E(as), \quad \text{then} \quad \mathfrak{z}\,[E_1(s)] = \frac{\partial}{\partial a}\mathfrak{z}\,[E(as)] \tag{1.40}$$

1.5 Sampled-Data System Transfer Function

The output of the linear system shown in Fig. 1.16 is a continuous function of time. However, for simplicity of analysis, it is assumed that

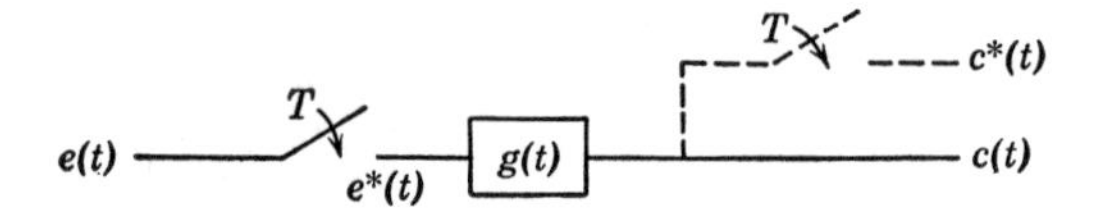

Figure 1.16 A typical linear sampled-data system

a fictitious sampler is introduced at the output synchronized with the input sampler for obtaining the sampled output. This restriction on obtaining the response only at the sampling instants will be relaxed in the discussion of the modified z-transform method.

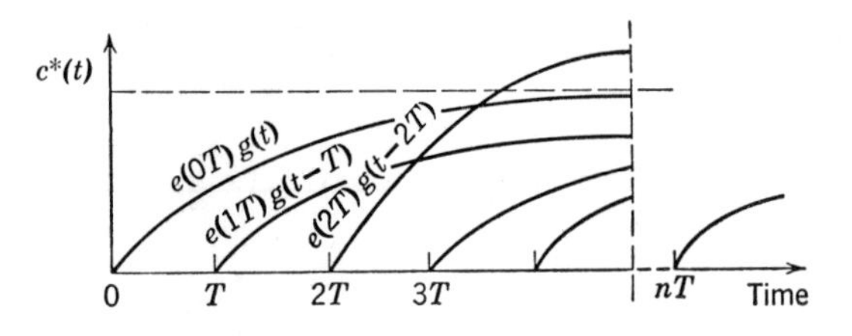

Figure 1.17 A typical output of the system in Fig. 1.16

Since the network or the system is linear, the sampled output can be obtained using the superposition series in the following form. Assuming that the system's impulsive response is as shown in Fig. 1.17, the output is obtained at any sampled instant, $t = nT$, by adding the impulsive responses for all time from zero to the instant $t = nT$. That is,

$$c(nT) = e(0T)\,g(nT) + e(1T)\,g(n-1)T + e(2T)\,g(n-2)T$$

$$+\cdots e(mT)\,g(n-m)T + \cdots e(nT)\,g(0T) = \sum_{m=0}^{n} e(mT)\,g(n-m)T \tag{1.41}$$

Since

$$g(n-m)T = 0, \qquad \text{from } m > n \tag{1.42}$$

thus

$$c^*(t) = \sum_{n=0}^{\infty} c(nT)\,\delta(t-nT) = \sum_{n=0}^{\infty}\left[\sum_{m=0}^{\infty} e(mT)\,g(n-m)T\right]\delta(t-nT) \tag{1.43}$$

By interchanging the summation signs, we obtain

$$c^*(t) = \sum_{m=0}^{\infty} e(mT) \sum_{n=0}^{\infty} g(n-m)T\,\delta(t-nT) \tag{1.44}$$

Taking the Laplace transform of equation (1.44) and putting $k = n - m$, we obtain

$$\mathcal{L}\,[c^*(t)] = \sum_{m=0}^{\infty} e(mT) \sum_{k=-m}^{k=\infty} g(kT)\,e^{-mTs}e^{-kTs} \tag{1.45}$$

But

$$g(kT) = 0, \qquad \text{for } k \text{ negative}$$

Thus

$$\mathcal{L}\,[c^*(t)] = \sum_{m=0}^{\infty} e(mT)e^{-mTs} \sum_{k=0}^{\infty} g(kT)\,e^{-kTs} \tag{1.46}$$

From the form of the z-transform in equation (1.46), the following relation is obtained:

$$\mathcal{L}\,[c^*(t)] = C^*(z) = E^*(z) \times G^*(z) \tag{1.47}$$

or

$$G^*(z) = \frac{C^*(z)}{E^*(z)} \tag{1.48}$$

Therefore, for a sampled-data system a transfer function $G^*(z)$ is obtained which relates the z-transform of the output to the z-transform of the input; it is given by the following expression:

$$G^*(z) = \mathcal{L}\,[g(t) \times \delta_T(t)] = \left[\sum_{n=1}^{N} \frac{A(s_n)}{B'(s_n)} \frac{1}{1 - e^{-T(s-s_n)}}\right]_{z=e^{Ts}} \tag{1.49†}$$

† It should be noted that z is substituted for e^{Ts} throughout this text.

where

$$\mathcal{L}\,[g(t)] = G(s) = \frac{A(s)}{B(s)} \tag{1.50}$$

$$B'(s_n) = \left.\frac{dB}{ds}\right|_{s \to s_n}, \qquad s_1, s_2, \cdots, s_n \text{ are the simple roots of } B(s)$$

and Fig. 1.18 presents the z-transfer function.

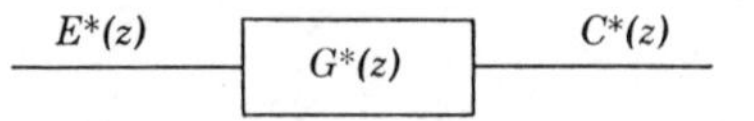

Figure 1.18 Mathematical representation of a sampled-data system

Alternately equation (1.48) can be found from the Laplace transform of equation (1.51).

$$C(s) = E^*(e^{sT}) \times G(s) \tag{1.51}$$

Applying the z-transform to equation (1.51), we obtain

$$C^*(z) = E^*(z) \times G^*(z) \tag{1.51a}$$

Physically, applying the z-transform to equation (1.51) means that the output is sampled as indicated in Fig. 1.16. We can also obtain the transform of the sampled output using relation (1.14) in the following form:

$$C^*(s) = \frac{1}{T} \sum_{k=-\infty}^{k=\infty} C(s + jk\omega_r) = \frac{1}{T} \sum_{k=-\infty}^{k=\infty} E^*(s + jk\omega_r)\, G(s + jk\omega_r) \tag{1.52}$$

Since $E^*(s + jk\omega_r)$ is periodic in $jk\omega_r$, it is equal to $E^*(s)$. Therefore, equation (1.52) becomes

$$C^*(s) = E^*(s) \times \frac{1}{T} \sum_{k=-\infty}^{k=\infty} G(s + jk\omega_r) \tag{1.53}$$

1.6 z-Transform Algebra

From the basic relation obtained in equation (1.48), we can find the transfer function of any linear system, open loop or closed loop. The transfer function of the basic configurations is obtained in this section, and a complete list of z-transform configurations is given in Table 2.2 (page 112). To indicate how to obtain the system transfer function, the following cases are discussed:

(*a*)

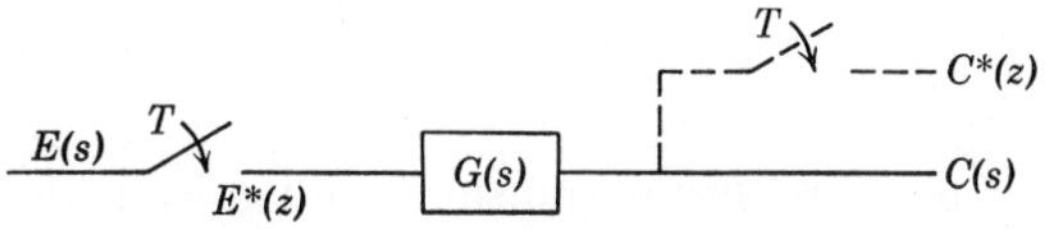

Figure 1.19 A sampled-data system

$$C^*(z) = E^*(z) \times G^*(z) \tag{1.54}$$

(*b*)

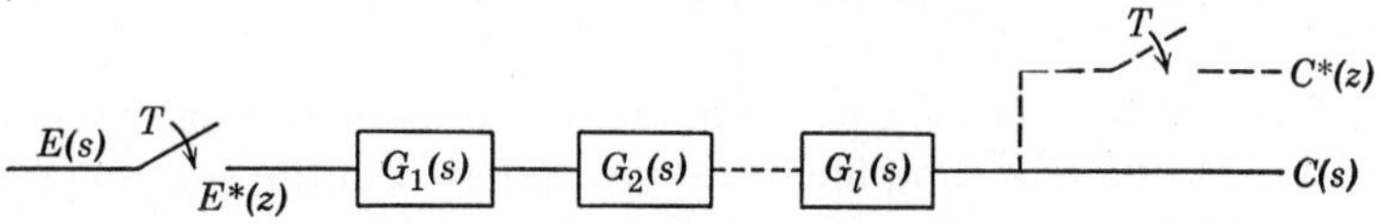

Figure 1.20 A sampled-data system with cascaded components

$$C^*(z) = E^*(z) \times G_1G_2 \cdots G_l{}^*(z)$$

where $G_1G_2 \cdots G_l{}^*(z) = \mathfrak{Z}\,[G_1(s) \times G_2(s) \times G_3(s) \times \cdots \times G_l(s)]$.

(*c*)

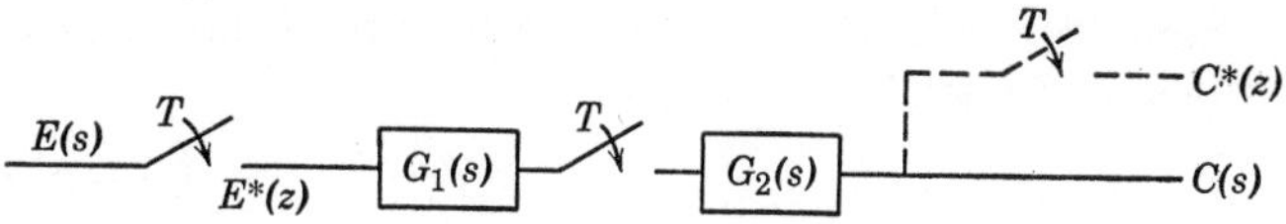

Figure 1.21 A sampled-data system with synchronized samplers

$$C^*(z) = E^*(z) \times G_1{}^*(z) \times G_2{}^*(z) \tag{1.55}$$

(*d*)

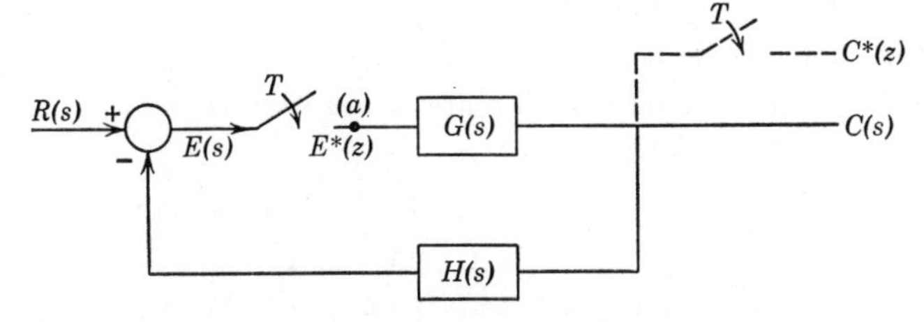

Figure 1.22 A sampled-data feedback control system

At point (*a*) the following relation exists:

$$E^*(z) = R^*(z) - E^*(z)\,GH^*(z) \tag{1.56}$$

And the z-transform of the output $C^*(z)$ is given by

$$C^*(z) = E^*(z) \times G^*(z) \tag{1.57}$$

Substituting $E^*(z)$ from relation (1.56) in $C^*(z)$, we obtain the transfer function of the feedback system:

$$C^*(z) = R^*(z) \frac{G^*(z)}{1 + HG^*(z)} \tag{1.58}$$

Similarly, we may obtain the transfer function in the form of z-transforms through the basic relations obtained in (*a*), (*b*), and (*c*).

1.7 Multiple Samplers with Different Periods

A multiple-sampler system is one with two or more pulsed elements operating at different sampling rates incorporated in the control system. In general, the sampling rates of the pulsed elements are not multiple integers of each other. However, there are digital controllers in which the output samples the information at a multiple rate of the input. Referred to as a multirate † controller, it can be easily analyzed from the general case discussed in this section.

In Fig. 1.23, a two-sampler system is shown; although the following analysis is applied to only two samplers, the procedure can be easily extended to general sampler systems.

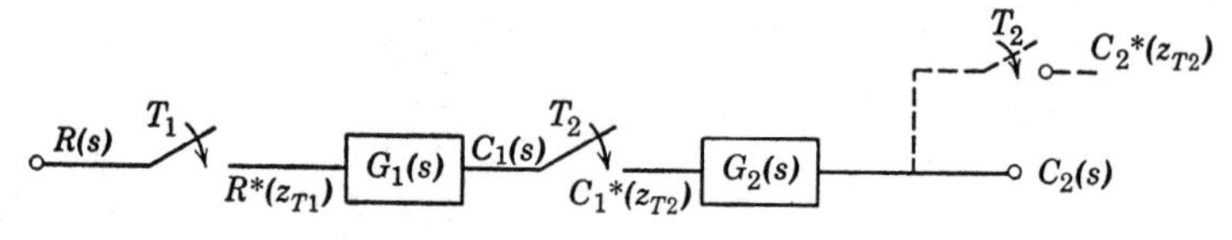

Figure 1.23 Two-sampler system

Since T_2 is not a multiple integer of T_1, we can always express T_2 in terms of T_1 if two integers b and q are found such that ‡

$$\frac{T_1}{T_2} = \frac{b}{q}, \qquad b, q = 1, 2, 3\text{—positive integers} \tag{1.59}$$

Obviously, such integers can always be found to any desired degree of accuracy to satisfy equation (1.59).

From Fig. 1.23, $C_1(s)$ can be expressed as follows:

$$C_1(s) = [R^*(z_{T1}) \times G_1(s)]_{z_{T1}=e^{T_1 s}} \tag{1.60}$$

† G. M. Kranc, "Compensation of an Error-Sampled System by a Multi-rate Controller," *Trans. A.I.E.E.*, Vol. 76, Pt. II, 1957, pp. 149–154.

‡ G. Farmanfarma, "Analysis of Multiple-Sampler Systems with Finite Pulse Width (Open Loop)," *A.I.E.E., Applications and Industry,* March 1958, pp. 20–28.

Since $R^*(z_{T1})$, the z-transform of the input $R(s)$ with respect to the period T_1, is a rational function of $e^{T_1 s}$, a typical term of $R^*(z_{T1})$ can be written as

$$R^*(e^{T_1 s}) = \frac{A}{1 - e^{-T_1(s-s_n)}} \tag{1.61}$$

where A is a constant and s_n is a typical root of $B(s)$ as expressed in equation (1.19). Thus, equation (1.60) can be rewritten as

$$C_1(s) = \frac{A}{1 - e^{-T_1(s-s_n)}} \times G_1(s) \tag{1.62}$$

which is equal to

$$C_1(s) = AG_1(s) \sum_{i=0,1,2,3}^{\infty} e^{-iT_1(s-s_n)} \tag{1.63}$$

By substituting equation (1.59) in equation (1.63), we can express the output $C_1(s)$ in terms of T_2:

$$C_1(s) = AG_1(s) \sum_{i=0}^{\infty} e^{-i(b/q)T_2(s-s_n)} \tag{1.64}$$

Equation (1.64) can be expanded, factored, and written as

$$C_1(s) = AG_1(s) \left\{ 1 + [1 + e^{-bT_2(s-s_n)} + e^{-2bT_2(s-s_n)} + \cdots] \times \sum_{i=1}^{q} e^{-(ib/q)T_2(s-s_n)} \right\} \tag{1.65}$$

which may also be written as

$$C_1(s) = \frac{AG_1(s)[1 + \sum_{i=1}^{q-1} e^{-i(b/q)T_2(s-s_n)}]}{1 - e^{-bT_2(s-s_n)}} \tag{1.66}$$

The output of the second sampler is the z-transform of equation (1.66) with respect to the period T_2; thus,

$$C_1^*(z_{T2}) = \mathfrak{z}_{T2}[C_1(s)] = \{\mathfrak{z}_{T2}[AG_1(s)]\} \times \frac{1 + \sum_{i=1}^{q-1} e^{-i(b/q)T_2(s-s_n)}}{1 - e^{-bT_2(s-s_n)}} \tag{1.67}$$

and the output $C_2(s)$ is

$$C_2(s) = C_1^*(e^{T_2 s}) \times G_2(s) \tag{1.68}$$

or its z-transform

$$C_2^*(z_{T2}) = C_1^*(z_{T2}) \times G_2^*(z_{T2}) \tag{1.69}†$$

where $G_2^*(z_{T2})$ is the z-transform of $G_2(s)$ with respect to the period T_2.

This procedure can be readily extended to the general case of multiple samplers. For instance, if the output of Fig. 1.23 is sampled with the period T_3, we can express the system function in terms of T_3, for it is always possible to express the ratio of T_2 to T_3 as follows:

$$\frac{T_2}{T_3} = \frac{b_1}{q_1}, \qquad \text{where } b_1, q_1 \text{ are positive integers} \tag{1.70}$$

1.8 Special Cases

a. *Multirate Systems*

In such systems T_2 is a submultiple integer of T_1; thus,

$$\frac{T_1}{T_2} = n = \frac{b}{q}, \qquad \text{where } n \text{ is an integer larger than unity.}$$

We substitute for $b/q = n$ in expression (1.64) to obtain

$$C_1(s) = AG_1(s) \sum_{i=0}^{\infty} e^{-inT_2(s-s_n)} \tag{1.71}$$

or

$$C_1(s) = AG_1(s) \times \frac{1}{1 - e^{-nT_2(s-s_n)}} \tag{1.72}$$

or

$$\mathfrak{z}_{T2}[C_1(s)] = C_1^*(z_{T2}) = \frac{1}{1 - e^{nT_2(s-s_n)}} \mathfrak{z}_{T2}[AG_1(s)] \tag{1.73}$$

The z-transform of the output, as shown in Fig. 1.23, is for this case

$$C_2^*(z_{T2}) = \left\{ \frac{1}{1 - e^{-nT_2(s-s_n)}} \mathfrak{z}_{T2}[AG_1(s)] \times G_2^*(z_{T2}) \right\} \tag{1.74}$$

Similarly, we may obtain the z-transform for the multirate system, for the case when $T_1/T_2 = 1/n$.

b. *Delayed Multiple Samplers*

Here the initial closure of the sampler T_2 is delayed by $\delta_1 T_2$ with respect to the first sampler as shown in Fig. 1.24.

† It should be noted that z_{Tn} is substituted for $e^{T_n s}$.

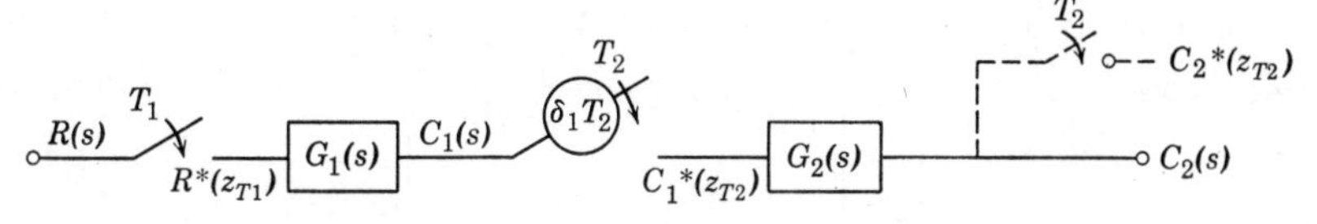

Figure 1.24 A two-sampler system with delay

In this case the delay $\delta_1 T_2$ can be incorporated in the impulsive response of $G_1(s)$, and the output of the second sampler can be expressed as

$$C_1^*(z_{T2}) = \left[\frac{1 + \sum_{i=1}^{q-1} e^{-i(b/q)T_2(s-s_n)}}{1 - e^{-bT_2(s-s_n)}}\right] \mathfrak{z}_{T2}\,[AG_1(s)] \qquad (1.75)$$

where

$$\mathfrak{z}_{T2}\,[G_1(s)] = G_1^*(z_{T2}, \delta) = \mathfrak{L}\,[g_1(t - \delta T_2) \times \delta_{T2}(t)] \qquad (1.76)\dagger$$

The transform $G_1^*(z_{T2}, \delta)$ can be obtained using (1.19) or from table of modified z-transform given in Chapter 2 with the proper substitution for m.

Illustrative Example

A two-sampler system shown in Fig. 1.25 is to be analyzed following the procedure discussed earlier. To determine $C_1^*(z)$ with period

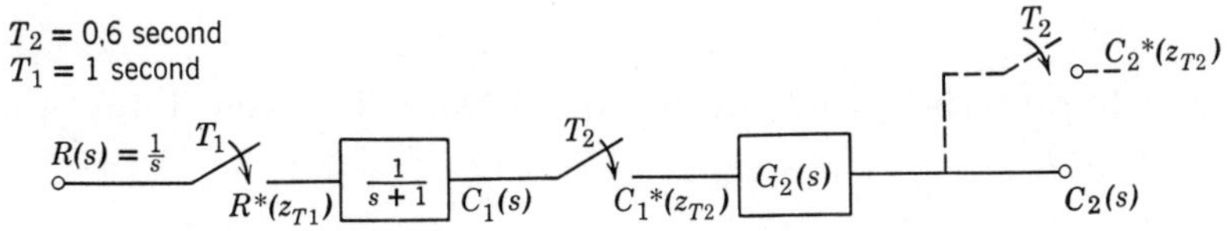

T_2 = 0,6 second
T_1 = 1 second

Figure 1.25 A multiple-sampler system

$T = T_2$, we must express $C_1(s)$ in terms of T_2. The ratio between T_1 and T_2 is given as

$$\frac{T_1}{T_2} = \frac{1}{0.6} = \frac{5}{3} \qquad \text{(i.e., } b = 5,\ q = 3\text{)} \qquad (1.77)$$

† For the case where δ is non-integer, the following relationship can be used to obtain $G_1^*(z_{T2}, \delta)$:

$$G_1^*(z_{T2}, \delta) = \mathfrak{L}\,[g_1(t - \delta T_2) \times \delta_{T2}(t)] = e^{-(k+1)T_2 s}\mathfrak{L}\,\{g_1[t + (1 - \delta_1)T_2] \times \delta_{T2}(t)\} \qquad (1.76a)$$

where $\delta = k + \delta_1$, k is a positive integer (or zero), and δ_1 is less than unity.

In this case, using relation (1.66), $R^*(z_{T1})$ may be written in terms of T_2 as

$$R^*(z_{T2}) = \left[\frac{1 + e^{-\frac{5}{3}T_2 s} + e^{-\frac{10}{3}T_2 s}}{1 - e^{-5T_2 s}}\right]_{z_{T2}=e^{T_2 s}} \tag{1.78}$$

Thus $C_1^*(z)$ in terms of T_2 can be written as

$$C_1^*(z_{T2}) = \frac{1}{1 - e^{-5T_2 s}}\left\{\mathfrak{z}_{T2}\left(\frac{1}{s+1}\right) + e^{-2T_2 s}\,\mathfrak{z}_{T2}\left[\frac{e^{\frac{1}{3}T_2 s}}{s+1}\right] + e^{-4T_2 s}\,\mathfrak{z}_{T2}\left[\frac{e^{\frac{2}{3}T_2 s}}{s+1}\right]\right\} \tag{1.79}$$

which reduces to

$$C_1^*(z_{T2}) = \frac{z_{T2}^{\,2}[z_{T2}^{\,4} + z_{T2}^{\,2}\, e^{-(T_2/3)} + e^{-\frac{2}{3}T_2}]}{(z_{T2}^{\,5} - 1)(z_{T2} - e^{-T_2})} \tag{1.80}$$

The total output can be expressed as

$$C_2^*(z_{T2}) = C_1^*(z_{T2})\,\mathfrak{z}_{T2}\,[G_2(s)] \tag{1.81}$$

A multirate feedback system is discussed in the next chapter where it is shown that the same techniques can be applied.

1.9 Characteristics of the Sampled-Data Transfer Function $G^*(z)$ †

The performance of sampled-data systems depends mainly on the form of its transfer function $G^*(z)$. This transfer function is related to the impulsive response of the system or to its Laplace transform $G(s)$ in the following relation:

$$G^*(z) = \mathfrak{L}\,[g(t) \times \delta_T(t)] = \left[\sum_{n=1}^{N} \frac{A(s_n)}{B'(s_n)} \times \frac{1}{1 - e^{-T(s-s_n)}}\right]_{z=e^{Ts}} \tag{1.82}$$

where $G(s) = A(s)/B(s)$, and it is assumed that the roots of $B(s)$ are simple. However, for multiple roots the characteristics to be derived remain the same.

From equation (1.82) the following characteristics of $G^*(z)$ are derived:

† E. I. Jury, "Analysis and Synthesis of Sampled-Data Control Systems," *Trans. A.I.E.E.*, Vol. 73, Pt. I, 1954, pp. 332–346.

1. $G^*(z)$ is periodic in s with the imaginary period $j(2\pi/T)$. This is evident from the following identity:

$$G^*(z) = \sum_{n=1}^{N} \frac{A(s_n)}{B'(s_n)} \frac{1}{1 - e^{Ts_n}e^{-T[s+j(2\pi/T)]}} = \sum_{n=1}^{N} \frac{A(s_n)}{B'(s_n)} \frac{1}{1 - e^{Ts_n}e^{-Ts}} \tag{1.83}$$

2. Asymptotic values of $G^*(z)$ as $s \to 0$ and $s \to jn(\omega_r/2)$ are real. This can be seen by substituting $s = 0$ and $s = jn(\omega_r/2)$ in equation (1.82) to obtain

$$G^*(z) = \sum_{n=1}^{N} \frac{A(s_n)}{B'(s_n)} \frac{1}{1 - e^{Ts_n}} = \text{real} \tag{1.84}$$

$$G^*(z) = \sum_{n=1}^{N} \frac{A(s_n)}{B'(s_n)} \frac{1}{1 + e^{Ts_n}} = \text{real} \tag{1.85}$$

Equations (1.84) and (1.85) are valid even if s_n is complex, since in physical systems complex quantities appear in conjugates.

3. The degree of the denominator of $G^*(z)$ in z^{-1} is equal to the degree of the denominator of $G(s)$ in s. This is evident from the fact that the summation in equation (1.82) is equal to the degree of $B(s)$ in s.

4. The poles of $G^*(z)$ in the s-plane are those of $G(s)$ plus an infinite number of poles separated by $j\omega_r$ at $s_n + jk\omega_r$. For $s = s_n + jk\omega_r$ in equation (1.82) is a pole of $G^*(z)$ in the s-plane, and s_n is also a pole of $G(s)$.

5. Insertion of zeros in $G(s)$ changes the coefficients $A(s_n)/B'(s_n)$ alone.

6. Changing the values of poles of $G(s)$ changes the coefficients $A(s_n)/B'(s_n)$ as well as the terms $1/[1 - e^{-T(s-s_n)}]$ as seen from equation (1.82).

7. Insertion of poles in $G(s)$ increases the number of terms of $G^*(z)$ in the summation in equation (1.82); that is, N becomes larger and $G^*(z)$ will have more terms of the form

$$\frac{A(s_n)}{B'(s_n)[1 - e^{-T(s-s_n)}]} \tag{1.86}$$

The last three characteristics can be utilized to obtain a correlation between the effect of changing poles and zeros of $G(s)$ on the sampled-data transfer function. These can be useful in compensating sampled-data control systems by linear networks, as will be discussed in Chapter 6.

1.10 Inverse z-Transform (Inversion Formula)

The actual output $c^*(t)$ at the sampling instants can be obtained from the z-transform $C^*(z)$ in two ways: (*a*) The residue method, (*b*) The power series expansion method.

a. The Residue Method

As noticed from equation (1.22), the z-transform of the output of any sampled-data system can be written as follows:

$$C^*(z) = \sum_{n=0}^{\infty} c(nT)\, z^{-n}$$

$$= c(0) + c(T)\, z^{-1} + c(2T)\, z^{-2} + \cdots + c(nT)\, z^{-n} + \cdots \quad (1.87)$$

The coefficients of this series are the output at discrete instants of time. Thus $c^*(t)$ can be found by determining the coefficients. One method of determining the coefficients for a known $c^*(t)$ is as follows: $c(T)$ can be recognized as the negative of the residue of $C^*(z)$ at infinity.† Thus, $c(T)$ can be found by evaluating the contour integral:

$$c(T) = \frac{1}{2\pi j} \int_{\Gamma} C^*(z)\, dz \quad (1.88)$$

where Γ is a closed contour enclosing the singularities of $C^*(z)$ but not enclosing infinity, and the direction of integration is counterclockwise. Multiplication of both sides of equation (1.87) by z^{-1} does not alter the region of convergence of the series. Thus, $c(0)$ can be found by evaluating

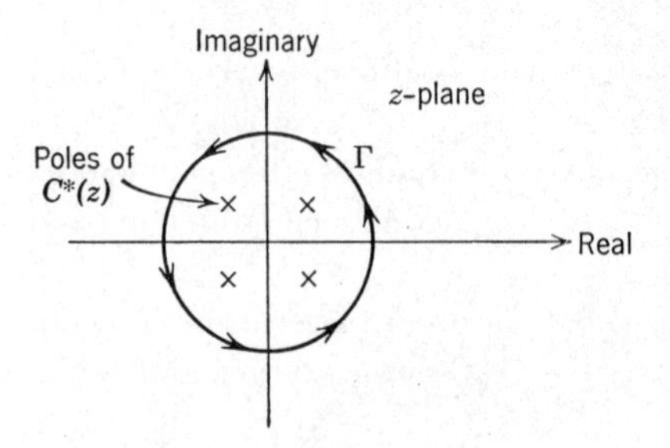

Figure 1.26 Path of integration in the z-plane

$$c(0) = \frac{1}{2\pi j} \int_{\Gamma} C^*(z)\, z^{-1}\, dz \quad (1.89)$$

since $c(0)$ is the residue of $C^*(z)\, z^{-1}$ at infinity. Unless $C^*(z)$ has a zero at $z = 0$, then $C^*(z)\, z^{-1}$ will have a pole at the origin and therefore Γ must enclose the origin and the poles of $C^*(z)$. Likewise, all other

† W. Kaplan, *Advanced Calculus*, Addison-Wesley Press, Cambridge, Mass., 1952, p. 567. D. F. Lawden, "A General Theory of Sampling Servo Systems," *Proc. I.E.E.* (*London*), Vol. 98, Pt. IV, 1951, pp. 31–36.

coefficients can be found by multiplying $C^*(z)$ by positive powers of z and finding the residue of the product at infinity. Multiplication of equation (1.87) by z^{n-1} increases the order of the singularity at infinity by $n - 1$. The function $C^*(z)\, z^{n-1}$ is still analytic outside the contour Γ except at infinity, and therefore $c(nT)$ can be found for all non-negative n by evaluation of

$$c(nT) = \frac{1}{2\pi j} \int_{\Gamma} C^*(z)\, z^{n-1}\, dz \tag{1.90}$$

The Γ-contour of integration in the z-plane that encloses the singularities of $C^*(z)$ is shown in Fig. 1.26.

Equation (1.90) is an expression for the inverse z-transform since $c^*(t)$ is given by the evaluation of equation (1.90) for all non-negative n. The actual output representation is

$$c^*(t) = \sum_{n=0}^{\infty} c(nT)\, \delta(t - nT) \tag{1.91}$$

The contour integral in equation (1.90) can be evaluated, using the Cauchy formula

$$c(nT) = \frac{1}{2\pi j} \int_{\Gamma} C^*(z)\, z^{n-1}\, dz = \text{sum of the residues of } C^*(z)\, z^{n-1} \tag{1.92}$$

The following cases are discussed for the inversion formula.

1. The poles of $C^*(z)$ are simple: Assume that

$$C^*(z) = \frac{F^*(z)}{G^*(z)} \tag{1.93}$$

When $G^*(z)$ has simple roots only, the residue at a simple singularity a is given by

$$\lim\, [(z - a)\, C^*(z)\, z^{n-1}]_{z \to a} = \lim \left[(z - a) \frac{F^*(z)}{G^*(z)}\, z^{n-1} \right]_{z \to a} \tag{1.94}$$

2. Poles of $C^*(z)$ given are not in a factored form: The residue at the singularity is

$$\text{Residue} = \left[\frac{F^*(z)}{G'^*(z)} \times z^{n-1} \right]_{z \to a_m} \tag{1.95}$$

where $G'^*(z) = \dfrac{dG^*(z)}{dz}$ and a_m is a singularity of $C^*(z)$.

EXAMPLE

$$C^*(z) = \frac{az}{\sin mz}, \qquad \text{poles at } z = \frac{k\pi}{m}, \; k = 0, 1, 2, \cdots \infty \tag{1.96}$$

$$c(nT) = \sum_{k=0}^{\infty} \frac{az^n}{m \cos mz}\bigg|_{z=\frac{k\pi}{m}} = \sum_{k=0}^{\infty} \frac{a(k\pi/m)^n}{m \cos k\pi} = \sum_{k=0}^{\infty} (-1)^k \frac{a}{m} (k\pi/m)^n \tag{1.97}$$

3. $C^*(z)$ has multiple poles: The residue at kth-order pole of $C^*(z)$ is given in the following expression: Residue at kth-order pole at a for singularity

$$b_1 = \frac{1}{k-1!} \frac{d^{k-1}}{dz^{k-1}} [C^*(z) \times (z-a)^k]\, s^{n-1}\Big|_{z\to a} \tag{1.98}$$

EXAMPLE

$$C^*(z) = \frac{z}{(z-\gamma)(z-1)^2} \tag{1.99}$$

$$c(nT) = \frac{1}{2\pi j} \int_\Gamma \frac{z^n}{(z-\gamma)(z-1)^2}\, dz$$

$$= \text{sum of the residues of } \frac{z^n}{(z-\gamma)(z-1)^2} \tag{1.100}$$

The singularities of the integrand in the z-plane are : (a) simple pole at $z = \gamma$ and (b) multiple poles at $z = 1$.

From 1 and 3,

$$c(nT) = \frac{\gamma^n}{(\gamma-1)^2} + \frac{1}{(2-1)!} \left(\frac{d}{dz} \frac{z^n}{z-\gamma}\right)_{z\to 1} \tag{1.101}$$

$$= \frac{\gamma^n}{(\gamma-1)^2} - \frac{1}{(1-\gamma)^2} + \frac{n}{1-\gamma} \tag{1.102}$$

The inverse z-transform is given by $c(nT) = \mathfrak{Z}^{-1}[C^*(z)]$, and the output time representation by

$$c^*(t) = \sum_{n=0}^{\infty} c(nT)\, \delta(t - nT) \tag{1.103}$$

Table 1.1 (page 56) gives an extensive list of the inversion integral for various values of $F^*(z)$. This table has been computed according to the rules given in this section.

b. The Power Series Method

The value of $c(nT)$ can also be obtained as the coefficient of z^{-n} in the power series expansion of $C^*(z)$ as a function of z^{-1}. From equation (1.22) it is observed that

$$C^*(z) = c_0 + c_1 z^{-1} + c_2 z^{-2} + c_3 z^{-3} + \cdots + c_n z^{-n} + \cdots \tag{1.104}$$

Therefore the inverse of this expression yields the output, if the inverse is obtained term by term:

$$c^*(t) = c_0\, \delta(t) + c_1\, \delta(t - T) + c_2\, \delta(t - 2T) + \cdots + c_n\, \delta(t - nT) + \cdots \tag{1.105}$$

The fact that the output of the inverse z-transform can also be obtained by the series expansion is of particular advantage in many cases where the evaluation of poles of $C^*(z)$ is not required.

Furthermore, the output coefficients $c_0, c_1, \cdots, c_n$ can also be obtained if the following conditions are imposed:

$$c_0 = \lim_{z \to \infty} C^*(z) \tag{1.106}$$

$$c_1 = \frac{-1}{1!} \lim_{z \to \infty} z^2 \frac{\partial C^*(z)}{\partial z} \tag{1.107}$$

$$c_2 = \frac{1}{2!} z^2 \lim_{z \to \infty} \frac{\partial}{\partial z} z^2 \frac{\partial C^*(z)}{\partial z} \tag{1.108}$$

$$\vdots \qquad \vdots$$

If $C^*(z)$ is given as a ratio of two polynomials in z^{-1}, the coefficients $c_0, c_1, \cdots, c_n$ are obtained as follows:

$$C^*(z) = \frac{p_0 + p_1 z^{-1} + p_2 z^{-2} + \cdots + p_n z^{-n}}{q_0 + q_1 z^{-1} + q_2 z^{-2} + \cdots + q_n z^{-n}} = c_0 + c_1 z^{-1} + c_2 z^{-2} + \cdots \tag{1.109}$$

$$p_0 = c_0 q_0 \tag{1.110}$$

$$p_1 = c_1 q_0 + c_0 q_1 \tag{1.111}$$

$$\vdots \qquad \vdots \qquad \vdots$$

$$p_n = c_n q_0 + c_{n-1} q_1 + c_{n-2} q_2 + \cdots c_0 q_n \tag{1.112}$$

It is noticed from the equations above that the output coefficients can also be obtained by synthetic division of the numerator by denominator of $C^*(z)$ given in the form shown in equation (1.109). The general form of output coefficients is obtained from the Appendix by letting $m \to 0$.

c. Theorems

1. Initial-value theorem. From relation (1.104), it is readily seen that the initial value of the output $\lim c^*(t)$ is given by

$$\lim_{t \to 0} c^*(t) = c_0\, \delta(t - 0T) = [\lim_{z \to \infty} C^*(z)]\, \delta(t) \tag{1.113}$$

2. Final-value theorem. The z-transform of a sampled function $c(nT)$ can be written, following equation (1.87), as

$$C^*(z) = \sum_{n=0}^{\infty} c(nT)\, z^{-n} = c(0^+) + \sum_{n=1}^{\infty} c(nT)\, z^{-n} \tag{1.114}$$

By using the translation theorem,† this equation gives

$$C^*(z) = c(0^+) + z^{-1} \sum_{n=0}^{\infty} c(n+1)T\, z^{-n} \tag{1.115}$$

or

$$\sum_{n=0}^{\infty} c(n+1)T\, z^{-n} = z[C^*(z) - c(0^+)] \tag{1.116}$$

Further, the z-transform of the first difference can be written

$$\begin{aligned} \mathfrak{z}\,[\Delta c(nT)] &= \mathfrak{z}\,[c(n+1)T] - \mathfrak{z}\,[c(nT)] \\ &= \sum_{n=0}^{\infty} c(n+1)T\, z^{-n} - \sum_{n=0}^{\infty} c(nT)\, z^{-n} \end{aligned} \tag{1.117}$$

By using equations (1.114) and (1.116), the transform of the first difference yields

$$\mathfrak{z}\,[\Delta c(nT)] = \frac{z-1}{z}\, C^*(z) - c(0^+) \tag{1.118}$$

This equation is useful in determining maxima and minima points of the response and the transform solution of difference equations.

Letting $z \to 1$, in equation (1.117), we note that the right side of equation (1.117) for this condition yields

$$\lim_{z \to 1} \mathfrak{z}\,[\Delta c(nT)] = \lim_{n \to \infty} \left[\sum_{n=0}^{n} c(n+1)T - \sum_{n=0}^{n} c(nT) \right] \tag{1.119}$$

† M. F. Gardner and J. L. Barnes, *Transients in Linear Systems*, Vol. 1, John Wiley & Sons, New York, 1942, pp. 236–241.

At the $(n-1)$th sampling period, the equation reduces to $\lim_{n\to\infty} c(nT) - c(0^+)$; therefore, from equations (1.118) and (1.119), the final-value theorem (if the limit exists) is given by

$$\lim_{n\to\infty} c(nT) = \lim_{z\to 1} \frac{z-1}{z} C^*(z) \tag{1.120}$$

3. Maxima and minima. The maximum or the minimum of the function can be obtained when the first difference $\Delta c(nT)$ changes sign. This can be found analytically by treating the discrete variable as continuous and first solving the following equation:

$$\Delta c(nT) = c(n+1)T - c(nT) = 0 \tag{1.121}$$

The solution of this equation generally yields a non-integer value of n. However, the actual value of n, which should be integer, for the maximum is the upper integer number of the value obtained from the solution of equation (1.121).

If the initial value of the function is zero, then from equation (1.118)

$$\mathfrak{z}\,[\Delta c(nT)] = (z-1)\, C^*(z) \tag{1.122}$$

or

$$\Delta c(nT) = \frac{1}{2\pi j}\int_\Gamma (z-1)\, C^*(z)\, z^{n-1}\, dz \tag{1.123}$$

and the point for maxima or minima can be obtained by first obtaining the zeros of $\Delta c(nT)$ or the zeros of the integral when equated to zero:

$$\Delta c(nT) = \frac{1}{2\pi j}\int_\Gamma C^*(z)\,(z-1) z^{n-1}\, dz = 0 \tag{1.124}$$

4. Complex translation. The complex-translation theorem given can be easily obtained by following the definition of the z-transform.

$$\mathfrak{z}\,[F(s+a)] = F^*(ze^{aT}), \qquad \mathfrak{z}\,[F(s-a)] = F^*(ze^{-aT}) \tag{1.125}$$

where $F^*(z) = \mathfrak{z}\,[F(s)]$.

$$\mathfrak{z}\,[F(s+a)] = \mathcal{L}\left[\sum_{n=0}^{\infty} e^{-at} f(t)\, \delta(t-nT)\right]$$

$$= \int_0^\infty \sum_{n=0}^{\infty} e^{-anT} f(nT)\, \delta(t-nT)\, e^{-st} dt$$

$$= \sum_{n=0}^{\infty} e^{-anT} f(nT)\, z^{-n} = \sum_{n=0}^{\infty} f(nT)\, (ze^{aT})^{-n} \tag{1.126}$$

but

$$\mathfrak{z}\,[F(s)] = \sum_{n=0}^{\infty} f(nT)\, z^{-n} = F^*(z) \tag{1.127}$$

Thus,

$$\mathfrak{z}\,[F(s + a)] = F^*(z_1)\big|_{z_1=(ze^{aT})} = F^*(ze^{aT}) \tag{1.128}$$

5. Differentiation with respect to second independent variable. The differentiation theorem given in the following equation is obtained from the definition of the z-transform as shown below.

$$\mathcal{L}\left[\frac{\partial}{\partial a} f^*(t, a)\right] = \frac{\partial}{\partial a} F^*(z, a) \tag{1.129}$$

$$\mathcal{L}\left[\frac{\partial}{\partial a} f^*(t, a)\right] = \mathcal{L}\left\{\sum_{n=0}^{\infty}\left[\frac{\partial}{\partial a} f(nT, a)\right]\delta(t - nT)\right\}$$

$$= \frac{\partial}{\partial a}\sum_{n=0}^{\infty} f(nT, a)\, z^{-n} = \frac{\partial}{\partial a} F^*(z, a) \tag{1.130}$$

6. Second independent variable limit value. The limiting value theorem given below has many applications in the design of sampled data and hence its inclusion is important.

$$\mathcal{L} \lim_{a\to a_0} [f^*(t, a)] = \lim_{a\to a_0} F^*(z, a) \tag{1.131}$$

where

$$F^*(z, a) = \mathcal{L}\,[f^*(t, a)] \tag{1.132}$$

7. Integration with respect to second independent variable. The integration theorem presented below is useful in evaluating the mean square error of sampled-data feedback systems, as discussed in Chapter 5.

$$\mathcal{L}\left[\int_0^a f^*(t, a)\, da\right] = \int_0^a F^*(z, a)\, da \tag{1.133}$$

where

$$F^*(z, a) = \mathcal{L}\,[f^*(t, a)] \tag{1.134}$$

8. Scale change theorem. The scale change theorem is useful in the normalization of tables of z-transforms.†

$$\text{If} \quad f(t) \to f(t/a) \tag{1.135}$$

and

$$T \to aT$$

† R. H. Barker, "The Pulse Transfer Function and Its Application to Sampling Servo Systems," *Proc. I.E.E. (London)*, Vol. 99, Pt. IV, 1952, pp. 302–317.

then

$$F^*(z)\Big|_{z=e^{sT}} \rightarrow F^*(z)\Big|_{z=e^{(aT)s}} \tag{1.136}$$

where a is the scale factor.

1.11 Stability Considerations

A linear sampled-data system is considered to be stable if for a bounded input always corresponds a bounded output. The stability conditions for such systems can be obtained if the sampled output of Fig. 1.16 is written as follows:

$$c^*(t) = \sum_{n=0}^{\infty} c(nT)\,\delta(t - nT) \tag{1.137}$$

where

$$c(nT) = \frac{1}{2\pi j}\int_\Gamma E^*(z)\,G^*(z)\,z^{n-1}\,dz \tag{1.138}$$

The output can be separated for the most part into steady state and transient terms. The output related to the steady-state part can be written as the sum of the following typical term:

$$(\text{Residue of } E^*(z)) \times G^*(z_m)\,z_m^{n-1} \tag{1.139}$$

where z_m is a typical pole of $E^*(z)$. Since the input is bounded, that is,

$$|z_m| \leq 1 \tag{1.140}$$

then the output is also bounded.

Similarly, a typical transient term of the output can be written

$$(\text{Residue of } G^*(z)) \times E^*(z_k)\,z_k^{n-1} \tag{1.141}$$

where z_k is a typical pole of $G^*(z)$. From expression 1.141, it is evident that in order for the output to be bounded or the system to be stable

$$|z_k| < 1 \tag{1.142}$$

the poles of $G^*(z)$ should be inside the unit circle.† Similarly, for the feedback system shown in Fig. 1.22 the terms of the output $c(nT)$ can be written as

$$c(nT) = \frac{1}{2\pi j}\int_\Gamma R^*(z)\,\frac{G^*(z)}{1 + HG^*(z)}\,z^{n-1}\,dz \tag{1.143}$$

and for the system to be stable the roots of $1 + HG^*(z)$ should lie inside the unit circle.

† H. M. James, N. B. Nichols, and R. S. Phillips, *Theory of Servomechanisms*, McGraw-Hill Book Company, New York, 1947, Chapter 6.

Although the output is stable at the sampling instants if the roots of $1 + HG^*(z)$ are inside the unit circle, there are some conditions in which the actual output is unstable. These rare conditions of hidden instability † will be discussed in Chapter 2. However, at this initial discussion of stability it is tacitly assumed that the output is considered only at the sampling instants.

1.12 Analytic Test for Stability

A sampled-data system is stable if all the roots (or zeros) of the system characteristic equation $F^*(z) = 0$ lie within the unit circle $|z| = 1$. A test for the locations of the zeros of the polynomial in z of $f^*(z)$ can be obtained by applying the Schur-Cohn ‡ criterion which states: If for the polynomial

$$F^*(z) = a_0 + a_1 z + a_2 z^2 + \cdots a_n z^n, \tag{1.144}$$

all the determinants

$$\Delta_k = \begin{vmatrix} a_0 & 0 & 0 & \cdots 0 & a_n & a_{n-1} & \cdots & a_{n-k+1} \\ a_1 & a_0 & 0 & \cdots 0 & 0 & a_n & \cdots & a_{n-k+2} \\ \vdots & \vdots & \vdots & \cdots & \vdots & \vdots & \cdots & \vdots \\ a_{k-1} & a_{k-2} & a_{k-3} & \cdots 0 & 0 & 0 & \cdots & a_n \\ \bar{a}_n & 0 & 0 & \cdots 0 & \bar{a}_0 & \bar{a}_1 & \cdots & \bar{a}_{k-1} \\ \bar{a}_{n-1} & \bar{a}_n & 0 & \cdots 0 & 0 & \bar{a}_0 & \cdots & \bar{a}_{k-2} \\ \vdots & \vdots & \vdots & \cdots & \vdots & \vdots & \cdots & \vdots \\ \bar{a}_{n-k+1} & \bar{a}_{n-k+2} & \bar{a}_{n-k+3} & \cdots \bar{a}_n & 0 & 0 & \cdots & \bar{a}_0 \end{vmatrix} \tag{1.145}$$

where

$$k = 1, 2, \cdots, n$$

and

$$\bar{a}_k = \text{conjugate of } a_k$$

are different from zero, $F^*(z)$ has no zeros on the unit circle $|z| = 1$ and

† E. I. Jury, "Hidden Oscillations in Sampled-Data Control Systems," *Trans. A.I.E.E.*, Vol. 75, Pt. II, 1956, pp. 391–395.

‡ M. Marden, *The Geometry of the Zeros of a Polynomial in a Complex Variable*, American Mathematical Society, New York, 1949, p. 152.

P number of zeros inside this circle that equal the number of variations in sign in the determinant sequence $1, \Delta_1, \Delta_2, \cdots, \Delta_n$.

For a stable sampled-data system all the zeros of the characteristic equations should lie inside the unit circle, which means that the determinant sequence $1, \Delta_1, \Delta_2, \cdots, \Delta_n$ must have n variations in sign, where n is the order of the characteristic equation.

Thus the stability criterion can be formulated as

$$\Delta_k < 0, \qquad k \text{ odd} \tag{1.146}$$

$$\Delta_k > 0, \qquad k \text{ even} \tag{1.147}$$

As an example, for a quadratic polynomial, $n = 2$, the following conditions for $1, \Delta_1, \Delta_2$ should exist:

$$\Delta_1 < 0, \qquad \Delta_2 > 0 \tag{1.148}$$

indicating that two variations in sign are necessary for the two zeros of the characteristic equation to lie inside the unit circle.

In this example Δ_1, Δ_2 are equal to

$$\Delta_1 = \begin{vmatrix} a_0 & a_2 \\ a_2 & a_0 \end{vmatrix} = a_0^2 - a_2^2 \tag{1.149}$$

$$\Delta_2 = \begin{vmatrix} a_0 & 0 & a_2 & a_1 \\ a_1 & a_0 & 0 & a_2 \\ a_2 & 0 & a_0 & a_1 \\ a_1 & a_2 & 0 & a_0 \end{vmatrix} = (a_0^2 - a_2^2)^2 - a_1^2(a_0 - a_2)^2 \tag{1.150}$$

In terms of the constants of the polynomial of the following characteristic equation,

$$a_0 + a_1 z + a_2 z^2 = 0 \tag{1.151}$$

the stability constraints are

$$a_0^2 - a_2^2 < 0 \tag{1.152}$$

$$(a_0^2 - a_2^2) - a_1^2(a_0 - a_2)^2 > 0 \tag{1.153}$$

Similarly, for a third-order system, $n = 3$, the following determinants are obtained:

$$\Delta_1 = a_0^2 - a_3^2 \tag{1.154}$$

$$\Delta_2 = (a_0^2 - a_3^2)^2 - (a_1 a_3 - a_0 a_2)^2 \tag{1.155}$$

$$\Delta_3 = (a_0^2 - a_3^2)^3 + (a_0 a_2 - a_1 a_3)^2(2a_3^2 - 2a_0^2 + a_2^2 - a_1^2) + (a_0 a_1 - a_2 a_3)^2(a_3^2 - a_0^2 + 2a_0 a_2 - 2a_1 a_3) \tag{1.156}$$

The system is stable if the following conditions are fulfilled:

$$\Delta_1 < 0, \qquad \Delta_2 > 0, \qquad \Delta_3 < 0 \tag{1.157}$$

that is, there are three changes of sign to ensure that the three roots of the characteristic equation are inside the unit circle.

Similar relations for higher-order systems that involve the evaluation of determinants of higher order can be obtained. A more practical procedure for testing stability which avoids evaluation of these higher-order determinants is presented as an alternate method.

If the closed region $|z| \leq 1$ is mapped into the region $Re[w] \leq 0$ of an auxiliary w-plane, the conditions for stability become exactly the Hurewitz criterion. The bilinear transformation †

$$z = \frac{w + 1}{w - 1} \tag{1.158}$$

is the simplest possible mapping of the unit circle into the left half of w-plane. In this manner the nth-degree polynomial in z is converted to a ratio of nth-degree polynomials in w, and the numerator is tested for its zeros.

Let the system equation in the z-plane be given by

$$A_0 z^n + A_1 z^{n-1} + \cdots + A_n = 0 \tag{1.159}$$

When mapped into the w-plane by this transformation, the zeros of the w-function are given by

$$B_0 w^n + B_1 w^{n-1} + \cdots + B_n = 0 \tag{1.160}$$

The relationship between the coefficients A_k and B_j is given by

$$B_j = \sum_{k=0}^{n} A_k \left[\binom{n-k}{j} - \binom{k}{1}\binom{n-k}{j-1} + \binom{k}{2}\binom{n-k}{j-2} - \cdots + (-1)^{j-1}\binom{k}{j-1}\binom{n-k}{1} + (-1)^j \binom{k}{j} \right] \tag{1.161}$$

where

$$\binom{\alpha}{\beta} = \frac{\alpha!}{\beta!(\alpha - \beta)!} \tag{1.162}$$

and

$$|(B_n)| = |(B_{n-j})| \tag{1.163}$$

For a second-order system whose characteristic equation is

$$A_0 z^2 + A_1 z + A_2 = 0 \tag{1.164}$$

† R. C. Oldenbourg and H. Sartorious, *The Dynamics of Automatic Controls*, American Society of Mechanical Engineers, New York, 1948, Chapter 5, pp. 189–193.

the constants B_j are:

$$B_0 = A_0 + A_1 + A_2 \tag{1.165}$$

$$B_1 = 2(A_0 - A_2) \tag{1.166}$$

$$B_2 = A_0 - A_1 + A_2 \tag{1.167}$$

By applying the Hurewitz criterion,

$$B_0 > 0, \qquad B_1 > 0, \qquad B_2 > 0 \tag{1.168}$$

Thus the stability conditions are

$$A_0 + A_1 + A_2 > 0 \tag{1.169}$$

$$A_0 - A_2 > 0 \tag{1.170}$$

$$A_0 - A_1 + A_2 > 0 \tag{1.171}$$

For a third-order system, $n = 3$, the characteristic equation is

$$A_0 z^3 + A_1 z^2 + A_2 z + A_3 = 0 \tag{1.172}$$

The stability conditions are †

$$B_0 = A_0 + A_1 + A_2 + A_3 > 0 \tag{1.173}$$

$$B_1 = 3(A_0 - A_3) + A_1 - A_2 > 0 \tag{1.174}$$

$$B_2 = 3(A_0 + A_3) - A_1 - A_2 > 0 \tag{1.175}$$

$$B_3 = A_0 - A_1 + A_2 - A_3 > 0 \tag{1.176}$$

$$B_1 B_2 - B_0 B_3 = 8(A_0^2 - A_3^2 - A_0 A_2 + A_1 A_3) > 0 \tag{1.177}$$

For a fourth-order system, $n = 4$, the Hurewitz constants are

$$B_0 = A_0 + A_1 + A_2 + A_3 + A_4 \tag{1.178}$$

$$B_1 = 4(A_0 - A_4) + 2(A_1 - A_3) \tag{1.179}$$

$$B_2 = 6(A_0 + A_4) - 2A_2 \tag{1.180}$$

$$B_3 = 4(A_0 - A_4) + 2(A_3 - A_1) \tag{1.181}$$

$$B_4 = A_0 - A_1 + A_2 - A_3 + A_4 \tag{1.182}$$

† B. H. Bharucha and E. I. Jury, "Analytic Tests of Stability of Linear Sampled Systems, Internal Memorandum No. 2, August 10, 1956, Electronics Research Laboratory, University of California, Berkeley.

The stability conditions are

$$B_j > 0, \qquad j = 0, 1, 2, 3, 4 \tag{1.183}$$

$$\Delta = B_1B_2 - B_0B_3 > 0 \tag{1.184}$$

$$B_3\Delta - B_1^2B_4 > 0 \tag{1.185}$$

For a fifth-order system, $n = 5$, the constants are

$$B_0 = A_0 + A_1 + A_2 + A_3 + A_4 + A_5 \tag{1.186}$$

$$B_1 = 5(A_0 - A_5) + 3(A_1 - A_4) + (A_2 - A_3) \tag{1.187}$$

$$B_2 = 10(A_0 + A_5) + 2(A_1 + A_4) - 2(A_2 + A_3) \tag{1.188}$$

$$B_3 = 10(A_0 - A_5) + 2(A_4 - A_1) + 2(A_3 - A_2) \tag{1.189}$$

$$B_4 = 5(A_0 + A_5) - 3(A_1 + A_4) + A_2 + A_3 \tag{1.190}$$

$$B_5 = A_0 - A_1 + A_2 - A_3 + A_4 - A_5 \tag{1.191}$$

Let

$$Y_1 = B_1B_2 - B_0B_3 \tag{1.192}$$

$$Y_2 = B_3Y_1 - B_1(B_1B_4 - B_0B_5) \tag{1.193}$$

The stability conditions are

$$B_j > 0, \qquad j = 0, 1, 2, \cdots, 5 \tag{1.194}$$

$$Y_1 > 0, \qquad Y_2 > 0 \tag{1.195}$$

$$B_4Y_2 - B_5[B_2Y_1 - B_0(B_1B_4 - B_0B_5)] > 0 \tag{1.196}$$

1.13 Mapping Theorems

a. Mapping from s-Plane to z-Plane

The transformation between the complex variables s and z is related in the following relation

$$z = e^{Ts} \tag{1.197}$$

To map the s-plane to z-plane the following contours are considered.

1. Mapping the imaginary axis of the s-plane.† Let $s = j\omega$, where ω is the variable; then z becomes $e^{jT\omega}$. When ω varies from 0 to $2\pi/T$, z describes in its plane one unit circle, and when ω varies from

† J. M. Raymond, "Analyse de functionement des systems physique discontinus," *Annales des Telecommunication*, Paris, Vol. 4, June–October, 1949.

$2\pi/T$ to $4\pi/T$, z describes the same unit circle. Hence, it is sufficient to map the strip between 0 and $2\pi/T$ into the z-plane as shown in Fig. 1.27.

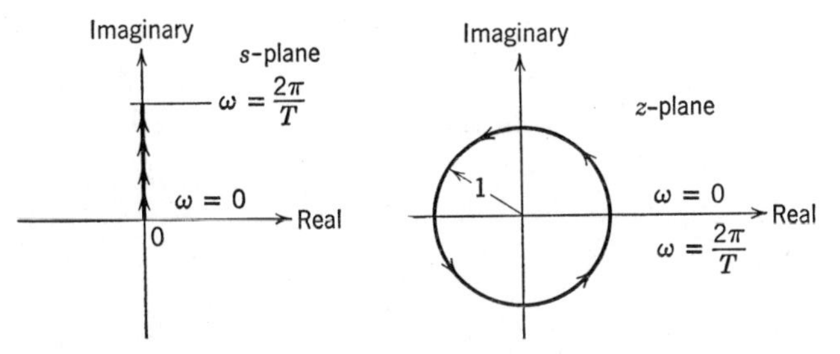

Figure 1.27 Mapping the $j\omega$-axis into the z-plane

2. Mapping the left half of the s-plane into the z-plane. From these considerations it is evident that to map the left half of the s-plane into the z-plane, mapping the rectangular region shown in Fig. 1.28a is sufficient. Thus on the point c let

$$s = -x + j\omega_r = -x + j\frac{2\pi}{T} \tag{1.198}$$

Then

$$z = e^{Ts} = e^{-Tx}e^{j2\pi} \tag{1.199}$$

when $x \to \infty$, $z \to 0$ as shown in Fig. 1.28b.

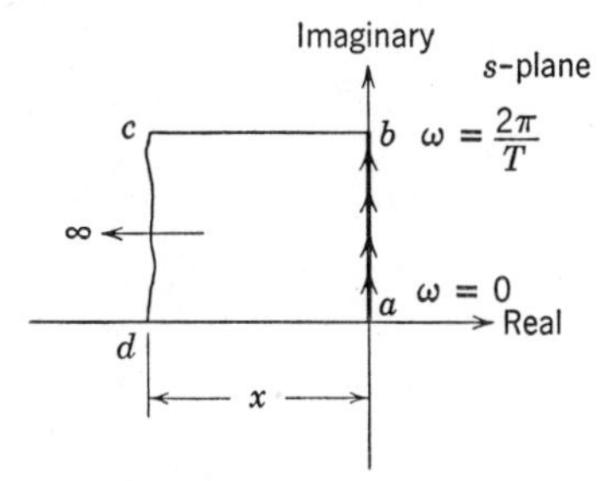

Figure 1.28*a* A strip in the left half of the s-plane

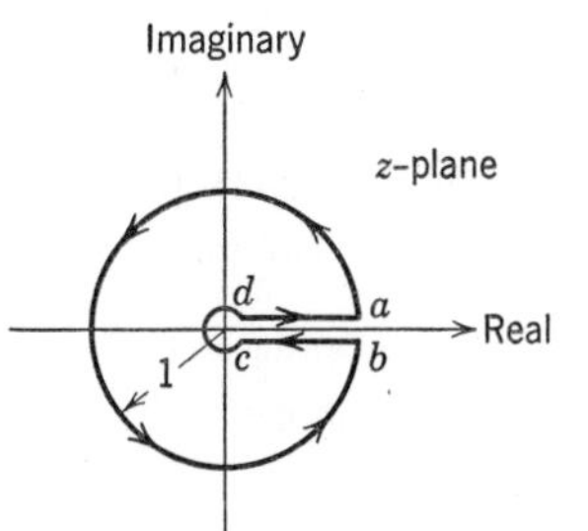

Figure 1.28*b* Mapping of Fig. 1.28a into the z-plane

3. Mapping the right half of the s-plane into the z-plane.† In this case it is sufficient, as explained in 1 and 2, to map a rectangular strip in the s-plane as shown in Fig. 1.29a.

† E. I. Jury, "Analysis and Synthesis of Sampled-Data Control Systems," Doctorate of Engineering Science Thesis, Columbia University, New York, April 1953.

On the point c,

$$s = x + j\frac{2\pi}{T} \tag{1.200}$$

or

$$z = e^{Tx}e^{j2\pi} \tag{1.201}$$

The mapping of this strip in the z-plane is shown in Fig. 1.29b.

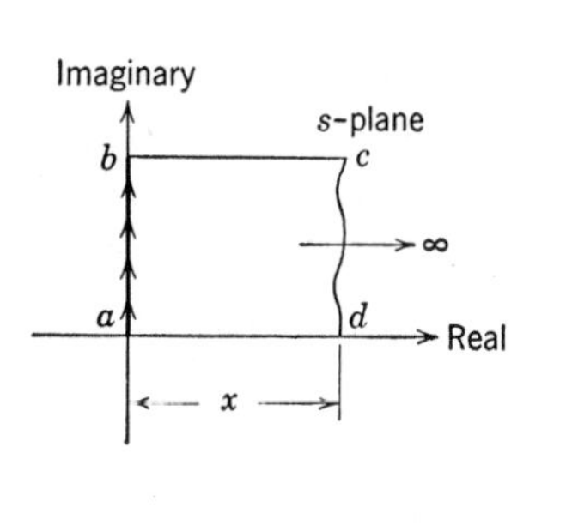

Figure 1.29a A strip in the right half of the s-plane

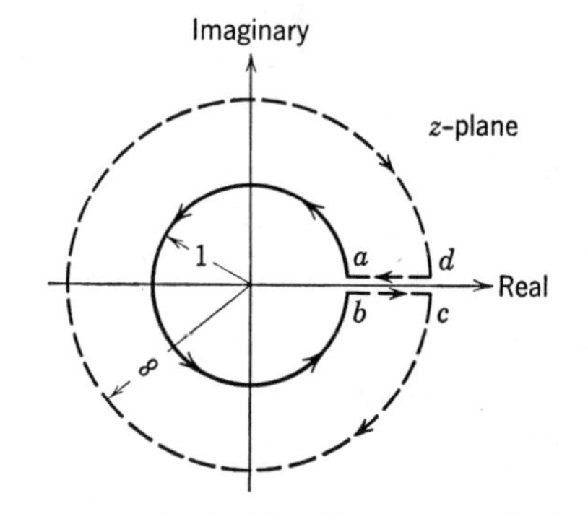

Figure 1.29b Mapping of the strip in Fig. 1.29a into the z-plane

4. Mapping a constant damping line shown in Fig. 1.30a from s-plane to z-plane. At any point along the straight line, s is given by the following relation

$$s = -x + j\omega \tag{1.202}$$

Thus

$$z = e^{-Tx}e^{jT\omega} \tag{1.203}$$

Equation (1.203) plots into a logarithmic spiral in the z-plane as shown in Fig. 1.30b.

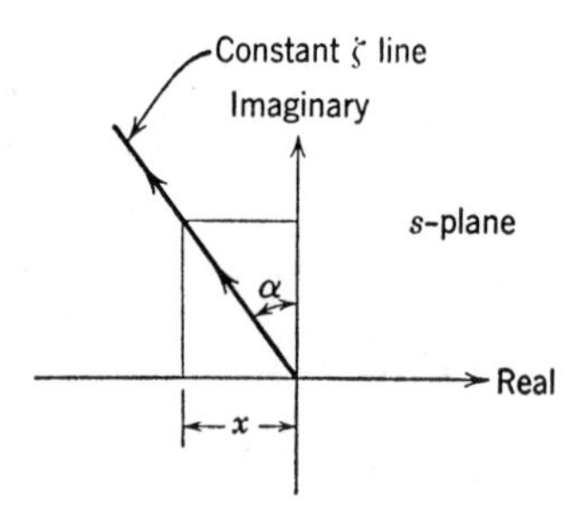

Figure 1.30a Constant damping line in the s-plane

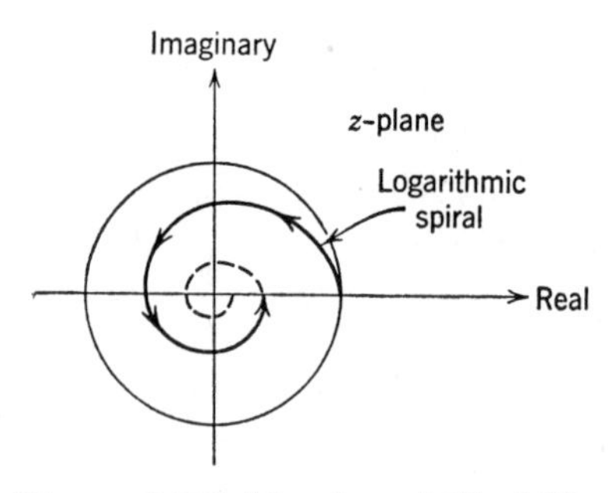

Figure 1.30b Mapping of Fig. 1.30a into the z-plane

b. Mapping from z-Plane to $G^*(z)$-Plane †

Since $G^*(z)$, the z-transform of $G(s)$, is a rational function of z as indicated in equation (1.49), we can apply Cauchy's mapping theorem from z-plane to $G^*(z)$-plane, stated as follows: If the point z in the z-plane describes a closed contour C in the positive sense (counterclockwise direction) as shown in Fig. 1.31, the point $G^*(z)$ in the $G^*(z)$-plane

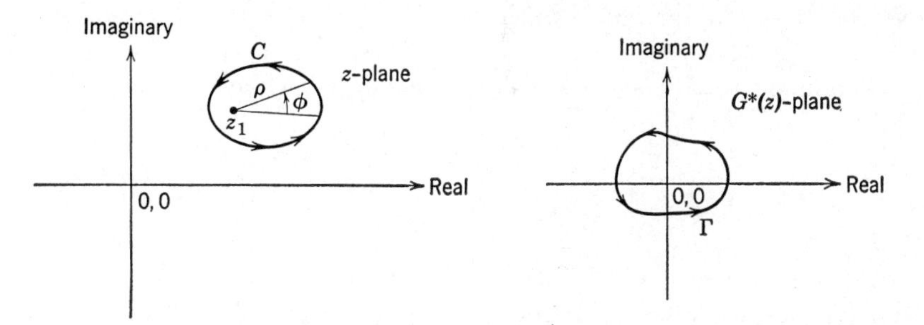

Figure 1.31 A closed contour in the $G^*(z)$-plane

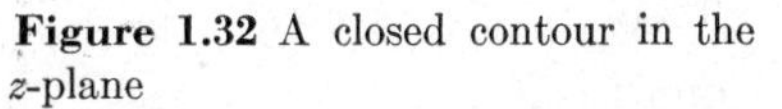

Figure 1.32 A closed contour in the z-plane

describes a closed contour Γ (Fig. 1.32). If the contour C encircles in a positive sense Z zeros and P poles (this takes into account the multiplicity of poles and zeros), the corresponding contour Γ in the $G^*(z)$-plane encircles the origin

$$N = Z - P \tag{1.204}$$

times in a positive sense.

The proof follows from the following considerations: Suppose that $G^*(z)$ has a single zero (root) at $z = z_1$

$$G^*(z) = A(z - z_1) \tag{1.205}$$

where A is constant. In polar form this becomes

$$G^*(z) = A\rho e^{j\phi} \tag{1.206}$$

It is evident that as the point z describes a contour C in the positive sense, the corresponding point in the $G^*(z)$-plane describes a contour Γ in a positive sense. The number of times that Γ encircles the origin is the total change in $\phi/2\pi$ which occurs when z traverses C once. Thus Γ encircles the origin once if C contains one zero z_1 at its interior. Similarly the contour Γ encircles the origin m times in a positive sense if the contour C encircles a root of mth order, or m distinct zeros.

† E. I. Jury, "Analysis and Synthesis of Sampled-Data Control Systems," Doctorate of Engineering Science Thesis, Columbia University, New York, April 1953.

Now consider a function $G^*(z)$ with a pole at $z = z_2$:

$$G^*(z) = \frac{A}{z - z_2} = \frac{A}{\rho} e^{-j\phi} \tag{1.207}$$

If the contour C encircles the pole $z = z_2$ in a positive sense, the contour Γ in the $G^*(z)$-plane encircles the origin once in a negative sense. This can be generalized as before; if the contour C encircles n poles in a positive sense, the contour Γ in the $G^*(z)$ encircles the origin n times in a negative sense.

Combining these considerations to include both the zeros and poles of $G^*(z)$, we obtain

$$G^*(z) = A \frac{(z - z_1)(z - z_3)(z - z_5) \cdots (z - z_m)}{(z - z_2)(z - z_4)(z - z_6) \cdots (z - z_n)}, \qquad m \leq n \tag{1.208}$$

As z describes in a positive sense a closed contour that encircles Z zeros and P poles, the phase angle of $G^*(z)$ changes by $+2\pi$ for each of the enclosed zeros and by -2π for each of the enclosed poles. The total number of times that the corresponding contour in the $G^*(z)$-plane encircles the origin in a positive sense is exactly $Z - P$.

The mapping theorem just given can be applied to determine the stability of sampled-data systems shown in Fig. 1.19, as follows: If $G^*(z)$ has all its zeros inside the unit circle, for the sampled-data system to be stable, the locus of $G^*(z)$ as z describes the unit circle in a positive sense must encircle the origin in a positive sense a number of times equal to the difference between its zeros and poles. This is evident, because in order for the system to be stable all its poles should lie inside the unit circle. (See the discussion of stability.)

1.14 Generalized Nyquist Criterion for Sampled-Data Control Systems

The mapping theorem discussed earlier can be applied to any function which is rational in z as follows:

$$Y^*(z) = 1 + G^*(z) \tag{1.209}$$

The map of a contour in the z-plane into the $G^*(z)$-plane can be obtained by shifting the corresponding map on the $Y^*(z)$-plane to the left by one unit. It follows that the contour C in the z-plane, described in a positive sense, will map into a contour Γ in the $G^*(z)$-plane that encircles the point $(-1, 0)$ in a positive sense $N = Z - P$.

The transfer locus is defined as the locus in the $G^*(z)$-plane for which C encloses all zeros and poles of $1 + G^*(z)$ that lie outside the unit circle. This locus will thus encircle the point $(-1, 0)$ a number of times that is the difference between the total number of zeros and the total number of poles of $1 + G^*(z)$ outside the unit circle. This mapping theorem can be applied for determining the stability of a sampled-data feedback system shown in Fig. 1.22. This is evident since the system is stable if, and only if, the number of zeros of $1 + G^*(z)$ outside or on the unit circle is zero.

If the mapping theorem is applied to a single-loop feedback sampled-data system whose open loop is stable ($G^*(z)$ has no poles outside the unit circle), the following theorem similar to the Nyquist criterion can be applied; that is: The sampled-data feedback system is stable if and only if the transfer locus of $G^*(z)$ does not pass through or encircle the point $(-1, 0)$ in the $G^*(z)$-plane.

1.15 Mapping the Transfer Locus $G^*(z)$ in the $G^*(z)$-Plane

First, consider that $G(s)$ consists of simple poles and no pole at the origin and of a denominator at least two degrees higher in s than the numerator. Furthermore, $G(s)$ is stable.

The z-transform of $G(s) = A(s)/B(s)$ using relation (1.49) yields

$$G^*(z) = \sum_{n=1}^{N} \frac{A(s_n)}{B'(s_n)} \frac{1}{1 - e^{-T(s-s_n)}} \tag{1.210}$$

where

$$G(s) = \frac{A(s)}{B(s)} \tag{1.211}$$

To obtain the transfer locus of equation (1.210), let z describe the outside of the unit circle in a positive sense as shown in Fig. 1.33. For the points a and b, let $z \to 1$; then

$$G^*(z) = \sum_{n=1}^{N} \frac{A(s_n)}{B'(s_n)} \frac{1}{1 - e^{Ts_n}} \tag{1.212}$$

is a positive real number. At the point $z = -1$

$$G^*(z) = \sum_{n=1}^{N} \frac{A(s_n)}{B'(s_n)} \frac{1}{1 + e^{Ts_n}} \tag{1.213}$$

is usually a negative real number (can also be positive under certain

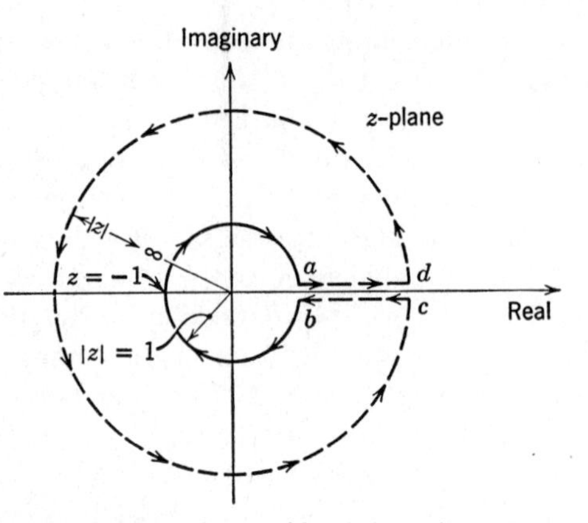

Figure 1.33 The locus of the outside of the unit circle in the z-plane

conditions). At point c let $\lim_{z\to\infty} z = \lim_{x\to\infty} x + jy$,

$$\lim_{\substack{z\to\infty \\ x\to\infty}} G^*(z) = \lim_{x\to\infty} \sum_{n=1}^{N} \frac{A(s_n)}{B'(s_n)} \frac{1}{1 - e^{Ts_n(x+jy)}} = \sum_{n=1}^{N} \frac{A(s_n)}{B'(s_n)} \tag{1.214}$$

But since $G(s)$ has a denominator two degrees higher in s than the numerator, its initial response is zero, which yields

$$\lim_{t\to 0} f(t) = \lim \sum_{n=1}^{N} \frac{A(s_n)}{B'(s_n)} e^{s_n t} = \sum_{n=1}^{N} \frac{A(s_n)}{B'(s_n)} = 0 \tag{1.215}$$

Therefore, the transfer locus of $G^*(z)$ in its plane is as indicated in Fig. 1.34.

It is noticed from Fig. 1.34, that the parallel straight lines on the real axis have no effect on the stability of the feedback system, because they never enclose the point $(-1, 0)$. Hence only the exterior boundary of the unit circle in the z-plane is sufficient for plotting the Nyquist (transfer)

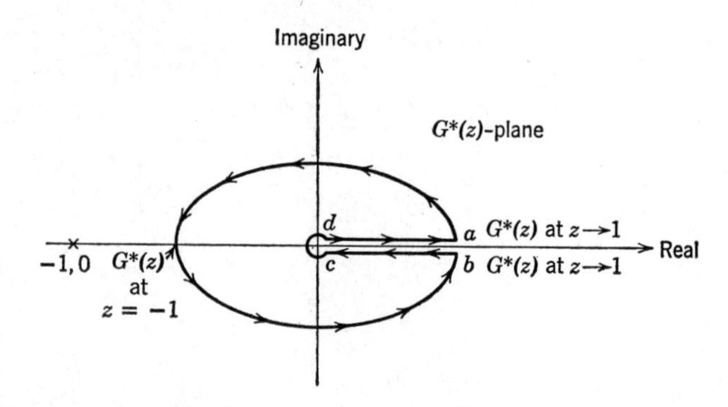

Figure 1.34 A typical locus of $G^*(z)$ as z describes the contour of Fig. 1.33

locus of $G^*(z)$ in its plane. Furthermore, $G^*(z)$ is symmetric along the real axis; thus only the upper half of the unit circle including the points $z = 1$, $z = -1$ is sufficient to plot the transfer locus.

Now consider that $G(s)$ has simple poles and a simple pole at the origin. The z-transform of $G(s)$ is given:

$$G^*(z) = \sum_{n=1}^{N} \frac{A(s_n)}{B'(s_n)} \frac{1}{1 - e^{-T(s-s_n)}} \tag{1.216}$$

For

$$s_n \to 0 \tag{1.217}$$

$$G^*(z) = \frac{A(0)}{B'(0)} \frac{z}{z-1} \tag{1.218}$$

$$B'(0) = \left.\frac{dB}{ds}\right|_{s\to 0} \tag{1.219}$$

Around the point $z \to 1$ or $s \to 0$, only the first term of the summation is significant; thus we can write near the point $z = 1$

$$\lim_{z\to 1} z = \lim_{\rho\to 0} (1 + \rho e^{j\theta}) \tag{1.220}$$

or

$$\lim_{z\to 1} G^*(z) = \lim_{\rho\to 0} \frac{A(0)}{B'(0)} \frac{1 + \rho e^{j\theta}}{\rho e^{j\theta}} = \lim_{\rho\to 0} \frac{A(0)}{B'(0)} \frac{1}{\rho e^{j\theta}} \tag{1.221}$$

where θ and ρ are the angle and radius of a small circle near the point $z = 1$ in the z-plane as shown in Fig. 1.35. When ρ describes the infinitely

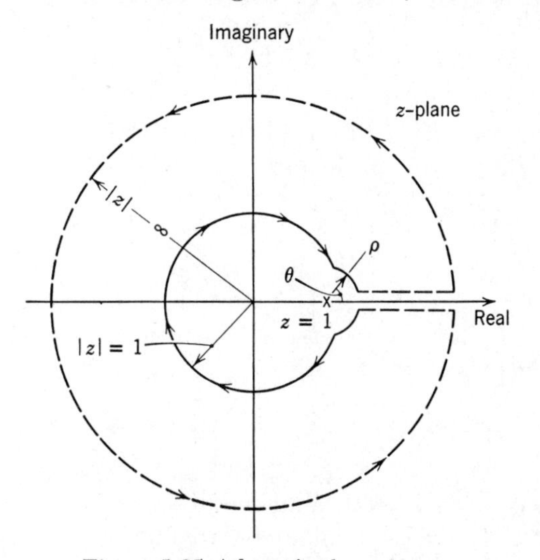

Figure 1.35 A locus in the z-plane

small semi-circle as θ varies from $+\pi/2$ to $-\pi/2$, the locus of $G^*(z)$ describes an infinitely large semi-circle from $-\pi/2$ to $+\pi/2$. A typical stable Nyquist locus for $G^*(z)$ given in equation (1.221) is shown in Fig. 1.36.

At the point $z = -1$, $G^*(z)$ is real. Since the parallel straight lines do not contribute to the stability test, they can be ignored in Nyquist plots; the outer boundary of the unit circle is sufficient for such a plot.

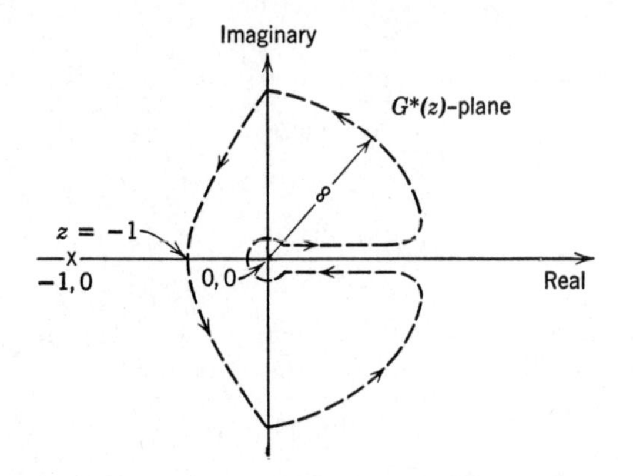

Figure 1.36 A typical locus of $G^*(z)$ as z describes the contour of Fig. 1.35

Third, consider that $G(s)$ has simple poles and a multiple pole at the origin of the order n. The z-transform can be written in this case using a relation similar to (1.18):

$$G^*(z) = \sum_{\text{poles of } G(s)} \text{Residue of } G(s) \frac{1}{1 - e^{sT}z^{-1}} \tag{1.222}$$

The term in $G^*(z)$ that corresponds to the nth-order pole at the origin can be generally written in the form

$$\frac{F^*(z)}{(z-1)^n} \tag{1.223}$$

Similarly as in the previous case let z near the point one be described as $1 + \rho e^{j\theta}$; then

$$\lim_{\rho \to 0} \frac{F^*(1 + \rho e^{j\theta})}{\rho e^{jn\theta}} \tag{1.224}$$

For the locus when ρ describes an infinitesimal circle from $-\pi/2$ to $\pi/2$, the locus $G^*(z)$ describes an infinitely large set of circles from $(n\pi/2)$ to

$(-n\pi/2)$. Typical Nyquist loci for systems when $n = 2$ and $n = 3$ are shown in Figs. 1.37 and 1.38.

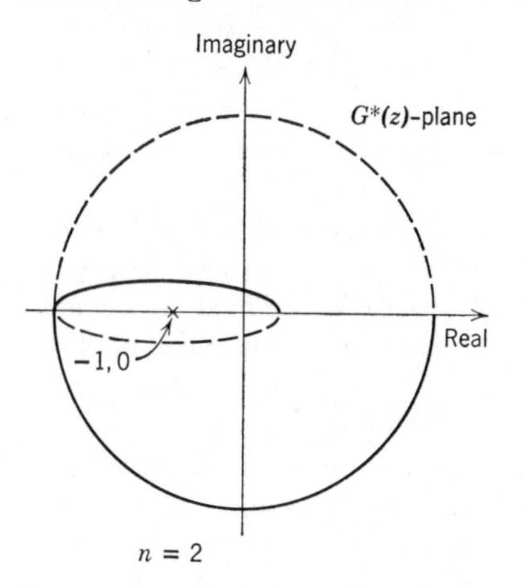

Figure 1.37 Typical plot of $G^*(z)$-locus for double pole at origin in $G(s)$-plane

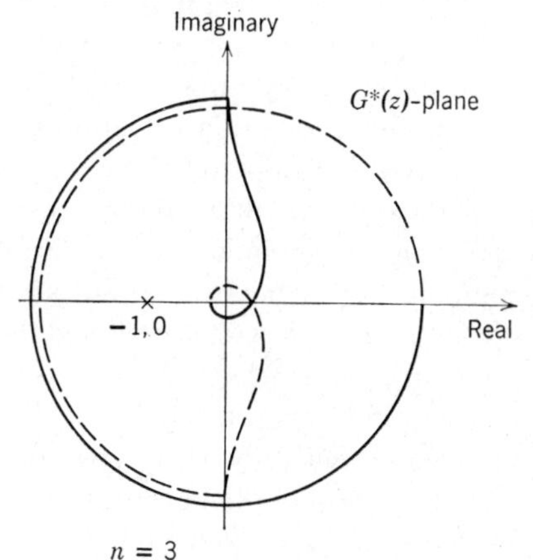

Figure 1.38 Typical plot of $G^*(z)$-locus for triple pole at origin in $G(s)$-plane

Finally, for the actual plot of $G^*(z)$ consider each term in the summation given below separately:

$$G^*(z) = \sum_{n=1}^{N} \frac{A(s_n)}{B'(s_n)} \frac{z}{z - e^{+Ts_n}} \tag{1.225}$$

The advantage of this method of plotting lies in the fact that each term in the summation is of the form

$$\frac{az}{z + b} \tag{1.226}$$

for the Nyquist locus when z describes the unit circle; the relation in equation (1.226) also describes a circle in the z-plane because of the bilinear transformation. Thus $G^*(z)$ for simple poles and a pole at the origin of $G(s)$ consists of circles and straight lines which are easy to plot; furthermore, this method of circle locus plotting leads eventually to synthesis and shaping in the $G^*(z)$-plane.

1.16 Hold Circuits

It has been shown at the beginning of this chapter that the sampler acts as an impulse modulator. As such, its output consists of the fundamental input frequency spectrum plus complementary frequency components as shown in Fig. 1.10. These complementary frequency components degenerate the input information to the sampler. In time domain the sampler output generates only short pulses (or in the limit impulses) of the input information as indicated in Fig. 1.6. Thus to recover the actual input information (or approximate form of the input) the sampler is followed by a hold circuit.

The frequency characteristic of this hold circuit should be of low-pass filter form to eliminate as much as possible the undesirable frequency components of the sampler output.† Alternately, the hold circuit is to reconstruct so far as it is practical the continuous function which has been previously sampled.

These hold circuits can be of different forms and circuitry; however, in this section only two types of hold circuits are to be considered, namely, zero-order hold circuit and first-order hold circuit. This classification is based on the complexity and the function of the hold to reproduce the sampled continuous function.

a. *Zero-Order Hold Circuit*

This type of hold converts a pulse train of finite width h shown in Fig. 1.39 into the form shown in Fig. 1.40, or in the limit as $h \to 0$, into a staircase function as shown in Figs. 1.41 and 1.42.

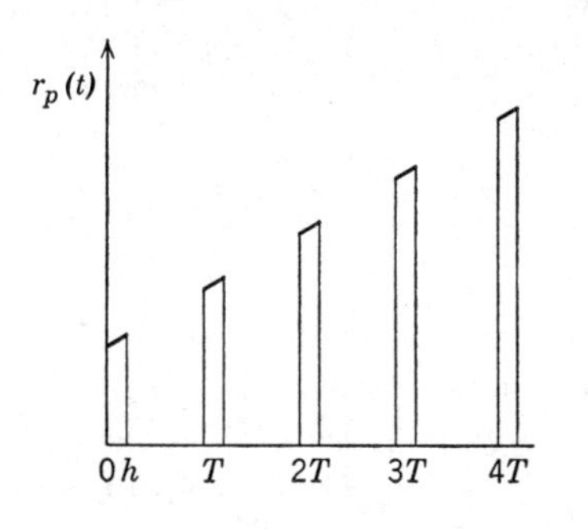

Figure 1.39 A typical input to sampler

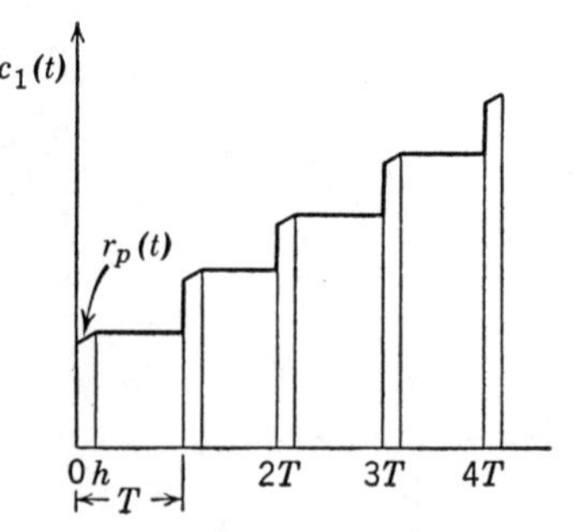

Figure 1.40 Output of sampler and hold

To obtain the transfer function of such a hold circuit consider Figs. 1.40 and 1.43, where the output transform $C_1(s)$ can be written consider-

† J. R. Ragazzini and L. A. Zadeh, "The Analysis of Sampled-Data Systems," *Trans. A.I.E.E.*, Vol. 71, Pt. II, 1952, pp. 225–232.

ing the superposition principle as follows:

$$C_1(s) = R_p(s) + \sum_{n=0}^{\infty} r(nT + h)\, e^{-nTs} \frac{e^{-hs} - e^{-Ts}}{s} \tag{1.227}$$

$$R_p(s) = \mathcal{L}\,[r_p(t)] \tag{1.228}$$

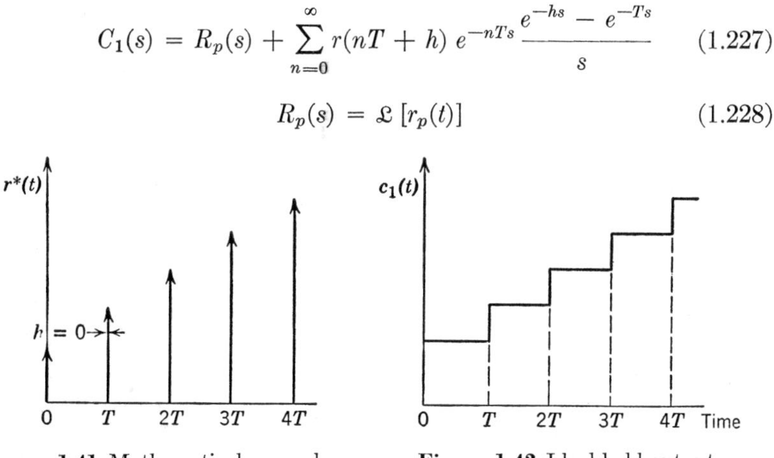

Figure 1.41 Mathematical sampler output

Figure 1.42 Ideal hold output

However, in the analysis of sampled-data systems the sampler output is assumed to be a sequence of impulses as shown in Fig. 1.41. Under this condition the output of the hold circuit is a set of flat-top pulses as indicated in Fig. 1.42 where it is assumed that the amplitude of these

Figure 1.43 A sampled-data system with zero-order hold

pulses are equal to the amplitude of the input signal at the sampling instants. The output of the hold circuit can therefore be written as

$$C_1(s) = \sum_{n=0}^{\infty} r(nT)\, e^{-nTs} \frac{1 - e^{-Ts}}{s} \tag{1.229}$$

which can also be written as

$$C_1(s) = R^*(z) \frac{1 - e^{-Ts}}{s} \tag{1.230}$$

since

$$R^*(z) = \left[\sum_{n=0}^{\infty} r(nT)\, e^{-nTs} \right]_{z=e^{Ts}} \tag{1.231}$$

Thus the total output becomes

$$C(s) = R^*(z) \frac{1 - e^{-Ts}}{s} KG_2(s) \tag{1.232}$$

Note that when zero-order hold is used, the task of amplifying the actual sampler output signals to the flat-top pulses shown in Fig. 1.42 is carried out by the hold circuit components. Therefore the gain K appearing in equation (1.232) is the actual gain of the amplifier following the hold circuit.

The zero-order transform function is presented as:

$$G_0(s) = \frac{(1 - e^{-Ts})}{s} = \frac{C_1(s)}{R^*(z)} \tag{1.233}$$

The frequency response of such a hold circuit can easily be obtained by letting $s \to j\omega$ in the transformed equation (1.233):

$$G_0(j\omega) = \frac{1}{j\omega}(1 - e^{-Tj\omega}) \tag{1.234}$$

or

$$|G_0(j\omega)| = \frac{1}{\omega}|1 - e^{-Tj\omega}| \tag{1.235}$$

Equation (1.235) can be reduced to the following form:

$$|G_0(j\omega)| = T\frac{\sin \omega T/2}{\omega T/2} \tag{1.236}$$

The frequency plot of equation (1.236) is shown in Fig. 1.44. This indicates that the higher-frequency components at the sampler output are filtered considerably in the output of the hold circuit.

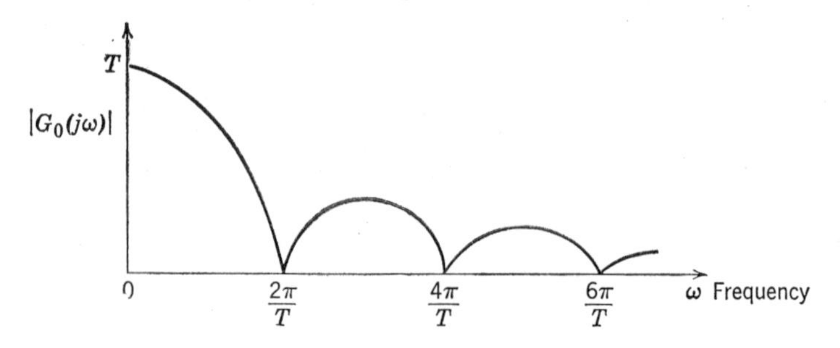

Figure 1.44 Frequency spectrum of zero-order hold

b. *First-Order Hold*

The output of a first-order hold circuit yields the signal amplitude at its input and its first difference. The first difference of the signal is obtained if the output in this hold equals the signal at the sampling instants and has a slope between the sampling instants equal to the slope of a straight line connecting the previous input samples. This is illustrated in Figs. 1.45 and 1.46.

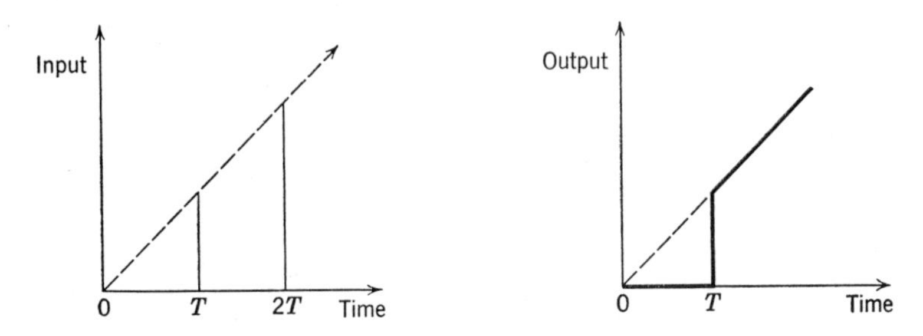

Figure 1.45 Input to first-order hold

Figure 1.46 Output of first-order hold

The transfer function can be obtained as the ratio of the output-input transforms. From Fig. 1.46, the transform of the hold circuit is †

$$G_I(s) = \frac{\dfrac{(T/s + 1/s^2)e^{-sT}}{Te^{-sT}}}{(1 - e^{-sT})^2} = \left(\frac{1}{s} + \frac{1}{Ts^2}\right)(1 - e^{-sT})^2 \quad (1.237)$$

The frequency plot of equation (1.237) where $s \to j\omega$ is shown in Fig. 1.47.

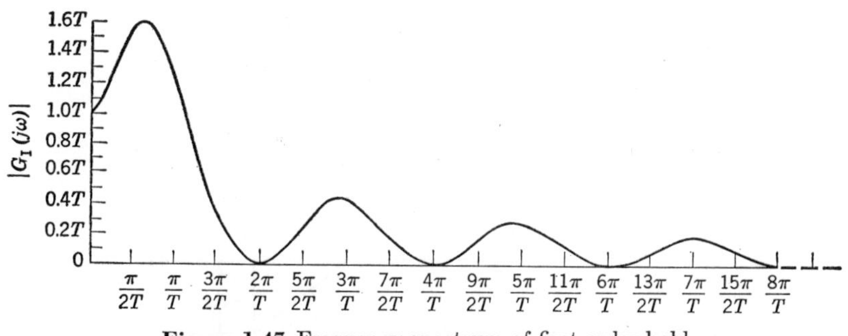

Figure 1.47 Frequency spectrum of first-order hold

† E. I. Jury and W. Schroeder, "Discrete Compensation of Sampled-Data and Continuous Control Systems," Electronics Research Laboratory Report, Series 60, Issue 154, December 14, 1955, University of California, Berkeley.

c. *Generalized First-Order Hold*

In this particular hold,† which is an extension of the first-order hold, the output circuit holds the signal amplitude at its input and adds to it a signal proportional to (the difference between the present and past sampled amplitude) the first difference. This proportional factor is denoted as A and varies from zero to unity. When it is zero we obtain the zero-order hold, and when it is unity we obtain the first-order hold. The transfer function of this generalized hold can be easily obtained from Figure 1.48.

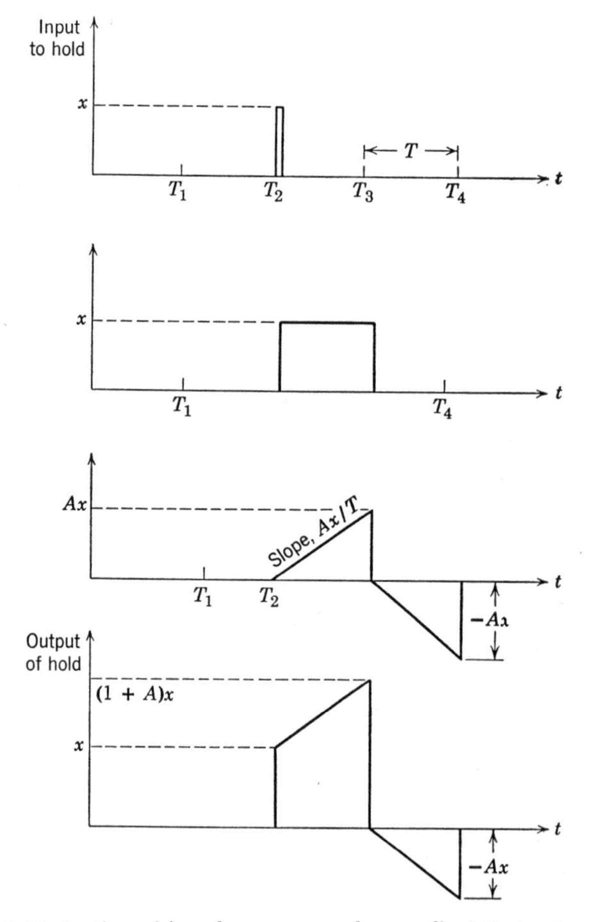

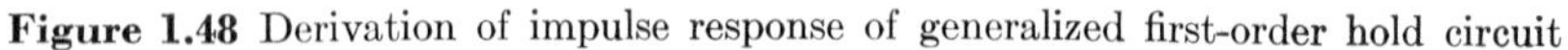

Figure 1.48 Derivation of impulse response of generalized first-order hold circuit

† Waldo I. Rogers, "Data Desampling Techniques in Digital Computer Control Systems," Master of Science Thesis, University of California, Los Angeles, June 1954.

Its final form can be expressed as follows for $x = 1$:

$$G_{Ig}(s) = \frac{A}{T}\left(\frac{1 - e^{-Ts}}{s}\right)^2 + \frac{(1 - e^{-Ts})(1 - Ae^{-Ts})}{s} \tag{1.238}$$

It is noticed from this equation that when $A \to 0$, $G_{Ig}(s) \to G_0(s)$, and when $A \to 1$, $G_{Ig}(s) \to G_I(s)$.

The advantage of having control on the value of A stems from the following observations. If the frequency distributions of the reference function are known, an optimum value of A can be found which will minimize the error between the actual input and the hold output for this particular band of frequencies. For low frequencies the value of A approaches unity. This is due to the fact that the shape of the function between two samples is nearly linear.

1.17 Physical Implementation of Hold Circuits

Since the hold circuit is used primarily for smoothing or extrapolating the sampled output of a digital computer before it is applied to the input of a control system, as shown in Fig. 1.49, it is appropriate to make use

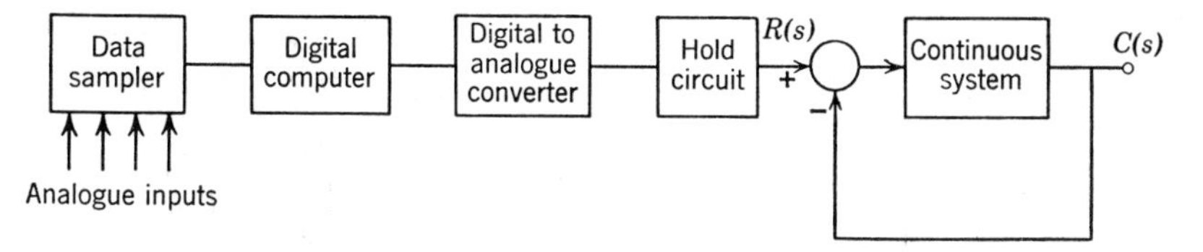

Figure 1.49 A simple feedback system controlled by a digital computer

of the computer to obtain the delay required in the hold. From Fig. 1.49 it is noticed that a time delay of one computation time is needed to obtain the desired impulsive response of the hold circuit. This suggests the adaption of the computer, itself, to perform this delay and the associated subtraction. Therefore, the digital computer, if present in the control system, can be used partially to obtain the first-order hold. Furthermore, it can also be conveniently used to generate a conic hold (the use of the three data points) or higher-order holds if required.

The second method to generate a hold is to simulate the transfer function of the hold. This can be done by the use of a sampler and active circuits, which can be easily simulated on an analogue computer.

The third method is to approximate the hold transfer function by linear passive network. There are several methods that can be applied, for instance, the Pade's approximation techniques or Ba Hli's method; the latter is discussed in detail in Chapter 6.

As an illustration of the Pade approximation, we can approximate the transfer function of the generalized first-order hold. Pade's second-order approximant of the ideal delay e^{-Ts} is given as follows:†

$$e^{-Ts} \cong \frac{1 - \frac{1}{2}Ts + \frac{1}{12}T^2s^2}{1 + \frac{1}{2}Ts + \frac{1}{12}T^2s^2} \tag{1.239}$$

Inserting this expression in equation (1.238), we obtain, after minor algebraic manipulations, a network approximation as follows:‡

$$G_{Ig}(s) \cong T \frac{1 + \left(\frac{1 + A}{2}\right) Ts + \left(\frac{1 - A}{12}\right) T^2s^2}{1 + Ts + \frac{5}{12}T^2s^2 + \frac{1}{12}T^3s^3 + \frac{1}{144}T^4s^4} \tag{1.240}$$

This transfer function can be synthesized by classical methods using RLC networks. In some practical cases, however, the value of capacitance and/or inductance required may be quite large, hence rendering the implementation of such a network impractical.

1.18 Other Hold Circuits

The zero-order hold has one main disadvantage, the introduction of phase lag. However, if such a hold circuit is used to drive an under-

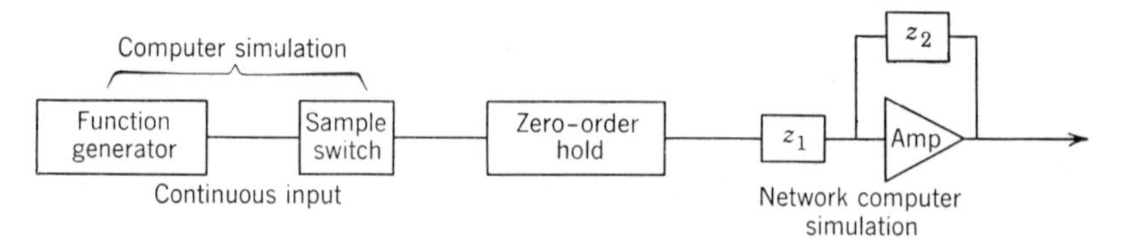

Figure 1.50 Zero-order hold plus overshoot network

† W. H. Kautz, "Network Synthesis for Specified Transient Response," M.I.T. Technical Report 209, April 23, 1952.

‡ Waldo I. Rogers, "Data Desampling Techniques in Digital Computer Control Systems," Master of Science Thesis, University of California, Los Angeles, June 1954.

damped network, an overshoot is obtained in the output of the combination. This overshoot is used to compensate for the inherent lag in the zero-order hold. This procedure might dispense with the use of first- or higher-order holds. A circuit indicating this is shown in Fig. 1.50.

TABLE 1.1

Extended List of z-Transforms and Their Inverse †

$F(s)$	$F^*(z)$	$f(nT)$
e^{-kTs}	z^{-k}	$\delta(n-k)T$
$\frac{1}{s}$	$\frac{z}{z-1}$	1
$\frac{1}{s+a}$	$\frac{z}{z-e^{-aT}}$	e^{-aTn}
$\frac{1}{s^2}$	$\frac{Tz}{(z-1)^2}$	Tn
$\frac{1}{s^2(s+a)}$	$\frac{(T/a)z}{(z-1)^2} - \frac{(1-e^{-aT})z}{a^2(z-1)(z-e^{-aT})}$	$\frac{1}{a}(Tn) - \frac{1-e^{-aTn}}{a^2}$
$\frac{a^2}{s(s^2+a^2)}$	$(1-\cos aT) \times \frac{(1+z)z}{(z-1)(z^2-2z\cos aT+1)}$	$(1-\cos aTn)$
$\frac{a}{s^2+a^2}$	$\frac{z \sin aT}{z^2-2z\cos aT+1}$	$\sin(aTn)$
$\frac{1}{s^3}$	$\frac{T^2 z(z+1)}{2(z-1)^3}$	$\frac{1}{2}(Tn)^2$
$\frac{1}{s^4}$	$\frac{T^3 z(z+1)}{2(z-1)^4} + \frac{T^3(z+2)z}{6(z-1)^3}$	$\frac{1}{3!}(Tn)^3$
$\frac{1}{s^5}$	$\frac{T^4 z}{24}\frac{(z^3+1)+11z(z+1)}{(z-1)^5}$	$\frac{(nT)^4}{4!}$

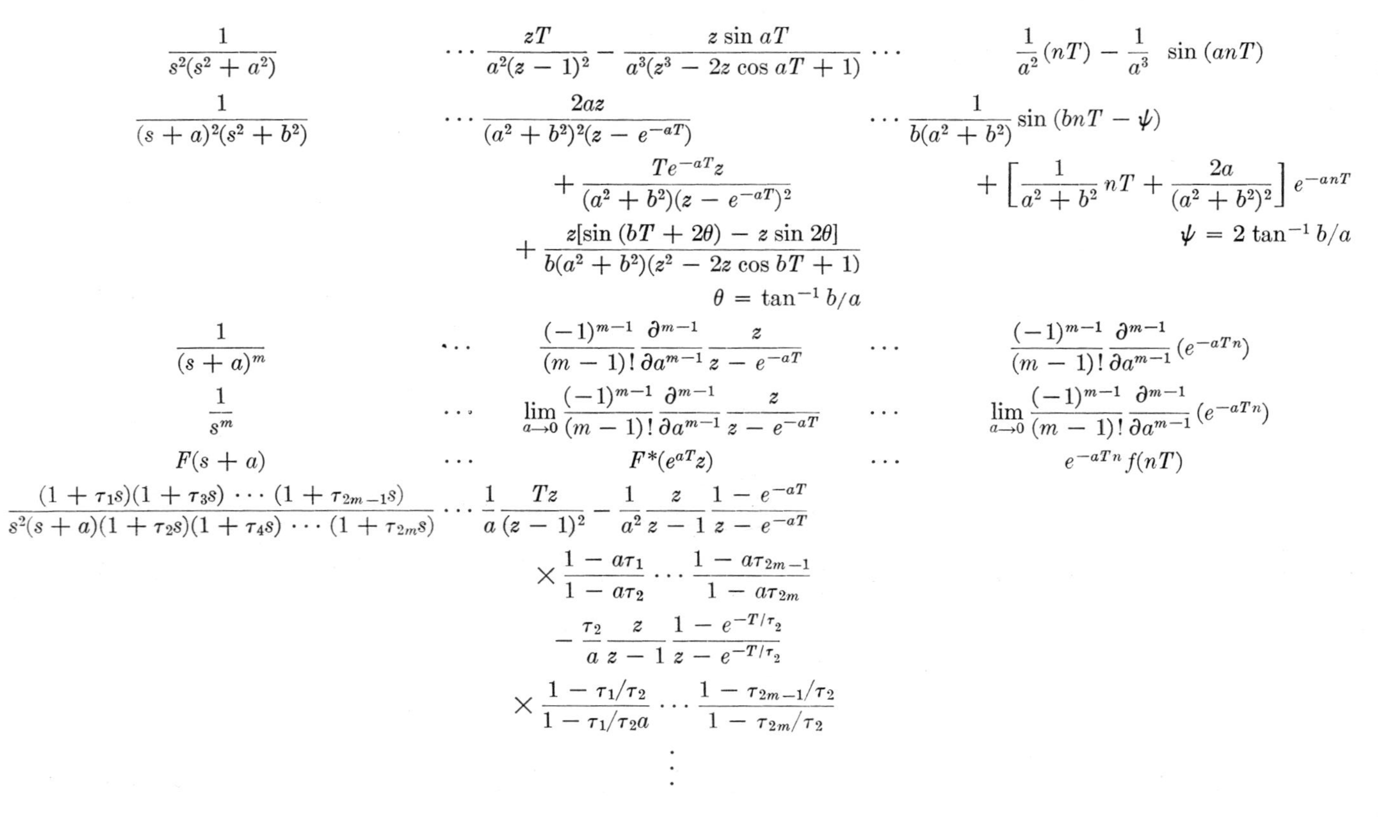

$\dfrac{1}{s^2(s^2+a^2)}$	$\cdots\ \dfrac{zT}{a^2(z-1)^2} - \dfrac{z \sin aT}{a^3(z^3 - 2z\cos aT + 1)}\ \cdots$	$\dfrac{1}{a^2}(nT) - \dfrac{1}{a^3}\ \sin(anT)$
$\dfrac{1}{(s+a)^2(s^2+b^2)}$	$\cdots\ \dfrac{2az}{(a^2+b^2)^2(z-e^{-aT})} + \dfrac{Te^{-aT}z}{(a^2+b^2)(z-e^{-aT})^2} + \dfrac{z[\sin(bT+2\theta) - z\sin 2\theta]}{b(a^2+b^2)(z^2-2z\cos bT+1)}$, $\theta = \tan^{-1} b/a$	$\cdots\ \dfrac{1}{b(a^2+b^2)}\sin(bnT-\psi) + \left[\dfrac{1}{a^2+b^2}nT + \dfrac{2a}{(a^2+b^2)^2}\right]e^{-anT}$, $\psi = 2\tan^{-1} b/a$
$\dfrac{1}{(s+a)^m}$	$\cdots\ \dfrac{(-1)^{m-1}}{(m-1)!}\dfrac{\partial^{m-1}}{\partial a^{m-1}}\dfrac{z}{z-e^{-aT}}\ \cdots$	$\dfrac{(-1)^{m-1}}{(m-1)!}\dfrac{\partial^{m-1}}{\partial a^{m-1}}(e^{-aTn})$
$\dfrac{1}{s^m}$	$\cdots\ \lim_{a\to 0}\dfrac{(-1)^{m-1}}{(m-1)!}\dfrac{\partial^{m-1}}{\partial a^{m-1}}\dfrac{z}{z-e^{-aT}}\ \cdots$	$\lim_{a\to 0}\dfrac{(-1)^{m-1}}{(m-1)!}\dfrac{\partial^{m-1}}{\partial a^{m-1}}(e^{-aTn})$
$F(s+a)$	$\cdots\ F^*(e^{aT}z)\ \cdots$	$e^{-aTn}f(nT)$
$\dfrac{(1+\tau_1 s)(1+\tau_3 s)\cdots(1+\tau_{2m-1}s)}{s^2(s+a)(1+\tau_2 s)(1+\tau_4 s)\cdots(1+\tau_{2m}s)}$	$\cdots\ \dfrac{1}{a}\dfrac{Tz}{(z-1)^2} - \dfrac{1}{a^2}\dfrac{z}{z-1}\dfrac{1-e^{-aT}}{z-e^{-aT}} \times \dfrac{1-a\tau_1}{1-a\tau_2}\cdots\dfrac{1-a\tau_{2m-1}}{1-a\tau_{2m}} - \dfrac{\tau_2}{a}\dfrac{z}{z-1}\dfrac{1-e^{-T/\tau_2}}{z-e^{-T/\tau_2}} \times \dfrac{1-\tau_1/\tau_2}{1-\tau_1/\tau_2 a}\cdots\dfrac{1-\tau_{2m-1}/\tau_2}{1-\tau_{2m}/\tau_2}$ $\vdots$	

TABLE 1.1 (*Continued*)

Extended List of z-Transforms and Their Inverse †

$F(s)$	$F^*(z)$	$f(nT)$
	$-\frac{\tau_{2m}}{a}\frac{z}{z-1}\frac{1-e^{-T/\tau_{2m}}}{z-e^{-T/\tau_{2m}}} \times \frac{1-\tau_1/\tau_{2m}}{1-1/\tau_{2m}a}\cdots\frac{1-\tau_{2m-1}/\tau_{2m}}{1-\tau_{2m-2}/\tau_{2m}}$	
$\frac{s}{s^2+a^2}$	$\frac{z(z-\cos aT)}{z^2-2z\cos aT+1}$	$\cos(aTn)$
$\frac{a}{(s+\alpha)^2+a^2}$	$\frac{z\,e^{-\alpha T}\sin aT}{z^2-2e^{-\alpha T}z\cos aT+e^{-2\alpha T}}$	$e^{-\alpha Tn}\sin(aTn)$
$\frac{1}{(s^2-\beta^2)s^2}$	$\frac{-z}{(2\beta^3)(z-e^{-\beta T})}+\frac{z}{(2\beta^3)(z-e^{\beta T})}-\frac{zT}{\beta^2(z-1)^2}$	
$\frac{k\pi/T}{s^2+(k\pi/T)^2}$	0	
$\frac{\pi/T}{s^2+(\pi/T)^2}$	0	
$\frac{\pi/T}{(s+\alpha)^2+(\pi/T)^2}$	0	
$\frac{s+\alpha}{(s+\alpha)^2+(\pi/T)^2}$	$\frac{z}{z+e^{-\alpha T}}$	

$\dfrac{s+a}{(s+\alpha)^2+(\pi/T)^2}$	$\cdots$	$\dfrac{z}{z+e^{-\alpha T}}$		
		$\dfrac{z}{(z-e^{-aT})(z-e^{-bT})}$	$\cdots$	$\dfrac{e^{-aTn}-e^{-bTn}}{e^{-aT}-e^{-bT}}$
		$\dfrac{z(a+bz)}{[(z-\alpha)^2+\beta^2](z-1)}$	$\cdots$	$\dfrac{a+b}{(1-\alpha)^2+\beta^2}+\dfrac{[(a+b\alpha)^2+(b\beta)^2]^{1/2}}{\beta[(\alpha-1)^2+\beta^2]^{1/2}} \times [\alpha^2+\beta^2]^{n/2}\sin(n\theta+\psi+\lambda)$ $\theta=\tan^{-1}\beta/\alpha,$ $\psi=-\tan^{-1}\beta/(\alpha-1),$ $\lambda=\tan^{-1}\dfrac{b\beta}{(a+b\alpha)}$
		$\dfrac{z}{(z-\gamma)[(z-\alpha)^2+\beta^2]}$	$\cdots$	$\dfrac{\gamma^n}{(\gamma-\alpha)^2+\beta^2}+\dfrac{1}{\beta[(\alpha-\gamma)^2+\beta^2]^{1/2}} (\alpha^2+\beta^2)^{n/2}\sin(n\theta+\psi)$ $\theta=\tan^{-1}\beta/\alpha,$ $\psi=\tan^{-1}\beta/(\alpha-\gamma)$
		$\dfrac{z}{(z-1)(z-\gamma)[(z-\alpha)^2+\beta^2]}$	$\cdots$	$\dfrac{1}{(1-\gamma)[(1-\alpha)^2+\beta^2]}+\dfrac{[\alpha^2+\beta^2]^{n/2}\sin(n\theta+\psi+\lambda)}{\beta[(\alpha-\gamma)^2+\beta^2]^{1/2}[(\alpha-1)^2+\beta^2]^{1/2}}+\dfrac{\gamma^n}{(\gamma-1)[(\gamma-\alpha)^2+\beta^2]}$ $\theta=\tan^{-1}\beta/\alpha,$ $\psi=-\tan^{-1}\beta/(\alpha-1),$ $\lambda=-\tan^{-1}\beta/(\alpha-\gamma)$

TABLE 1.1 (*Continued*)

Extended List of z-Transforms and Their Inverse †

$F(s)$	$F^*(z)$	$f(nT)$
	$\dfrac{z(z+a_0)}{(z-1)(z-\gamma)[(z-\alpha)^2+\beta^2]}$	$\cdots \dfrac{(1+a_0)}{(1-\gamma)[(1-\alpha)^2+\beta^2]} + \dfrac{(\gamma+a_0)\gamma^n}{(\gamma-1)[(\gamma-\alpha)^2+\beta^2]} + \dfrac{[\alpha^2+\beta^2]^{n/2}[(a_0+\alpha)^2+\beta^2]^{1/2}}{\beta[(\alpha-1)^2+\beta^2]^{1/2}[(\alpha-\gamma)^2+\beta^2]^{1/2}} \sin(n\theta+\psi+\lambda)$ $\theta = \tan^{-1}\beta/\alpha,$ $\psi = \psi_1+\psi_2,$ $(\psi_1 = -\tan^{-1}\beta/(\alpha-1)$ $\psi_2 = -\tan^{-1}\beta/(\alpha-\gamma) = \tan^{-1}\dfrac{\beta}{(a_0+\alpha)}$
	$\dfrac{z}{(z-\gamma)(z-1)^2}$	$\cdots \dfrac{\gamma^n}{(\gamma-1)^2} + \dfrac{n}{(1-\gamma)} - \dfrac{1}{(1-\gamma)^2}$
	$\dfrac{z(z+a_0)}{(z-\gamma)(z-1)^2}$	$\cdots \dfrac{\gamma+a_0}{(\gamma-1)^2}\gamma^n + \dfrac{1+a_0}{1-\gamma}n + \left[\dfrac{1}{1-\gamma} - \dfrac{a_0+1}{(1-\gamma)^2}\right]$

$\dfrac{z}{(z-\gamma)^2(z-1)^3}$	…	$\dfrac{n\gamma^{n-1}}{(\gamma-1)^3}-\dfrac{3\gamma^n}{(\gamma-1)^4}+\dfrac{1}{2}\left[\dfrac{n(n-1)}{(1-\gamma)^2}-\dfrac{4n}{(1-\gamma)^3}+\dfrac{6}{(1-\gamma)^4}\right]$
$\dfrac{z(z+a_0)}{(z-\gamma)^2(z-1)^2}$	…	$\dfrac{(\gamma+a_0)n\gamma^{n-1}+\gamma^n}{(\gamma-1)^2}-\dfrac{2\gamma^n(\gamma+a_0)}{(\gamma-1)^3}+\dfrac{n(1+a_0)+1}{(1-\gamma)^2}-\dfrac{2(1+a_0)}{(1-\gamma)^3}$
$a+\dfrac{1}{T}\ln\left(\dfrac{z-e^{-aT}}{z-1}\right)$	…	$\left(\dfrac{1-e^{-anT}}{nT}\right)$
$\dfrac{z}{z+a}$	…	$a^n\cos\pi n$
$\dfrac{z}{z+e^{-\alpha T}}$	…	$e^{-\alpha Tn}\cos\pi n$
$\dfrac{z(z-e^{-\alpha T}\cos aT)}{z^2-2z\,e^{-\alpha T}\cos aT+e^{-2\alpha T}}$	…	$e^{-\alpha Tn}\cos aTn$
$K\dfrac{z\prod_{i=1}^{m}(z-\mu_i)\prod_{i=1}^{g}[(z-\zeta_i)^2+\gamma_i^2]}{(z-1)\prod_{i=1}^{q}(z-\rho_i)\prod_{i=1}^{l}[(z-\alpha_i)^2+\beta_i^2]}$ $2l+q>2g+m$	…	$A_0\Big[1+\sum_{k=1}^{l}M_k\dfrac{\beta_{0k}^2[\alpha_k^2+\beta_k^2]^{n/2}}{\beta_k[(\alpha_k-1)^2+\beta_k^2]^{1/2}}\times\sin(n\theta_k+\lambda_k+\psi_k)+\sum_{k=1}^{q}(-1)r_k^{+k}N_k(\rho_k)^n\Big]$ $A_0=K\dfrac{\prod_{i=1}^{m}(1-\mu_i)\prod_{i=1}^{g}[(1-\zeta_i)^2+\gamma_i^2]}{\prod_{i=1}^{q}(1-\rho_i)\prod_{i=1}^{l}[(1-\alpha_i)^2+\beta_i^2]}$

TABLE 1.1 (*Continued*)

Extended List of z-Transforms and Their Inverse †

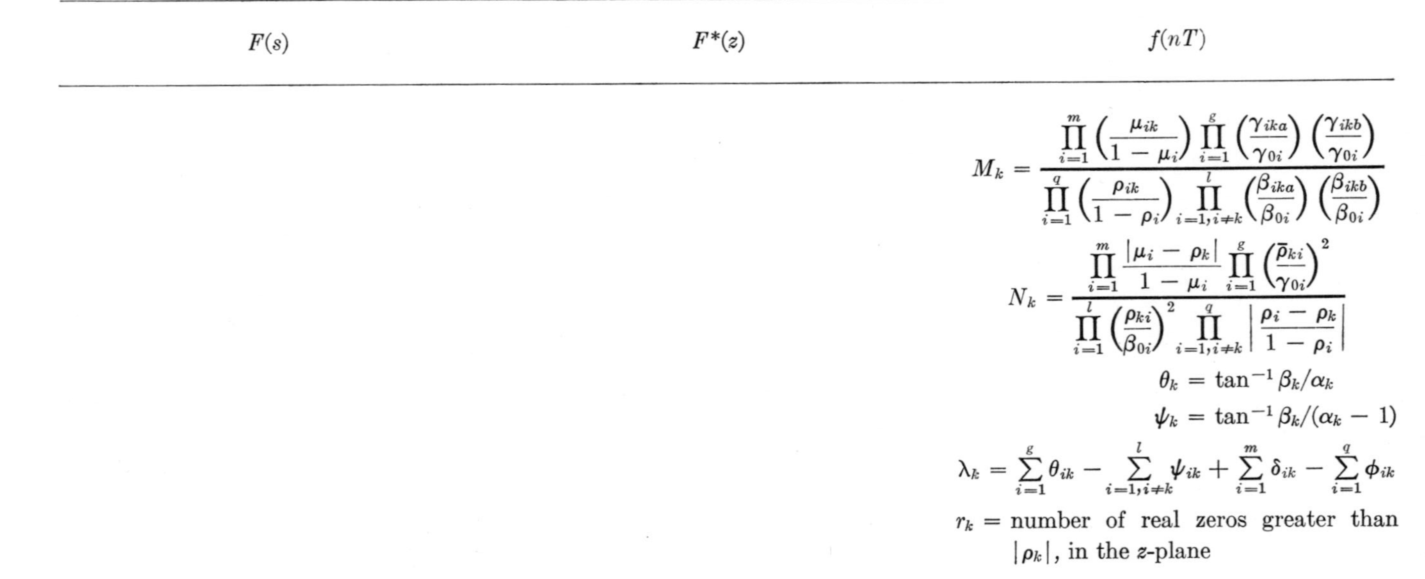

$F(s)$	$F^*(z)$	$f(nT)$
		$M_k = \dfrac{\prod_{i=1}^{m}\left(\dfrac{\mu_{ik}}{1-\mu_i}\right)\prod_{i=1}^{g}\left(\dfrac{\gamma_{ika}}{\gamma_{0i}}\right)\left(\dfrac{\gamma_{ikb}}{\gamma_{0i}}\right)}{\prod_{i=1}^{q}\left(\dfrac{\rho_{ik}}{1-\rho_i}\right)\prod_{i=1, i\neq k}^{l}\left(\dfrac{\beta_{ika}}{\beta_{0i}}\right)\left(\dfrac{\beta_{ikb}}{\beta_{0i}}\right)}$
		$N_k = \dfrac{\prod_{i=1}^{m}\dfrac{\lvert\mu_i-\rho_k\rvert}{1-\mu_i}\prod_{i=1}^{g}\left(\dfrac{\bar{\rho}_{ki}}{\gamma_{0i}}\right)^2}{\prod_{i=1}^{l}\left(\dfrac{\rho_{ki}}{\beta_{0i}}\right)^2\prod_{i=1, i\neq k}^{q}\left\lvert\dfrac{\rho_i-\rho_k}{1-\rho_i}\right\rvert}$
		$\theta_k = \tan^{-1}\beta_k/\alpha_k$
		$\psi_k = \tan^{-1}\beta_k/(\alpha_k - 1)$
		$\lambda_k = \sum_{i=1}^{g}\theta_{ik} - \sum_{i=1, i\neq k}^{l}\psi_{ik} + \sum_{i=1}^{m}\delta_{ik} - \sum_{i=1}^{q}\phi_{ik}$
		r_k = number of real zeros greater than $\lvert\rho_k\rvert$, in the z-plane

Note: The explanation of z-transforms notations in this table is as follows:

$\alpha_k \pm j\beta_k$ = location of kth pair of complex poles inside the unit circle
$\zeta_k \pm j\gamma_k$ = location of kth pair of complex zeros in the z-plane
ρ_k = location of kth real pole inside the unit circle
μ_k = location of kth real zero in the z-plane
$\beta_{0k}^2 = (1 - \alpha_k)^2 + \beta_k^2$
$\gamma_{0k}^2 = (1 - \zeta_k)^2 + \gamma_k^2$
ρ_{ik} = distance from ρ_i to $\alpha_k + j\beta_k$
μ_{ik} = distance from μ_i to $\alpha_k + j\beta_k$
β_{ika} = distance from $\alpha_i + j\beta_i$ to $\alpha_k + j\beta_k$
β_{ikb} = distance from $\alpha_i - j\beta_i$ to $\alpha_k + j\beta_k$
γ_{ika} = distance from $\zeta_i + j\gamma_i$ to $\alpha_k + j\beta_k$
γ_{ikb} = distance from $\zeta_i - j\gamma_i$ to $\alpha_k + j\beta_k$
$\bar{\rho}_{ik}$ = distance from ρ_i to $\zeta_k + j\gamma_k$

$$\theta_{ik} = \theta_{ika} + \theta_{ikb} = \tan^{-1}\frac{\beta_k - \gamma_i}{\alpha_k - \zeta_i} + \tan^{-1}\frac{\beta_k + \gamma_i}{\alpha_k - \zeta_i}$$

$$\psi_{ik} = \psi_{ika} + \psi_{ikb} = \tan^{-1}\frac{\beta_k - \beta_i}{\alpha_k - \alpha_i} + \tan^{-1}\frac{\beta_k + \beta_i}{\alpha_k - \alpha_i}$$

$$\delta_{ki} = \tan^{-1}\frac{\beta_k}{\alpha_k - \mu_i}$$

$$\theta_{ik} = \tan^{-1}\frac{\beta_k}{\alpha_k - \rho_i}$$

† E. I. Jury, "Analysis and Synthesis of Sampled-Data Control Systems," *Trans. A.I.E.E.*, Vol. 73, Pt. I, 1954, pp. 332–346.

CHAPTER 2

Modified z-Transform Method

2.0 Introduction—Response between the Sampling Instants

The use of digital computers as the compensating component of a feedback system requires the description of the output at all instants of time. In such mixed systems in which part of the information is sampled and part of it is described continuously as a function of time, the problem of output behavior between the sampling instants is of much importance. Indeed, the digital transfer function or its programming function can be correctly obtained in most cases only if the output is described as a continuous function of time. Thus four methods have been developed whereby we can obtain information about the system's behavior between the sampling instants. A method often used, called the modified z-transform, is discussed in detail in this chapter. This method is an extension of the z-transform, and indeed most of the theorems and derivations discussed in the preceding chapter can be obtained from the modified z-transform by effecting the limiting case, as the following material will show.

Before introducing a detailed discussion of this method it is desirable to present a brief description of the other existing methods which serve mainly as analysis and can be extended for actual design.

2.1 Submultiple of the Sampling Period Method †

In this method a fictitious sampler with a period of $T' = T/n$ is introduced in series with the actual sampler that describes the sampled-data system as shown in Fig. 2.1.

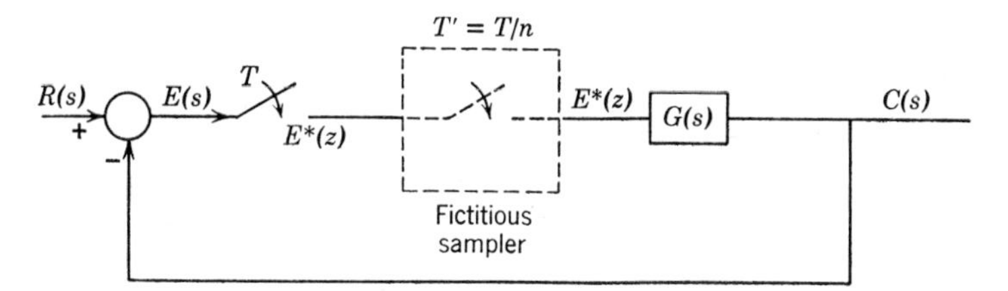

Figure 2.1 Sampled-data feedback system with fictitious sampler

In this scheme the actual error transform is presented as follows:

$$E^*(z) = \frac{R^*(z)}{1 + G^*(z)} = A_0 + \frac{A_1}{z} + \frac{A_2}{z^2} + \frac{A_3}{z^3} + \cdots \tag{2.1}$$

Suppose the period of the fictitious sampler is half the period T of the actual sampler, that is,

$$T' = T/n = T/2 \tag{2.2}$$

then

$$E^*(z) = A_0 + \frac{0}{z} + \frac{A_1}{z^2} + \frac{0}{z^3} + \frac{A_2}{z^4} + \frac{0}{z^5} + \frac{A_3}{z^6} + \cdots \tag{2.3}$$

Thus it is noticed that if z is replaced by z^2 in equation (2.1), we obtain $E^*(z)$ as follows:

$$E^*(z) = \frac{R^*(z^2)}{1 + G^*(z^2)} \tag{2.4}$$

The output for the new sampling period is

$$C^{*\prime}(z) = \frac{R^*(z^2)}{1 + G^*(z^2)} \times G^{*\prime}(z) \qquad (2.5)\ ‡$$

where $G^{*\prime}(z)$ = z-transform of $G(s)$ with respect to the period $T' = T/2$.

† W. K. Linvill and R. W. Sittler, *I.R.E. Convention Record*, New York, Pt. I, 1953, pp. 99–104. G. V. Lago and John G. Truxal, "The Design of Sampled-Data Feedback Systems," *Trans. A.I.E.E.*, Vol. 73, Pt. II, 1954, pp. 247–253.

‡ Since z is $e^{sT/2}$, which can be represented as z_2, this equation can be written as

$$C^*(z_2) = \frac{R^*(z_2{}^2)}{1 + G^*(z_2{}^2)} G^*(z_2) \tag{2.5a}$$

Equation (2.5) yields the output at half-points between sampling instants. Similarly we obtain the output at one-quarter the sampling period if $n = 4$. Therefore, by varying n in integer values, we can obtain the response between the sampling instants.

2.2 Impulsive-Response Method

This method is a direct application of the impulsive response of the system and the superposition theorem. Consider the system shown in Fig. 2.2. The response $c(t)$ is given by the following expression: †

$$c(t) = g_0(t) + g_1(t) + g_2(t) + g_3(t) + \cdots \tag{2.6}$$

where $g_0(t)$ is the impulsive response to the error for the first sampling instant and $g_1(t)$ is the system impulsive response to the error at the end

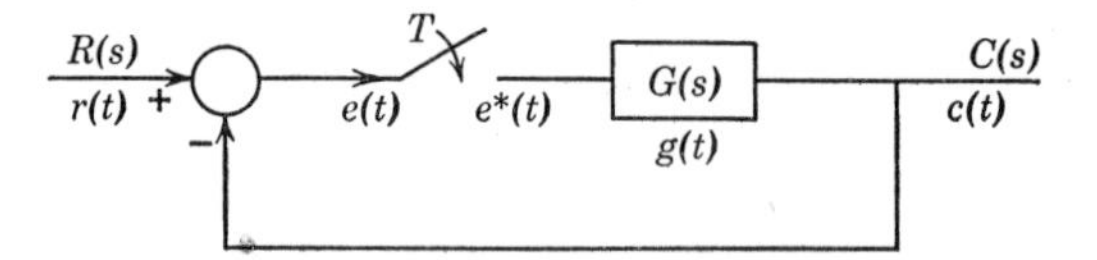

Figure 2.2 Sampled-data feedback system with unity feedback

of the first sampling period. Similarly, $g_2(t), g_3(t) + \cdots$ are the impulsive responses for the values of the error at each sampling period.

2.3 Real-Convolution Method

In this method the Laplace transform of the output is obtained from Fig. 2.3, as follows:

$$C(s) = E^*(s) \times G(s) \tag{2.7}$$

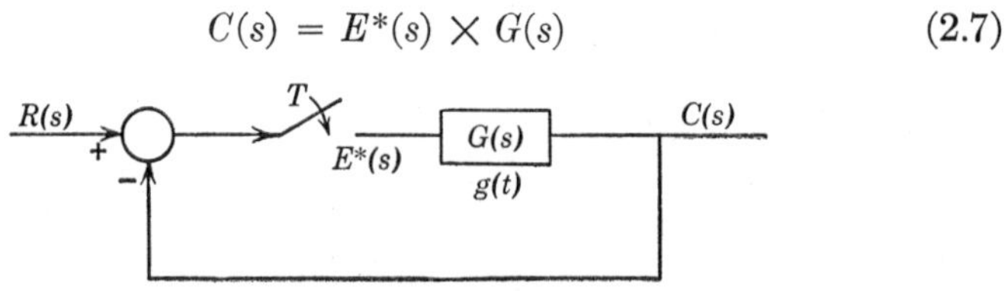

Figure 2.3 Sampled-data feedback system

Using the convolution theorem, we obtain the inverse of equation (2.7):

$$c(t) = \int_0^t e^*(\tau)\, g(t - \tau)\, d\tau \tag{2.8}$$

† G. V. Lago and John G. Truxal, "The Design of Sampled-Data Feedback Systems," *Trans. A.I.E.E.*, Vol. 73, Pt. II, 1954, pp. 247–253.

Since the error $e^*(t)$ is available only at the sampling instants, thus

$$c(t) = \sum_{n=0}^{n=m} [r(nT) - c(nT)]\, g(t - nT), \quad \text{for } mT \leq t \leq (m+1)T \tag{2.9}$$

Actually this method † is the same as the method mentioned above. Furthermore, the output can be obtained as the inverse Laplace of equation (2.7) as follows:

$$c(t) = \frac{1}{2\pi j} \int_{c-j\infty}^{c+j\infty} C(s)\, e^{st}\, ds = \frac{1}{2\pi j} \int_{c-j\infty}^{c+j\infty} E^*(s)\, G(s)\, e^{st}\, ds \tag{2.10}$$

Usually equation (2.10) yields the output as an infinite series in time and requires the evaluation of the singularities of the integrand.

2.4 z-Transform and Impulsive-Response Combination Method ‡

This method, formulated by Sklansky and Ragazzini, makes use of both the impulsive-response and the z-transform methods. Consider a

Figure 2.4 Sampled-data system with one time constant

linear system shown in Fig. 2.4 and given as

$$c(t) = A_1\, e(0T)\, e^{-a_1 t}, \qquad 0 \leq t < T \tag{2.11}$$

The output between the first and second sampling period is given from the impulsive-response and superposition theorems as shown in Fig. 2.5.

$$c(t) = A_1\, e(0T)\, e^{-a_1 t} + A_1\, e(1T)\, e^{-a_1(t-T)} \qquad T \leq t < 2T \tag{2.12}$$

Equation (2.12) can be written as

$$c(t) = [A_1\, e(0T)\, e^{-a_1 T} + A_1\, e(1T)]\, e^{-a_1(t-T)} \tag{2.13}$$

but

$$A_1\, e(0T)\, e^{-a_1 T} + A_1\, e(1T) = c(1T) \tag{2.14}$$

where $c(1T)$ is the output at the first sampling period.

† G. W. Johnson, D. P. Lindorff, and C. G. A. Nordling, "Extension of Continuous-Data Design Technique to Sampled-Data Control Systems, *Trans. A.I.E.E.*, Vol. 74, Pt. II, 1955, pp. 252–263.

‡ J. Sklansky and J. R. Ragazzini, "Analysis of Errors in Sampled-Data Feedback Systems," *Trans. A.I.E.E.*, Vol. 74, Pt. II, 1955, pp. 5–7.

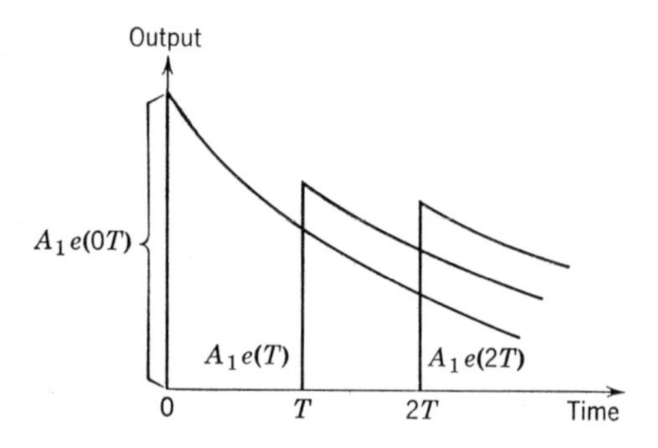

Figure 2.5 Output response of system in Fig. 2.4

From the inverse z-transform of the output $c(1T)$ can be found. Similarly, the output at any time is given by

$$c_1(t) = c_1(nT)\, e^{-a_1(t-nT)} \qquad nT \leq t < (n+1)T \tag{2.15}$$

If $G(s)$ is composed of many time constants, these can be found by partial fraction expansion, shown as parallel paths in Fig. 2.6. Furthermore, if a hold circuit is used, the term $1 - e^{-Ts}$ is factored and the term $1/s$ is considered with $G(s)$, as shown in Fig. 2.7.

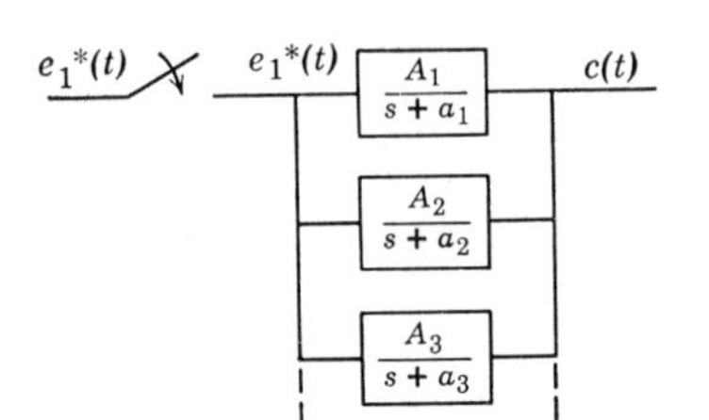

Figure 2.6 Sampled-data system with parallel components

The output is composed of additions of the various outputs of the channels, that is,

$$c(t) = c_1(t) + c_2(t) + c_3(t) + \cdots \tag{2.16}$$

The coefficients $c_1(nT)$, $c_2(nT)$ can be obtained from the z-transform of the appropriate channels, which yield

$$C^*(z) = \frac{R^*(z)\, G^*(z)}{1 + HG^*(z)} \tag{2.17}$$

$$c(nT) = \mathfrak{z}^{-1}\,[C^*(z)] \tag{2.18}$$

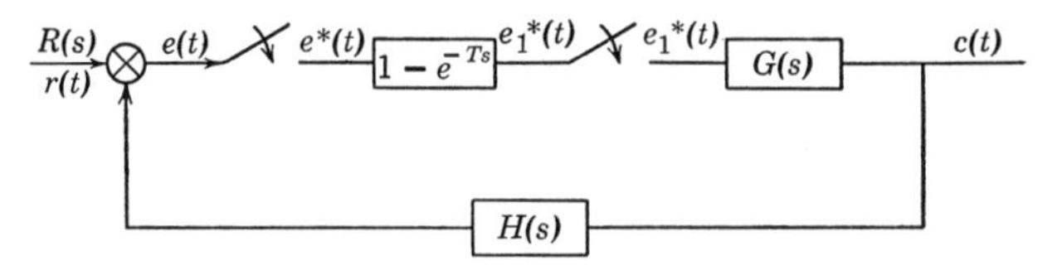

Figure 2.7 A typical sampled-data feedback system

This method is usually applicable to the analysis of the actual response and can be extended to check on the design of sampled-data feedback systems.

2.5 Introduction to the Modified z-Transform Method †

It has been shown in Chapter 1 that the z-transform method can be systematically applied to the analysis of sampled-data control systems. The analysis based on this method yields the response only at the sampling time. This z-transform method can be modified to yield the response at all times, and this method is called the modified z-transform method. It will be shown later in this chapter that the z-transform is only a special case of the general method of the modified z-transform.

Thus, the application of the modified z-transform method to the analysis of sampled-data control systems is analogous to the application of ordinary Laplace transform to the continuous control systems.

a. Modified z-Transform of Sampled-Data Transfer Function ‡

Since the output of a sampled-data system is continuous while its input is sampled, a transfer function can be developed to relate the continuous output transform to the actual input. Consider a sampled-data system shown in Fig. 2.8. If the output is considered only at the sampling

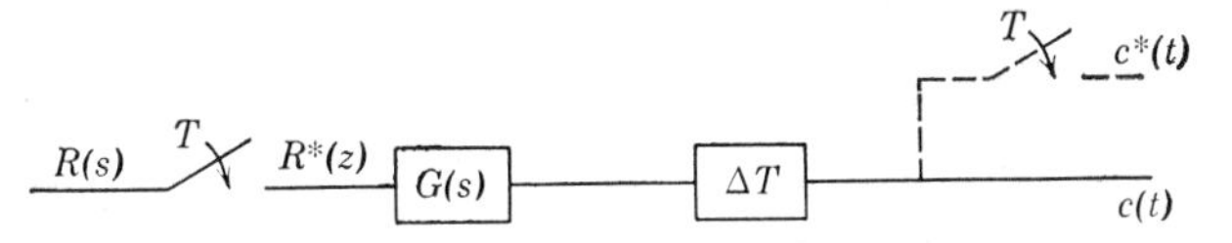

Figure 2.8 Sampled-data system with fictitious delay, ΔT

instants, a fictitious sampler is introduced at the output, which is synchronized with the actual input sampler as shown in Fig. 2.8. Based on this analysis the z-transform of the transfer function is developed and is given by the following equation

$$G^*(z) = \mathcal{L}\,[g(t) \times \delta_T(t)] \tag{2.19}$$

† This method is based on the extension of R. H. Barker's method of fictitious delay, given in "The Pulse Transfer Function and Its Application to Sampling Servo Systems," *Proc. I.E.E. (London)*, Vol. 99, Pt. IV, 1952, pp. 302–317. Similar results have been developed independently by J. S. Cypkin, *Differenzengleichungen Der Impuls-Und Regeltechnik*, Veb Verlag Technik, Berlin, 1956, Chapter 2.

‡ E. I. Jury, "Synthesis and Critical Study of Sampled-Data Control Systems," *Trans. A.I.E.E.*, Vol. 75, Pt. II, 1956, pp. 141–151.

This transfer function relates the sampled output to the input. The actual output is continuous as shown in Fig. 2.9, and the z-transform of the output yields only the values at the sampling instants. However, to scan the actual output a fictitious delay can be introduced at the output [denoted as (ΔT)]; when this fictitious delay is varied between zero and the sampling period, the actual output can be obtained.†

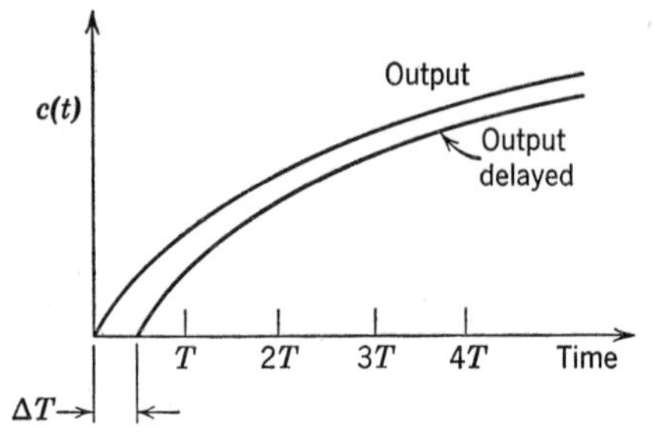

Figure 2.9 Output and fictitiously delayed output of system in Fig. 2.8

Using this concept of artificial delay which is considered negative in this work but can also be positive, we can write a new transfer function which is a function of z and the delay, Δ:

$$G^*(z, \Delta) = \mathcal{L}\,[g(t - \Delta T) \times \delta_T(t)] \tag{2.20}$$

where

$$\mathcal{L}\,[g(t - \Delta T)] = G(s)\, e^{-\Delta s T} \tag{2.21}$$

Equation (2.20) can be evaluated using the real multiplication theorem in the following form:

$$G^*(z, \Delta) = \frac{1}{2\pi j} \int_{c-j\infty}^{c+j\infty} G(p)\, e^{-\Delta p T} \frac{1}{1 - e^{-T(s-p)}}\, dp \tag{2.22}$$

The integral in equation (2.22) can be evaluated either in the right half or left half of the complex plane p as shown in Figs. 1.8 and 1.15. However, to assure the convergence of the integral on the infinite semi-circle, a change in the notation of the variable is required so that the value of the integral on the infinite semi-circle vanishes. This change of variable notation is the following:

$$\Delta = 1 - m \tag{2.23}$$

† R. H. Barker, "The Pulse Transfer Function and Its Application to Sampling Servo Systems," *Proc. I.E.E. (London)*, Vol. 99, Pt. IV, 1952, pp. 302–317.

Therefore equation (2.22) becomes

$$G^*(z, m) = e^{-sT} \frac{1}{2\pi j} \int_{c-j\infty}^{c+j\infty} G(p)\, e^{mpT} \frac{1}{1 - e^{-T(s-p)}}\, dp \qquad (2.24)\dagger$$

because

$$\mathcal{L}\,[g(t - \Delta T) \times \delta_T(t)] = e^{-sT}\, \mathcal{L}\,[g(t + mT) \times \delta_T(t)] \qquad (2.25)$$

By integration in the left half of the complex p-plane, as shown in Fig. 1.15, the modified z-transform of $G(s)$ equals ‡

$$G^*(z, m) = z^{-1} \sum_{\text{poles of } G(s)} \text{Residue of } G(s) \frac{e^{msT}}{1 - e^{sT} z^{-1}} \qquad (2.26)\S$$

If m approaches unity in equation (2.26), we obtain the z-transform. In case of discontinuous impulsive response of $G(s)$, the inverse for this value of m yields the response at the lower value of the discontinuity, that is, at 0^-, T^-, $2T^-$, $3T^-$, $\cdots$. Furthermore, if equation (2.26) is multiplied by z and we let $m \to 0$, the z-transform is obtained and the inverse yields the response at the sampling instants; in the case of discontinuity in the response, the inverse yields the upper value of the discontinuity, that is, at 0^+, T^+, $2T^+$, $\cdots$.

Generally, for continuous system response the following relation exists:

$$G^*(z) = \lim_{m \to 0} z\, G^*(z, m) = \lim_{m \to 1} G^*(z, m) \qquad (2.27)$$

Thus, it is noticed that the z-transform is a special case of the modified z-transform, and for all types of responses the z-transform is obtained from the following relation:

$$G^*(z) = \lim_{m \to 0} z\, G^*(z, m) \qquad (2.28)$$

† Strictly, $G^*(z, \Delta) = G^*(z, 1-m)$; however, for notational convenience the form $G^*(z, m)$ is used in this text instead of $G^*(z, 1-m)$.

‡ E. I. Jury, "Additions to the Modified z-Transform Method," *I.R.E. Wescon Convention Record*, Pt. IV, August 21, 1957, pp. 136–156.

§ For the case in which $G(s) = A(s)/B(s)$ has simple poles, equation (2.26) can be written as:

$$G^*(z, m) = z^{-1} \left[\sum_{n=1}^{N} \frac{A(s_n)}{B'(s_n)} \frac{e^{ms_nT}}{1 - e^{-T(s-s_n)}} \right]_{z=e^{Ts}} \qquad (2.26a)$$

where $s_1, s_2, \cdots, s_n$ are the simple roots of $B(s)$.

EXAMPLE

Suppose that $G(s)$ in Fig. 2.8 is

$$G(s) = \frac{K}{s + a} \tag{2.29}$$

The z-transform of equation (2.29) yields

$$G^*(z) = K\frac{z}{z - e^{-aT}} \tag{2.30}$$

The modified z-transform of $G(s)$ can be obtained using equation (2.26a) to yield

$$G^*(z, m) = K\frac{e^{-maT}}{z - e^{-aT}} \tag{2.31}$$

Since $G(s)$ has a discontinuous impulsive response, the z-transform can be obtained from the modified z-transform using relation (2.28).

$$G^*(z) = K\frac{z}{z - e^{-aT}} \tag{2.32}$$

which is identical to equation (2.30). However, by letting $m \to 1$ in expression (2.31), we obtain a form that is not identical to the z-transform.

Table 2.1 (page 104) lists extensive forms of the modified z-transform for various forms of $G(s)$. This table can also be used to obtain the z-transform using the relationship expressed in equation (2.28).

Evaluating equation (2.25) by integrating in the right half of the p-plane which encloses all the singularities of $1/(1 - e^{-Ts})$, we obtain an alternate form as an infinite series formula for the modified z-transform as follows:

$$G^*(e^{Ts}, m) = \frac{1}{T}\sum_{k=-\infty}^{k=\infty} G(s + jk\omega_r)\, e^{-(s+kj\omega_r)(1-m)T} \tag{2.33}$$ †

This equation can be used advantageously in the statistical analysis of sampled-data systems.

† For the case $g(0^+) \neq 0$, equation (2.33) should be modified to read:

$$G^*(e^{Ts}, m) = \frac{1}{T}\sum_{k=-\infty}^{k=\infty} G(s + jk\omega_r)\, e^{-(s+kj\omega_r)(1-m)T} + \frac{1}{2}\, g(0^+)$$

2.6 Input-Output Relationship

Since the input to the system is of sampled form, its z-transform is $R^*(z)$. The output is obtained by simply multiplying the input z-transform by the modified z-transform of the transfer function $G(s)$ as follows:

$$C^*(z, m) = R^*(z) \times G^*(z, m) \tag{2.34}$$

where $C^*(z, m)$ denotes the modified z-transform of the output.

Furthermore, if the Laplace transform of the output is obtained in the following expression:

$$C(s) = R^*(z) \times G(s) \tag{2.35}$$

the modified z-transform of equation (2.35) is

$$C^*(z, m) = R^*(z) \times G^*(z, m) \tag{2.36}$$

This relationship can be utilized advantageously for obtaining various input-output relationships for sampled-data configurations in the form of the modified z-transform.

2.7 Modified z-Transform Algebra

The modified z-transform can be systematically applied to obtain the transfer function of any sampled-data system configuration.† This is evident from the relations (2.35) and (2.36), as shown below.

1. Assume a configuration of Fig. 2.10. The Laplace transform of the output is given as

$$C(s) = R^*(s) \times G_1{}^*(s) \times G_2(s) \tag{2.37}$$

Figure 2.10 Sampled-data system with synchronized sampler

The modified z-transform of equation (2.37) is

$$C^*(z, m) = \mathfrak{Z}_m\,[C(s)] = R^*(z)\, G_1{}^*(z) \times G_2{}^*(z, m) \tag{2.38}$$

2. Similarly, for a configuration shown in Fig. 2.11 the output Laplace transform is:

$$C(s) = [R^*(z) \times G_1(s) \times G_2(s)]_{z=e^{Ts}} \tag{2.39}$$

† E. I. Jury, "Additions to the Modified z-Transform Method," *I.R.E. Wescon Convention Record*, Pt. IV, August 21, 1957, pp. 136–156.

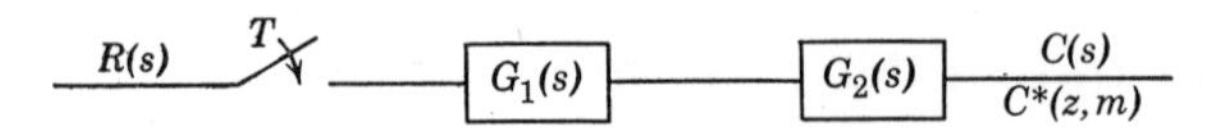

Figure 2.11 Sampled-data system with two cascaded components

The modified z-transform of the output is

$$C^*(z, m) = R^*(z) \times G_1G_2^*(z, m) \tag{2.40}$$

where

$$G_1G_2^*(z, m) = \mathfrak{Z}_m [G_1(s) \times G_2(s)] \tag{2.41}$$

3. For a simple feedback system shown in Fig. 2.12, the output Laplace transform is

$$C(s) = R^*(z) \frac{G(s)}{1 + HG^*(z)} \tag{2.42}$$

The modified z-transform is

$$C^*(z, m) = R^*(z) \frac{G^*(z, m)}{1 + HG^*(z)} \tag{2.43}$$

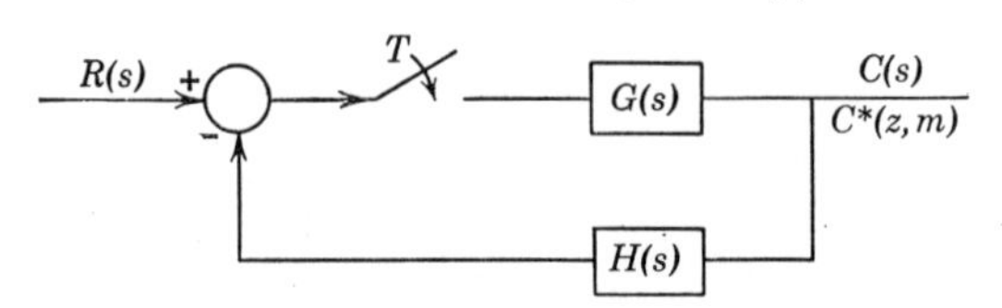

Figure 2.12 Sampled-data feedback control system

4. To obtain the modified z-transform of the output of a configuration shown in Fig. 2.13, first obtain the Laplace transform of the output as follows:

$$C(s) = [R(s) - C^*(z)\, H(s)]\, G(s) \tag{2.44}$$

or

$$C(s) = R(s)\, G(s) - C^*(z)\, H(s)\, G(s) \tag{2.45}$$

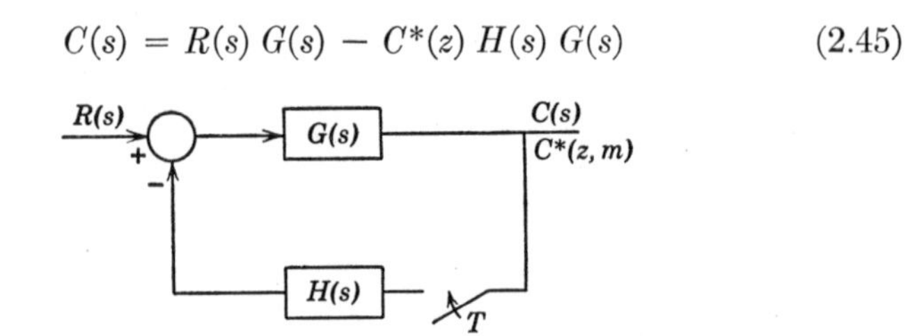

Figure 2.13 Sampled-data control system with sampler in feedback path

Apply the z-transform to equation (2.45) to obtain for $C^*(z)$ the following relation:

$$C^*(z) = RG^*(z) - C^*(z)\,HG^*(z) \tag{2.46}$$

or

$$C^*(z) = \frac{RG^*(z)}{1 + HG^*(z)} \tag{2.47}$$

Substituting $C^*(z)$ in equation (2.45) yields

$$C(s) = R(s)\,G(s) - \frac{RG^*(s)}{1 + HG^*(z)} H(s)\,G(s) \tag{2.48}$$

Apply the modified z-transform to equation (2.48):

$$C^*(z, m) = \mathfrak{z}_m\,[C(s)] = RG^*(z, m) - \frac{RG^*(z)}{1 + HG^*(z)} HG^*(z, m) \tag{2.49}$$

Following these algebraic rules, we can obtain the transfer function of any system configuration. Table 2.2 (page 112) indicates the modified z-transform of various sampled-data systems configurations.

2.8 Multiple-Sampler Systems

Just as with the multiple-sampler case discussed in the preceding chapter using the z-transform, we can apply the same technique for the modified z-transform method. For instance, consider a two-sampler system shown in Fig. 2.14, when T_2 and T_1 are of two different periods.

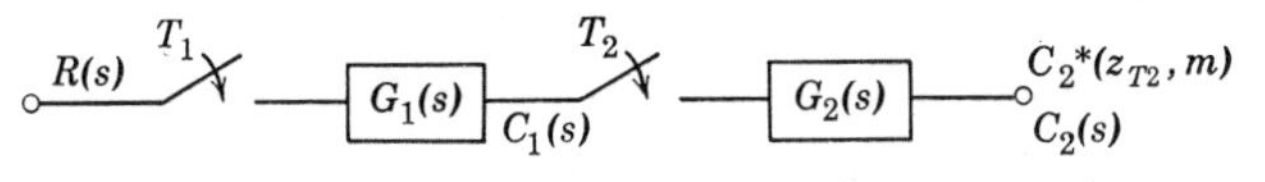

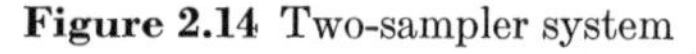
Figure 2.14 Two-sampler system

The Laplace transform $C_2(s)$ can be written, following the procedure of the preceding chapter, as

$$C_2(s) = [R^*(z_{T2})\,G_1^*(z_{T2}) \times G_2(s)]_{z_{T2}=e^{T_2 s}} \tag{2.50}$$

The modified z-transform of equation (2.50) yields

$$C_2^*(z_{T2}, m) = R^*(z_{T2})\,G_1^*(z_{T2}) \times G_2^*(z_{T2}, m) \tag{2.51}$$

where $R^*(z_{T2})$ is $\mathfrak{z}_{T1}\,[R(s)]$ expressed in terms of z_{T2} using equation (1.66).

To extend these techniques to a feedback sampled-data system, consider the system shown in Fig. 2.15. To simplify the calculations, it is assumed that $T_2/T_1 = 1/n$ and that n is an integer larger than unity.

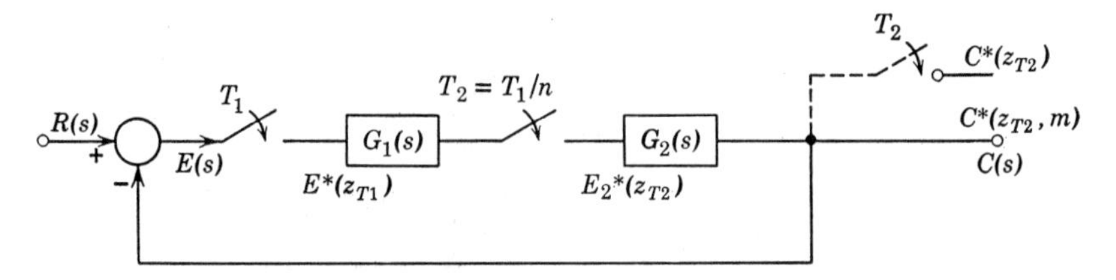

Figure 2.15 Multirate error-sampled feedback system

The output modified z-transform can be written directly as

$$C^*(z_{T2}, m) = E^*(z_{T1}) \times G_1^*(z_{T2}) \times G_2^*(z_{T2}, m) \tag{2.52}$$

The output z-transform can also be written:

$$C^*(z_{T2}) = E^*(z_{T1}) \times G_1^*(z_{T2}) \times G_2^*(z_{T2}) \tag{2.53}$$

The error $E^*(z_{T1})$ equals

$$E^*(z_{T1}) = R^*(z_{T1}) - C^*(z_{T1}) \tag{2.54}$$

The output $C^*(z_{T1})$ can be obtained from $C^*(z_{T2})$ using the following identity: †

$$C^*(z_{T1}) = \frac{T_2}{T_1} \sum_{k=0}^{(T_1/T_2)-1} C^*\left[z_{T2} \exp\left(j\frac{2\pi k}{T_1/T_2}\right)\right] = \mathfrak{z}_{T1}\,[C^*(z_{T2})] \tag{2.55}$$

Applying equation (2.55) to equation (2.53), we obtain:

$$\begin{aligned} C^*(z_{T1}) &= \mathfrak{z}_{T1}\,[C^*(z_{T2})] = \mathfrak{z}_{T1}\,[E^*(z_{T1}) \times G_1^*(z_{T2})\, G_2^*(z_{T2})] \\ &= E^*(z_{T1})\, \mathfrak{z}_{T1}\,[G_1^*(z_{T2})\, G_2^*(z_{T2})] \end{aligned} \tag{2.56}$$

Substituting equation (2.56) into (2.54) results in

$$E^*(z_{T1}) = R^*(z_{T1}) \frac{1}{1 + \mathfrak{z}_{T1}\,[G_1^*(z_{T2})\, G_2^*(z_{T2})]} \tag{2.57}$$

Equation (2.57) is substituted into equation (2.52), which finally gives

† J. Sklansky, "Network Compensation of Error-Sampled Feedback Systems," Doctoral Dissertation, Columbia University, New York, 1955. See also derivation on page 244.

the form of the output modified z-transform:

$$C^*(z_{T2}, m) = R^*(z_{T1}) \frac{G_1^*(z_{T2})\, G_2^*(z_{T2}, m)}{1 + \mathfrak{z}_{T1}\,[G_1^*(z_{T2})\, G_2^*(z_{T2})]}$$

$$= R^*(z_{T2}) \frac{G_1^*(z_{T2})\, G_2^*(z_{T2}, m)}{1 + \mathfrak{z}_{T1}\,[G_1^*(z_{T2})\, G_2^*(z_{T2})]} \qquad (2.58)$$

where $R^*(z_{T2})$ is $\mathfrak{z}_{T1}\,[R(s)]$ expressed in terms of z_{T2}.

For the case $T_1/T_2 = b/q$, where b and q are any integers, the same techniques can be extended; however, the final form is more involved.† This general case can also be deduced from the multiple-sampler feedback case discussed in Chapter 9 by effecting the limiting case.

2.9 Inverse Modified z-Transform

The actual output can be obtained from the modified z-transform through a mathematical process called the inverse modified z-transform, denoted by $\mathfrak{z}_m^{-1}$. Just as with the z-transform, there are two methods for obtaining the inverse time function, namely the inversion integral and the power series method.

2.10 Inversion Integral

The inverse modified z-transform can be obtained by using the following integral similar to the z-transform, that is,

$$c(n, m)T = \frac{1}{2\pi j} \int_\Gamma C^*(z, m)\, z^{n-1}\, dz \qquad (2.59)$$

where Γ is a path of integration in the z-plane that encloses all the singularities of the integrand in equation (2.59).

Since m is constant in the integration (for integration is only in the z-plane), the same tables calculated for the inverse z-transform in Chapter 1 can still be applied for the inverse modified z-transform.

The output is generally a function of n and m where n takes integer values and m varies continuously between zero and unity yielding the

† G. M. Kranc, "Input-Output Analysis of Multi-rate Feedback Systems," *I.R.E. Trans. on Automatic Control*, PGAC-3, November 1957, pp. 21–28.

total response. The time t is related to n by the following relation:

$$t = (n - 1 + m)T \tag{2.60}$$

Thus the output for all instants of time is readily obtained with the modified z-transform. To obtain the response at the sampling instants, let $m \to 1$ in expression (2.60). In case of discontinuous response this yields the lower value of the discontinuity, that is, at $(0)^-$, $(T)^-$, $(2T)^-$. To obtain the values at 0^+, T^+, $2T^+$, or in other words the responses obtainable from the z-transform, let $m = 0$ and let n be the next higher integer value than the value used for n, in equation (2.60) when $m = 1$.

Therefore this method yields the response of both discontinuities and also the response between the sampling instants.

EXAMPLE

Suppose that the input to Fig. 2.8 is a step function and that it is applied to the same $G(s)$ given in the example on page 72; then the modified z-transform of the output is

$$C^*(z, m) = K \frac{z}{z-1} \times \frac{e^{-maT}}{z - e^{-aT}} \tag{2.61}$$

The output is obtained as

$$c(n, m)T = \frac{1}{2\pi j} \int_\Gamma K \frac{z}{z-1} \times \frac{e^{-maT}}{z - e^{-aT}} z^{n-1}\, dz \tag{2.62}$$

It is noticed that m is constant in the integration; thus

$$c(n, m)T = \frac{1}{2\pi j} K e^{-maT} \int_\Gamma \frac{z^n\, dz}{(z-1)(z - e^{-aT})} \tag{2.63}$$

The singularities of the integrand are at $z = 1$ and at $z = e^{-aT}$; thus the output equals the sum of the residues:

$$c(n, m)T = K e^{-amT} \frac{1 - e^{-aTn}}{1 - e^{-aT}} \tag{2.64}$$

$$t = (n - 1 + m)T \tag{2.65}$$

Since the response is discontinuous at the sampling instants, to obtain the value at 0^+ let $m \to 0$, $n \to 1$; at 0^- let $m \to 1$, $n \to 0$. We obtain the value at T^-, T^+, and so on in the same way.

2.11 Power Series Method for Obtaining the Actual Response

Just as in the z-transform, the modified z-transform can be expanded in a power series in z^{-1} as follows:

$$C^*(z, m) = z^{-1} \sum_{n=0}^{\infty} c_n(m)\, z^{-n} \tag{2.66}$$

or

$$z\, C^*(z, m) = c_0(m)\, z^{-0} + c_1(m)\, z^{-1} + c_2(m)\, z^{-2} + \cdots + c_n(m)\, z^{-n}, \qquad |z| > 1 \tag{2.67}$$

It is noticed from these equations that the modified z-transform of the output is first multiplied by z before expansion. This is done in order that the time t in equation (2.60) can be expressed as $t = (n + m)T$.

The coefficients $c_0(m)$, $c_1(m)$, $c_n(m)$ are the terms of the power series expansion of $z\, C^*(z, m)$. The values $c_0(m)$, $c_1(m)$,† $\cdots$, when m varies continuously between zero and unity, give the response at all times. Furthermore, it is noticed that when $m \to 0$ the response at the sampling instants is obtained as indicated in equation (2.27).

The values of $c_0(m)$, $c_1(m)$, $\cdots$, $c_n(m)$ are obtained from $C^*(z, m)$ by the following procedure. From equation (2.67) it is noticed that

$$c_0(m) = \lim_{z\to\infty} z\, C^*(z, m), \qquad 0 \le m \le 1 \tag{2.68}$$

$$c_1(m) = -\frac{1}{1!} \lim_{z\to\infty} z^2 \frac{\partial}{\partial z} [z\, C^*(z, m)], \qquad 0 \le m \le 1 \tag{2.69}$$

$$c_2(m) = \frac{1}{2!} \lim_{z\to\infty} z^2 \frac{\partial}{\partial z} \left\{ z^2 \frac{\partial}{\partial z} [z\, C^*(z, m)] \right\}, \qquad 0 \le m \le 1$$

$$\vdots \tag{2.70}$$

$$c_n(m) = (-1)^n \frac{1}{n!} \lim_{z\to\infty} z^2 \frac{\partial}{\partial z} [\cdots], \qquad 0 \le m \le 1$$

† It should be noted that the relation between $c(t)$ and $c_n(m)$ is given by

$$c_n(m) = c[(n + m)T]$$

If $z\, C^*(z, m)$ is presented as ratio of two polynomials in z as follows:

$$z\, C^*(z, m) = \frac{p_0(m) + p_1(m)\, z^{-1} + p_2(m)\, z^{-2} + p_3(m)\, z^{-3} + \cdots + p_n(m)\, z^{-n}}{1 + q_1 z^{-1} + q_2 z^{-2} + q_3 z^{-3} + \cdots + q_n z^{-n}} \tag{2.71}$$

then

$$\begin{aligned}
c_0(m) &= p_0(m) \\
c_1(m) &= p_1(m) - p_0(m)\, q_1 = p_1(m) - q_1\, c_0(m) \\
c_2(m) &= p_2(m) - q_1\, c_1(m) - q_2\, c_0(m) \\
c_3(m) &= p_3(m) - q_1\, c_2(m) - q_2\, c_1(m) - q_3\, c_0(m) \\
&\vdots
\end{aligned} \tag{2.72}$$

Thus, it is noticed that the coefficients $p_0(m)$, $p_1(m) - p_0(m)\, q_1$, $\cdots$ are obtained by synthetic division of the numerator in equation (2.71) by its denominator similar to the z-transform method. Incidentally, the response at the sampling instants, a special case of the total response, is obtained when $m = 0$. The general form of $c_n(m)$ is given in the Appendix.

For systems whose response has no discontinuity, the following relation is useful to check the accuracy of calculation:

$$\lim_{m \to 1} c_{n-1}(m) = \lim_{m \to 0} c_n(m) \tag{2.73}$$

Furthermore, in case of discontinuous response, the left side of equation (2.73) yields the lower value of discontinuity and the right side yields the upper value of discontinuity.

2.12 Theorems Relating to the Modified z-Transform

a. Initial- and Final-Value Theorems

1. Initial-value theorem. From equation (2.67) it is noticed that the initial value is obtained when $m \to 0$ in the expression for $c_0(m)$; thus:

$$\lim_{t \to 0} c(n, m)T = \lim_{\substack{z \to \infty \\ m \to 0}} z\, C^*(z, m) \tag{2.74}$$

2. Final-value theorem. The modified z-transform of the output can be expanded in partial fractions as:

$$C^*(z, m) = \frac{A_0(m)\, z}{z - 1} + \frac{A_1(m)\, z}{z - a_1} + \frac{A_2(m)\, z}{z - a_2} + \cdots \tag{2.75}$$

The inverse of equation (2.75) can be written as:

$$c(n, m)T = A_0(m) + A_1(m)\, a_1{}^n + A_2(m)\, a_2{}^n + \cdots \tag{2.76}$$

For a stable output, $a_1, a_2, \cdots$ are inside the unit circle, that is, as n approaches infinity, equations (2.75) and (2.76) give the final-value theorem as follows:

$$\lim_{n\to\infty} c(n, m)T = A_0(m) = \lim_{z\to 1} \frac{z - 1}{z}\, C^*(z, m) \tag{2.77}$$

If $A_0(m)$ is a function of m, the final-value theorem readily yields the steady-state ripple in the continuous output. If no ripple exists, A_0 is not a function of m and the final value is the same as at the sampling instants. This method can be used to obtain the final value noted on p. 30.

b. Theorem for Differentiation with Respect to m

$$\mathfrak{z}_m \left[\frac{\partial}{\partial m} f(n, m)T \right] = \frac{\partial}{\partial m} F^*(z, m) \tag{2.78}$$

or

$$\frac{\partial}{\partial m} f(n, m)T = \mathfrak{z}_m{}^{-1} \left[\frac{\partial}{\partial m} F^*(z, m) \right]$$

This follows from a similar Laplace transform theorem:

$$\mathfrak{L} \left\{ \frac{\partial}{\partial m} [f(t - (1 - m)T) \times \delta_T(t)] \right\} = \frac{\partial}{\partial m} \sum_{n=0}^{\infty} f(n, m)T\, z^{-n} \tag{2.79}†$$

but

$$\sum_{n=0}^{\infty} f(n, m)T\, z^{-n} = F^*(z, m) \tag{2.79a}$$

Therefore

$$\mathfrak{z}_m \left[\frac{\partial}{\partial m} f(n, m)T \right] = \frac{\partial}{\partial m} F^*(z, m) \tag{2.80}$$

This theorem can be applied advantageously for obtaining maxima or minima of the response, as will be shown later.

† It should be noted that $f(n, m)T = f(n - 1 + m)T$.

EXAMPLE

Suppose that $F(s)$ is given as

$$F(s) = \frac{\pi}{s^2 + \pi^2} \tag{2.81}$$

and that its modified z-transform is

$$F^*(z, m) = \frac{\sin \pi m}{z + 1} \tag{2.82}$$

$$\frac{\partial}{\partial m} F^*(z, m) = \frac{m \cos m\pi}{z + 1} \tag{2.83}$$

The inverse modified z-transform of this equation is

$$\mathfrak{Z}_m^{-1} \left(\frac{m \cos m\pi}{z + 1} \right) = (-1)^n m \cos m\pi \tag{2.84}$$

On the other hand

$$f(n, m)T = \mathfrak{Z}_m^{-1} [F^*(z, m)] = (-1)^n \sin m\pi \tag{2.85}$$

And the derivative of this with respect to m is

$$\frac{\partial}{\partial m} [f(n, m)T] = (-1)^n m \cos m\pi \tag{2.86}$$

Equation (2.86) is identical to equation (2.84), as indicated in the differentiation theorem.

c. *Translational Theorem*

$$\mathfrak{Z}_m [F(s + b)] = e^{-bT(m-1)} F^*(ze^{bT}, m) \tag{2.87}$$

$$\mathfrak{Z}_m [F(s - b)] = e^{bT(m-1)} F^*(ze^{-bT}, m) \tag{2.88}$$

where

$$\mathfrak{Z}_m [F(s)] = F^*(z, m) \tag{2.89}$$

Proof: From the definition of the modified z-transform the following can be written:

$$\mathfrak{Z}_m [F(s + b)] = \mathfrak{L} [e^{-b(t-\Delta T)} f(t - \Delta T) \times \delta_T(t)] \tag{2.90}$$

since

$$\Delta = 1 - m \tag{2.91}$$

Equation (2.90) becomes

$$\mathfrak{Z}_m [F(s + b)] = z^{-1} \sum_{n=0}^{\infty} e^{-bmT} f_n(m) (e^{bT}z)^{-n} \tag{2.92}$$

or

$$\mathfrak{z}_m [F(s + b)] = e^{-bmT} z^{-1} \sum_{n=0}^{\infty} f_n(m) (e^{bT}z)^{-n} \tag{2.93}$$

If equation (2.93) is multiplied and divided by e^{-bT}, then

$$\mathfrak{z}_m [F(s + b)] = e^{-bT(m-1)}(e^{+bT}z)^{-1} \sum_{n=0}^{\infty} f_n(m) (e^{bT}z)^{-n} \tag{2.94}$$

By definition

$$F^*(z, m) = z^{-1} \sum_{n=0}^{\infty} f_n(m) z^{-n} \tag{2.95}$$

or

$$F^*(ze^{bT}, m) = (e^{bT}z)^{-1} \sum_{n=0}^{\infty} f_n(m) (e^{bT}z)^{-n} \tag{2.96}$$

By substituting equation (2.96) into (2.94), it is noticed that equation (2.87) is verified. Similarly equation (2.88) can be obtained if $+b$ is replaced by $-b$ in equation (2.90).

EXAMPLE

Assume $F(s)$ as follows:

$$F(s) = \frac{1}{s(s + a)} \tag{2.97}$$

To obtain $\mathfrak{z}_m [F(s + b)]$, apply the translation theorem as follows: From Table 2.1 and from equation (2.87)

$$\mathfrak{z}_m [F(s)] = \frac{1}{a}\left(\frac{1}{z - 1} - \frac{e^{-amT}}{z - e^{-aT}}\right) \tag{2.98}$$

$$\mathfrak{z}_m [F(s + b)] = \frac{1}{a}\left(\frac{1}{ze^{bT} - 1} - \frac{e^{-amT}}{ze^{bT} - e^{-aT}}\right) \times e^{-bT(m-1)} \tag{2.99}$$

Equation (2.99) can be reduced to

$$\mathfrak{z}_m [F(s + b)] = \frac{1}{a}\left[\frac{e^{-bmT}}{z - e^{-aT}} - \frac{e^{-mT(a+b)}}{z - e^{-(a+b)T}}\right] \tag{2.100}$$

Equation (2.100) is exactly the modified z-transform of

$$F(s + b) = \frac{1}{s + b} \times \frac{1}{s + a + b} \tag{2.101}$$

which can be found from Table 2.1 or from equation (2.26).

d. Limiting-Value Theorem

$$\mathfrak{z} \lim_{a \to a_0} [f(n, a)T] = \lim_{a \to a_0} [F^*(z, a)] \tag{2.102}$$

Proof: By definition

$$\mathfrak{z} \lim_{a \to a_0} [f(n, a)T] = \mathfrak{L} \lim_{a \to a_0} [f(t, aT) \times \delta_T(t)] \tag{2.103}$$

$$= \sum_{n=0}^{\infty} \lim_{a \to a_0} [f(n, a)T\, z^{-n}] \tag{2.104}$$

Since the summation is independent of a, thus:

$$\mathfrak{z} \lim_{a \to a_0} [f(n, a)T] = \lim_{a \to a_0} \sum_{n=0}^{\infty} f(n, a)T\, z^{-n} \tag{2.105}$$

but

$$\sum_{n=0}^{\infty} f(n, a)T\, z^{-n} = F^*(z, a) \tag{2.106}$$

Thus the theorem is shown. As a corollary to this theorem, the following can be written:

$$\mathfrak{z}_m [\lim_{m \to m_0} f(n, m)T] = \lim_{m \to m_0} F^*(z, m), \qquad 0 \leq m \leq 1 \tag{2.102a}$$

Example

Let $F(s)$ equal

$$F(s) = \frac{1}{s + a}, \qquad f(n, aT) = e^{-naT} \tag{2.107}$$

$$\mathfrak{z}\,[F(s)] = \frac{z}{z - e^{-aT}} \tag{2.108}$$

but

$$\mathfrak{z} \lim_{a \to 0} [f(n, aT)] = \mathfrak{z}\ (\text{unit step}) = \frac{z}{z - 1} \tag{2.109}$$

and

$$\lim_{a \to 0} \mathfrak{z} \left[\frac{1}{s + a}\right] = \lim_{a \to 0} \frac{z}{z - e^{-aT}} = \frac{z}{z - 1} \tag{2.110}$$

which verifies the theorem.

e. Theorem for Integration with Respect to the Variable a

$$\mathfrak{z} \left[\int_0^a f(n, a)T\, da\right] = \int_0^a F^*(z, a)\, da, \qquad a > 0 \tag{2.111}$$

Proof: From definition of z-transform

$$\mathfrak{z}\left[\int_0^a f(n, a)T\,da\right] = \sum_{n=0}^{\infty}\left[\int_0^a f(n, a)T\,da\right] z^{-n} \tag{2.112}$$

Since the summation is independent of a, thus

$$\mathfrak{z}\left[\int_0^a f(n, a)T\,da\right] = \int_0^a \left[\sum_{n=0}^{\infty} f(n, a)T\,z^{-n}\right] da \tag{2.113}$$

but

$$\sum_{n=0}^{\infty} f(n, a)T\,z^{-n} = F^*(z, a) \tag{2.114}$$

therefore

$$\mathfrak{z}\left[\int_0^a f(n, a)T\,da\right] = \int_0^a F^*(z, a)\,da \tag{2.115}$$

As a corollary to this theorem the following can be written:

$$\mathfrak{z}_m\left[\int_0^m f(n, m)T\,dm\right] = \int_0^m F^*(z, m)\,dm \tag{2.111a}$$

EXAMPLE

If we know the z-transform of the following,

$$\mathfrak{z}\,(e^{-anT}) = \frac{z}{z - e^{-aT}} \tag{2.116}$$

how can we obtain

$$\int_0^a \frac{z}{z - e^{-aT}}\,da \tag{2.117}$$

This integral equals

$$\int_0^a \frac{z}{z - e^{-aT}}\,da = z\left[\frac{a}{z} - \frac{1}{z(-T)}\ln\,(z - e^{-aT})\right]_0^a \tag{2.118}$$

$$= a + \frac{1}{T}\ln\frac{z - e^{-aT}}{z - 1}$$

From the theorem,

$$\int_0^a \frac{z}{z - e^{-aT}}\,da = \int_0^a e^{-anT}\,da = -\frac{e^{-anT}}{nT} + \frac{1}{nT} \tag{2.119}$$

Thus the z-transform of the following function is

$$\mathfrak{z}\left(\frac{1 - e^{-anT}}{nT}\right) = a + \frac{1}{T} \ln \frac{z - e^{-nT}}{z - 1} \qquad (2.120)$$

f. Maxima and Minima Theorems

There are several methods of finding maxima-minima and inflection points of the system response. First from the inversion integral we obtain $c(n, m)T$, from which maxima or minima can be found by the following procedures:

1. If $c(n, m)T$ can be brought to the form $c(t)$ where $t = (n - 1 + m)T$, ordinary differentiation with time determines maxima or minima points, in the same way as for ordinary continuous systems:

$$\frac{\partial c(t)}{\partial t} = 0 \qquad (2.121)$$

However, it is not always possible to bring $c(n, m)T$ into $c(t)$ explicitly; thus other methods should be investigated.

2. If the maximum is near the maximum at the sampling instants, which is usually the case, we can obtain $n_{\max}$ or $c(n_{\max}, m)$ which can be differentiated with respect to m to obtain $m_{\max}$; that is,

$$\frac{\partial c(n_{\max}, m)T}{\partial m} = 0 \qquad (2.122)$$

Thus the actual maximum can be obtained as $c(n_{\max}, m_{\max})T$.

3. In some cases the actual output is of the form

$$c(n, m)T = f(m)\, c(nT) \qquad (2.123)$$

The maximum can be obtained by differentiating with respect to m:

$$\frac{\partial f(m)}{\partial m} c(nT) = 0 \qquad (2.124)$$

A value of $m_{\max}$ is found which determines the maximum for $n = 1, 2, \cdots$—any integer.

4. If from method 2 $c(n_{\max}, m)$ equals a constant, the actual maximum is the same as at the sampling instants and is constant between the sampling instants.

5. If

$$\frac{\partial c(n_{\max}, m)}{\partial m} \neq 0, \qquad \text{for } 0 \leq m \leq 1 \tag{2.125}$$

the actual maximum coincides with the maximum at the sampling instants.

6. In general we can use the following relation,

$$\frac{\partial c(n, m)}{\partial m} = 0 \tag{2.126}$$

which yields a value of $m_{\max} = f(n)$. Since n should be an integer and $0 \leq m \leq 1$, the maximum point can be located by a few trials in satisfying equation (2.126).

Furthermore, the power series method of response yields the maximum in two ways:

$$(a) \quad \frac{\partial c_0(m)}{\partial m} = 0, \quad \frac{\partial c_1(m)}{\partial m} = 0, \quad \frac{\partial c_2(m)}{\partial m} = 0 \cdots, \quad 0 \leq m \leq 1 \tag{2.127}$$

Differentiate each of the functions as above and find a value of m which satisfies these conditions.

(*b*) From the theorem on differentiation, we can differentiate the modified z-transform of the output with respect to m and then expand in powers of z^{-1}; the coefficients from the power series expansion determine the maxima or minima if they vanish for values of m between zero and unity. This is presented in the following equation.

$$\frac{\partial z\, C^*(z, m)}{\partial m} = c'_0(m)\, z^{-0} + c'_1(m)\, z^{-1} + c'_2(m)\, z^{-2} + \cdots + c'(m)\, z^{-n} \tag{2.128}$$

where we set

$$c'_0(m) = 0, \quad c'_1(m) = 0, \quad \cdots, \quad c'_n(m) = 0 \tag{2.128a}$$

The solution of the above equation for $0 < m < 1$, yields the maxima or minima points.

The advantage of the use of the derivative of $C^*(z, m)$ lies in the fact that it is simpler to expand in a power series of z^{-1}.

g. Mean Square Value Theorem

$$\mathfrak{z}\,[G(s) \times G(-s)]_{\substack{z=e^{j\omega T}\\ s=j\omega}} = T\, \left| G^*(z, m)_{z=e^{j\omega T}} \right|^2 \tag{2.129}$$

Proof: From the infinite series form of the z-transform, we can write the following relations:

$$\mathfrak{z}\,[G(s)] = \frac{1}{T}\sum_{k=-\infty}^{k=\infty} G(s + jk\omega_r) \tag{2.130}$$

$$\mathfrak{z}\,[G(s) \times G(-s)] = \frac{1}{T}\sum_{k=-\infty}^{k=\infty} G(s + jk\omega_r) \times G(-s - jk\omega_r) \tag{2.131}$$

Letting $s \to j\omega$ in this expression and noting that $G(j\omega)$ is the conjugate of $G(-j\omega)$, we find that

$$\mathfrak{z}\,[G(s) \times G(-s)]_{s=j\omega} = \frac{1}{T}\sum_{k=-\infty}^{k=\infty} |G(j\omega + jk\omega_r)|^2 \tag{2.132}$$

This relation has been introduced by Barker † and other authors.‡

From the infinite series form of the modified z-transform, the following can be written:

$$G^*(e^{j\omega T}, m) = \frac{1}{T}\sum_{n=-\infty}^{n=\infty} G(j\omega + jn\omega_r)\, e^{-j(1-m)(\omega+n\omega_r)T} \tag{2.133}$$

Let

$$\hat{G}^*(e^{j\omega T}, m) = \text{conjugate of } G^*(e^{j\omega T}, m) \tag{2.134}$$

Then

$$\hat{G}^*(e^{j\omega T}, m) = \frac{1}{T}\sum_{k=-\infty}^{k=\infty} \hat{G}(j\omega + jk\omega_r)\, e^{j(1-m)(\omega+k\omega_r)T} \tag{2.135}$$

Multiply equations (2.133) and (2.135) and note that, for the linear system,

$$G(j\omega) = \hat{G}(-j\omega) \tag{2.136}$$

Thus

$$|G(e^{j\omega T}, m)|^2 = \frac{1}{T}\Bigg[\sum_{n=-\infty}^{n=\infty} |G(j\omega + jn\omega_r)|^2 + \sum_{\substack{n=-\infty \\ n\neq k}}^{n=\infty}\ \sum_{k=-\infty}^{k=\infty} G(j\omega + jn\omega_r)\, G(-j\omega - kj\omega_r)\, e^{-j(k-n)\omega_r(1-m)T}\Bigg] \tag{2.137}$$

The mean value of the second summation term, evaluated from $m = 0$ to $m = 1$, is zero since for $n \neq k$, $e^{-jk\omega_r(1-m)T}$ is orthogonal to $e^{-jn\omega_r(1-m)T}$

† R. H. Barker, "The Pulse Transfer Function and Its Application to Sampling Servo Systems," *Proc. I.E.E. (London)*, Vol. 99, Pt. IV, pp. 302–317.

‡ J. Sklansky and J. K. Ragazzini, "Analysis of Errors in Sampled-Data Feedback Systems," *Trans. A.I.E.E.*, Vol. 74, Pt. II, 1955, pp. 5–7.

with respect to the interval (0, 1) in m. Therefore

$$\overline{\left| G^*(e^{j\omega T}, m) \right|^2} = \frac{1}{T^2} \sum_{n=-\infty}^{n=\infty} |G(j\omega + jn\omega_r)|^2 \tag{2.138}$$

This relation has been shown by Mori.† Now, by noting equations (2.138) and (2.132), the following theorem is shown.

$$\mathfrak{z}\,[G(s) \times G(-s)] = T \int_0^1 |G^*(z, m)_{z=e^{j\omega T}}|^2 \, dm \tag{2.139}$$

$$= T \, \overline{\left| G^*(z, m)_{z=e^{j\omega T}} \right|^2}$$

EXAMPLE

Assume $G(s)$ given as

$$G(s) = \frac{1}{s + a} \tag{2.140}$$

Then

$$G(s) \times G(-s) = \frac{-1}{s^2 - a^2} = \frac{1}{2a}\left(\frac{1}{s + a} - \frac{1}{s - a}\right) \tag{2.141}$$

The z-transform of equation (2.141) can be obtained from tables to give

$$\mathfrak{z}\,[G(s) \times G(-s)]_{z=e^{j\omega T}} = \frac{e^{j\omega T}}{2a}\left(\frac{1}{e^{j\omega T} - e^{-aT}} - \frac{1}{e^{j\omega T} - e^{+aT}}\right) \tag{2.142}$$

which yields the following:

$$\mathfrak{z}\,[G(s) \times G(-s)] = \frac{1 - e^{-2aT}}{2a(1 - 2e^{-aT} \cos \omega T + e^{-2aT})} \tag{2.142a}$$

Similarly, the modified z-transform of equation (2.140) is

$$G^*(z, m) = \mathfrak{z}_m\left(\frac{1}{s + a}\right) = \frac{e^{-amT}}{z - e^{-aT}} \tag{2.143}$$

and

$$G^*(e^{j\omega T}, m) = \frac{e^{-amT}}{e^{j\omega T} - e^{-aT}} \tag{2.144}$$

or

$$|G^*(e^{j\omega T}, m)|^2 = \frac{e^{-2amT}}{1 - e^{-aT + j\omega T} - e^{-aT - j\omega T} + e^{-2aT}} \tag{2.145}$$

† Masahiro Mori, "Statistical Treatment of Sampled-Data Control Systems for Actual Random Inputs," *Rept. Inst. Ind. Sci. Univ. Tokyo*, 1956.

which finally yields

$$|G^*(e^{j\omega T}, m)|^2 = \frac{e^{-2amT}}{1 - 2e^{-aT}\cos\omega T + e^{-2aT}} \tag{2.146}$$

The mean square value is

$$\overline{\left| G^*(e^{j\omega T}, m) \right|^2} = \int_0^1 \frac{e^{-2amT}}{1 - 2e^{-aT}\cos\omega T + e^{-2nT}}\, dm \tag{2.147}$$

which yields

$$\overline{\left| T\, G^*(e^{j\omega T}, m) \right|^2} = \frac{1 - e^{-2aT}}{(1 - 2e^{-aT}\cos\omega T + e^{-2aT})2a} \tag{2.148}$$

Equation (2.148) is exactly equivalent to equation (2.142*a*), which is expected from the theorem.

It should be noted that to obtain the mean square value of the modified transfer function this theorem is easier to use in most cases than the ordinary integration with respect to m.

2.13 Stability Considerations

It was indicated in Chapter 1 that a sampled-data control system shown in Fig. 2.16 is stable if the zeros of $1 + G^*(z)$ lie inside the unit circle. There are some cases in which the system is stable at the sam-

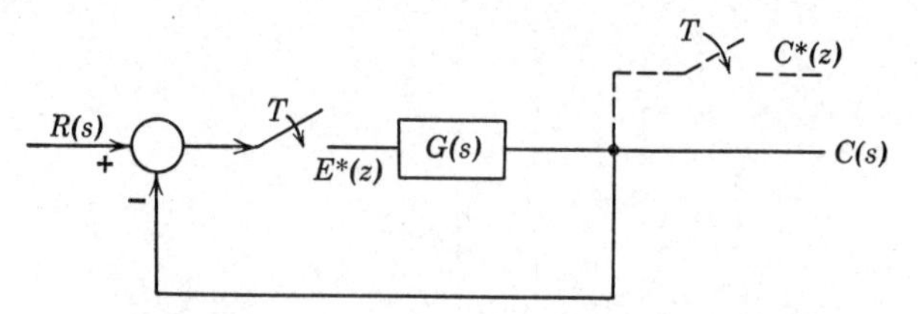

Figure 2.16 Error-sampled feedback system

pling instants but unstable in between the sampling instants. These cases are rare and exist only if $G(s)$ is unstable and of special form as noted below.

The modified z-transform and the z-transform of the output in Fig. 2.16 are

$$C^*(z, m) = R^*(z)\frac{G^*(z, m)}{1 + G^*(z)} \tag{2.149}$$

$$C^*(z) = R^*(z)\frac{G^*(z)}{1 + G^*(z)} \tag{2.150}$$

If $G^*(z)$ is given as

$$G^*(z) = \frac{A(z)}{B(z)} \tag{2.151}$$

the modified z-transform can be of the form

$$G^*(z, m) = \frac{A_1(z, m)}{B_1(z)} \tag{2.152}$$

where $B_1(z)$ is a polynomial in z which has more roots than $B(z)$; these roots do not appear at the z-transform of the output as seen from equation (2.150).

Equation (2.149) can be written following relations (2.151) and (2.152) as follows:

$$C^*(z, m) = R^*(z) \frac{A_1(z, m)}{A(z) + B(z)} \times \frac{B(z)}{B_1(z)} \tag{2.153}$$

From the output the following deductions are evident:

1. If $B_1(z)$ has no roots outside the unit circle, the stability † of the system depends on the roots $A(z) + B(z)$ or of $1 + G^*(z)$ as seen from equation (2.153). In this case the system is stable at the sampling instants if it is stable in between the sampling instants and vice versa.
2. If $B_1(z)$ has a root outside the unit circle, the system can be stable at the sampling instants but unstable in between. However, this case arises because $G(s)$ is unstable, which yields a root of $B_1(z)$ outside the unit circle which does not appear at $B(z)$.

In conclusion, the tests for stability whether graphical or analytical should be applied to the roots of the following equation:

$$[A(z) + B(z)] \times [B_1(z)] = 0 \tag{2.154}$$

The system is stable if the roots are inside the unit circle; and if one of the roots are outside the unit circle, the system is unstable.

2.14 Properties of Modified z-Transform Transfer Function

If $G(s)$ has simple poles, equation (2.26) can be written as

$$G^*(z, m) = z^{-1} \sum_{n=1}^{N} \frac{A(s_n)}{B'(s_n)} e^{ms_nT} \frac{1}{1 - e^{-T(s-s_n)}} \tag{2.155}$$

† E. I. Jury, "Hidden Oscillations in Sampled-Data Control Systems," *Trans. A.I.E.E.*, Vol. 75, Pt. II, 1956, pp. 391–395.

From equation (2.155) the following properties are apparent:

1. $G^*(z, m)$ is periodic in s with the imaginary period $j\omega_r$.
2. $G^*(z, m)$ is real for values of $s = 0$, and $s = jn\omega_r/2$ as noticed from equation (2.155).
3. The degree of the denominator of $z\,G^*(z, m)$ in z^{-1} is equal to the degree of denominator $G(s)$ in s.
4. The poles of $z\,G^*(z, m)$ in the s-plane are those of $G(s)$ plus an infinite number of poles separated by $j\omega_r$ at $s_n + jk\omega_r$.
5. The zero of $G^*(z, m)$ in the z-plane are not fixed but are dependent on the value of m which lies between $0 \leq m \leq 1$.
6. Changing the values of the poles of $G(s)$ changes the coefficients

$$\frac{A(s_n)}{B'(s_n)}\,e^{ms_nT} \tag{2.156}$$

as well as the terms

$$\frac{1}{1 - e^{-T(s-s_n)}} \tag{2.157}$$

in $G^*(z, m)$.

7. Insertion of zeros in $G(s)$ changes the coefficients $A(s_n)/B'(s_n)$ alone.
8. Insertion of poles of $G(s)$ increases the number of terms of $G^*(z, m)$ in the summation of equation (2.155); that is N becomes larger and $G^*(z, m)$ will have more terms of the form:

$$\frac{A(s_n)\,e^{ms_nT}}{B'(s_n)[1 - e^{-T(s-s_n)}]} \tag{2.158}$$

These properties are the same for $G(s)$, which has multiple poles or contains pure delays.

Illustrative Example

To illustrate the several mathematical concepts and derivations developed in the discussion of the modified z-transform, the following example is chosen.

Assume a sampled-data system shown in Fig. 2.17. Given:

$$D^*(z) = \frac{z - 0.736}{z - 0.368} \tag{2.159}$$

$$G(s) = \frac{K}{s(s+1)} \tag{2.160}$$

$$T = 1 \text{ second} \tag{2.161}$$

$$K = 1.91$$

This is a second-order system compensated with a digital compensator or pulsed network having the transfer function $D^*(z)$ of the form indicated.

The following investigations will be discussed: (*a*) how to obtain the actual response for a step input using the modified z-transform; (*b*) how

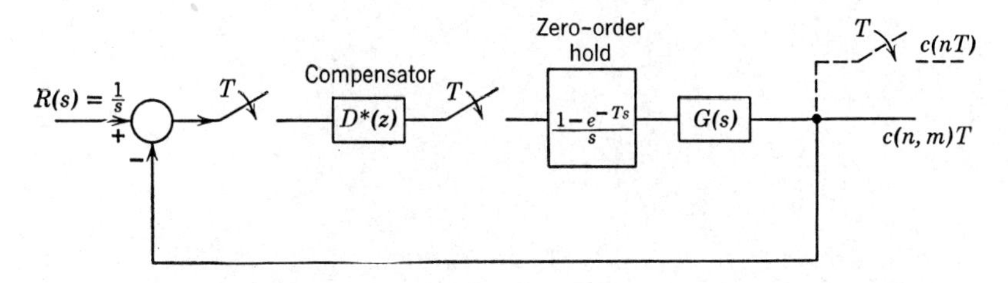

Figure 2.17 Sampled-data feedback system for illustrative example

to obtain the initial, final values as well as the maximum of the output and peak time; (*c*) how to obtain the maximum gain that tends the system to be unstable; (*d*) how to obtain the response at the sampling instants from the modified z-transform.

1. *The overall transfer function* in the form of modified z-transform can be either obtained from Table 2.2 or derived from the modified z-transform algebra discussed earlier. The modified z-transform of the output is:

$$C^*(z, m) = R^*(z) \frac{D^*(z)\, G^*(z, m)}{1 + G^*(z)\, D^*(z)} \tag{2.162}$$

where

$$G^*(z, m) = \mathfrak{z}_m \left[\frac{1 - s^{-Ts}}{s} \times \frac{K}{s(s+1)} \right] \tag{2.163}$$

$$G^*(z) = \mathfrak{z} \left[\frac{1 - e^{-Ts}}{s} \times \frac{K}{s(s+1)} \right] \tag{2.164}$$

$$R^*(z) = \mathfrak{z}\,[R(s)] \tag{2.165}$$

To obtain the modified z-transform of $(1 - e^{-Ts})/s \times G(s)$, Table 2.1 of modified z-transform can be used to obtain the function $\mathfrak{z}_m\,[G(s)/s]$, since the modified z-transform of $(1 - e^{-Ts})$ is $(1 - z^{-1})$; thus

$$G^*(z, m) = 1.91 \left[\frac{\left\{ \begin{array}{l} (m-1)(z^2 - 1.368z + 0.368) \\ \quad + (z - 0.368) + e^{-m}(z^2 - 2z + 1) \end{array} \right\}}{z(z-1)(z-0.368)} \right] \tag{2.166}$$

The z-transform of

$$\frac{1 - e^{-Ts}}{s} \times \frac{K}{s(s + 1)}$$

can be obtained either from tables of z-transforms or by letting $m = 1$ in expression (2.166), to obtain

$$G^*(z) = \frac{0.704(z + 0.72)}{(z - 0.368)(z - 1)} \tag{2.167}$$

Now

$$R^*(z) = \frac{z}{z - 1} \tag{2.168}$$

The modified z-transform of the output equals

$$C^*(z, m) = \frac{1}{z - 1}\left[\frac{\left\{\begin{matrix}1.91(z - 0.736)[z^2(m - 1) + e^{-m} + z(2.368 \\ - 1.368m - 2e^{-m}) + 0.368m + e^{-m} - 0.736]\end{matrix}\right\}}{(z^3 - 1.032z^2 + 0.861z - 0.507)}\right] \tag{2.169}$$

The characteristic equation is a cubic whose roots are

$$z_1 = 0.775$$
$$z_{2,3} = 0.131 \pm j\sqrt{0.641} = 0.311 \pm j0.8 \tag{2.170}$$

To obtain the actual response, apply first the inversion formula:

$$c(n, m)T = \frac{1}{2\pi j}\int_\Gamma \frac{\left\{\begin{matrix}1.91(z - 0.736)[z^2(m - 1 + e^{-m}) + z(2.37 \\ - 1.37m - 2e^{-m}) + 0.37m + e^{-m} - 0.736]\end{matrix}\right\}}{\left\{\begin{matrix}(z - 1)(z - 0.775)(z - 0.131 + j0.8) \\ \times (z - 0.131 - j0.8)\end{matrix}\right\}} z^{n-1}\, dz \tag{2.171}$$

where Γ is a closed path in the z-plane which encloses the singularities of the integrand. The output can be obtained as the sum of the residues or can be found from tables of inverse z-transform since m is constant in the integration; $c(n, m)T$ = sum of the residues at the singularities of the integrand. The singularities are at

$$z = 1$$
$$z_2 = 0.775 \tag{2.172}$$
$$z_{3,4} = 0.131 \pm j0.8$$

Thus the output is found from the sum of the residues as follows:

$$\begin{aligned} c(n, m)T &= 1.01 + 1.57 \times 10^{-2}(0.775)^{n-1}(1.84n - e^{-m} - 10) \\ &\quad + 1.96(m + e^{-m} - 1)(0.812)^{n+1} \cos [(n + 1)80.8^\circ + 131^\circ] \\ &\quad + 1.96(2.368 - 1.368m - 2e^{-m})(0.812)^{n} \cos (n80.8 + 131^\circ) \\ &\quad + 1.96(e^{-m} + 0.368m - 0.736) \times (0.812)^{n-1} \cos [(n - 1)80.8 + 131^\circ] \end{aligned} \tag{2.173}$$

The output is plotted in Fig. 2.18.

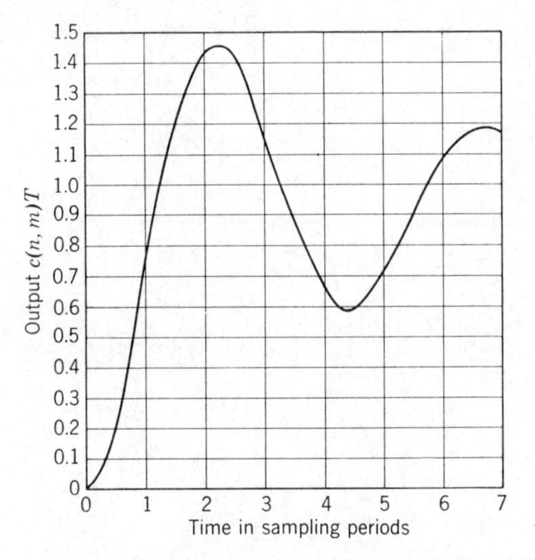

Figure 2.18 Continuous output of system in Fig. 2.17

2. *The initial value* can be found as follows:

$$c(0^+) = \lim_{\substack{z \to \infty \\ m \to 0}} z\, C^*(z, m) = 0, \tag{2.174}$$

For *final value*

$$\lim_{n \to \infty} c(n, m)T = \lim_{z \to 1} \frac{z - 1}{z} C^*(z, m) = 1 \tag{2.175}$$

To find the maximum and peak time, first obtain $n_{\max}$. Since $c(0) = 0$, thus

$$\Delta c(nT) = \mathfrak{z}^{-1} [(z - 1)\, C^*(z)] \tag{2.176}$$

which yields for $\Delta c(nT)$,

$$\Delta c(nT) = 0.703[0.0552(0.775)^n + (0.812)^n \cos (n80.8 - 48.3)] \tag{2.177}$$

For n_{max}, solve $\Delta c(nT) = 0$. This occurs approximately when the following relation is satisfied:

$$\cos(n80.8 - 48.3) = 0 \tag{2.178}$$

or when $n = 1.71$

Thus n_{max} is equal to 2,

$$n_{max} = 2 \tag{2.179}$$

Substituting this value of n_{max} in expression of $c(n, m)T$, we obtain

$$\begin{aligned} c(n_{max}, m)T &= 1.01 + 1.22 \times 10^{-2}(1.84 - e^{-m} - 10) \\ &\quad + 1.03(m + e^{-m} - 1) + 0.482(2.368 - 1.368m - 2e^{-m}) \\ &\quad - 1.35(e^{-m} + 0.368m - 0.736) \end{aligned} \tag{2.180}$$

for the maximum:

$$\frac{\partial c(n_{max}, m)T}{\partial m} = 0 = -0.112 - e^{-m}(-1.29) \tag{2.181}$$

or

$$m = 2.42$$

Since m should lie between zero and unity, in this case n_{max} should be 3; thus:

$$\begin{aligned} c(3, m)T &= 1.01 + 0.06(m + e^{-m} - 1) \\ &\quad + 1.025(2.368 - 1.368m - 2e^{-m}) + 0.482(e^{-m} + 0.368m - 0.736) \end{aligned} \tag{2.182}$$

or

$$\frac{\partial c(3, m)T}{\partial m} = 0 = 1.293 + e^{-m}\, 1.638 \tag{2.183}$$

or

$$m = 0.235$$

The peak time is found from the following relation:

$$\tau_p = (n - 1 + m) = (3 - 1 + 0.235) = 2.235 \text{ seconds} \tag{2.184}$$

and the maximum is

$$c(3, 0.235) = 1.44 \tag{2.185}$$

3. *The maximum gain* for stability limit can be obtained from the stability conditions given in Chapter 1 or alternately from the following relation:

$$|D^*(z)\, G^*(z)| = 1, \qquad \text{ang } D^*(z)\, G^*(z) = \pi \tag{2.186}$$

or

$$|D^*(z)\,G^*(z)| = 0.368K_{\max}\left|\frac{(z-0.736)(z+0.72)}{(z-0.368)^2(z-1)}\right| = 1 \qquad (2.187)$$

which yields $K_{\max}$ for values of z satisfying the angle condition

$$K_{\max} = 3.24 \qquad (2.188)$$

4. *The response* at the sampling instants can be obtained by letting $m = 1$ in expression (2.173), which yields

$$\begin{aligned} c(nT) &= 1.01 + 1.57 \times 10^{-2}(0.775)^{n-1}(1.84 - 0.368 - 10) \\ &\quad + 1.96(1 + 0.368 - 1)(0.812)^{n+1}\cos[(n+1)80.8^\circ + 131^\circ] \\ &\quad + 1.96(2.368 - 1.368 - 2 \times 0.368) \times (0.812)^n \cos(n80.8^\circ + 131^\circ) \end{aligned} \qquad (2.189)$$

The above reduces to

$$\begin{aligned} c(nT) &= 1.01 - 0.1728 \times (0.775)^n \\ &\quad - 0.8349 \times (0.812)^n \cos(n \times 80.8^\circ - 5.95^\circ) \end{aligned} \qquad (2.189a)$$

2.15 Analysis of Sampled-Data Systems with Pure Delay †

The modified z-transform method can be easily applied to obtain the response of sampled-data control system with pure delay. First consider a system with transportation lag in the forward path as shown in

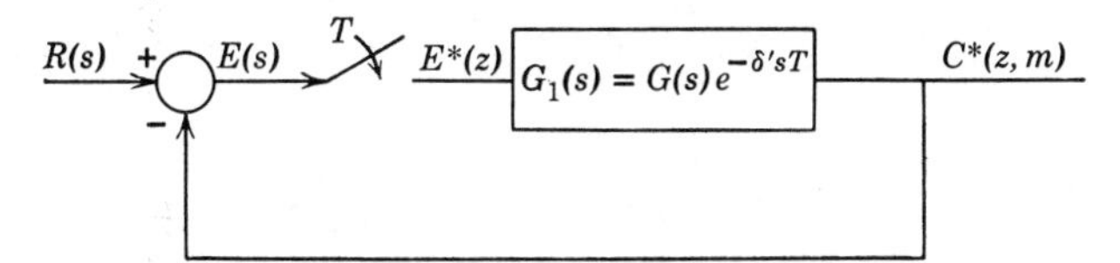

Figure 2.19 Sampled-data feedback system with pure delay in the forward path

Fig. 2.19. The output modified z-transform is given by the following relation

$$C^*(z, m) = R^*(z)\,\frac{G_1^*(z, m)}{1 + G_1^*(z)} \qquad (2.190)$$

† E. I. Jury, "Additions to the Modified z-Transform Method," *I.R.E. Wescon Convention Record*, Pt. IV, August 21, 1957, pp. 136–151. Also, W. Schroeder, "Analysis and Synthesis of Sampled-Data and Continuous Control Systems with Pure Time Delays," Electronics Research Laboratory Report, Series 60, Issue 156, June 8, 1956, University of California, Berkeley.

where

$$G_1^*(z, m) = \mathfrak{Z}_m[G_1(s)] \tag{2.191}$$

$$G_1^*(z) = \mathfrak{Z}[G_1(s)] \tag{2.192}$$

1. For the case when the delay is an integer number, that is,

$$\delta' = k, \quad k = \text{integer}$$

then

$$G_1(s) = G(s)\, e^{-ksT} = z^{-k}\, G(s) \tag{2.193}$$

$$G_1^*(z, m) = z^{-k}\, G^*(z, m)$$

$$G_1^*(z) = G_1^*(z, m)\big|_{m\to 1}$$

The output $c(n, m)T$ is given by the following integral:

$$c(n, m) = \frac{1}{2\pi j}\int_\Gamma C^*(z, m)\, z^{n-1}\, dz, \qquad 0 \le m \le 1 \tag{2.194}$$

2. If the delay is less than unity, that is,

$$\delta' < 1 = \delta \tag{2.195}$$

then

$$G_1(s) = G(s)\, e^{-\delta sT} \tag{2.195a}$$

To obtain the modified z-transform of equation (2.195a), consider the following extended definition of modified z-transform:

$$G_1^*(z, \Delta) = \mathfrak{L}\,[g_1(t - (\Delta - \delta)T) \times \delta_T(t)] \tag{2.196}$$

where $g_1(t) = g(t - \delta)$ and $g(t) = \mathfrak{L}^{-1}[G(s)]$.

It should be noticed that when $\Delta = \delta$, the response at the sampling instants is obtained. Furthermore equation (2.196) can be written in terms of $g(t)$ as follows:

$$G_1^*(z, \Delta) = \mathfrak{L}\,[g(t - \delta T - \Delta T + \delta T) \times \delta_T(t)]$$

$$= \mathfrak{L}\,[g(t - \Delta T) \times \delta_T(t)] \tag{2.197}$$

This relation is identically the modified z-transform of $G(s)$; thus by using the notation $m = 1 - \Delta$, $G_1^*(z, \Delta)$ becomes

$$G_1^*(z, m) = G^*(z, m) \tag{2.198}$$

$$G_1^*(z) = G_1^*(z, m)\big|_{m=1-\delta}, \qquad 0 \le m \le 1$$

The output in this case is given by

$$c(n, m)T = \frac{1}{2\pi j} \int_{\Gamma} R^*(z) \frac{G_1^*(z, m)}{1 + G_1^*(z)} z^{n-1}\, dz \tag{2.199}$$

$$t = (n - m_\delta + m)T,\ m_\delta = 1 - \delta,\ 0 \leq m \leq 1$$

The response at the sampling instants is obtained when $m = m_\delta = 1 - \delta$. It is noticed that from the extended definition of the modified z-transform we can make use of tables if $G^*(z, m)$ [the modified z-transform of $G(s)$] to obtain $G_1^*(z, m)$.

3. Similarly for the case δ' is a non-integer larger than unity,

$$\delta' = k + \delta, \qquad \delta < 1 \tag{2.200}$$

$$G_1^*(z, m) = z^{-k} G^*(z, m)$$

$$G_1^*(z) = G_1^*(z, m)\,|_{m=1-\delta}$$

the output is

$$c(n, m)T = \frac{1}{2\pi j} \int_{\Gamma} C^*(z, m)\, z^{n-1}\, dz \tag{2.201}$$

$$t = (n - m_\delta + m)T,\ m_\delta = 1 - \delta,\ 0 \leq m \leq 1$$

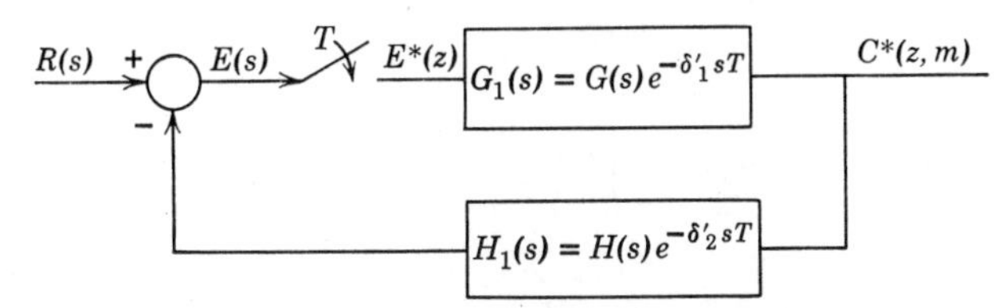

Figure 2.20 Sampled-data feedback system with pure delays in the forward and feedback paths

4. For the more general case of delay both the forward and feedback paths are as shown in Fig. 2.20; then:

$$\delta'_1 = k + \delta_1 \tag{2.202}$$

$$\delta'_2 = l + \delta_2$$

where k and l are integers and $\delta_1 + \delta_2 < 1$. The output is given

$$C^*(z, m) = \frac{R^*(z)}{1 + G_1H_1^*(z)} \times G_1^*(z, m) \tag{2.203}$$

where

$$G_1^*H_1^*(z, m) = z^{-(k+l)} \times GH^*(z, m) \tag{2.204}$$

$$G_1H_1^*(z) = G_1H_1^*(z, m)\,|_{m=1-(\delta_1+\delta_2)}$$

In the case that $\delta_1 + \delta_2$ is larger than unity, the integer value of unity can be included in $k + l$ and the remainder is non-integer. Furthermore

$$G_1^*(z, m) = z^{-k} G^*(z, m) \tag{2.205}$$

The inverse modified z-transform of the output is given as

$$c(n, m)T = \frac{1}{2\pi j} \int_\Gamma C^*(z, m) z^{n-1} dz, \tag{2.206}$$

$$t = (n - m_{\delta 1} + m)T, m_{\delta 1} = 1 - \delta_1, 0 \le m \le 1$$

The response at the sampling instants is obtained from this expression by letting $m = m_{\delta 1}$.

EXAMPLE

Assume a system with pure delay shown in Fig. 2.21 where the following quantities are given: †

$$\delta' = 1.25 = k + \delta = 1 + 0.25$$

$$G(s) = \frac{1}{s+1}, \qquad T = 1 \tag{2.207}$$

$$G_1^*(z, m) = z^{-1} G^*(z, m) = z^{-1} \mathfrak{z}_m \left[\frac{1 - e^{-Ts}}{s(s+1)}\right]$$

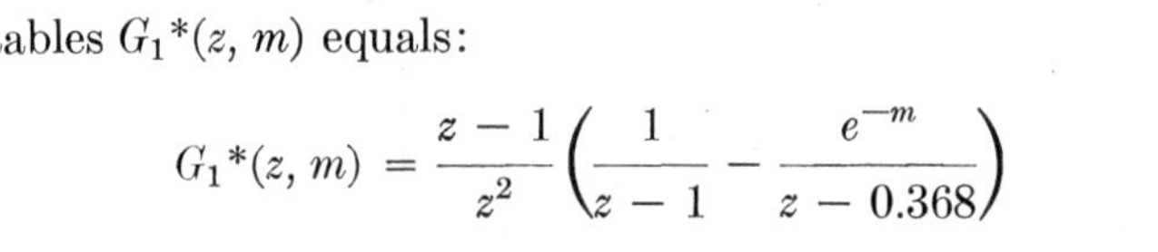

Figure 2.21 Error-sampled feedback system for illustrative example

From tables $G_1^*(z, m)$ equals:

$$G_1^*(z, m) = \frac{z-1}{z^2}\left(\frac{1}{z-1} - \frac{e^{-m}}{z - 0.368}\right) \tag{2.208}$$

The z-transform of $G_1(s)$ equals

$$G_1^*(z) = G_1^*(z, m)\big|_{m=1-\delta} = G_1^*(z, m)\big|_{m=0.75}$$

$$= \frac{z-1}{z^2}\left(\frac{1}{z-1} - \frac{0.473}{z - 0.368}\right) \tag{2.209}$$

† A. R. Bergen and J. R. Ragazzini, "Sampled-Data Processing Techniques for Feedback Control Systems," *Trans. A.I.E.E.*, Vol. 73, Pt. II, 1954, pp. 236–247.

The modified z-transform of the output for step input is given by

$$C^*(z, m) = R^*(z) \frac{G_1^*(z, m)}{1 + G_1^*(z)}$$

$$= \frac{z}{(z-1)} \left(\frac{z - 0.368 - e^{-m} z + e^{-m}}{z^3 - 0.368z^2 + 0.527z + 0.105} \right) \qquad (2.210)$$

The actual output is given as

$$c(n, m)T = \frac{1}{2\pi j} \int_\Gamma \frac{[z(1 - e^{-m}) + e^{-m} - 0.368]}{(z-1)(z+0.17)(z - 0.269 + j0.74)(z - 0.269 - j0.74)} z^n \, dz \qquad (2.211)$$

The evaluation of this integral by the residue method yields

$$\begin{aligned} c(n, m)T &= 0.5 + (0.63 - 1.37e^{-m})(-0.17)^n \\ &\quad + 1.35(0.787)^{n+1}(1 - e^{-m}) \cos [(n + 1)70° + 76°] \\ &\quad + 1.52(0.787)^n(e^{-m} - 0.368) \cos (n \times 70° + 76°) \qquad (2.212) \\ t &= (n - m_\delta + m),\ 0 \le m \le 1,\ m_\delta = 1 - \delta = 0.75 \end{aligned}$$

The plot of this function is shown in Fig. 2.22. The response can also be obtained by the power series method, which avoids the evaluation of the poles of $C^*(z, m)$.

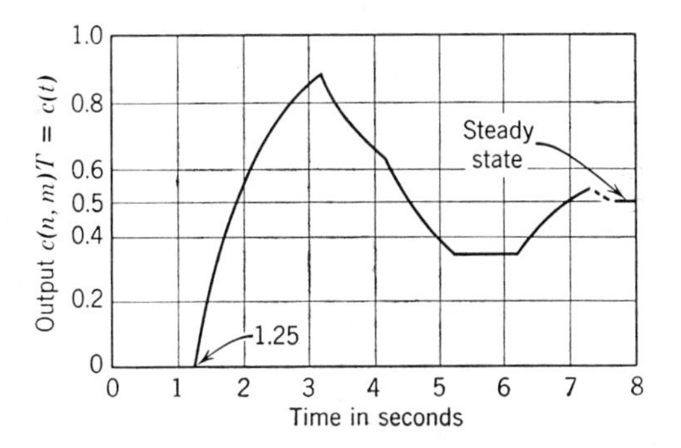

Figure 2.22 Output response of system in Fig. 2.21

2.16 Application of the Modified z-Transform for Obtaining the Inverse Laplace Transform

It has been shown that the inverse modified z-transform yields the continuous response of sampled-data systems in a closed form. Furthermore, the continuous output can also be obtained by finding the inverse Laplace transform of the output. Thus the inverse Laplace and modified z-transform for a particular system are equivalent mathematically.

$$c(t) = \mathfrak{L}^{-1}[C(s)] = \mathfrak{Z}_m^{-1}[C^*(z, m)] \qquad t = (n - 1 + m)T \tag{2.213}$$

The output Laplace transform of a sampled-data system usually consists of functions of e^{Ts} and s, and its inverse generally consists of transient and steady-state solutions. The steady-state part is generally of infinite-series form. By applying the steady-state condition of the modified z-transform, we may obtain a closed form of several convergent infinite series.

EXAMPLE

Assume $C(s)$ as follows:

$$C(s) = \frac{1}{1 - e^{-Ts}} \times \frac{1}{s + a} \tag{2.214}$$

The inverse Laplace transform is expressed as

$$c(t) = \frac{1}{2\pi j} \int_{c-j\infty}^{c+j\infty} \frac{e^{st}}{(1 - e^{-Ts})(s + a)}\, ds \tag{2.215}$$

The integrand in equation (2.215) has simple poles at $s = -a$ and $s = \pm j2\pi k/T$, $k = 0, 1, 2 \cdots$. Evaluating the integral we obtain †

$$c(t) = \frac{e^{-at}}{1 - e^{aT}} + \frac{1}{aT} + \frac{2}{T} \sum_{k=1}^{\infty} \frac{a \cos \dfrac{2\pi k}{T} t + \dfrac{2\pi k}{T} \sin \dfrac{2\pi k}{T} t}{a^2 + \left(\dfrac{2\pi k}{T}\right)^2} \tag{2.216}$$

The first term of equation (2.216) can be considered as the transient part and the other terms as the steady-state part. Thus the steady state

† E. I. Jury, "Synthesis and Critical Study of Sampled-Data Control Systems," *Trans. A.I.E.E.*, Vol. 75, Pt. II, 1956, pp. 141–151, discussion by G. Farmanfarma.

is

$$c(t)_{ss} = \frac{1}{aT} + \frac{2}{T}\sum_{k=1}^{\infty} \frac{a \cos \frac{2\pi k}{T} t + \frac{2\pi k}{T} \sin \frac{2\pi k}{T} t}{a^2 + \left(\frac{2\pi k}{T}\right)^2} \tag{2.217}$$

if the substitution $t = (n - 1 + m)T$ is inserted in equation (2.217); then the following expression is found:

$$c(t)_{ss} = \frac{1}{aT} + \frac{2}{T}\sum_{k=1}^{\infty} \frac{a \cos 2\pi km + \frac{2\pi k}{T} \sin 2\pi km}{a^2 + \left(\frac{2\pi k}{T}\right)^2} \tag{2.218}$$

The modified z-transform of equation (2.214) can be found using Table 2.1 as follows:

$$C^*(z, m) = \mathfrak{Z}_m [C(s)] = \frac{z}{z - 1}\frac{e^{-amT}}{z - e^{-aT}}, \qquad 0 \leq m \leq 1 \tag{2.219}$$

The steady-state output is obtained by applying the final-value theorem

$$c(t)_{ss} = \lim_{z \to 1} \frac{z - 1}{z} C^*(z, m) = \frac{e^{-amT}}{1 - e^{-aT}} \tag{2.220}$$

or multiplying the numerator and denominator respectively by e^{aT} to get

$$c(t)_{ss} = \frac{e^{aT(1-m)}}{e^{aT} - 1} \tag{2.221}$$

Equating the steady-state part of the alternate expressions of equations (2.218) and (2.221), we obtain:

$$\sum_{k=1}^{\infty} \frac{a \cos 2\pi km + \frac{2\pi k}{T} \sin 2\pi km}{a^2 + \left(\frac{2\pi k}{T}\right)^2} = \frac{T\, e^{aT(1-m)}}{2(e^{aT} - 1)} - \frac{1}{2a} \tag{2.222}$$

Thus a closed form of an infinite series is obtained by the final-value theorem of the modified z-transform. Table 2.3 (page 118) presents a short list of a closed form of convergent infinite series based on the modified z-transform.

TABLE 2.1

Pairs of Modified z-Transforms †

$G(s)$	$G^*(z, m)$ ‡	
	1.0 Simple Forms of $G(s)$	
$\frac{1}{s}$	$\frac{1}{z-1}$	(1.01)
$\frac{1}{s+a}$	$\frac{e^{-amT}}{z-e^{-aT}}$	(1.02)
	2.0 Quadratic Denominators of $G(s)$	
$\frac{1}{s^2}$	$\frac{mT}{z-1} + \frac{T}{(z-1)^2}$	(2.01)
$\frac{1}{(s+a)^2}$	$Te^{-amT}\left[\frac{m}{z-e^{-aT}} + \frac{e^{-aT}}{(z-e^{-aT})^2}\right]$	(2.02)
$\frac{1}{(s+a)(s+b)}$	$\frac{1}{b-a}\left(\frac{e^{-amT}}{z-e^{-aT}} - \frac{e^{-bmT}}{z-e^{bT}}\right)$	(2.03)
$\frac{s+a_0}{(s+a)(s+b)}$	$\frac{1}{b-a}\left[\frac{(a_0-a)e^{-amT}}{z-e^{aT}} - \frac{(a_0-b)e^{-bmT}}{z-e^{-bT}}\right]$	(2.04)
$\frac{1}{(s+\alpha)^2+\beta^2}$	$\frac{e^{-\alpha mT}}{\beta}\frac{z \sin m\beta T + e^{-\alpha T}\sin[(1-m)\beta T]}{z^2 - 2ze^{-\alpha T}\cos\beta T + e^{-2\alpha T}}$	(2.05)
$\frac{s+a_0}{(s+\alpha)^2+\beta^2}$	$e^{-\alpha mT}\sec\phi\,\frac{z\cos(m\beta T+\phi) - e^{-\alpha T}\cos[(1-m)\beta T-\phi]}{z^2 - 2ze^{-\alpha T}\cos\beta T + e^{-2\alpha T}}$, $\tan\phi = \frac{\alpha - a_0}{\beta}$	(2.06)

$\dfrac{1}{s^2+\beta^2}$	$\dfrac{1}{\beta}\dfrac{z\sin m\beta T+\sin(1-m)\beta T}{z^2-2z\cos\beta T+1}$	(2.07)
$\dfrac{1}{s^2-\beta^2}$	$\dfrac{1}{\beta}\dfrac{z\sinh m\beta T+\sinh[(1-m)\beta T]}{z^2-2z\cosh\beta T+1}$	(2.08)
$\dfrac{s}{s^2+\beta^2}$	$\dfrac{z\cos m\beta T-\cos[(1-m)\beta T]}{z^2-2z\cos\beta T+1}$	(2.09)
$\dfrac{s}{s^2-\beta^2}$	$\dfrac{z\cosh m\beta T-\cosh(1-m)\beta T}{z^2-2z\cosh\beta T+1}$	(2.10)
$\dfrac{s+a_0}{s^2+\beta^2}$	$\dfrac{\sqrt{a_0{}^2+\beta^2}}{\beta^2}\dfrac{z\cos(m\beta T-\phi)-\cos(1-m)\beta T+\phi}{z^2-2z\cos\beta T+1}$ $\quad \tan\phi=\dfrac{a_0}{\beta}$	(2.11)

Some special forms of $G(s)$

$\dfrac{k\pi/T}{s^2+(k\pi/T)^2}$	$\dfrac{\sin mk\pi}{z+(-1)^{k+1}}$
$\dfrac{\pi/T}{s^2+(\pi/T)^2}$	$\dfrac{\sin m\pi}{z+1}$
$\dfrac{\pi/T}{(s+\alpha)^2+(\pi/T)^2}$	$\dfrac{e^{-\alpha mT}\sin m\pi}{z+e^{-\alpha T}}$
$\dfrac{(s+\alpha)}{(s+\alpha)^2+(\pi/T)^2}$	$e^{-\alpha mT}\dfrac{\cos m\pi}{z+e^{-\alpha T}}$
$\dfrac{s+a}{(s+\alpha)^2+(\pi/T)^2}$	$\dfrac{e^{-\alpha mT}}{z+e^{-\alpha T}}\left[\dfrac{T(a-\alpha)}{\pi}\sin m\pi+\cos m\pi\right]$

TABLE 2.1 (*Continued*)

Pairs of Modified z-Transforms †

$G(s)$	$G^*(z, m)$ ‡	
	3.0 Cubic Denominators of $G(s)$	
$\frac{1}{s^3}$	$\frac{T^2}{2}\left[\frac{m^2}{z-1}+\frac{2m+1}{(z-1)^2}+\frac{2}{(z-1)^3}\right]$	(3.01)
$\frac{1}{(s+a)^3}$	$\frac{T^2e^{-amT}}{2}\left[\frac{m^2}{z-e^{-aT}}+\frac{(2m+1)e^{-aT}}{(z-e^{-aT})^2}+\frac{2e^{-2aT}}{(z-e^{-aT})^3}\right]$	(3.02)
$\frac{1}{s^2(s+\alpha)}$	$\frac{1}{\alpha}\left[\frac{e^{-\alpha mT}}{\alpha(z-e^{-\alpha T})}+\frac{T}{(z-1)^2}+\frac{mT-1/\alpha}{(z-1)}\right]$	(3.03)
$\frac{s+a_0}{s^2(s+\alpha)}$	$\frac{1}{\alpha}\left[\frac{a_0-\alpha}{\alpha}\frac{e^{-\alpha mT}}{(z-e^{-\alpha T})}+\frac{a_0T}{(z-1)^2}+\left(a_0mT+1-\frac{a_0}{\alpha}\right)\frac{1}{z-1}\right]$	(3.04)
$\frac{s^2+a_1s+a_0}{s^2(s+\alpha)}$	$\frac{1}{\alpha}\left[\frac{a^2-a_1\alpha+a_0}{\alpha}\frac{e^{-\alpha mT}}{z-e^{-\alpha T}}+\frac{a_0T}{(z-1)^2}+\left(a_0mT+a_1-\frac{a_0}{\alpha}\right)\frac{1}{z-1}\right]$	(3.05)
$\frac{1}{s(s+a)(s+b)}$	$\frac{1}{ab(z-1)}+\frac{e^{-amT}}{a(a-b)(z-e^{-aT})}+\frac{e^{-bmT}}{b(b-a)(z-e^{-bT})}$	(3.06)
$\frac{s+a_0}{s(s+a)(s+b)}$	$\frac{a_0}{ab}\frac{1}{z-1}+\frac{a_0-a}{a(a-b)}\frac{e^{-amT}}{z-e^{-aT}}+\frac{a_0-b}{b(b-a)}\frac{e^{-bmT}}{z-e^{-bT}}$	(3.07)
$\frac{s^2+a_1s+a_0}{s(s+a)(s+b)}$	$\frac{a_0}{ab}\frac{1}{z-1}+\frac{a^2-a_1a+a_0}{a(a-b)}\frac{e^{-amT}}{z-e^{-aT}}+\frac{b^2-a_1b+a_0}{b(b-a)}\frac{e^{-bmT}}{z-e^{-bT}}$	(3.08)

$$\frac{1}{(s+a)(s+b)(s+c)} \qquad \frac{1}{(b-a)(c-a)}\frac{e^{-amT}}{z-e^{-aT}} + \frac{1}{(a-b)(c-b)}\frac{e^{-bmT}}{z-e^{-bT}} + \frac{1}{(a-c)(b-c)}\frac{e^{-cmT}}{z-e^{-cT}} \tag{3.09}$$

$$\frac{s+a_0}{(s+a)(s+b)(s+c)} \qquad \frac{a_0-a}{(b-a)(c-a)}\frac{e^{-amT}}{z-e^{-aT}} + \frac{a_0-b}{(a-b)(c-b)}\frac{e^{-bmT}}{z-e^{-bT}} + \frac{a_0-c}{(a-c)(b-c)}\frac{e^{-cmT}}{z-e^{-cT}} \tag{3.10}$$

$$\frac{s^2+a_1s+a_0}{(s+a)(s+b)(s+c)} \qquad \frac{a^2-aa_1+a_0}{(c-a)(b-a)}\frac{e^{-amT}}{z-e^{-aT}} + \frac{b^2-ba_1+a_0}{(a-b)(c-b)}\frac{e^{-bmT}}{z-e^{-bT}} + \frac{c^2-ca_1+a_0}{(a-c)(b-c)}\frac{e^{-cmT}}{z-e^{-cT}} \tag{3.11}$$

$$\frac{1}{s(s+\alpha)^2} \qquad \frac{1}{\alpha^2}\left\{\frac{1}{z-1} - e^{-\alpha mT}\left[\frac{1+\alpha mT}{z-e^{-\alpha T}} + \frac{\alpha T e^{-\alpha T}}{(z-e^{-\alpha T})^2}\right]\right\} \tag{3.12}$$

$$\frac{s+a_0}{s(s+\alpha)^2} \qquad \frac{1}{\alpha^2}\left\{\frac{a_0}{z-1} + e^{-\alpha mT}\left[\frac{m\alpha T(a_0-\alpha)-a_0}{z-e^{-\alpha T}} + \frac{(a_0-\alpha)\alpha T e^{-\alpha T}}{(z-e^{-\alpha T})^2}\right]\right\} \tag{3.13}$$

$$\frac{s^2+a_1s+a_0}{s(s+\alpha)^2} \qquad \frac{1}{\alpha^2}\left\{\frac{a_0}{z-1} + e^{-\alpha mT}\left[\frac{\alpha^2-a_0+mT\alpha(a_1\alpha-\alpha^2-a_0)}{z-e^{-\alpha T}} + \frac{\alpha T(a_1\alpha-\alpha^2-a_0)e^{-\alpha T}}{(z-e^{-\alpha T})^2}\right]\right\} \tag{3.14}$$

$$\frac{1}{(s+b)(s+\alpha)^2} \qquad \frac{1}{(\alpha-b)^2}\left\{\frac{e^{-bmT}}{z-e^{-bT}} + e^{-\alpha mT}\left[\frac{mT(\alpha-b)-1}{z-e^{-\alpha T}} + \frac{(\alpha-b)Te^{-\alpha T}}{(z-e^{-\alpha T})^2}\right]\right\} \tag{3.15}$$

$$\frac{s+a_0}{(s+b)(s+\alpha)^2} \qquad \frac{1}{(b-\alpha)^2}\left\{\frac{(a_0-b)e^{-bmT}}{z-e^{-bT}} + e^{-\alpha mT}\left[\frac{(b-a_0)+(a_0-\alpha)(b-\alpha)mT}{z-e^{-\alpha T}} + \frac{(a_0-\alpha)(b-\alpha)Te^{-\alpha T}}{(z-e^{-\alpha T})^2}\right]\right\} \tag{3.16}$$

$$\frac{s^2+a_1s+a_0}{(s+b)(s+\alpha)^2} \qquad \frac{1}{(b-\alpha)^2}\left\{(b^2-a_1b+a_0)\frac{e^{-bmT}}{z-e^{-bT}} + (\alpha^2-2\alpha b+a_1b-a_0)\frac{e^{-\alpha mT}}{z-e^{-\alpha T}}\right.$$

$$\left. + (\alpha^2-a_1\alpha+a_0)(b-\alpha)Te^{-\alpha mT}\left[\frac{m}{z-e^{-\alpha T}} + \frac{e^{-\alpha T}}{(z-e^{-\alpha T})^2}\right]\right\} \tag{3.17}$$

$$\frac{1}{s[(s+\alpha)^2+\beta^2]} \qquad \frac{1}{\alpha^2+\beta^2}\left\{\frac{1}{z-1} - e^{-\alpha mT}\sec\phi\,\frac{z\cos(m\beta T+\phi) - e^{-\alpha T}\cos[(1-m)\beta T-\phi]}{z^2-2ze^{-\alpha T}\cos\beta T + e^{-2\alpha T}}\right\}$$

$$\tan\phi = \frac{-\alpha}{\beta} \tag{3.18}$$

TABLE 2.1 (*Continued*)

Pairs of Modified z-Transforms †

$G(s)$	$G^*(z, m)$ ‡	
	3.0 Cubic Denominators of $G(s)$ (*Continued*)	
$\dfrac{s + a_0}{s[(s+\alpha)^2 + \beta^2]}$	$\dfrac{a_0}{\alpha^2+\beta^2}\left\{\dfrac{1}{z-1} - e^{-\alpha mT} \sec\phi \dfrac{z\cos(m\beta T + \phi) - e^{-\alpha T}\cos[(1-m)\beta T - \phi]}{z^2 - 2ze^{-\alpha T}\cos\beta T + e^{-2\alpha T}}\right\}$ $\tan\phi = \dfrac{\alpha^2 + \beta^2 - \alpha a_0}{a_0\beta}$	(3.19)
$\dfrac{1}{(s+b)[(s+\alpha)^2 + \beta^2]}$	$\dfrac{1}{(\alpha-b)^2+\beta^2}\left\{\dfrac{e^{-bmT}}{z-e^{-bT}} - e^{-\alpha mT} \sec\phi \dfrac{z\cos(m\beta T + \phi) - e^{-\alpha T}\cos[(1-m)\beta T - \phi]}{z^2 - 2ze^{-\alpha T}\cos\beta T + e^{-2\alpha T}}\right\}$ $\tan\phi = \dfrac{b-\alpha}{\beta}$	(3.20)
$\dfrac{s^2 + a_1 s + a_0}{s[(s+\alpha)^2 + \beta^2]}$	$\dfrac{1}{\alpha^2+\beta^2}\left\{\dfrac{a_0}{z-1} + (\alpha^2+\beta^2-a_0)e^{-\alpha mT} \sec\phi \dfrac{z\cos(m\beta T + \phi) - e^{-\alpha T}\cos[(1-m)\beta T - \phi]}{z^2 - 2ze^{-\alpha T}\cos\beta T + e^{-2\alpha T}}\right\}$ $\tan\phi = \dfrac{\alpha - a_1}{\beta} - \dfrac{a_0(2\alpha - a_1)}{\beta(\alpha^2+\beta^2-a_0)}$	(3.21)
$\dfrac{s + a_0}{(s+b)[(s+\alpha)^2 + \beta^2]}$	$\dfrac{a_0 - b}{(\alpha-b)^2+\beta^2}\left\{\dfrac{e^{-bmT}}{z-e^{-bT}} - e^{-\alpha mT} \sec\phi \dfrac{z\cos(m\beta T + \phi) - e^{-\alpha T}\cos[(1-m)\beta T - \phi]}{z^2 - 2ze^{-\alpha T}\cos\beta T + e^{-2\alpha T}}\right\}$ $\tan\phi = \dfrac{(a_0-\alpha)(b-\alpha) - \beta^2}{(a_0-b)\beta}$	(3.22)

$$\frac{s^2 + a_1 s + a_0}{(s+b)[(s+\alpha)^2 + \beta^2]} \qquad \frac{1}{(\alpha - b)^2 + \beta^2}\left\{(b^2 - a_1 b + a_0)\frac{e^{-bmT}}{z - e^{-bT}} + (\alpha^2 + \beta^2 - 2\alpha b + a_1 b - a_0)e^{-\alpha m T}\sec\phi \right.$$

$$\left. \frac{z\cos[m\beta T + \phi] - e^{-\alpha T}\cos[(1-m)\beta T - \phi]}{z^2 - 2ze^{-\alpha T}\cos\beta T + e^{-2\alpha T}}\right\}$$

$$\tan\phi = \frac{\alpha + \dfrac{(\alpha^2\beta^2)(b - a_1) + 2a_0\alpha - a_0 b}{\alpha^2 + \beta^2 - 2\alpha b + a_1 b - a_0}}{\beta} \qquad (3.23)$$

$$\frac{1}{s(s^2+\beta^2)} \qquad \frac{1}{\beta^2}\left\{\frac{1}{z-1} - \frac{z\cos m\beta T - \cos[(1-m)\beta T]}{z^2 - 2z\cos\beta T + 1}\right\} \qquad (3.24)$$

$$\frac{s + a_0}{s(s^2+\beta^2)} \qquad \frac{a_0}{\beta^2}\left\{\frac{1}{z-1} - \sec\phi\,\frac{z\cos(m\beta T - \phi) - \cos[(1-m)\beta T + \phi]}{z^2 - 2z\cos\beta T + 1}\right\}$$

$$\tan\phi = \frac{a_0}{\beta} \qquad (3.25)$$

$$\frac{s^2 + a_1 s + a_0}{s(s^2+\beta^2)} \qquad \frac{1}{\beta^2}\left\{\frac{a_0}{z-1} + (\beta^2 - a_0)e^{-\alpha m T}\sec\phi\,\frac{z\cos(m\beta T - \phi) - e^{-\alpha T}\cos[(1-m)\beta T + \phi]}{z^2 - 2ze^{-\alpha T}\cos\beta T + e^{-2\alpha T}}\right\}$$

$$\tan\phi = \frac{a_1\beta}{\beta^2 - a_0} \qquad (3.26)$$

$$\frac{s + a_0}{(s+b)(s^2+\beta^2)} \qquad \frac{a_0 - b}{\beta^2 + b^2}\left\{\frac{e^{-bmT}}{z - e^{-bT}} - \sec\phi\,\frac{z\cos(m\beta T + \phi) - \cos[(1-m)\beta T - \phi]}{z^2 - 2z\cos\beta T + 1}\right\}$$

$$\tan\phi = \frac{a_0 b - \beta^2}{(a_0 - b)\beta} \qquad (3.27)$$

$$\frac{s^2 + a_1 s + a_0}{(s+b)(s^2+\beta^2)} \qquad \frac{1}{\beta^2 + b^2}\left\{(b^2 - a_1 b + a_0)\frac{e^{-bmT}}{z - e^{-bT}} + (\beta^2 + a_1 b - a_0)\sec\phi\,\frac{z\cos(m\beta T + \phi) - \cos[(1-m)\beta T - \phi]}{z^2 - 2z\cos\beta T + 1}\right\}$$

$$\tan\phi = \frac{\beta^2(b - a_1) - a_0 b}{\beta(\beta^2 a_1 b - a_0)} \qquad (3.28)$$

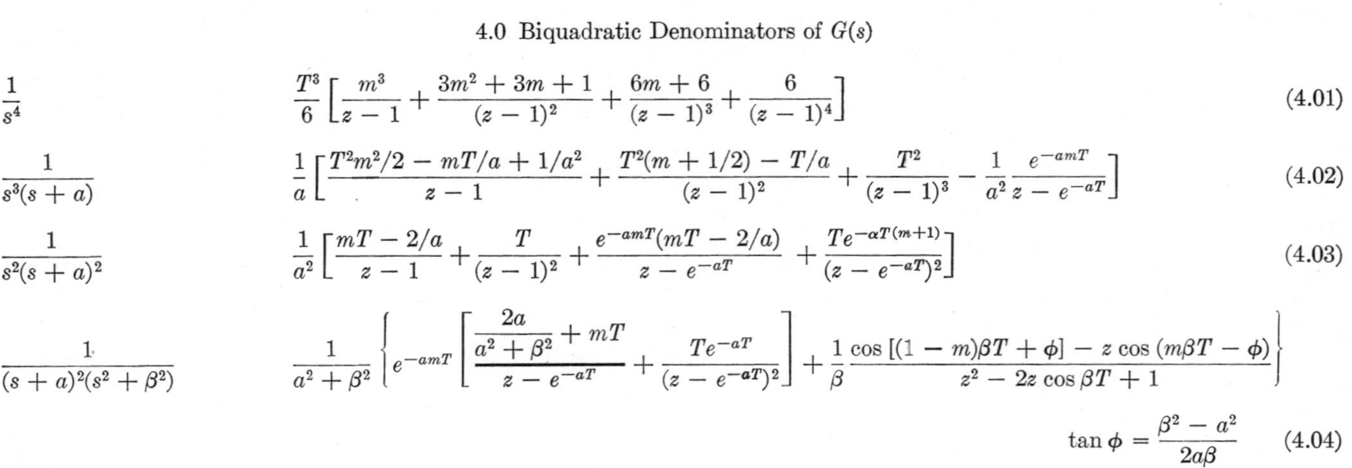

TABLE 2.1 (*Continued*)

Pairs of Modified z-Transforms †

$G(s)$	$G^*(z, m)$ ‡	
	4.0 Biquadratic Denominators of $G(s)$	
$\frac{1}{s^4}$	$\frac{T^3}{6}\left[\frac{m^3}{z-1}+\frac{3m^2+3m+1}{(z-1)^2}+\frac{6m+6}{(z-1)^3}+\frac{6}{(z-1)^4}\right]$	(4.01)
$\frac{1}{s^3(s+a)}$	$\frac{1}{a}\left[\frac{T^2m^2/2-mT/a+1/a^2}{z-1}+\frac{T^2(m+1/2)-T/a}{(z-1)^2}+\frac{T^2}{(z-1)^3}-\frac{1}{a^2}\frac{e^{-amT}}{z-e^{-aT}}\right]$	(4.02)
$\frac{1}{s^2(s+a)^2}$	$\frac{1}{a^2}\left[\frac{mT-2/a}{z-1}+\frac{T}{(z-1)^2}+\frac{e^{-amT}(mT-2/a)}{z-e^{-aT}}+\frac{Te^{-aT(m+1)}}{(z-e^{-aT})^2}\right]$	(4.03)
$\frac{1}{(s+a)^2(s^2+\beta^2)}$	$\frac{1}{a^2+\beta^2}\left\{e^{-amT}\left[\frac{\frac{2a}{a^2+\beta^2}+mT}{z-e^{-aT}}+\frac{Te^{-aT}}{(z-e^{-aT})^2}\right]+\frac{1}{\beta}\frac{\cos[(1-m)\beta T+\phi]-z\cos(m\beta T-\phi)}{z^2-2z\cos\beta T+1}\right\}$ $\tan\phi=\frac{\beta^2-a^2}{2a\beta}$	(4.04)

$\dfrac{1}{s^2(s^2+\beta^2)}$	$\dfrac{1}{\beta^2}\left\{\dfrac{mT}{z-1}+\dfrac{T}{(z-1)^2}-\dfrac{1}{\beta}\dfrac{z\sin\beta mT+\sin[(1-m)\beta T]}{z^2-2z\cos\beta T+1}\right\}$	(4.05)
$\dfrac{1}{s^2[(s+\alpha)^2+\beta^2]}$	$\dfrac{2\alpha}{(\alpha^2+\beta^2)^2}\left\{\dfrac{T(\alpha^2+\beta^2)/2\alpha}{(z-1)^2}+\dfrac{[mT(\alpha^2+\beta^2)/2\alpha]-1}{z-1}+\sec\phi\, e^{-\alpha mT}\dfrac{z\cos(m\beta T+\phi)-e^{-\alpha T}\cos[(1-m)\beta T-\phi]}{z^2-2ze^{-\alpha T}\cos\beta T+e^{2\alpha T}}\right\}$ $\tan\phi=\dfrac{\beta^2-\alpha^2}{2\alpha\beta}$	(4.06)
$\dfrac{s+a_0}{s^2[(s+\alpha)^2+\beta^2]}$	$\dfrac{1}{\beta_0^4}\left\{\dfrac{\beta_1^2+a_0\beta^2 mT}{z-1}+\dfrac{a_0\beta_0^2T}{(z-1)^2}-\beta_1^2e^{-\alpha mT}\sec\phi\,\dfrac{z\cos(m\beta T+\phi)-e^{-\alpha T}\cos[(1-m)\beta T-\phi]}{z^2-2ze^{-\alpha T}\cos\beta T+e^{-2\alpha T}}\right\}$ $\beta_0^2=\alpha^2+\beta^2;\ \beta_1^2=\beta_0^2-2\alpha a_0$ $\tan\phi=-\dfrac{\alpha\beta_1^2+a_0\beta_0^2}{\beta\beta_1^2}$ When $a_0=\alpha$, $\tan\phi=-\dfrac{2\alpha\beta}{\beta^2-\alpha^2}$	(4.07)

E. I. Jury, "Additions to the Modified z-Transform Method," *I.R.E. Wescon Convention Record*, Pt. IV, August 21, 1957, pp. 136–156. Similar tables of modified z-transform are presented by R. H. Barker, "The Pulse Transfer Function and Its Applications to Sampling Servo Systems," *Proc. I.E.E.* (*London*), Vol. 99, Pt. IV, 1952, pp. 302–307.

† A few entries of Barker's table (British Crown Copyright) in a modified form have been included in the table above for which the permission of the Controller of Her Britannic Majesty's Stationary Office has been obtained.

‡ It should be noted that $G^*(z)$ can be obtained by multiplying $G^*(z, m)$ by z and letting m go to zero.

TABLE 2.2

Sampled-Data Systems Configurations †

No.	Figure	$C^*(z)$	$C^*(z, m)$
1	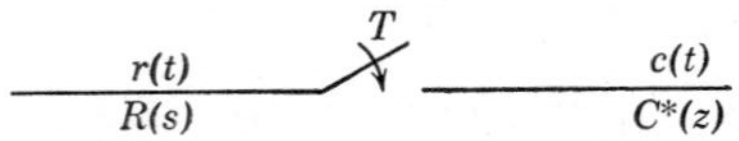 $r(t)$, $R(s)$, T, $c(t)$, $C^*(z)$	$R^*(z)$	$R^*(z)$
2	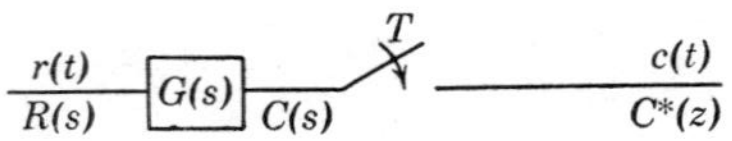 $r(t)$, $R(s)$, $G(s)$, $C(s)$, T, $c(t)$, $C^*(z)$	$RG^*(z)$	$RG^*(z)$
3	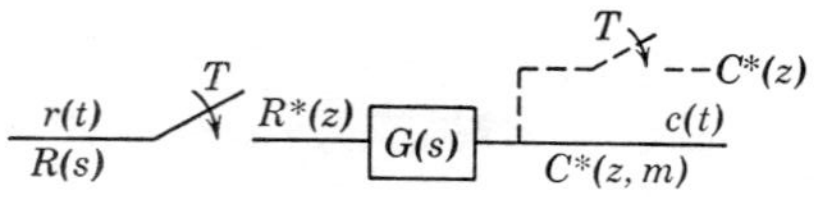 $r(t)$, $R(s)$, T, $R^*(z)$, $G(s)$, T, $C^*(z)$, $c(t)$, $C^*(z, m)$	$R^*(z)\ G^*(z)$	$R^*(z)\ G^*(z, m)$
4	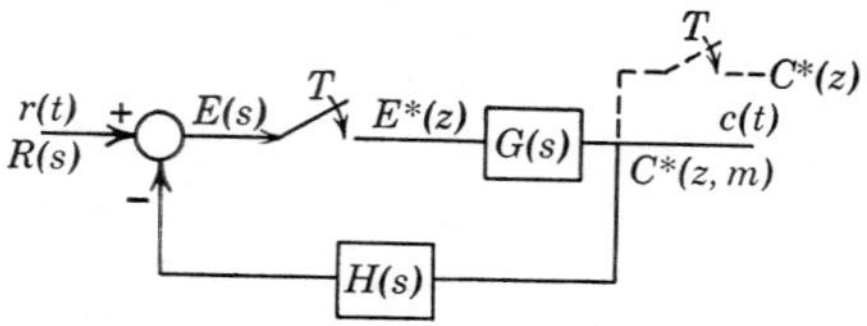 $r(t)$, $R(s)$, +, −, $E(s)$, T, $E^*(z)$, $G(s)$, $H(s)$, T, $C^*(z)$, $c(t)$, $C^*(z, m)$	$\dfrac{R^*(z)\ G^*(z)}{1 + HG^*(z)}$	$\dfrac{R^*(z)\ G^*(z, m)}{1 + HG^*(z)}$

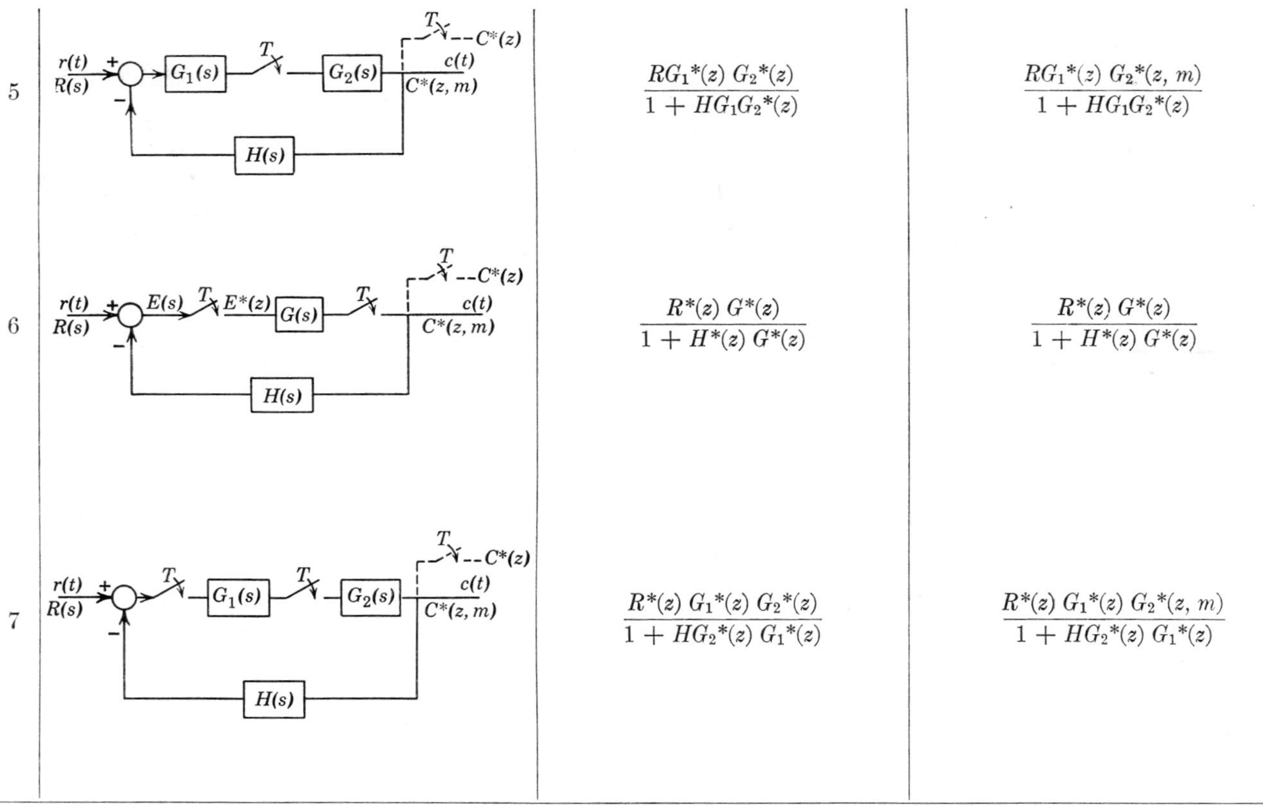

5		$\dfrac{RG_1^*(z)\,G_2^*(z)}{1+HG_1G_2^*(z)}$	$\dfrac{RG_1^*(z)\,G_2^*(z,m)}{1+HG_1G_2^*(z)}$
6		$\dfrac{R^*(z)\,G^*(z)}{1+H^*(z)\,G^*(z)}$	$\dfrac{R^*(z)\,G^*(z)}{1+H^*(z)\,G^*(z)}$
7		$\dfrac{R^*(z)\,G_1^*(z)\,G_2^*(z)}{1+HG_2^*(z)\,G_1^*(z)}$	$\dfrac{R^*(z)\,G_1^*(z)\,G_2^*(z,m)}{1+HG_2^*(z)\,G_1^*(z)}$

TABLE 2.2 (*Continued*)

Sampled-Data Systems Configurations †

No.	Figure	$C^*(z)$	$C^*(z, m)$
8	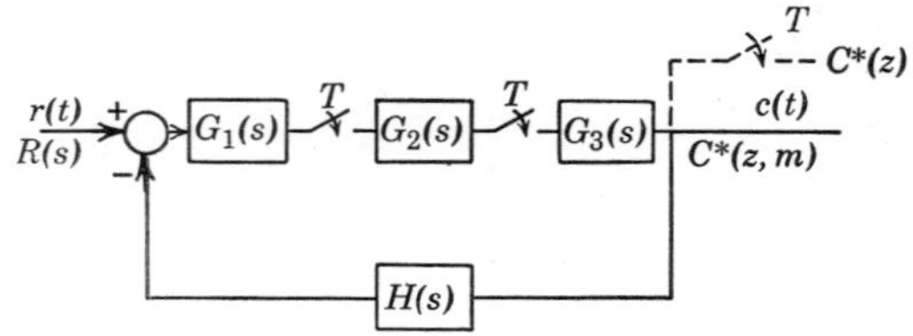 $r(t)$, $R(s)$, +, −, $G_1(s)$, T, $G_2(s)$, T, $G_3(s)$, T, $C^*(z)$, $c(t)$, $C^*(z, m)$, $H(s)$	$\dfrac{R\,G_1^*(z)\;G_2^*(z)\;G_3^*(z)}{1 + HG_1G_3^*(z)\;G_2^*(z)}$	$\dfrac{R\,G_1^*(z)\;G_2^*(z)\;G_3^*(z, m)}{1 + HG_1G_3^*(z)\;G_2^*(z)}$
9	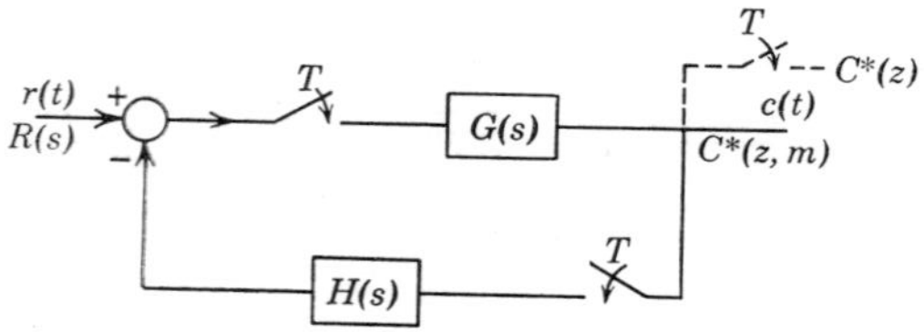 $r(t)$, $R(s)$, +, −, T, $G(s)$, T, $C^*(z)$, $c(t)$, $C^*(z, m)$, $H(s)$, T	$\dfrac{R^*(z)\;G^*(z)}{1 + H^*(z)\;G^*(z)}$	$\dfrac{R^*(z)\;G^*(z, m)}{1 + H^*(z)\;G^*(z)}$
10	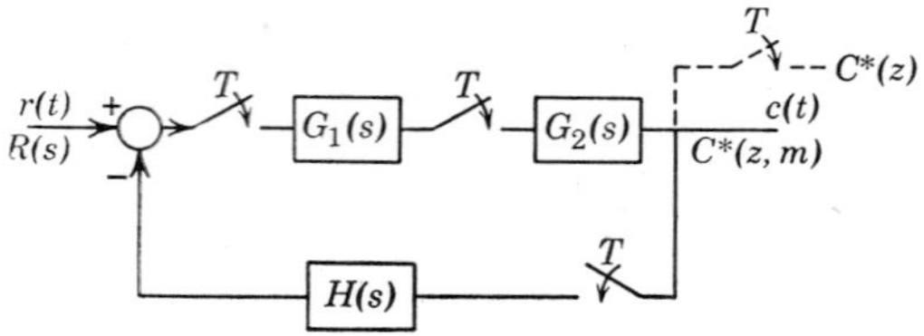 $r(t)$, $R(s)$, +, −, T, $G_1(s)$, T, $G_2(s)$, T, $C^*(z)$, $c(t)$, $C^*(z, m)$, $H(s)$, T	$\dfrac{R^*(z)\;G_1^*(z)\;G_2^*(z)}{1 + H^*(z)\;G_1^*(z)\;G_2^*(z)}$	$\dfrac{R^*(z)\;G_1^*(z)\;G_2^*(z, m)}{1 + H^*(z)\;G_1^*(z)\;G_2^*(z)}$

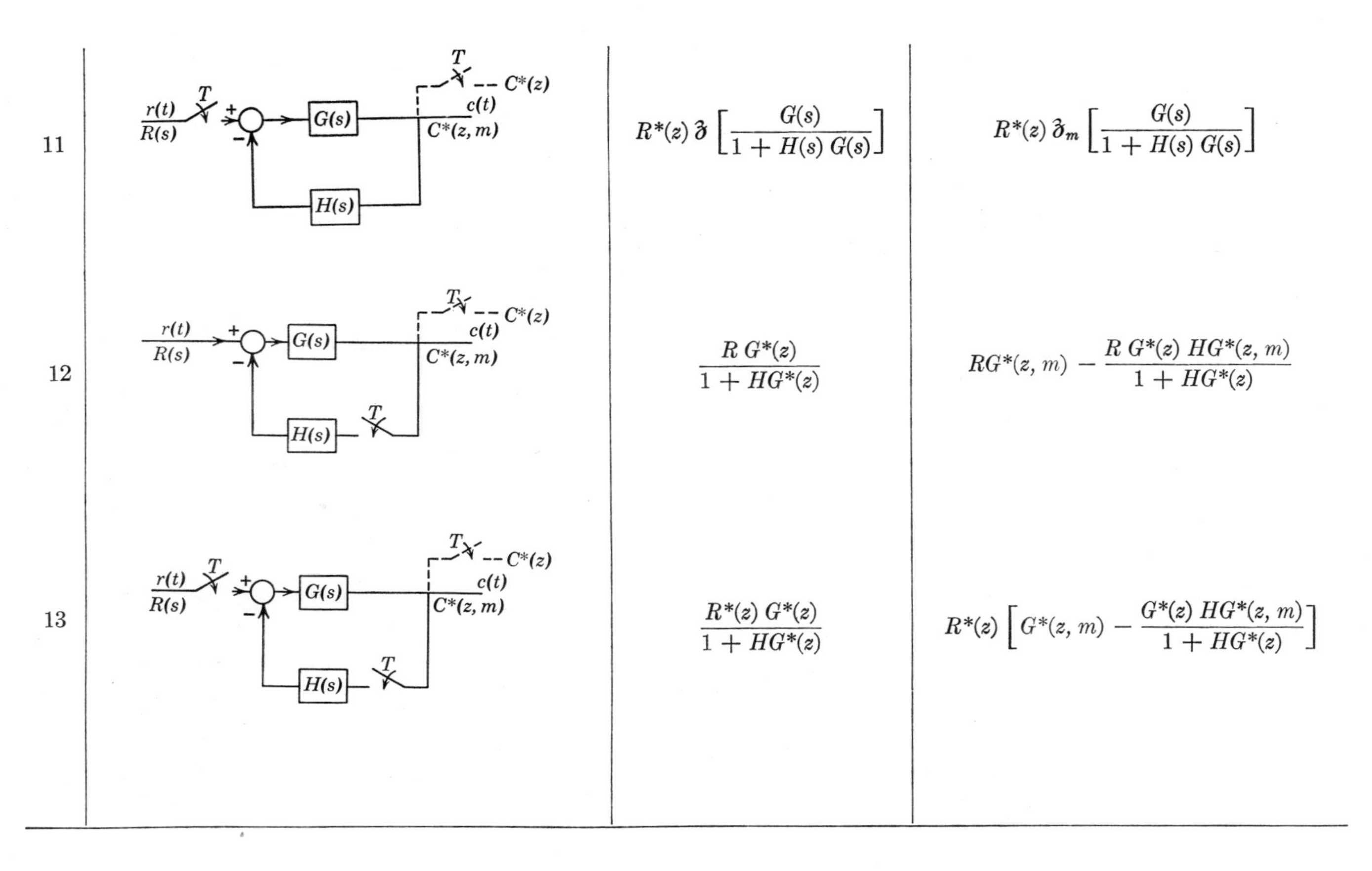

11		$R^*(z)\,\mathfrak{z}\left[\dfrac{G(s)}{1+H(s)\,G(s)}\right]$	$R^*(z)\,\mathfrak{z}_m\left[\dfrac{G(s)}{1+H(s)\,G(s)}\right]$
12		$\dfrac{R\,G^*(z)}{1+HG^*(z)}$	$RG^*(z, m) - \dfrac{R\,G^*(z)\;HG^*(z, m)}{1+HG^*(z)}$
13		$\dfrac{R^*(z)\,G^*(z)}{1+HG^*(z)}$	$R^*(z)\left[G^*(z, m) - \dfrac{G^*(z)\;HG^*(z, m)}{1+HG^*(z)}\right]$

TABLE 2.2 (*Continued*)

Sampled-Data Systems Configurations †

No.	Figure	$C^*(z)$	$C^*(z, m)$
14	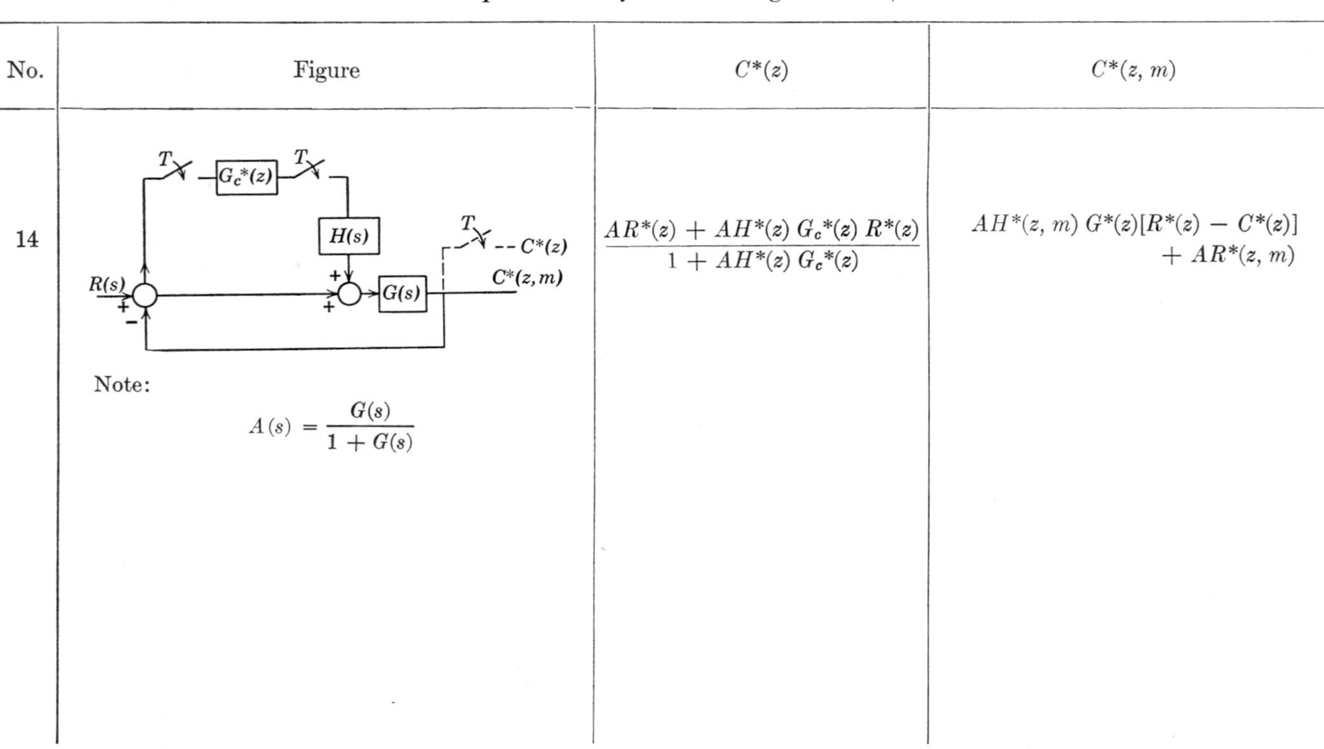 Note: $A(s) = \frac{G(s)}{1 + G(s)}$	$\frac{AR^*(z) + AH^*(z)\, G_c^*(z)\, R^*(z)}{1 + AH^*(z)\, G_c^*(z)}$	$AH^*(z, m)\, G^*(z)[R^*(z) - C^*(z)] + AR^*(z, m)$

15	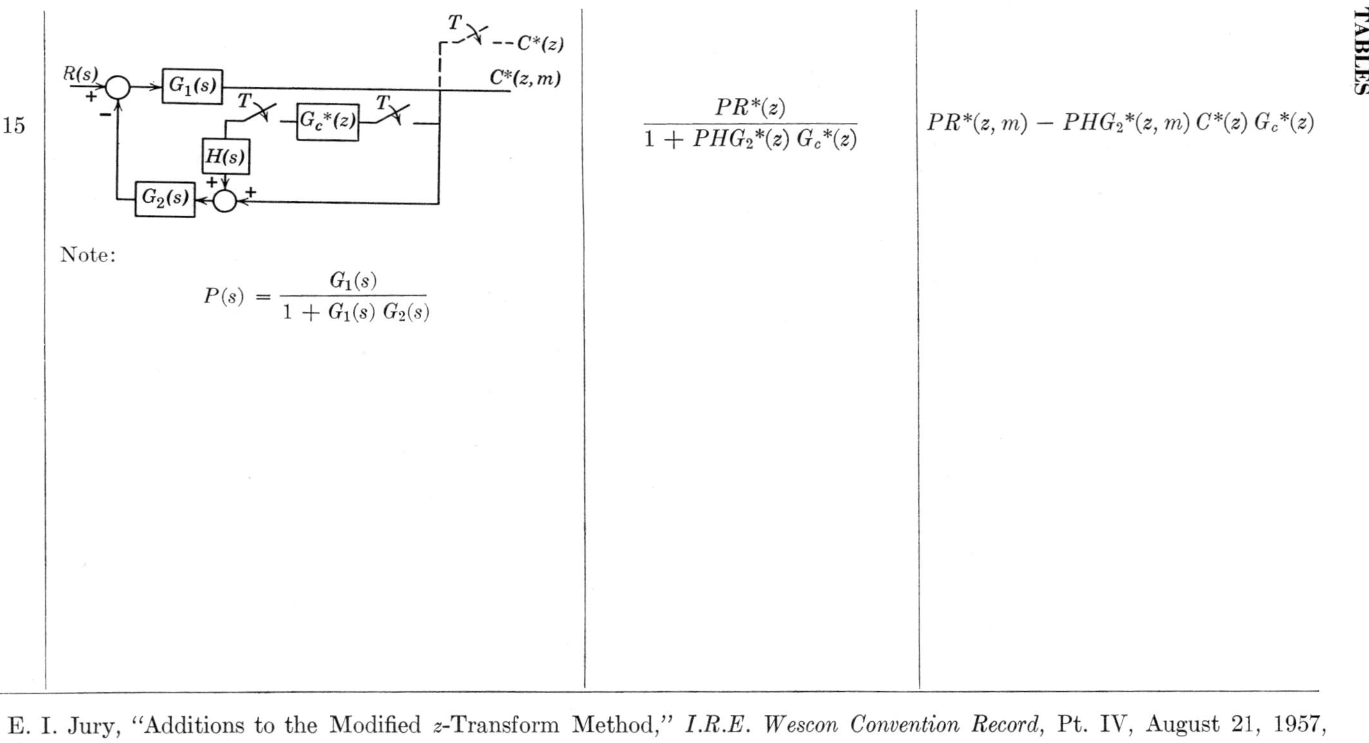 Note: $P(s) = \frac{G_1(s)}{1 + G_1(s)\,G_2(s)}$	$\frac{PR^*(z)}{1 + PHG_2^*(z)\,G_c^*(z)}$	$PR^*(z, m) - PHG_2^*(z, m)\,C^*(z)\,G_c^*(z)$

E. I. Jury, "Additions to the Modified z-Transform Method," *I.R.E. Wescon Convention Record*, Pt. IV, August 21, 1957, pp. 136–156.

† All samplers are assumed in synchronism. $m = 1 - \Delta$, Δ is the fictitious delay; m varies $0 - 1$.

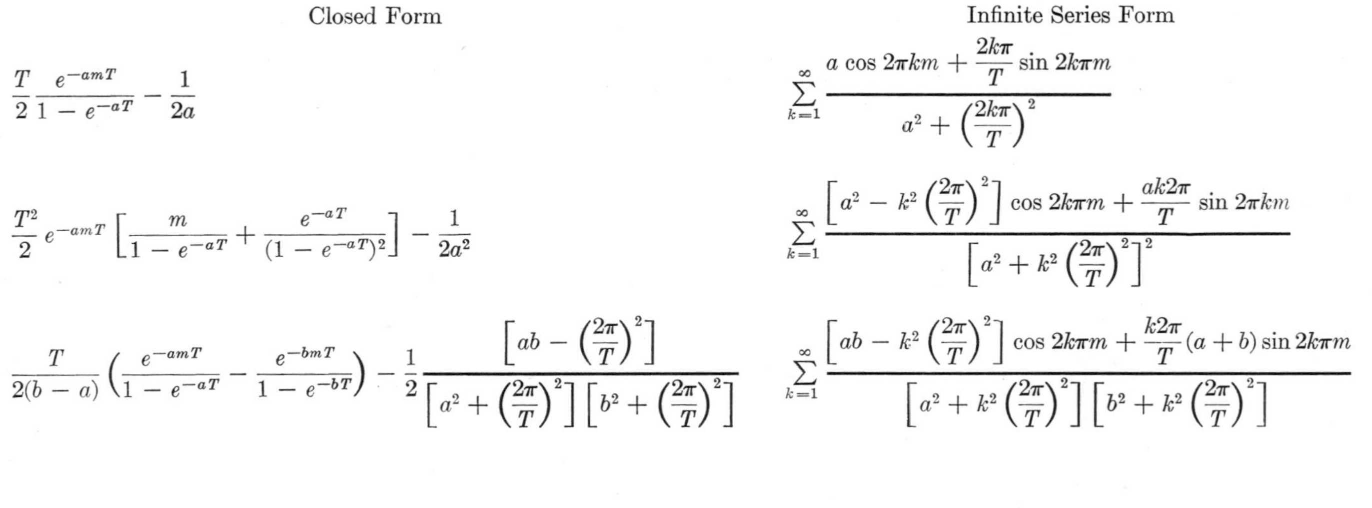

TABLE 2.3

Closed Form of Infinite Series

Closed Form	Infinite Series Form
$\frac{T}{2}\frac{e^{-amT}}{1-e^{-aT}}-\frac{1}{2a}$	$\sum_{k=1}^{\infty}\frac{a\cos 2\pi km+\frac{2k\pi}{T}\sin 2k\pi m}{a^2+\left(\frac{2k\pi}{T}\right)^2}$
$\frac{T^2}{2}e^{-amT}\left[\frac{m}{1-e^{-aT}}+\frac{e^{-aT}}{(1-e^{-aT})^2}\right]-\frac{1}{2a^2}$	$\sum_{k=1}^{\infty}\frac{\left[a^2-k^2\left(\frac{2\pi}{T}\right)^2\right]\cos 2k\pi m+\frac{ak2\pi}{T}\sin 2\pi km}{\left[a^2+k^2\left(\frac{2\pi}{T}\right)^2\right]^2}$
$\frac{T}{2(b-a)}\left(\frac{e^{-amT}}{1-e^{-aT}}-\frac{e^{-bmT}}{1-e^{-bT}}\right)-\frac{1}{2}\frac{\left[ab-\left(\frac{2\pi}{T}\right)^2\right]}{\left[a^2+\left(\frac{2\pi}{T}\right)^2\right]\left[b^2+\left(\frac{2\pi}{T}\right)^2\right]}$	$\sum_{k=1}^{\infty}\frac{\left[ab-k^2\left(\frac{2\pi}{T}\right)^2\right]\cos 2k\pi m+\frac{k2\pi}{T}(a+b)\sin 2k\pi m}{\left[a^2+k^2\left(\frac{2\pi}{T}\right)^2\right]\left[b^2+k^2\left(\frac{2\pi}{T}\right)^2\right]}$

E. I. Jury, "Additions to the Modified z-Transform Method," *I.R.E. Wescon Convention Record*, Pt. IV, August 21, 1957, pp. 136–156.

CHAPTER 3

Root-Locus Method of Analysis of Sampled-Data Control Systems†

The performance of sampled-data control systems is evaluated on the transient-response basis when a unit step input or other types of inputs are applied to the system. Consider, for instance, a sampled-data control

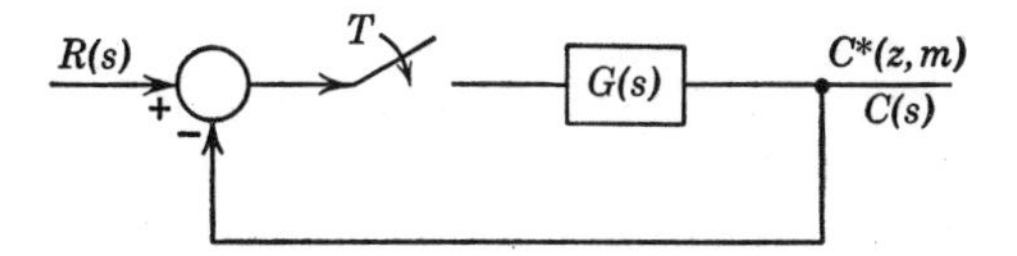

Figure 3.1 Error-sampled feedback system

system shown in Fig. 3.1. The overall transfer function which describes such a system is given by the following equation:

$$\frac{C^*(z, m)}{R^*(z)} = \frac{G^*(z, m)}{1 + G^*(z)} \tag{3.1}$$

where $G^*(z)$, $G^*(z, m)$ are the z-transform and the modified z-transform of $G(s)$, and $R^*(z)$ is the z-transform of the input function $R(s)$.

† E. I. Jury, "Correlation Between Root-Locus and Transient Response of Sampled-Data Control Systems," *Trans. A.I.E.E.*, Vol. 74, Pt. II, 1955, pp. 337–346.

To obtain information on the system performance the roots of $1 + G^*(z)$ in equation (3.1) have to be evaluated. A graphical method for obtaining the roots of the characteristic equation can be obtained from the root-locus.

The root-locus is the locus of all values of z in the z-plane which when substituted in $G^*(z)$ makes its phase angle $(2k - 1)\pi$ where k is an integer number. It is also the conformal transformation of the negative real axis of the $G^*(z)$-plane on the z-plane.

If a sampled-data control system is characterized by equation (3.1), the poles of the overall transfer function will evidently be all the values of z that make $G^*(z) = -1$. In attempting to find values of z that make the transfer function $G^*(z)$ equal to -1, the value -1 is considered as a vector whose angle is $(2k - 1)\pi$ and whose magnitude is unity. First, the problem may be considered of finding the locus for which the angle condition alone is satisfied; that is, plot the locus of z for the open-loop transfer function $G^*(z)$ so that the addition of all angles of the various terms of $G^*(z)$ add up to $(2k - 1)\pi$. Since $G^*(z)$ generally consists of rational polynomials in z, the same rules applied in the s-plane for the continuous system can be exactly applied to the z-plane. Thus, the locus can be easily plotted using a Spirule or the procedures explained later. After the locus has thus been determined, we consider the second condition, that is, that the magnitude of $G^*(z)$ be unity at a particular value of z which corresponds to a phase angle of $(2k - 1)\pi$. This procedure determines the maximum allowable value or range of values of the gain K, which makes the sampled-data system stable or causes it to have a certain overshoot and peak time response.

In plotting the root-locus as mentioned earlier, it is assumed that the poles of the overall transfer function in equation (3.1) are only the roots of $1 + G^*(z)$ which is the case in most sampled-data control systems. However, in cases of hidden oscillations, † the poles of $G^*(z, m)$ are not the same as those of $G^*(z)$; thus the roots of $1 + G^*(z)$ do not constitute all the poles of the transfer function, and in these rare cases the additional poles appear in the modified z-transform of $C^*(z, m)$, which equation (3.1) correctly describes.

3.1 The Root-Locus Plot

The root-locus may be generalized by the following relation:

$$\text{ang}\, G^*(z) = \psi \tag{3.2}$$

† E. I. Jury, "Hidden Oscillations in Sampled-Data Control Systems," *Trans. A.I.E.E.*, Vol. 75, Pt. II, 1956, pp. 391–395.

where ψ may be any angle varying from zero to $\pm\pi$. For various values of ψ, a family of constant ψ (constant-phase angle loci) may be constructed which are analogous to those used in continuous systems. The root-locus is a particular one of these loci where $\psi = \pm\pi$.

Typical constant-phase angle loci will be derived as follows: For case 1,

$$G^*(z) = 1/z \tag{3.3}$$

Since z is complex, which can be written as $x + jy$, $\psi = -\tan^{-1} y/x$, and the family of constant ψ loci has the following equation:

$$y = (-\tan \psi)x \tag{3.4}$$

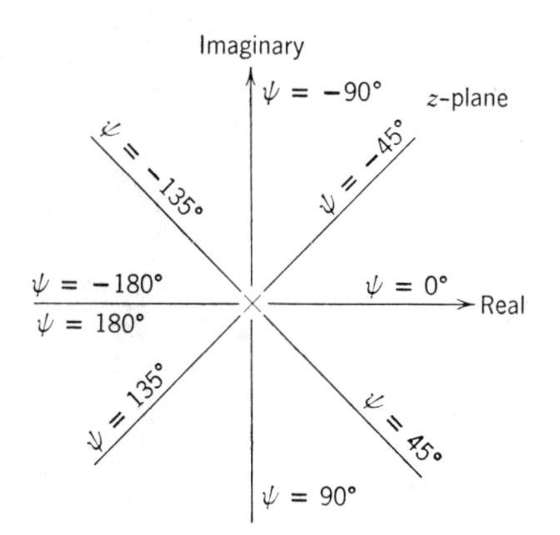

Figure 3.2 Phase angle loci of $1/z$

Equation (3.4) indicates that constant ψ loci are straight lines as shown in Fig. 3.2. For case 2,

$$G^*(z) = \frac{1}{z - 1} \tag{3.5}$$

In this case $\psi = -\tan^{-1} y/(x - 1)$, and the equation of constant-phase loci is

$$y = (-\tan \psi)x + \tan \psi \tag{3.6}$$

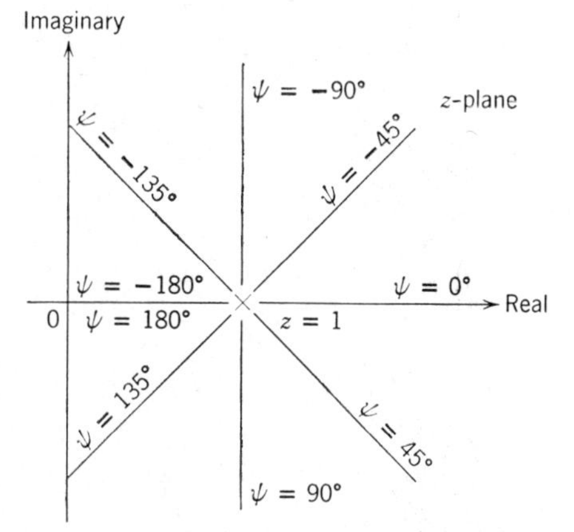

Figure 3.3 Phase angle loci of $1/(z - 1)$

Equation (3.6) is a family of straight lines as shown in Fig. 3.3.

For case 3,

$$G^*(z) = \frac{z - b}{z - a} \tag{3.7}$$

where a and b are real. The phase angle ψ in this case can be shown to be

$$\psi = \tan^{-1}\frac{y}{x - b} - \tan^{-1}\frac{y}{x - a} \tag{3.8}$$

By putting $N = \tan\psi$ in equation (3.8), the constant ψ loci equation after some algebraic manipulation can be written as follows:

$$\left(x - \frac{a + b}{2}\right)^2 + \left(y - \frac{b - a}{2N}\right)^2 = \left(\frac{a - b}{2}\right)^2 + \left(\frac{b - a}{2N}\right)^2 \tag{3.9}$$

Equation (3.9) is a family of circles as shown in Fig. 3.4. It is noted that the root-locus is the constant ψ locus, for which ψ is equal to $(2k - 1)\pi$.

Since the z-transform of the transfer function $G^*(z)$ is generally regarded as consisting of combinations of the mentioned three cases, the

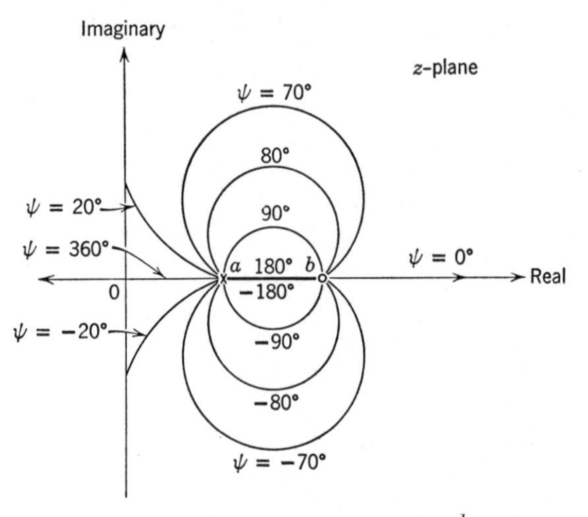

Figure 3.4 Phase angle loci of $\dfrac{z - b}{z - a}$

three basic forms of $G^*(z)$ discussed will suffice to cover most forms of $G^*(z)$. These constant ψ loci for the basic forms can be superimposed to yield the constant ψ loci for $G^*(z)$. The root-locus is obtained by choosing the constant ψ locus for which ψ is equal to $(2k - 1)\pi$. To

TABLE 3.1

Root-Locus Plots

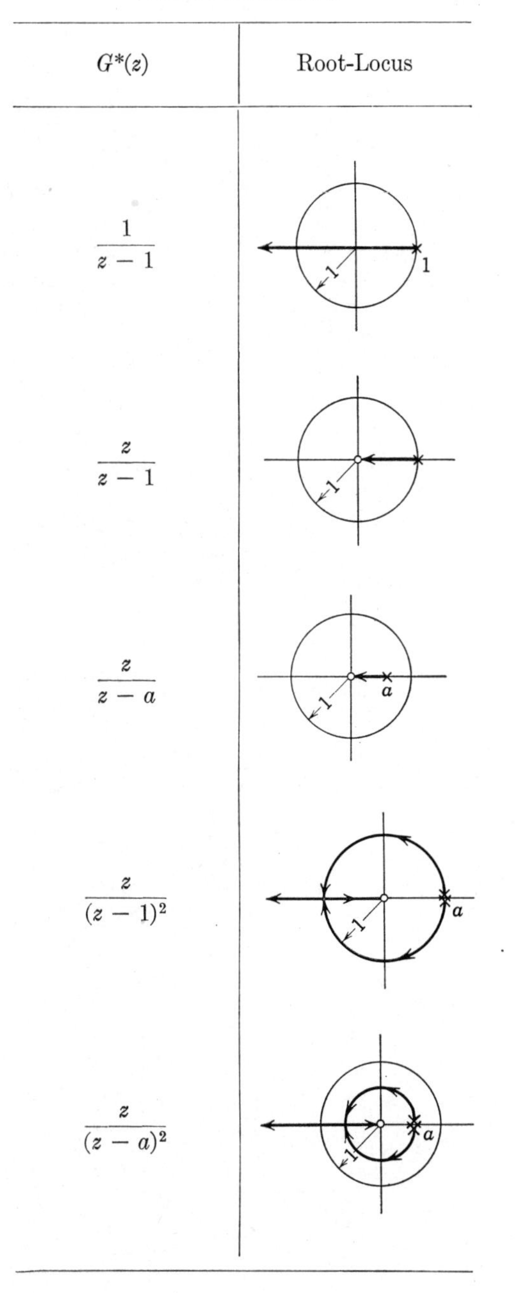

$G^*(z)$	Root-Locus
$\dfrac{1}{z-1}$	
$\dfrac{z}{z-1}$	
$\dfrac{z}{z-a}$	
$\dfrac{z}{(z-1)^2}$	
$\dfrac{z}{(z-a)^2}$	

TABLE 3.1 (*Continued*)

Root-Locus Plots

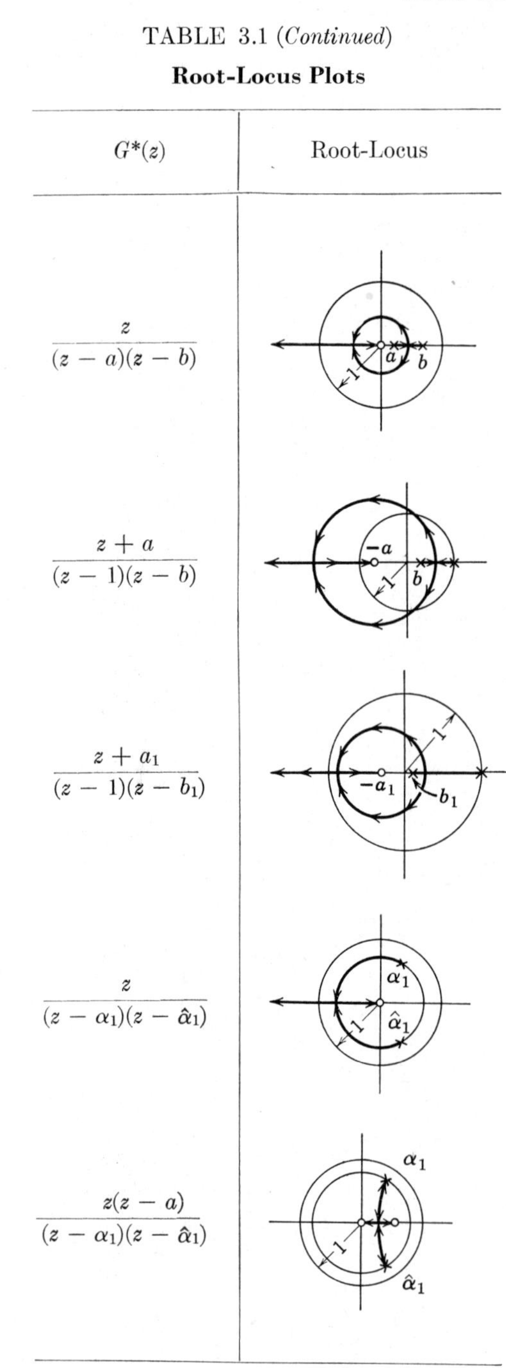

$G^*(z)$	Root-Locus
$\dfrac{z}{(z-a)(z-b)}$	1, a, b
$\dfrac{z+a}{(z-1)(z-b)}$	$-a$, 1, b
$\dfrac{z+a_1}{(z-1)(z-b_1)}$	1, $-a_1$, b_1
$\dfrac{z}{(z-\alpha_1)(z-\hat{\alpha}_1)}$	α_1, 1, $\hat{\alpha}_1$
$\dfrac{z(z-a)}{(z-\alpha_1)(z-\hat{\alpha}_1)}$	α_1, 1, $\hat{\alpha}_1$

obtain the roots of $1 + G^*(z)$ in equation (3.1), we can apply the magnitude condition, that is, $|G^*(z)| = 1$, which yields the actual roots.

As mentioned before, $G^*(z)$ generally consists of poles and zeros in the z-plane; thus the rules applied for plotting the root-locus in the continuous case can still be used for plotting the root-locus in the z-plane. These rules are of certain value in indicating the characteristics and the properties of the root-locus. Namely, the root-locus is always symmetrical about the real axis in the z-plane, and the asymptotes and the branch points are similar to the continuous case. Intercepts with the horizontal axis can be obtained easily from the continuous case, and also the properties on the centroid and types of poles and zeros are similar to the continuous case.

Table 3.1 shows typical root-loci plots for certain functions of $G^*(z)$.† These plots can be constructed either from the constant ψ loci or from the rules indicated in the continuous case. The Spirule facilitates plotting the root-loci and can be used to the same advantage as in continuous control systems.

3.2 Synthesis in the z-Plane Using the Root-Locus Method

The root-locus describes the roots of equation (3.1) as a function of the gain. For a certain gain the roots are determined for the original

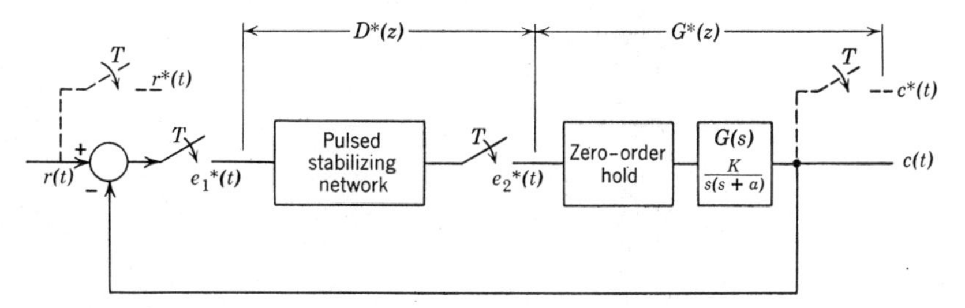

Figure 3.5 Error-sampled feedback system with compensating pulsed network

system. In most cases the designer is concerned with shaping the original root-locus to yield more acceptable roots.

The root-locus can be shaped by using pulsed networks or digital computers in the series path as shown in Fig. 3.5.

† Masahiro Mori, "Root-Locus Method of Pulse Transfer Function for Sampled-Data Control Systems," *I.R.E. Trans. on Automatic Control*, PGAC-3, November 1957, pp. 13–20.

The shaped root-locus can be constructed by superimposing the phase angle loci of the cascaded components of $G^*(z)$ and $D^*(z)$ on the z-plane and determining the points that give a sum of $(2k - 1)\pi$.

Shaping the root-locus to yield the desired roots can be accomplished by adjusting the constants of the stabilizing component in the loop, which might be a digital computer or a pulsed network. In so doing, a qualitative picture may be obtained of how the original root-locus tends to change, depending on the form of this stabilizing component. In view of the fact that most second- or higher-order sampled-data systems become less stable as the gain increases, the problem of shaping the root-locus in the z-plane is more complicated than it is in the continuous case; hence trial and error procedures are more prevalent in the synthesis of such systems than in the continuous ones. The compensating effect of pulsed networks is limited by the actual practical considerations of the range of constants. However, digital computers can be utilized more freely, for they are subjected to fewer restrictions.

Illustrative Example

Assume a sampled-data control system in Fig. 3.5 having a zero-order hold circuit; $G(s)$ is of the following form:

$$G(s) = \frac{K}{s(s + a)} \tag{3.10}$$

The corresponding $G^*(z)$ of this second-order system in series with zero-order hold circuit is

$$G^*(z) = \frac{KT}{a(z - 1)} - \frac{K}{a^2}\frac{1 - e^{-aT}}{z - e^{-aT}} \tag{3.11}$$

The root-locus equation can be obtained by letting ψ, the phase angle of $G^*(z)$, equal π. From this condition the following equation is derived: †

$$y^2 + (x + b)^2 = b^2 + b + e^{-aT}(b + 1) \tag{3.12}$$

where

$$b = \frac{1 - e^{-aT} - aTe^{-aT}}{aT - 1 + e^{-aT}} \tag{3.13}$$

Equation (3.12) is a circle in the z-plane which indicates part of the root-locus. These circles have been plotted for various values of T as shown in Fig. 3.6.

† E. I. Jury, "Correlation Between Root-Locus and Transient Response of Sampled-Data Control Systems," *Trans. A.I.E.E.*, Vol. 74, Pt. II, 1955, pp. 427–436 (Appendix).

It is noticed that the roots for maximum allowable gain for stability are complex when T is small and real when T becomes large. The transi-

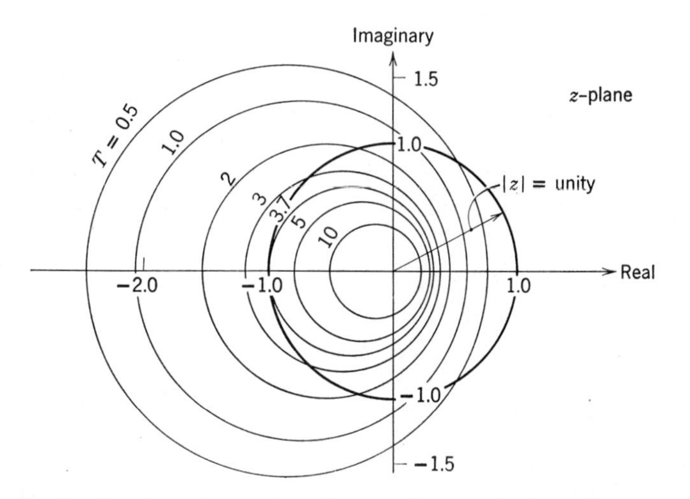

Figure 3.6 Family of root-locus plots of system in example for various values of T

tion between these types of roots occurs when $T = 3.7$. Therefore, this system can become unstable at either one of two frequencies: (1) when $\omega = \pi/T$, and (2) when $\omega < \pi/T$.

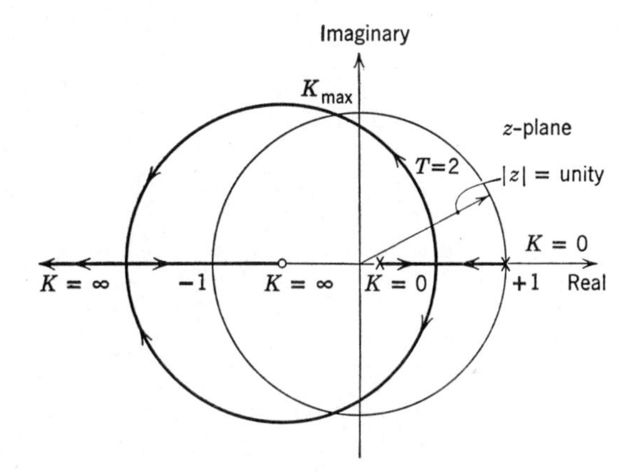

Figure 3.7 Root-locus plot for $T = 2$

As an illustration, two root-loci are plotted in Figs. 3.7 and 3.8, for T equal to 2 and 5 respectively and a equal to unity in equation (3.12).

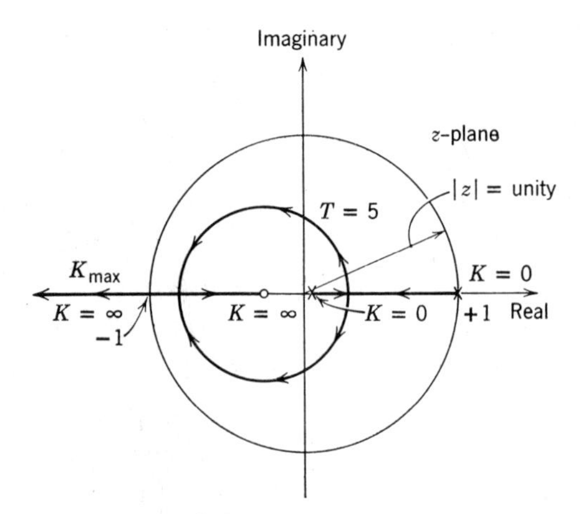

Figure 3.8 Root-locus plot for $T = 5$

If the values $T = 1$, $a = 1$ are inserted in equation (3.11), then

$$G^*(z) = \frac{0.368K}{z - 1} \times \frac{z + 0.72}{z - 0.368} \tag{3.14}$$

The constant-phase loci of equation (3.14) are obtained by superimposing the phase angle loci of the two components of $G^*(z)$, that is, the straight lines and circles. The root-locus is obtained by determining the points which give a sum of ± 180 degrees. The various constant-phase loci and the root-locus are constructed in Fig. 3.9.

Part of the root-locus equation can be obtained from (3.12) as

$$y^2 + (x + 0.72)^2 = (1.368)^2 \tag{3.15}$$

This equation indicates a circle of radius 1.368 and center at $(-0.72, 0)$, which tallies with the graphical construction of Fig. 3.9.

The gain K can be found from equation (3.14) as follows:

$$K = \left| \frac{(z - 1)(z - 0.368)}{z + 0.72} \right| \frac{1}{0.368} \tag{3.16}$$

The actual roots for a value of $K = 1$ are obtained from the root-locus shown in Fig. 3.9. For this example these roots are

$$z_{1,2} = 0.5 \pm j\sqrt{0.38} \tag{3.17}$$

The maximum allowable gain K_m which determines the limit of stability

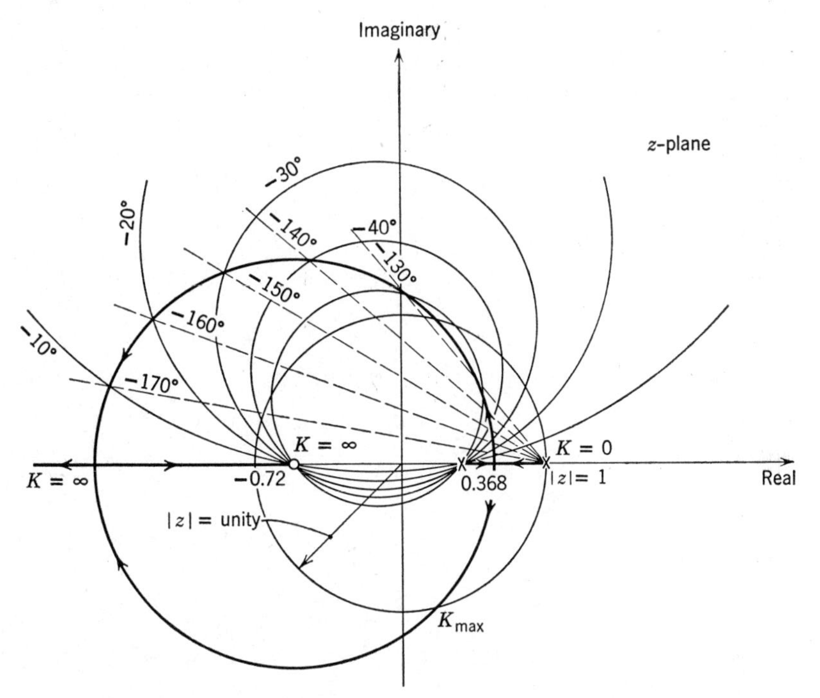

Figure 3.9 Construction of the root-locus of uncompensated system in example

is obtained at the intersection of the root-locus with the unit circle, at which point the roots are

$$z_{1,2} = 0.24 \pm j0.97 \tag{3.18}$$

Here K_m is equal to 2.43, which is the limit of stability for this particular system.

Suppose that the system described in equation (3.14) is to be improved by using a pulsed network or a digital compensator as shown in Fig. 3.5; then the transfer function $D^*(z)$ of the compensating system can be written in terms of poles and zeros in the z-plane, and its simplest form is the following:

$$D^*(z) = A\frac{z - B}{z - C} \tag{3.19}$$

The choice of the compensator in the form given in equation (3.19) will further stabilize the system if $B > C$; or, in other words, the original root-locus is shaped so that the new root-locus tends more toward the inside of the unit circle, as may be noticed from the constant-phase loci of this function and the shaped root-locus in Fig. 3.10.

The gain constant of the pulsed network or the discrete compensator is designated by A and chosen within the compensator limits. Assume

$$A = 1.0, \quad B = 0.736, \quad C = 0.368$$

Then equation (3.19) becomes

$$D^*(z) = \frac{z - 0.736}{z - 0.368} \tag{3.20}$$

The compensated open-loop z-transform is then

$$D^*(z)\, G^*(z) = \frac{z - 0.736}{z - 0.368} \frac{z + 0.72}{z - 0.368} \frac{0.368K}{z - 1} \tag{3.21}$$

The root-locus of $1 + D^*(z)\, G^*(z)$ is as shown in Fig. 3.10, and the value of the gain K can be found as follows:

$$K = \frac{1}{0.368} \left| \frac{(z - 1)(z - 0.368)}{z + 0.72} \frac{z - 0.368}{z - 0.736} \right| \tag{3.22}$$

If a pair of the new roots of the compensated system are assumed to be the same distance from the origin as the roots of the uncompensated locus when K equals 1, the new roots from Fig. 3.10 are

$$z_{1,2} = 0.13 \pm j0.79, \qquad z_3 = 0.775 \tag{3.23}$$

The gain for these roots is

$$K = 1.91 \tag{3.24}$$

The limiting value of gain K_m in this case can be found when the shaped root-locus crosses the unit circle, which yields the following roots:

$$z_{1,2} = -0.1 \pm j0.995, \qquad z_3 = 0.744 \tag{3.25}$$

This limiting value is

$$K_m = 3.24 \tag{3.26}$$

Thus it is noticed that the compensated system is more stable than the original one, but the values of gain are still limited for stability. This is characteristic of all higher-order sampled-data control systems, that is, the roots always tend to move outside the unit circle when the gain is increased.

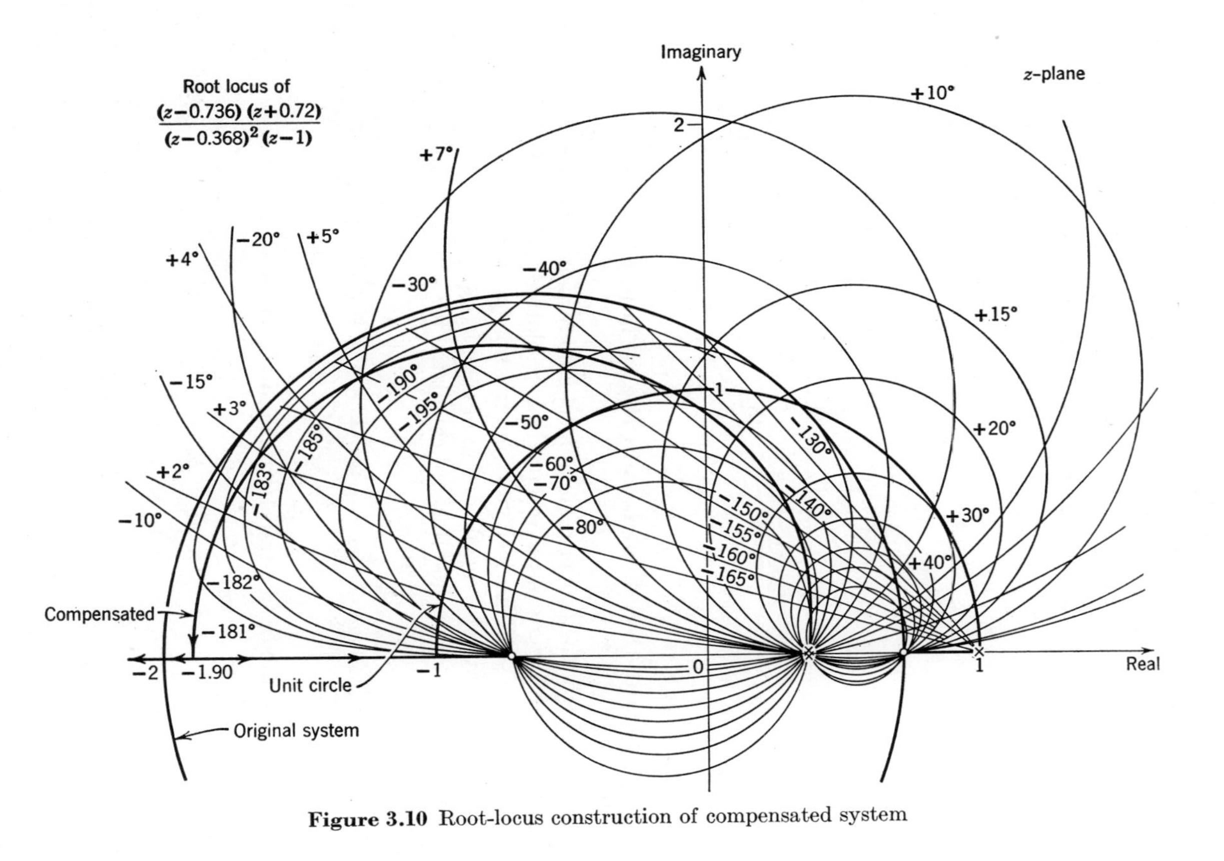

Figure 3.10 Root-locus construction of compensated system

The response quantities of the original and the compensated systems for step input are compared in Table 3.2.

TABLE 3.2

Transient Response of Original and Compensated Systems

Term	Symbol	Original	Compensated
Complex roots	$z_{1,2}$	$0.5 \pm j0.62$	$0.13 \pm j0.79$
Real roots	z_3		0.775
Distance of complex roots from origin of unit circle	$\sqrt{z_1 z_2}$	0.795	0.795
Gain	K	1	1.905
Maximum gain	K_m	2.43	3.24
Peak overshoot, per cent	M_p	45	44
Peak time, seconds	τ_p	3.45	2.23

3.3 Constant-Overshoot Loci in the z-Plane †

The choice of the proper roots to meet step response specifications can be easily made if constant-overshoot loci are plotted for the sampled-data control system. These loci yield information on the system response which aid considerably in the design of such systems.

Such constant-overshoot loci are calculated for second-order sampled-data control systems, that is,

$$G(s) = \frac{\omega_0^2(1 - e^{-Ts})}{s^2(s + 2\omega_0\eta)} \tag{3.27 ‡}$$

The output modified z-transform is found as follows:

$$C^*(z, m) = R^*(z)\frac{G^*(z, m)}{1 + G^*(z)} \tag{3.28}$$

For step input the output response equals

$$c(n, m)T = \frac{1}{2\pi j}\int_\Gamma \frac{z}{z - 1}\frac{G^*(z, m)}{1 + G^*(z)} z^{n-1}\,dz \tag{3.29}$$

† E. I. Jury, "Synthesis and Critical Study of Sampled-Data Control Systems," *Trans. A.I.E.E.*, Vol. 75, Pt. II, 1956, pp. 141–151.

‡ In this equation, ω_0 equals undamped natural frequency of the second-order system, η equals damping ratio of the system.

where $G^*(z, m)$, $G^*(z)$ are the modified z-transform and the z-transform respectively of

$$(1 - e^{-Ts})/s \times G(s) \tag{3.30}$$

The maximum of the response can be found by using the following relation:

$$\frac{\partial c(n_{\max}, m)}{\partial m} = 0 \tag{3.31}$$

In order to keep the overshoot constant, both $(\omega_0 T)$ and η are variables.

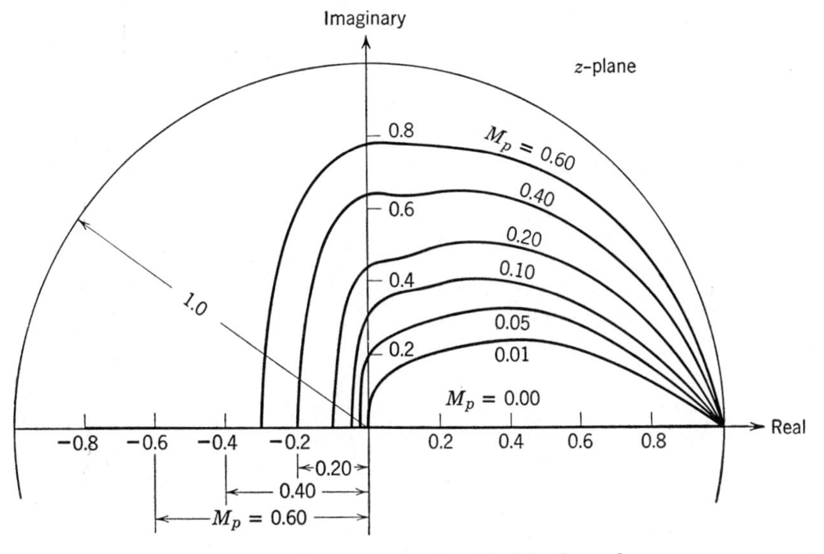

Figure 3.11 Constant overshoot loci in the z-plane

Those constant-overshoot loci are plotted in Fig. 3.11, where it is noticed that the roots of $1 + G^*(z)$ can be real or imaginary, depending on the values of $\omega_0 T$ and η.

These constant-overshoot loci can be used for higher-order sampled-data control systems when dominance holds.† Thus these loci are important in the root-locus shaping discussed in the preceding section.

For the second-order system discussed earlier, the locus of the roots of $1 + G^*(z)$ is plotted in Fig. 3.12 and computed in Table 3.3. For this locus $\omega_0 T$ is held constant and η is variable, yielding the corresponding overshoot. These plots will aid in the design of this type of sampled-data control system.

† See the next section.

TABLE 3.3

Relationship between Location of Roots and Time Sequence Response Overshoot for Second-Order Sampled-Data Control System

Location	Root	M_p, per cent	
		Overshoot	η
	$\omega_0 T = 1.0$		
$0.568 \pm j0.752$	z_1	82	0.3
$+0.500 \pm j0.618$	z_2	40	0.5
$0.444 \pm j0.436$	z_3	15	0.8
$0.426 \pm j0.320$	z_4	5	1.0
$0.416 \pm j0.195$	z_5	0.37	1.2
0.412	z_6	0	1.35
0.513, 0.310	z_7	0	1.4
	$\omega_0 T = 2$		
$-0.026 \pm j0.971$	z_1	94	0.4
$\pm 0.854j$	z_2	73	0.5
$0.083 \pm j0.598$	z_3	35	0.8
$0.132 \pm j0.478$	z_4	20	1.0
$0.174 \pm j0.380$	z_5	8	1.2
$0.208 \pm j0.291$	z_6	4	1.4
$0.237 \pm j0.205$	z_7	0.62	1.6
$0.261 \pm j0.091$	z_8	0 †	1.8
$+0.27$	z_9	0	1.9005
	$\omega_0 T = 3$		
$-0.500 \pm j0.795$	z_1	105	0.5
$-0.240 \pm j0.568$	z_2	49	0.8
$-0.124 \pm j0.482$	z_3	25	1.0
$-0.003 \pm j0.384$	z_4	15	1.3
$+0.080 \pm j0.302$	z_5	7	1.6
$0.156 \pm j0.195$	z_6	0.85	2.0
0.299, 0.190	z_7	0.00	2.4
	$\omega_0 T = 4$		
-0.818 ‡	z_0	222	0.6
$-0.673 \pm j0.222$	z_1	148	0.7
$-0.554 \pm j0.283$	z_2	122	0.8
$-0.375 \pm j0.330$	z_3	84	1.0
$-0.246 \pm j0.336$	z_4	49	1.2
$-0.111 \pm j0.314$	z_5	22	1.5
$-0.017 \pm j0.277$	z_6	8	1.8
$+0.031 \pm j0.248$	z_7	6	2.0
$+0.105 \pm j0.180$	z_8	1	2.4
$+0.159 \pm j0.082$	z_9	0 §	2.8
0.190, 0.154	z_{10}	0	2.92

† At integer instant only.
‡ Convergence not apparent until $n = 26$.
§ At integer instant only.

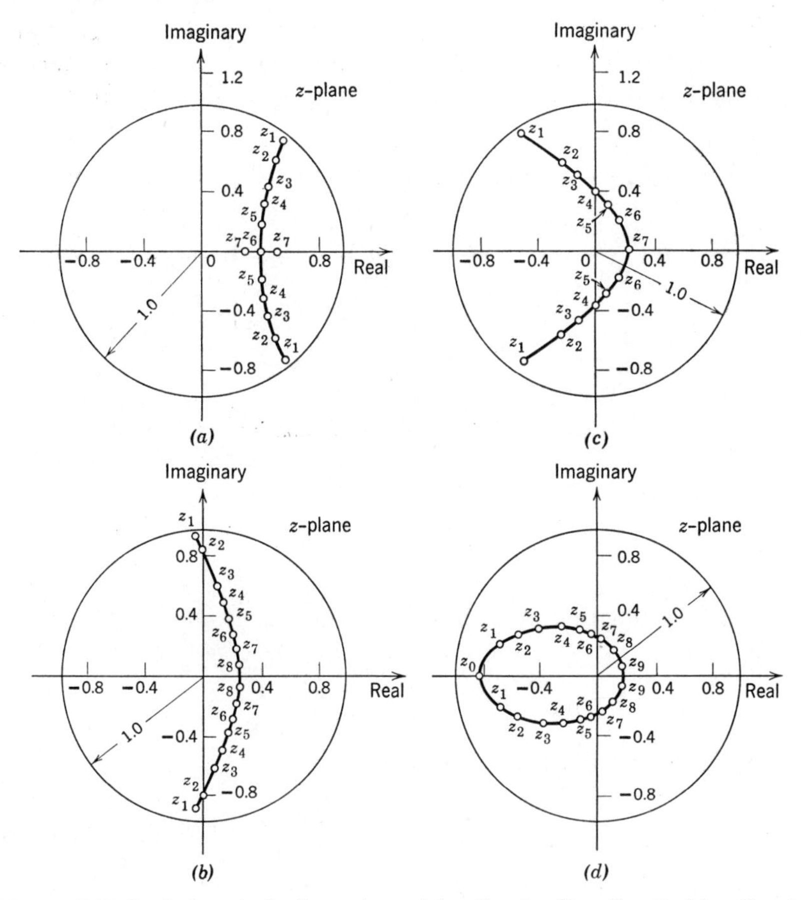

Figure 3.12 Loci of roots in the z-plane: (a) $\omega_0 T = 1$; (b) $\omega_0 T = 2$; (c) $\omega_0 T = 3$; (d) $\omega_0 T = 4$

3.4 Approximate Equations for Transient Overshoot and Peak Time

For a sampled-data control system shown in Fig. 3.13, assume that the input-output modified z-transform can be represented as follows:

$$\frac{C^*(z, m)}{R^*(z)} = \frac{G^*(z, m)}{1 + HG^*(z)} = K\frac{A(z, m)}{B(z)} \tag{3.32}$$

where

$$B(z) = \prod_{l=1}^{v} (z - q_l) \tag{3.33}$$

It is assumed that (1) no multiple poles of $C^*(z, m)/R^*(z)$ exist; (2) the order in z of $B(z)$ is higher than of $A(z, m)$, as encountered in practical systems; and (3) the roots of $B(z)$ are within the unit circle, that is, the

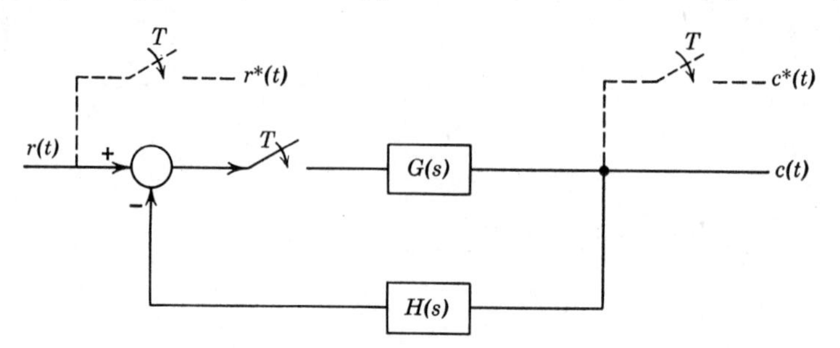

Figure 3.13 Error-sampled feedback system

system is stable. For step input,

$$R^*(z) = \frac{z}{z-1} \tag{3.34}$$

Substituting equation (3.34) in equation (3.32), we obtain

$$C^*(z, m) = K \frac{z}{z-1} \frac{A(z, m)}{B(z)} \tag{3.35}$$

The inverse modified z-transform of $C^*(z, m)$ is

$$c(n, m)T = \frac{1}{2\pi j} \int_\Gamma K \frac{A(z, m)}{(z-1)\,B(z)} z^n\,dz \tag{3.36}$$

where Γ is a contour of integration in the z-plane that encloses all the singularities of the integrand in equation (3.36). By performing the integration, it can be noted that equation (3.36) is

$$c(n, m)T = K \frac{A(1)}{B(1)} + \sum_{q_l=\text{real}} \frac{KA(q_l, m)}{(q_l - 1)\,B'(q_l)} (q_l)^n$$

$$+ \sum_{q_l=\alpha_l+j\beta_l} 2 \left| \frac{KA(q_l, m)}{(q_l - 1)\,B'(q_l)} \right|$$

$$\times (\alpha_l^2 + \beta_l^2)^{n/2} [\cos n\theta_l + \text{ang}\, A(q_l, m) - \text{ang}\,(q_l - 1) - \text{ang}\, B'(q_l)]$$

(3.37) †

† It should be noted the steady-state output is of the same form as the step input, thus $A(z, m)|_{z=1} = A(1)$.

where

$$\tan \theta_l = \frac{\beta_l}{\alpha_l} \qquad \text{and} \qquad B'(q_l) = \frac{dB}{dz}\bigg|_{z=q_l} \tag{3.38}$$

Assume that a pair of predominate poles exists $(\alpha_0 \pm j\beta_0)$ near the unit circle and that all other poles are concentrated near the origin of the unit circle. Then all the modes of equation (3.37) may be neglected except the constant term and those due to the pair of predominate poles $(\alpha_0 \pm j\beta_0)$; thus

$$c(n, m)T = K\frac{A(1)}{B(1)} + 2\left|\frac{KA(z_0, m)}{(z_0 - 1)\,B'(z_0)}\right| |z_0|^n$$
$$\times \cos\,[n\theta_0 + \text{ang}\,A(z_0, m) - \text{ang}\,(z_0 - 1) - \text{ang}\,B'(z_0)] \tag{3.39}$$

where

$$z_0 = \alpha_0 + j\beta_0 \tag{3.40}$$

$$B'(z_0) = \frac{dB}{dz}\bigg|_{z=z_0} \tag{3.41}$$

Suppose that the response of such a system is generally as shown in Figs. 3.14 and 3.15. It is noticed in Fig. 3.15 that the peak time does

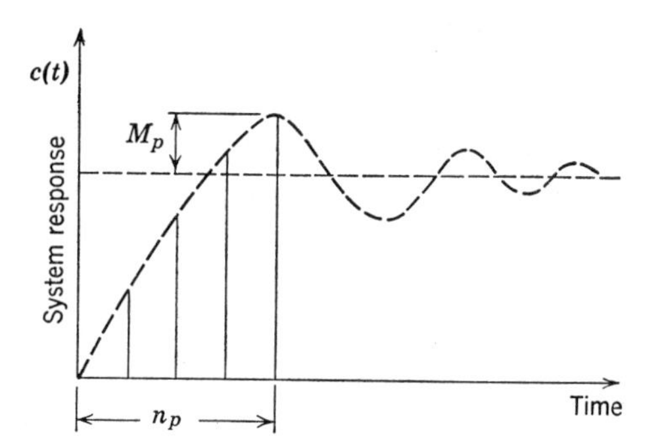

Figure 3.14 A typical output when the maximum occurs at sampling instants

not coincide with the sampling instants. In this case the M_p and τ_p can be found by using the procedures discussed in Chapter 2.

Obtain first the maximum at the sampling instants. Letting $m \to 1$ in expression (3.39), we obtain the response at the sampling instants $c(nT)$. To obtain n_p, apply the following condition and solve for n_p which ought to be an integer:

$$c(n + 1)T - c(nT) = 0 \tag{3.42}$$

The solution of equation (3.42) generally yields a value of n which is non-integer; however, the value of n_p to be used is the upper integer value of the actual n obtained. The value of n_p thus obtained can be substituted in equation (3.39) to obtain $c(n_p, m)T$.

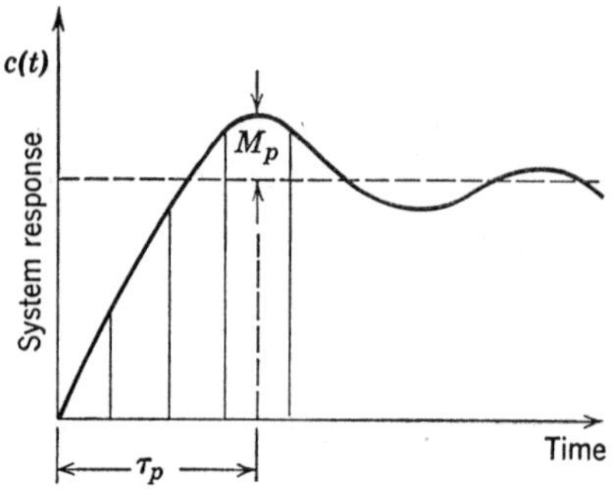

To obtain the value of m for the actual output, the following expression is used:

$$\frac{\partial c(n_p, m)T}{\partial m} = 0 \qquad (3.43)$$

The solution of equation (3.43) yields a value $m = m_p$ between zero and unity, and the peak time τ_p is the following:

$$\tau_p = (n_p - 1 + m_p)T \qquad (3.44)$$

Figure 3.15 A typical output when the maximum occurs between sampling instants

The actual maximum is obtained when n_p and m_p are substituted in expression (3.39); thus

$$M_p = c(n_p, m_p)T - K\frac{A(1)}{B(1)} \qquad (3.45)$$

When equation (3.43) is not satisfied with the given restrictions on m, the actual output coincides at the sampling instants as shown in Fig. 3.14. Thus n_p can be found from equation (3.42). In the following derivation, for simplicity it is assumed that the solution of equation (3.42) yields an integer value of n. However, the results can be easily modified if n is a non-integer, for in this case the actual value of n will be the upper integer value of the value obtained.†

By substituting equation (3.39) in (3.42), letting $m \to 1$, it can be shown that

$$n_p = \frac{1}{\theta_0}\left[\frac{\pi}{2} - \text{ang}\, A(z_0) + \text{ang}\, B'(z_0)\right] \qquad (3.46)$$

If n_p in equation (3.42) is a non-integer, the actual value of n_p will be

$$n_{pa} = n_p + Y_n \qquad (3.47)$$

where Y_n is a correction factor that will bring the value of n_{pa} to be integer.

† E. I. Jury, "Effect of Pole and Zero Location on the Transient Response of Sampled-Data Systems," *Trans. A.I.E.E.*, Vol. 74, Pt. II, 1955, pp. 41–48.

Since for simplicity it was assumed that n_p is an integer value, the first overshoot is obtained by substituting equation (3.46) in (3.39), and noting (3.45);

$$M_p = \frac{2}{[(\alpha_0 - 1)^2 + \beta_0{}^2]^{1/2}} \left| \frac{KA(z_0)}{B'(z_0)} \right| \times |z_0|^{n_p} \sin \text{ang} (z_0 - 1) \quad (3.48)$$

which can be simplified further to yield

$$M_p = \frac{2\beta}{[(\alpha_0 - 1)^2 + \beta_0{}^2]} \left| \frac{KA(z_0)}{B'(z_0)} \right| \left| z_0 \right|^{n_p} \quad (3.49)$$

The accuracy of the assumption which resulted in the two approximate relations for n_p and M_p may be explained readily. From the general solution of equation (3.37), a certain simple mode is considered; that is, the mode

$$\frac{KA(q_1)}{(q_1 - 1)\, B'(q_1)} (q_1)^n \quad (3.50)$$

This mode will die to a small per cent of its initial value when $n_p = 3$; and if n_p is larger, the effect of this simple pole is small even if

$$\frac{KA(q_1)}{(q_1 - 1)\, B'(q_1)} \quad (3.51)$$

is large. It can be shown that the coefficient

$$\frac{KA(q_1)}{(q_1 - 1)\, B'(q_1)} \quad (3.52)$$

is small if this root q_1 is not too close to other roots. In case a certain mode must be accounted for, the magnitude of this mode at n_p can be evaluated from the proper term of the general equation (3.37) and added to the result of equation (3.39) as a second approximation.

Equation (3.46) can be rewritten as

$$n_p\theta_0 = \frac{\pi}{2} - \text{(sum of angles from zeros to the predominate pole } \alpha_0 + j\beta_0) + \text{(sum of angles from other poles to the predominate pole } \alpha_0 + j\beta_0) \quad (3.52a)$$

Thus it may be concluded that zeros decrease n_p, and additional poles increase n_p. Furthermore, n_p is inversely proportional to θ_0.

M_p, from equation (3.49) can be written as the product of the following two terms

$[\alpha_0^2 + \beta_0^2]^{n_p/2}$ (This quantity is always less than unity, since the predominate poles are inside the unit circle.)

$\dfrac{K}{(\alpha_0 - 1)^2 + \beta_0^2}$ × (product of distances from zeros to the predominate pole $\alpha_0 + j\beta_0$)/(product of distances from all poles to the predominate pole $\alpha_0 + j\beta_0$, excluding the distance between the two predominate poles)

It is evident from the first term that the smaller n_p is, the larger M_p becomes; thus the choice of n_p and M_p requires a compromise. For a zero-displacement error system K must fulfill the condition that in steady state the output equals the input; thus

$$K = \frac{\prod_{l=1}^{v}(1 - q_l)}{\prod_{i=1}^{u}(1 - p_i)}, \qquad p_i \text{ are zeros of } A(z, m)\Big|_{m\to 1} \tag{3.53}$$

Substituting for K into equation (3.49), we obtain

M_p = [(Product of distances from all poles to the point (1, 0), excluding distances from two predominate poles to the point (1, 0)/(product of distances from all poles to predominate pole $\alpha_0 + j\beta_0$, excluding the distance between predominate poles)] × [(product of distances from zeros to the predominate pole $\alpha_0 + j\beta_0$)/[product of distance from all zeros to the point (1, 0)] × $[|z_0|^{n_p}]$ (3.54)

In equation (3.46) n_p can be written as

$$n_p = \frac{1}{\theta_0}\left[\pi - \sum_{\text{all zeros}} \gamma + \sum_{\substack{\text{all poles except}\\ \text{predominate pair}}} \phi\right] \tag{3.55}$$

where ϕ and γ are as shown in Fig. 3.16. By substituting for n_p in equation (3.54),

$$M_p = \left[\prod \text{(all poles except predominate pair)} \frac{aO}{ab} |z_0|^{\phi/\theta_0} \text{(due to additional poles)}\right] \times \left[\prod \text{(all zeros)} \frac{db}{dO} |z_0|^{-\gamma/\theta_0} \text{(due to zeros)}\right] \times |z_0|^{\pi/\theta_0} \text{(constant term)} \tag{3.56}$$

where aO, ab db, dO are the distances as shown in Fig. 3.16.

In discussing the effect of real poles on M_p, it is evident from Fig. 3.17, that if a pole is near the origin of the unit circle, then $a0/ab$ is nearly unity and the effect of this pole configuration on both M_p and n_p is not substantial. In contrast to this, if a pole configuration is as shown in

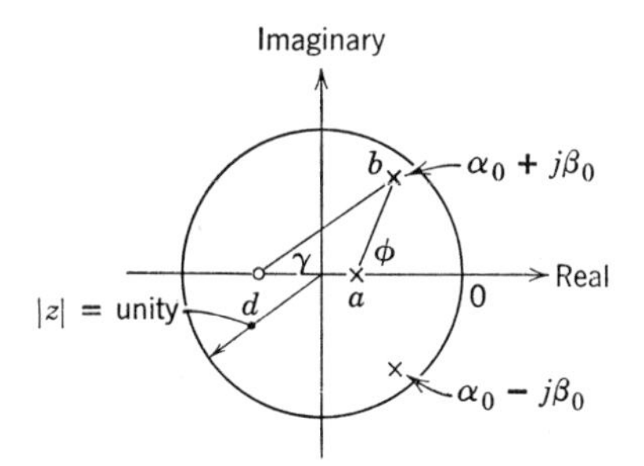

Figure 3.16 Location of predominate poles in the z-plane

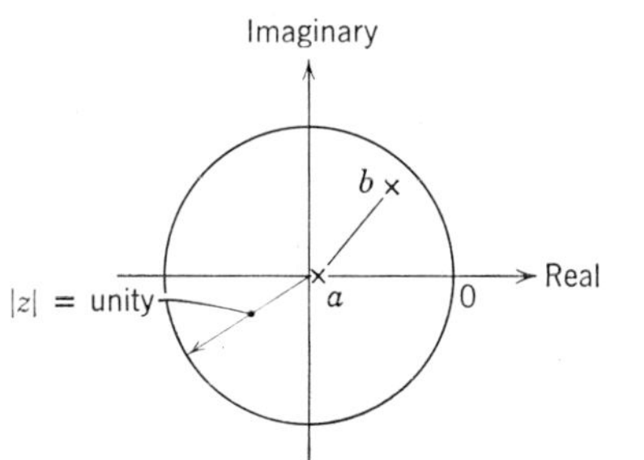

Figure 3.17 Effect on M_p and n_p when a third root is near the origin of the unit circle in the z-plane

Fig. 3.18, then $a0/ab \gg 1$, and M_p will increase considerably. Thus it can be deduced that the response will be highly oscillatory if the poles are coinciding. Finally, if a pole configuration is as shown in Fig. 3.19, then $a0/ab < 1$, and M_p is reduced, compared to the case of Fig. 3.18. Similar conclusions can be deduced when the additional poles are complex inside the unit circle.

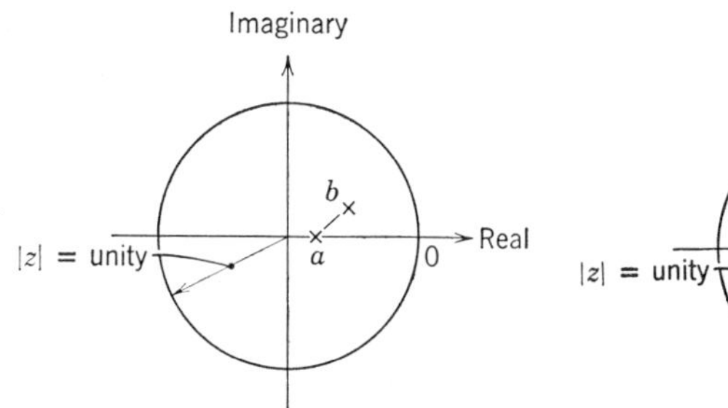

Figure 3.18 Effect on M_p and n_p when $a0 > ab$

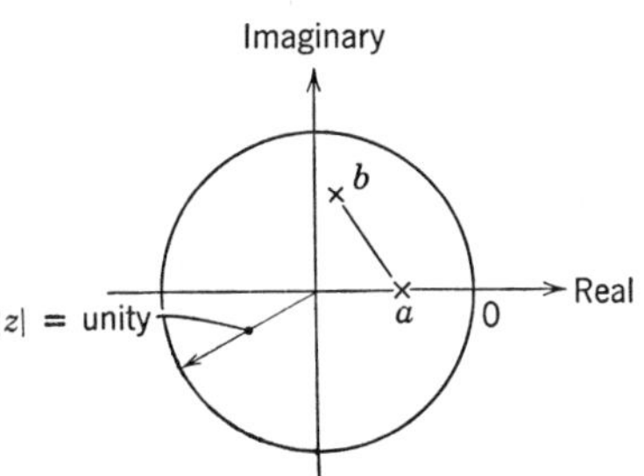

Figure 3.19 Effect on M_p and n_p when $a0 < ab$

The effect of zeros on M_p and n_p can be deduced from the second bracket of equation (3.54), where it is noticed that for a zero configuration as shown in Fig. 3.20 $db/d0 \approx 1$, and γ is small. The effects on both M_p and n_p are small. In contrast, when a zero is near the point (1, 0), then $db/d0 > 1$, and M_p is increased tremendously; thus a zero near the point (1, 0) is not desirable. However, when a zero is outside the unit circle, as shown in Fig. 3.21, then $db/d0 \approx 1$, and M_p will not increase considerably. In conclusion, it ought to be mentioned that real and complex poles might exist in any location inside the unit circle, but zeros of

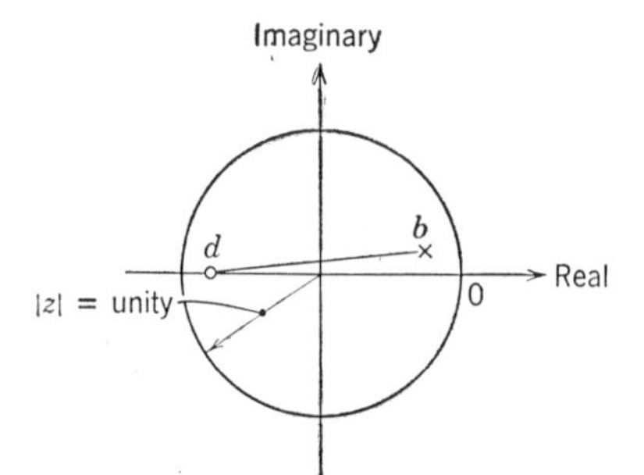

Figure 3.20 Effect on M_p and n_p when $db/d0 \approx 1$

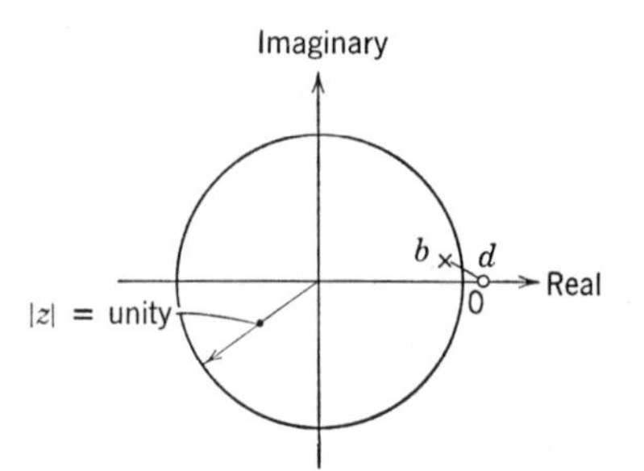

Figure 3.21 Effect on M_p and n_p when a zero exists outside the unit circle

the overall transfer function may be located anywhere inside or outside the unit circle.

3.5 Correlation between Frequency Locus and Root-Locus

The frequency locus $G^*(z)$ of any sampled-data control system is the locus of all points of $G^*(z)$ in the $G^*(z)$-plane as z traverses the unit circle. This locus is the conformal transformation of the whole unit circle of the z-plane on the $G^*(z)$-plane. Figure 3.1 indicates a typical sampled-data control system whose frequency locus for various values of gain K is shown in Fig. 3.22.

Since the frequency locus is the conformal transformation of the unit circle in the z-plane, the frequency locus itself cannot give the values of the poles of $C^*(z, m)$ in equation (3.1). Any attempt to find these poles by means of correspondence between the z- and $G^*(z)$-plane requires some transformation along a certain curve inside the unit circle where the desired poles are located. Thus the frequency locus may be generalized by putting

$$z = A_n e^{j\phi} \tag{3.57}$$

into the transfer function $G^*(z)$. (For a stable system the particular values of z to be considered should lie inside the unit circle.)

By using A_n as a parameter, a family of constant A_n loci is obtained. The usual frequency locus is the constant A_n locus, A_n equaling unity.

If the radial lines from the origin of the z-plane are conformally transformed on the $G^*(z)$-plane, a family of constant ϕ loci is obtained. By means of these two families of loci, a curvilinear square in $G^*(z)$-plane can

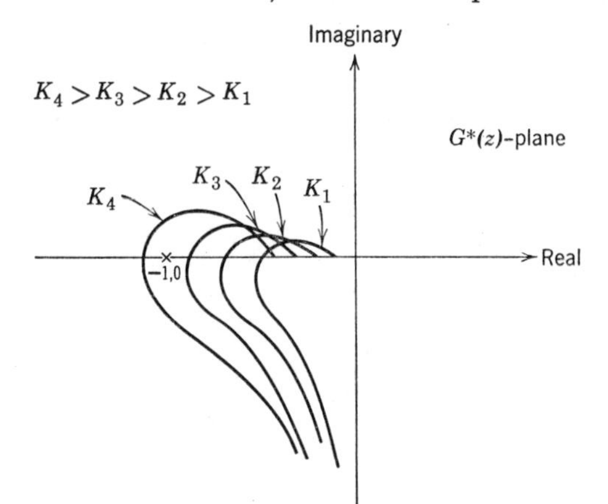

Figure 3.22 Typical frequency loci of $G^*(z)$

be found which encloses the point $(-1, 0)$, and by taking successively closer approximation in the values of z, the poles of equation (3.1) can be found to any desired accuracy. Typical families of constant A_n and

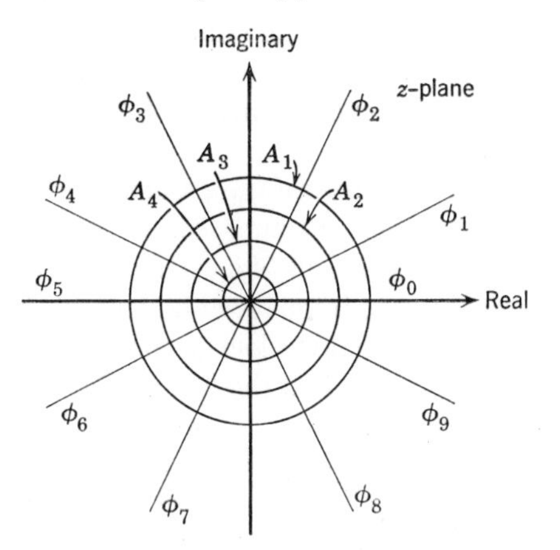

Figure 3.23 Family of constant ϕ loci and constant A_n loci in the z-plane

constant ϕ and their conformal transformation in the $G^*(z)$-plane are shown in Figs. 3.23 and 3.24.

The frequency locus $G^*(z)$ can also be obtained from the root-locus once the roots have been determined. This can be easily accomplished

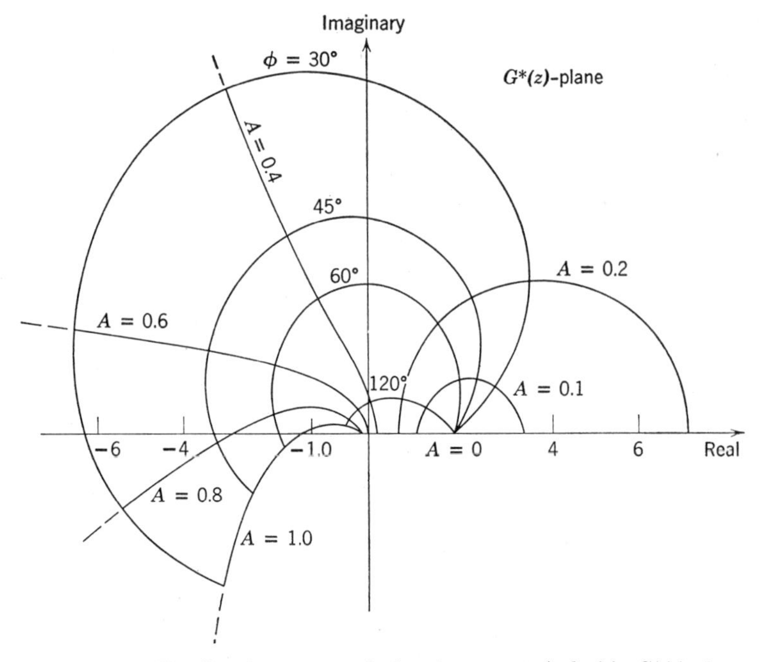

Figure 3.24 Family of constant ϕ loci and constant A_n loci in $G^*(z)$-plane

by letting z traverse the unit circle and finding the vector magnitude and phase from the roots to the unit circle. In this way the roots and the zeros yield the overall frequency response of the sampled-data control system.

From the correspondence between the z and the $G^*(z)$ plane, any information concerning the system encompassed on the $G^*(z)$-plane may be obtained from the z-plane by means of a certain transformation. To find the actual correlation between frequency and transient responses, advantage can be taken of the fact that the loci on the $G^*(z)$-plane give information on the frequency response, and the loci on the z-plane give information on the transient response.

Furthermore, for the second-order system the frequency locus will cross the negative real axis either at one or at two distinct points as shown in Figs. 3.25*a*, 3.25*b*, and 3.25*c*.

For small values of $(\omega_0 T)$ the frequency locus $G^*(z)$ generally crosses the real axis at two points when the roots of $1 + G^*(z)$ are in the right half of the unit circle as shown in Fig. 3.12*a*. For large values of $(\omega_0 T)$, the locus crosses the real axis only at one point when the roots lie in the negative half of the unit circle as shown in Figs. 3.12*c* and 3.12*d*.

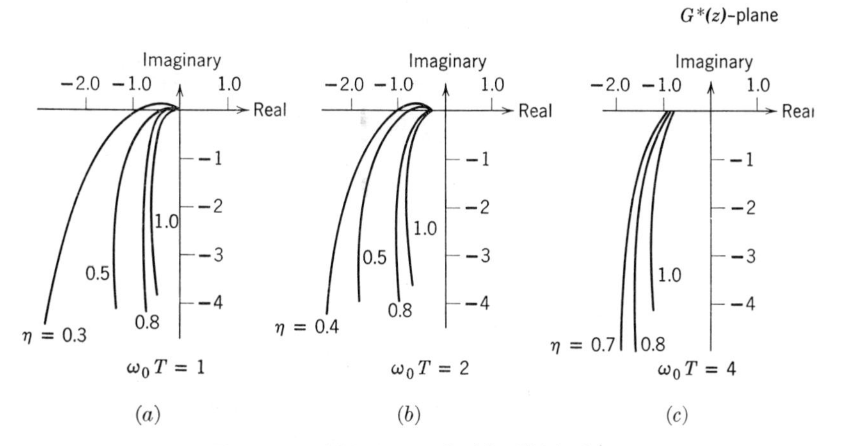

Figure 3.25 Frequency loci in $G^*(z)$-plane

3.6 Steady-State Error from Root-Locus

a. Steady-State Error at the Sampling Instants

The z-transform of the error at the sampling instants for a system configuration shown in Fig. 3.1 is given as

$$E^*(z) = R^*(z) \frac{1}{1 + G^*(z)} \tag{3.58}$$

Equation (3.58) can be described as follows:

$$E^*(z) = R^*(z) \frac{\text{Poles of } G^*(z)}{\text{Roots of } 1 + G^*(z)} \tag{3.59}$$

For the steady-state error apply the final value theorem to equation (3.59); thus

$$e_{ss}(nT) = \lim_{z \to 1} \frac{z-1}{z} \times R^*(z) \frac{1}{1 + G^*(z)} \tag{3.60}$$

or

$$e_{ss}(nT) = \lim_{z \to 1} \frac{z-1}{z} \times R^*(z) \frac{\prod \text{distances of poles of } G^*(z) \text{ to } (1, 0)}{\prod \text{distances of roots to } (1, 0)} \tag{3.61}$$

The steady-state error at the sampling instants can be obtained from the root-locus plot of $G^*(z)$ as ratio of distances.

For a step input, equation (3.61) becomes

$$e_{ss}(nT) = \frac{\prod \text{distances of poles of } G^*(z) \text{ to } (1, 0)}{\prod \text{distances of roots to } (1, 0)} \tag{3.62}$$

It is noticed from this equation that the steady-state error is zero if a pole of $G^*(z)$ exists at $z = 1$.

Similarly, for a ramp input,

$$R^*(z) = \frac{Tz}{(z - 1)^2} \tag{3.63}$$

Equation (3.62) becomes

$$e_{ss}(nT) = \lim_{z \to 1} \frac{T}{z - 1} \frac{\prod \text{distances of poles of } G^*(z) \text{ to } (1, 0)}{\prod \text{distances of roots to } (1, 0)} \tag{3.64}$$

Thus, the steady-state error for ramp input is zero if $G^*(z)$ has a multiple pole at z equal to unity.

Similar deductions can be obtained for a higher-order input if the system is stable.

b. *Steady-State Error for the Continuous Output*

In the previous discussion relations for the steady state at the sampling instants are obtained from the root-locus. However, the error (difference between input and output) is continuous and can be found from the following relations.

The modified z-transform of the output is given as

$$C^*(z, m) = R^*(z) \times \frac{G^*(z, m)}{1 + G^*(z)} \tag{3.65}$$

To obtain the steady-state output apply the final-value theorem for the modified z-transform:

$$c_{ss}(t) = \lim_{\substack{z \to 1 \\ 0 \leq m \leq 1}} \frac{z - 1}{z} \times R^*(z) \frac{G^*(z, m)}{1 + G^*(z)} \tag{3.66}$$

The actual steady-state error is

$$e_{ss}(t) = r(t) - c_{ss}(t) \tag{3.67}$$

where $r(t)$ equals the continuous input.

Furthermore, the actual steady-state error can also be obtained from the modified z-transform:

$$E^*(z, m) = R^*(z, m) - C^*(z, m) \tag{3.68}$$

$$e_{ss}(t) = \lim_{\substack{z \to 1 \\ 0 \leq m \leq 1}} \frac{z - 1}{z} E^*(z, m) \tag{3.69}$$

The last relation is applicable for all higher-order inputs if the system is stable.

In most cases the limit of $E^*(z, m)$ when $z \to 1$ is independent of m, and thus the root-locus relations presented in Section a can be applied.

CHAPTER 4

Frequency Response Method of Analysis of Sampled-Data Systems

In the preceding chapters the z-transform method, which is essentially a generalized form of the Laplace transform, has been applied for the exact analysis of sampled-data systems. In this chapter the conventional Laplace transform theory used for the analysis of continuous systems is applied to sampled-data systems. Block diagram reductions and error coefficients procedure often used for the continuous system analysis are extended to the sampled-data systems. Furthermore, Nyquist diagrams and Bode logarithmic plots are used for the frequency analysis of sampled-data control systems whereby design in the frequency domain can be useful.

4.1 Sampler Representation as a Block Diagram

In Chapter 1, it is indicated that if the sampler is ideal, it can be considered as a device producing a train of impulses at its output. † This action is based on the mathematical equation which describes the sampler

† It should be noted that this ideal representation is only valid if the gain following the sampler is multiplied by the actual pulse width.

in time as follows:

$$e^*(t) = e(t) \times \delta_T(t) = e(t) \sum_{n=-\infty}^{n=\infty} \delta(t - nT) \tag{4.1}$$

where $e(t)$ is the input function applied to the sampler and $\delta_T(t)$ is a string of unit impulses separated by the sampling period T. It has been shown in equation (1.14) that the Laplace transform of equation (4.1) is given by,

$$E^*(s) = \frac{1}{T} \sum_{k=-\infty}^{k=\infty} E(s + jk\omega_r), \qquad k = \text{integer}, \ \omega_r = \frac{2\pi}{T} \tag{4.2}$$

It is noticed from equation (4.2) that if the input $e(t)$ has one frequency component ω_1, the sampler generates all the higher frequencies as discussed in Chapter 1. Further, the sampler can be represented by an impulse modulator M as shown in Fig. 4.1, and the sampling process can

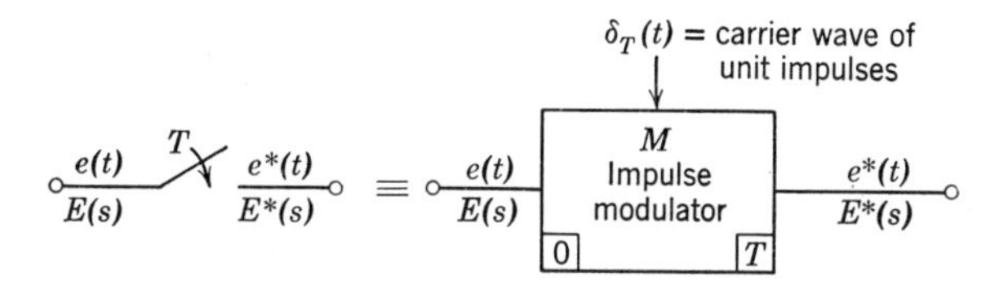

Figure 4.1 Block representation of sampler with zero delay to the input

be viewed as the amplitude modulation of a train of impulses by the input signal.

In the case $e(t)$ has a non-zero value at $t = 0^+$, equation (4.2) should be modified † as

$$E^*(s) = \frac{1}{T} \sum_{k=-\infty}^{k=\infty} E(s + jk\omega_r) + \frac{1}{2} e(0^+) \tag{4.3}$$

where $e(0^+)$ is the value of the time function at $t = 0^+$. This modification is brought about because in evaluating equation (4.2) for this case only half the impulse ‡ at $t = 0$ is accounted for. Since in most sampled-data control systems $e(t)$, the error, is zero at $t = 0^+$, equation (4.2) is used in most calculations.

† G. V. Lago, "Additions to Sampled Data Theory," *Proc. Natl. Electronic Conf.*, Vol. 10, February 1955, pp. 403–408.

‡ W. K. Linvill, "Sampled-Data Control Systems Studied through Comparison of Sampling with Amplitude Modulation," *Trans. A.I.E.E.*, Vol. 70, Pt. II, 1951, pp. 1779–1788.

4.2 Characteristics of the Impulse Modulator

From equation (4.2), which describes the impulse modulator, the following characteristics are evident.

1. The sampler output is periodic in s with the imaginary period $j\omega_r$. In the s-plane $E^*(s)$ has periodic strips separated by $j\omega_r$ as shown in Fig. 4.2.

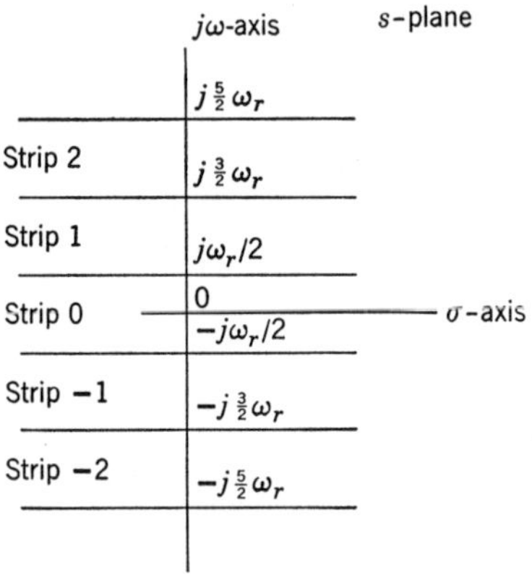

2. If s increases along the $j\omega$-axis, the output amplitude spectrum $|E^*(j\omega)|$ as a function of frequency contains a primary component plus complementary components. The useful information is contained in the primary component, and the complementary components produce the sampler ripple in the system output. This is shown in Fig. 1.10.

3. The amplitude spectrum is an even function of frequency, and phase function is an odd function of frequency within each strip.

Figure 4.2 Periodicity strip of $E^*(s)$ in s-plane

4. In order to recover the input signal, the sampling frequency ω_r should be larger than or equal to twice the highest frequency component of the input signal (Shannon's sampling theorem):

$$\omega_r \geq 2\omega \tag{4.4}$$

5. If $E(s)$ is a rational function in s, then $E^*(s)$ is always a rational function in e^{Ts}. This characteristic shows the equivalence between the z-transform method and the Laplace transform method.

6. The impulse modulator is a linear device that can be described as an amplitude modulator, equations (4.1) and (4.2), but cannot be described by a conventional transfer function. Further, since the sampling process is linear, the output for a sum of inputs is equal to the sum of the responses from the inputs applied one at a time.

7. For $s = 0$ and $s = \pm j(k\omega_r/2)$, $E^*(s)$ is always real. This is noticed from Fig. 4.2 or equation (1.49).

8. If the frequency locus of $E^*(s)$, that is, $s \to j\omega$, is plotted for frequencies 0 to $\omega_r/2$, the locus for frequencies $\omega_r/2$ to ω_r is the reflection about the real axis of the 0 to $\omega_r/2$ locus.

4.3 Input-Output Relationship

If it is assumed that impulse-modulated signals are applied to a relaxed continuous filter as shown in Fig. 4.3, we can apply the conventional

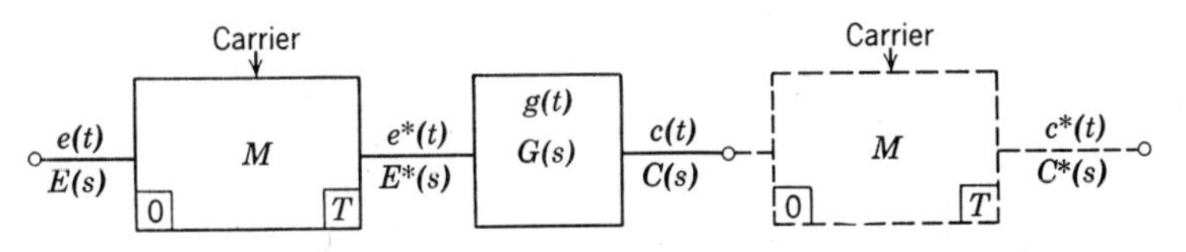

Figure 4.3 Linear-sampled-data system

Laplace transform to obtain the output transform as follows:

$$C(s) = E^*(s) \times G(s) = \left[\frac{1}{T}\sum_{k=-\infty}^{k=\infty} E(s + jk\omega_r)\right] G(s) \tag{4.5}$$

If only the output at the sampling instants is required, we can apply relation (4.2) to obtain

$$C^*(s) = \frac{1}{T}\sum_{k=-\infty}^{k=\infty} E^*(s + jk\omega_r)\, G(s + jk\omega_r) \tag{4.6}$$

But $E^*(s)$ is a periodic function with period $j\omega_r$. Hence,

$$E^*(s + jk\omega_r) = E^*(s) \tag{4.7}$$

Substituting equation (4.7) into (4.6) yields

$$C^*(s) = E^*(s) \times \frac{1}{T}\sum_{k=-\infty}^{k=\infty} G(s + jk\omega_r) \tag{4.8}$$

or

$$C^*(s) = E^*(s) \times G^*(s) \tag{4.9}$$

It is of importance to indicate that both $G^*(s)$ and $C^*(s)$ have the same characteristics enumerated earlier for $E^*(s)$.

In a similar manner the output at half the sampling period can be obtained by fictitiously introducing an impulse modulator at the output to operate † at $T/2$. This is shown in Fig. 4.4.

† W. K. Linvill and R. W. Sittler, "Design of Sampled-Data Systems by Extension of Conventional Techniques," Report R-222, M.I.T., July 1953.

The output transform at half the sampling period $C^{**}(s)$ can be written as †

$$C^{**}(s) = E^*(s) \times \frac{1}{T/2} \sum_{k=-\infty}^{k=\infty} G(s + jk2\omega_r) \tag{4.10}$$

which can be rewritten as

$$C^{**}(s) = E^*(s) \times G^{**}(s) \tag{4.10a}$$

In most cases $G^{**}(s)$ can be obtained from $G^*(s)$ by replacing every T in $G^*(s)$ by $T/2$.

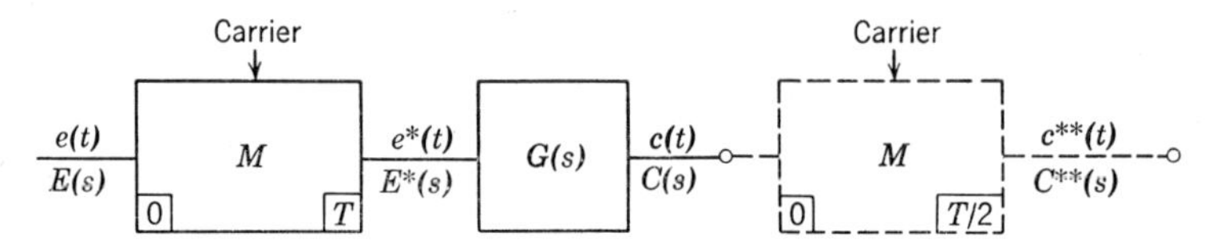

Figure 4.4 Method for obtaining response between sampling instants

This procedure can be extended to obtain more information about the response between sampling instants by introducing a fictitious modulator ‡ whose duty cycle is T/n, where n is a positive integer.

4.4 Output Response

To obtain the total output $c(t)$ we can apply the ordinary inverse Laplace transform method to equation (4.5):

$$c(t) = \mathcal{L}^{-1}[C(s)] = \frac{1}{2\pi j} \int_{c-j\infty}^{c+j\infty} E^*(s)\, G(s)\, e^{st}\, ds \tag{4.11}$$

or

$$c(t) = \mathcal{L}^{-1}\left[\frac{1}{T} \sum_{k=-\infty}^{k=\infty} E(s + jk\omega_r) \times G(s)\right] \tag{4.12}$$

Since $E^*(s)$ is of infinite summation form in s, the transfer output transform $C(s)$ consists of an infinite number of poles in the s-plane. These infinite poles give rise to an infinite time series as expected from equation (4.12). In some cases we can approximate $E^*(s)$ with few terms by ignoring the high-frequency components. By this approximation we

† W. K. Linvill and R. W. Sittler, "Design of Sampled-Data Systems by Extension of Conventional Techniques," Report R-222, M.I.T., July 1953.

‡ R. F. Nease, "Analysis and Design of Non-linear Sampled-Data Control Systems," W.A.D.C. Technical Note 57-162, M.I.T., June 1957.

can easily obtain the time function as the sum of the responses of the few components of $E^*(s)$. This approximation procedure facilitates the analysis of sampled-data feedback systems from both the time and frequency response approaches.

4.5 Equivalence of Inverse Laplace Transform to Inverse Modified z-Transform Method

In Chapter 2 the theory of the modified z-transform method has been applied to obtain the exact output of a sampled-data system in a closed form. Similarly, the principle of this method can be applied to equation (4.5), to scan the total output. If a fictitious delay of $\Delta T = (1 - m)T$ is introduced in the output as shown in Fig. 4.5, and if a fictitious impulse

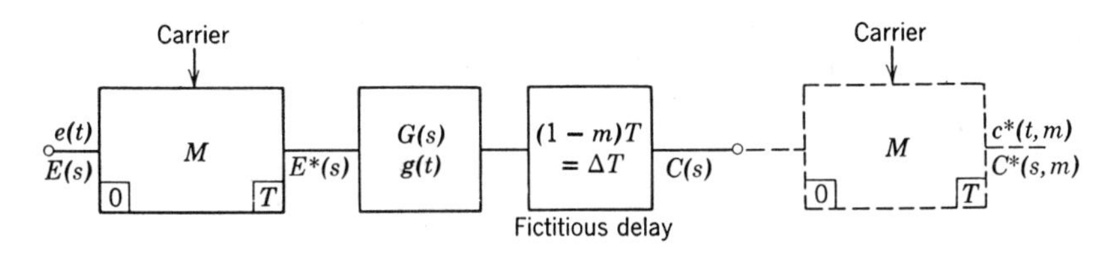

Figure 4.5 Method for obtaining total response

modulator is further included, we can scan the total output when Δ varies between zero and unity. This procedure is exactly the same as the modified z-transform method except that the sampler is replaced by an impulse modulator and the variable s is used instead of z.

Using equation (2.33) of Chapter 2 we can write for the output $C^*(s, m)$ the following equation:

$$C^*(s, m) = E^*(s) \times \frac{1}{T} \sum_{k=-\infty}^{k=\infty} G(s + jk\omega_r)\, e^{-(s+jk\omega_r)(1-m)T} \tag{4.13}$$

It has been indicated earlier that if $E(s)$ and $G(s)$ are rational functions of s with a denominator of higher degree in s than the numerator, as is usually the case in sampled-data systems, then $E^*(s)$ and $G^*(s)$ are rational functions of e^{Ts}. Therefore we can rewrite equation (4.13) in a different form as

$$C^*(e^{sT}, m) = E^*(e^{sT}) \times G^*(e^{sT}, m) \tag{4.14}$$

If we replace e^{sT} by z, equation (4.13) is exactly the modified z-transform of equation (4.5). Therefore, the inverse modified z-transform of equation (4.14) yields time function impulses whose areas are the values of $c(t)$ at any time.

The inverse modified z-transform of equation (4.13) can be expressed, following equation (2.50), as

$$c(n, m)T = \frac{1}{2\pi j}\int_{\Gamma} C^*(z, m)\, z^{n-1}\, dz \tag{4.15}$$

where Γ is a closed path in the z-plane that encloses all poles of $C^*(z, m)$ and

$$t = (n - 1 + m)T, \quad n\text{-integer}, \quad 0 \leq m \leq 1 \tag{4.16}$$

Therefore, whenever $C(s)$ the output transform of a sampled-data system is of mixed form, that is, rational in both e^{Ts} and s, we can apply the inverse modified z-transform method to obtain a closed form of $c(t)$ in terms of n and m. This procedure also gives a closed form of the infinite series obtained from the inverse Laplace transform. Furthermore, the ripple produced by the sampler can be easily determined by applying the final-value theorem developed for the modified z-transform.

ILLUSTRATIVE EXAMPLE

To illustrate the equivalence between the inverse modified z-transform and inverse Laplace transform, consider the system shown in Fig. 4.6.

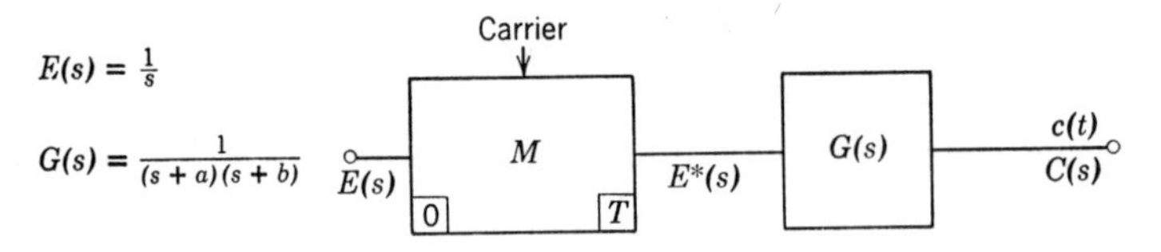

Figure 4.6 Illustrative example

In this system the output Laplace transform is given by equation (4.5) as follows:

$$C(s) = E^*(s) \times G(s) \tag{4.17}$$

The form used for $E(s)$ is given by equation (4.3) in view of the fact that $E(s)$ has an impulsive response which is not zero at $t = 0^+$; therefore

$$C(s) = \frac{1}{T}\sum_{k=-\infty}^{k=\infty} \frac{1}{(s + jk\omega_r)} \times \frac{1}{(s + a)(s + b)} + \frac{1}{2}\frac{1}{(s + a)(s + b)} \tag{4.18}$$

Equation (4.18) can be expanded to give

$$C(s) = \frac{1}{T}\left[\frac{1}{s}\frac{1}{(s+a)(s+b)}\right] + \frac{1}{T}\left[\frac{1}{s+j\omega_r}\frac{1}{(s+a)(s+b)}\right]$$
$$+ \frac{1}{T}\left[\frac{1}{s-j\omega_r}\frac{1}{(s+a)(s+b)}\right] + \frac{1}{T}\left[\frac{1}{s+2j\omega_r}\frac{1}{(s+a)(s+b)}\right]$$
$$+ \frac{1}{T}\left[\frac{1}{s-2j\omega_r}\frac{1}{(s+a)(s+b)}\right] + \cdots + \frac{1}{2}\frac{1}{(s+a)(s+b)} \tag{4.19}$$

It is seen that equation (4.19) is of infinite series form, its pole configuration in the s-plane is represented in Fig. 4.7.

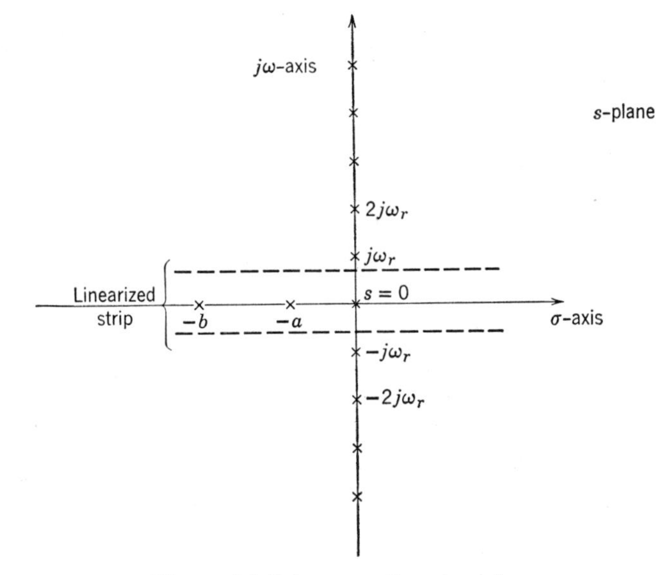

Figure 4.7 Pole-zero pattern in s-plane

To obtain the response $c(t)$, we can obtain the various responses of the terms in equation (4.19) by taking the inverse Laplace transform of each term. For instance, the first-order solution in the linearized strip of Fig. 4.7 is obtained by

$$c_1(t) = \mathcal{L}^{-1}\left[\frac{1}{T}\left(\frac{1}{s}\frac{1}{s+a}\frac{1}{s+b}\right)\right] + \frac{1}{2}\mathcal{L}^{-1}\left[\frac{1}{(s+a)(s+b)}\right] \tag{4.19a}$$

and the ripple solution is generated by the higher-frequency components. In some cases we are interested in the low-frequency behavior of the system; thus equation (4.19) can be approximated by only a few terms.

For instance, in this example attention is focused only on the first-order solution and the first two side bands; then

$$C(s) \cong \frac{1}{T}\frac{1}{s}\frac{1}{(s+a)(s+b)} + \frac{1}{T}\frac{1}{(s+a)(s+b)}\left(\frac{1}{s+j\omega_r} + \frac{1}{s-j\omega_r}\right) + \frac{1}{2}\frac{1}{(s+a)(s+b)}$$

$$= \frac{1}{T}\frac{1}{s}\frac{1}{(s+a)(s+b)} + \frac{1}{T}\frac{1}{(s+a)(s+b)} \times \frac{2s}{s^2+\omega_r^2} + \frac{1}{2}\frac{1}{(s+a)(s+b)} \tag{4.20}$$

The approximate solution can be found from the inverse Laplace transform to yield

$$c_a(t) = \frac{1}{T}\left[\frac{1}{ab} + \frac{be^{-at} - ae^{-bt}}{ab(a-b)}\right] + \frac{2}{T}\left\{\frac{1}{a-b}\left[\frac{a}{\omega_r^2+a^2}e^{-at} - \frac{b}{\omega_r^2+b^2}e^{-bt}\right]\right\} + \frac{1}{2}\frac{e^{-at}-e^{-bt}}{b-a}$$
$$+ \frac{2}{T}\frac{\cos(\omega_r t - \phi)}{\sqrt{(ab-\omega_r)^2 + \omega_r^2(a+b)^2}}, \qquad \phi = \tan^{-1}\frac{\omega_r(a+b)}{ab-\omega_r^2} \tag{4.21}$$

The total response can be obtained by adding the response contributions of all the higher harmonics in equation (4.19). The final form is given in equation (4.22):

$$c(t) = \frac{1}{b-a}\left[\frac{e^{-at}}{1-e^{aT}} - \frac{e^{-bt}}{1-e^{bT}}\right] + \frac{1}{T}\left\{\frac{ab - \left(\frac{2\pi}{T}\right)^2}{\left[a^2 + \left(\frac{2\pi}{T}\right)^2\right]\left[b^2 + \left(\frac{2\pi}{T}\right)^2\right]}\right.$$
$$\left. + 2\sum_{k=1}^{\infty}\frac{\left[ab - k^2\left(\frac{2\pi}{T}\right)^2\right]\cos\frac{2k\pi t}{T} + \frac{2\pi k}{T}(a+b)\sin\frac{2\pi kt}{T}}{\left[a^2 + k^2\left(\frac{2\pi}{T}\right)^2\right]\left[b^2 + k^2\left(\frac{2\pi}{T}\right)^2\right]}\right\} \tag{4.22 †}$$

† In evaluating equation (4.22) the following form is used for $C(s)$:

$$C(s) = \frac{1}{1-e^{-Ts}}\frac{1}{(s+a)(s+b)}$$

This form is given in an infinite series, which is a complicated form to deal with in the final investigation of the response. However, this difficulty can be easily removed if the modified z-transform is used as shown in the following: $E^*(s)$ for the step input can be written in terms of e^{Ts} as

$$E^*(s) = \frac{1}{T} \sum_{k=-\infty}^{k=\infty} \frac{1}{s + jk\omega_r} + \frac{1}{2} = \frac{1}{1 - e^{-Ts}} \tag{4.23}$$

and

$$C(s) = E^*(s)\, G(s) = \frac{1}{1 - e^{-Ts}} \times \frac{1}{(s+a)(s+b)} \tag{4.24}$$

Since equation (4.24) is of mixed form, that is, both e^{Ts} and s appear; the response $c(t)$ using the inverse Laplace transform yields the infinite series form. However, from equation (4.14), the modified z-transform of equation (4.23) can be written

$$C^*(z, m) = \frac{z}{z-1} \times \mathfrak{z}_m \left[\frac{1}{(s+a)(s+b)}\right] \tag{4.25}$$

where $\mathfrak{z}_m \left[\frac{1}{(s+a)(s+b)}\right]$ is the modified z-transform of

$$G(s) = \frac{1}{(s+a)(s+b)}$$

which is given by equation (4.13). It can also be readily obtained from tables of modified z-transform to yield

$$\mathfrak{z}_m \left[\frac{1}{(s+a)(s+b)}\right] = \frac{1}{b-a}\left(\frac{e^{-amT}}{z - e^{-aT}} - \frac{e^{-bmT}}{z - e^{-bT}}\right) \tag{4.26}$$

Therefore, equation (4.25) reduces to

$$C^*(z, m) = \frac{z}{z-1} \times \frac{1}{b-a}\left(\frac{e^{-amT}}{z - e^{-aT}} - \frac{e^{-bmT}}{z - e^{-bT}}\right) \tag{4.27}$$

The inverse modified z-transform of equation (4.27) can be obtained using equation (4.15) or through tables of inverse z-transform and in this case gives

$$c(n, m)T = \frac{1}{b-a}\left(\frac{e^{-amT}}{1 - e^{-aT}} - \frac{e^{-bmT}}{1 - e^{-bT}}\right)$$

$$+ \frac{1}{b-a}\left(\frac{e^{-amT}}{e^{-aT} - 1} e^{-aTn} - \frac{e^{-bmT}}{e^{-bT} - 1} e^{-bTn}\right) \tag{4.28}$$

$$t = (n - 1 + m)T, \quad n = \text{integer}, \quad 0 \le m \le 1$$

The first bracketed term of equation (4.28) yields the steady-state response, or in this case the steady-state ripple, and the second term in the transient term. Hence, by transforming into the z-plane, the infinite poles in the s-plane become a single pole in the z-plane; therefore the solution is obtained in a closed form which can be easily plotted and investigated.

4.6 Block Diagram Representation of Sampled-Data Systems

It has been shown in the preceding sections that the sampler operation can be represented in a block diagram indicating the impulse modulation process. The output of the impulse modulator block M is usually fed

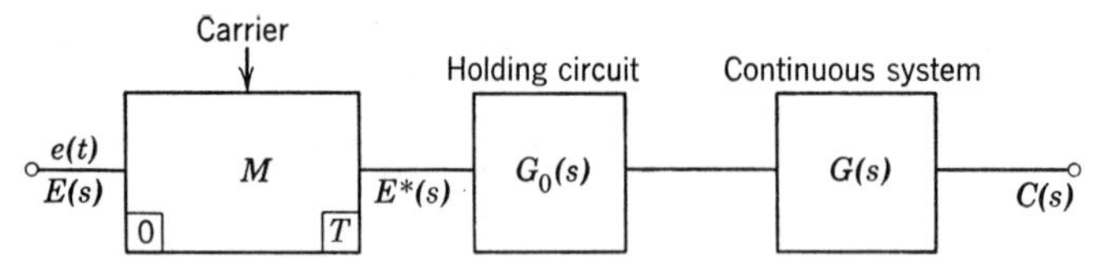

Figure 4.8 Practical sampled-data system

into a holding or smoothing circuit whose output is fed into a linear filter $G(s)$ as shown in Fig. 4.8.

The output $C(s)$ can be written in the following form:

$$C(s) = [E(s)M]\, G_0(s)\, G(s) \tag{4.29}$$

but

$$[E(s)M] = E^*(s) \tag{4.30}$$

Therefore

$$C(s) = E^*(s)\, G_0(s)\, G(s) \tag{4.31}$$

If the output transform at the sampling instants is required, we can multiply equation (4.31) by M to get

$$C^*(s) = [C(s)M] = E^*(s)\,[G_0G(s)M] = E^*(s)\, G_0\, G^*(s) \tag{4.32}$$

From equation (4.32) the following relations exist:

$$\begin{aligned} &(a) \quad CM = C^* \\ &(b) \quad G_0GM = GG_0M = G_0G^* = GG_0{}^* \end{aligned} \tag{4.33}$$

In many applications a digital computer is inserted in a continuous system for digital control purposes, especially in a feedback system. To describe a digital computer in a block diagram, we should recognize that the input to the computer is sampled, and the computer operation, if linear, is described by a transfer function denoted as $D^*(e^{sT})$. The output of the computer is clamped by a zero-order hold. Therefore, the block diagram of a digital computer is represented in Fig. 4.9.

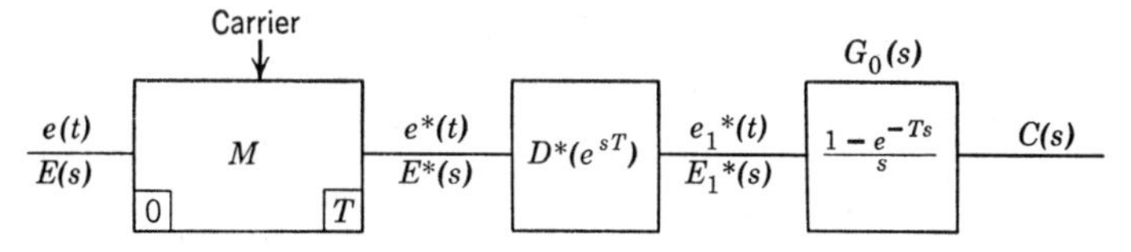

Figure 4.9 Block diagram representation of a digital computer

In this case the output transform is written as

$$C(s) = E(s)M\,D^*(e^{sT}) \times G_0(s) \tag{4.34}$$

or

$$C(s) = E^*(s) \times D^*(e^{sT}) \times G_0(s) \tag{4.35}$$

In practical operation of a digital computer, there exists a time delay in the computation † $e^{-\delta sT}$, which can be combined with $G_0(s)$. Since $E^*(s)$ can also be written as $E^*(e^{sT})$, equation (4.35) is of mixed combination in e^{sT} and s, whereby the modified z-transform method is best suited for the analysis in time function as explained in the preceding example.

In addition to (a) and (b), equations (4.34) and (4.35) give the following identities.‡

$$\left.\begin{aligned}
&(c)\quad D^*(e^{sT})\,G(s) \neq G(s)\,D^*(e^{sT})\\
&(d)\quad D_1^*(e^{sT})\,D_2^*(e^{sT}) = D_2^*(e^{sT})\,D_1^*(e^{sT})\\
&(e)\quad MD^*(e^{sT}) \neq D^*(e^{sT})M, \text{ unless } e(t) \text{ is discrete}\\
&(f)\quad MD^*(e^{sT})\,GM = MD^*G^*\\
&(g)\quad G_1MG_2M = G_1^*G_2^*\\
&(h)\quad \text{If } E = R - C, \text{ then } E^* = EM = (R - C)M\\
&\qquad\qquad\qquad\qquad\qquad = RM - CM = R^* - C^*
\end{aligned}\right\} \tag{4.36}$$

The identities (a)–(h) can be advantageously utilized in the block reduction relationships of sampled-data control systems. Table 4.1 (page 160) lists various block diagram reduction for sampled data systems.

† John M. Salzer, "System Compensation with a Digital Computer," *I.R.E. National Convention Record*, Pt. V, March 1954, pp. 179–186.

‡ W. K. Linvill and R. W. Sittler, "Design of Sampled-Data Systems by Extension of Conventional Techniques," Report R-222, M.I.T., July 1953.

TABLE 4.1

Block Diagram Reduction for Sampled-Data Systems

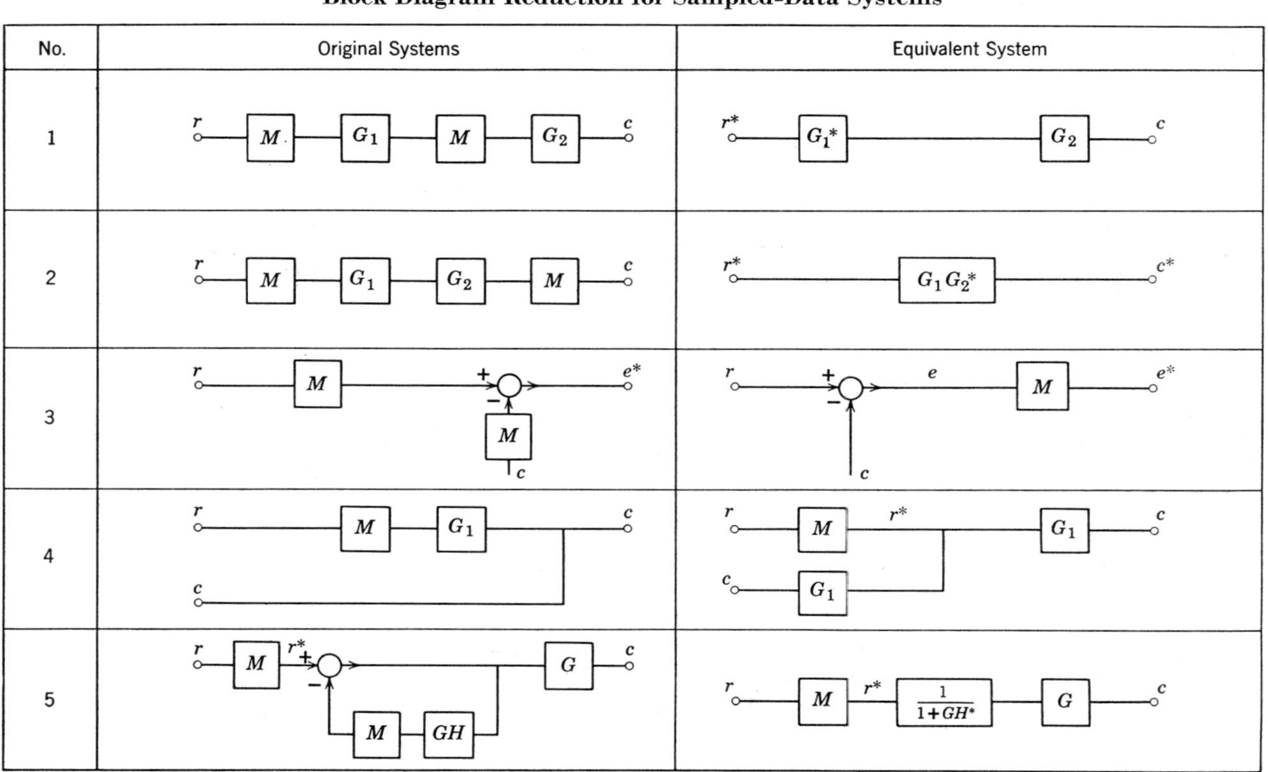

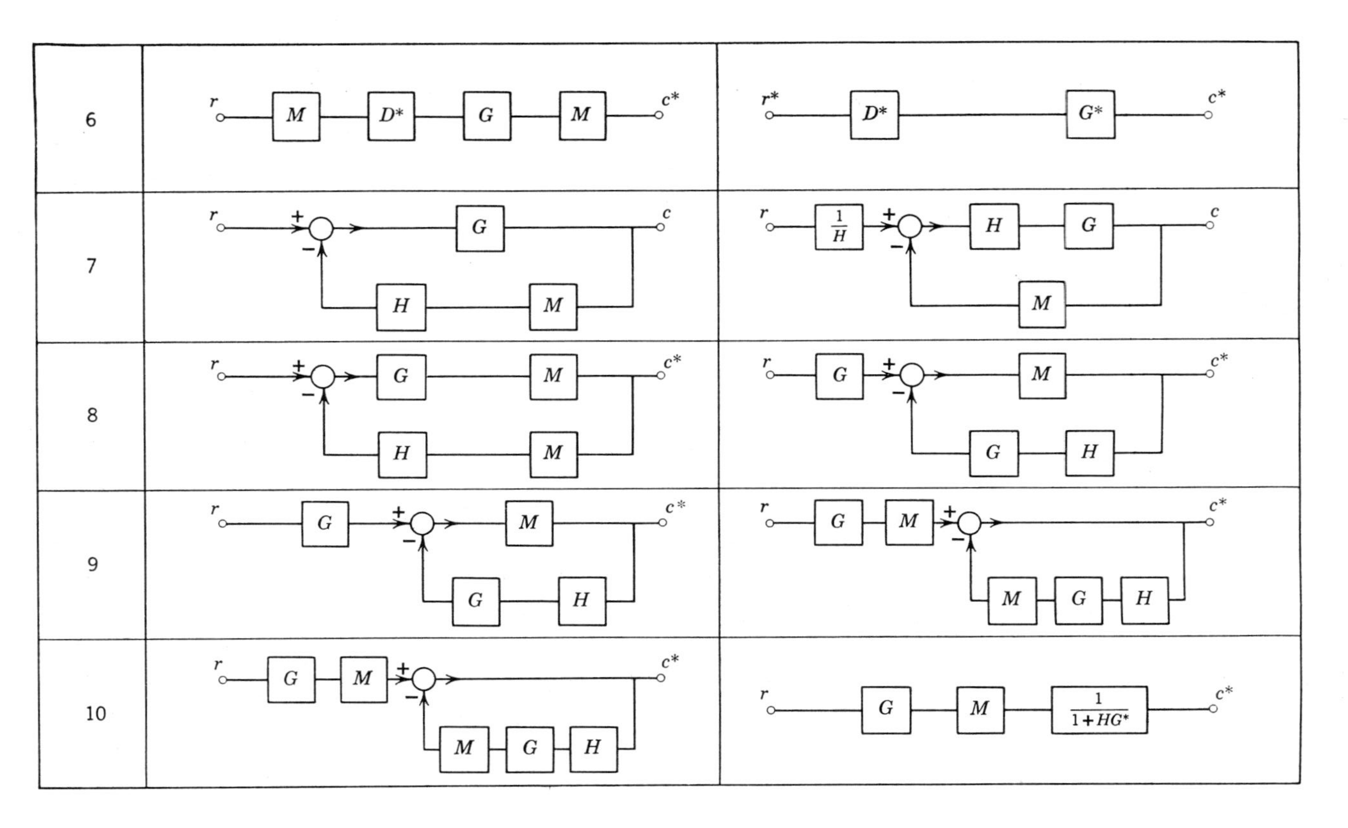
6
7
8
9
10

TABLE 4.1 (*Continued*)

Block Diagram Reduction for Sampled-Data Systems

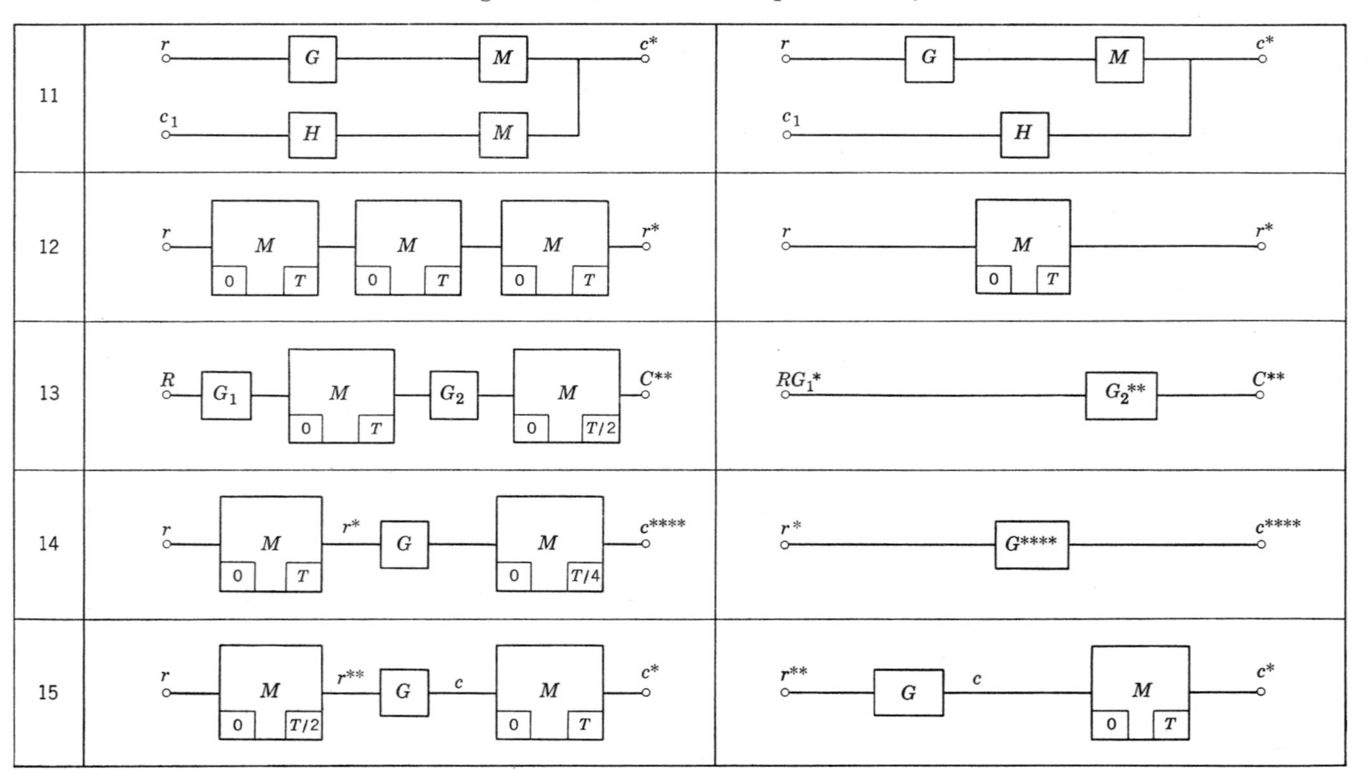

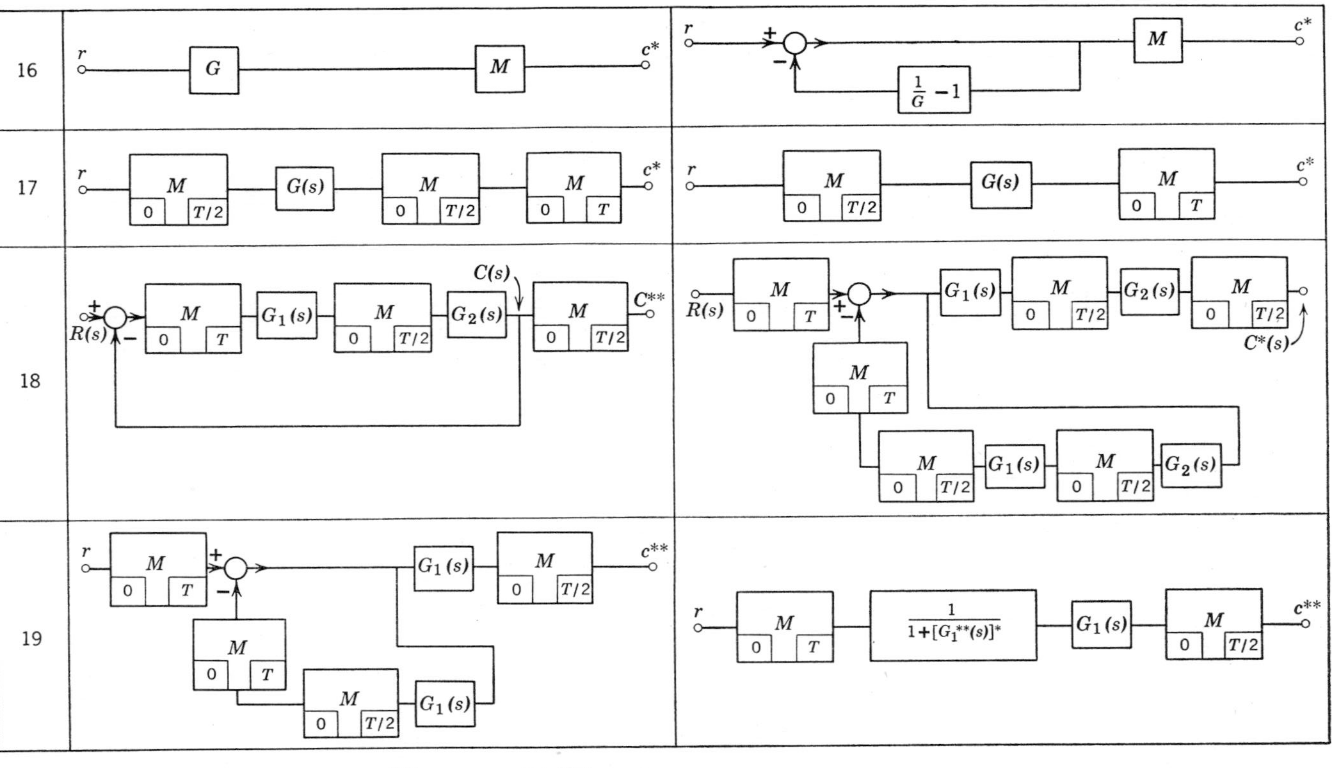

Note: $[G_1^{**}(s)]^* = \frac{1}{2}[G_1^{**}(e^{sT/2}) + G_1^{**}(e^{j\pi+sT/2})] = G_1^*(s)$

4.7 Sampled-Data Feedback System

Consider the sampled-data feedback system shown in Fig. 4.10. To obtain the transfer function which describes the system, the following two relations exist:

$$C(s) = E^*(s)\, G_0(s)\, G_1(s) \tag{4.37}$$

$$E(s) = R(s) - C(s)\, H(s) \tag{4.38}$$

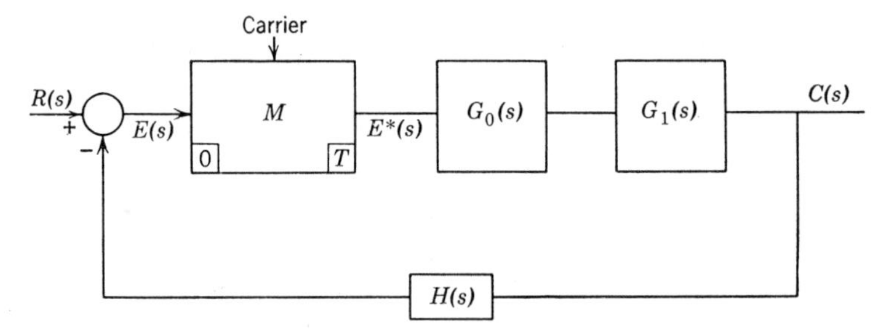

Figure 4.10 Error-sampled feedback system

If equation (4.38) is multiplied by M and we use relation (h) of (4.36), we obtain

$$E^*(s) = R^*(s) - CH^*(s) \tag{4.39}$$

Substituting $C(s)$ of (4.37) into equation (4.38) and using relation (4.39), we obtain

$$E^*(s) = R^*(s) - E^*(s)HG_0G_1{}^*(s) \tag{4.40}$$

or

$$E^*(s) = \frac{R^*(s)}{1 + HG_0G_1{}^*(s)} \tag{4.41}$$

and the output from equation (4.37) yields

$$C(s) = \frac{R^*(s)\, G_0(s)\, G_1(s)}{1 + HG_0G_1{}^*(s)} \tag{4.42}$$

If the output at the sampling instants is desired, multiply the equation by M:

$$C^*(s) = \frac{R^*(s)}{1 + HG_0G_1{}^*(s)} \times G_0G_1{}^*(s) \tag{4.43}$$

Equation (4.42) can also be written in the expanded form as

$$C(s) = \frac{1}{T} \sum_{k=-\infty}^{k=\infty} R(s + jk\omega_r) \frac{G_0(s)\, G_1(s)}{1 + \dfrac{1}{T} \sum_{k=-\infty}^{k=\infty} HG_0G_1(s + jk\omega_r)} \tag{4.44}$$

4.8 Analysis Procedures

The analysis of a sampled-data feedback system usually involves the determination of absolute stability and of the actual response for certain inputs which determine the relative stability behavior. As with the continuous feedback system, there are two methods of approach, namely, the time domain method through the inverse Laplace transform and the root-locus method, and the frequency response method through the Nyquist and Bode diagrams. The first three chapters have dealt in sufficient detail with the root-locus method and time domain response; therefore, the remainder of this chapter will discuss in detail the frequency response methods in the s-plane.

4.9 Stability Considerations

For a linear system, the stability of the system is defined as the existence of a bounded output for a bounded input. Or, the transform $C(s)$ of an error-sampled data feedback system, as given in equation (4.44), has no poles in the right half of the system. It is noticed from the expression of $C(s)$, given below, that the poles in the right half-plane of the s-plane can only appear from the denominator, for the open loop and the input are assumed to be stable:

$$C(s) = \frac{1}{T} \sum_{k=-\infty}^{k=\infty} R(s + jk\omega_r) \frac{G_0(s)\, G_1(s)}{1 + \frac{1}{T} \sum_{k=-\infty}^{k=\infty} HG_0G_1(s + jk\omega_r)} \tag{4.45}$$

The sufficient condition for stability of the system is obtained if the zeros of $1 + \frac{1}{T} \sum HG_0G_1(s + jk\omega_r)$ as given below are in the left half of the s-plane.†

$$1 + \frac{1}{T} \sum_{k=-\infty}^{k=\infty} HG_0G_1(s + jk\omega_r) = 0 \tag{4.46}$$

Since $\sum HG_0G_1$ is periodic in s with period $j\omega_r$, all the roots of equation (4.46) come in groups. If there is one root of equation (4.46) in the right half-plane, there will be an infinite number of roots each separated by multiples of $j\omega_r$. Nyquist and Routh criterions can be applied for test of stability.

† W. K. Linvill, "Sampled-Data Control Systems Studied through Comparison of Sampling with Amplitude Modulation," *Trans. A.I.E.E.*, Vol. 70, Pt. II, 1951, pp. 1779–1788.

In most cases encountered in sampled-data and feedback systems, the open-loop transfer function, $H(s)\,G_0(s)\,G_1(s)$, is of low-pass form characteristics having cutoff characteristics near or below the signal frequencies. Further, if ω_r is large (or the sampling period is small), we can approximate the infinite summation of equation (4.46) by only a few terms, usually for $k = 0, \pm 1$. In using this approximation, equation (4.46) becomes

$$1 + \frac{1}{T}[HG_0G_1(s) + HG_0G_1(s + j\omega_r) + HG_0G_1(s - j\omega_r) + \cdots] = 0 \tag{4.47}$$

Based on this approximation, the Routh criterion for stability can be applied for testing whether any root of equation (4.47) exists in the right half of the s-plane. The main disadvantage of this analytic test for stability in the s-plane lies in the high degrees of polynomials involved in equation (4.47), particularly if more terms of the series are considered.†

4.10 Nyquist Test for Stability in the s-Plane

In addition to the analytic test for stability, a graphical test for stability can be applied. This well-known test is the Nyquist criterion where s assumes the value of $j\omega$. The Nyquist locus can easily be obtained by affecting the approximation indicated. Thus, the Nyquist locus is applied to the following approximate function:

$$\frac{1}{T}[HG_0G(j\omega)] + \frac{1}{T}[HG_0G(j\omega + j\omega_r)] + \frac{1}{T}[HG_0G(j\omega - j\omega_r)] + \cdots \tag{4.48}$$

The Nyquist locus in the s-plane has the following characteristics:

1. Periodicity in the frequency $j\omega_r$.
2. Symmetry along the real axis.
3. Real value of $\sum$ for $\omega = \omega_r/2$.

On the basis of these main characteristics, we may vary the frequency ω from zero to $\omega_r/2$. The usual test for enclosure of the point $(-1, 0)$ in the s-plane can be readily applied, just as with the continuous feedback system.

The main advantages of this approximation are that similar response characteristics of the continuous case can easily be extended to sampled-

† John J. Truxal, *Control System Synthesis*, McGraw-Hill Book Company, New York, 1955, p. 526.

data systems, and $HG_0G_1(s)$ need not be given in terms of poles and zeros but can be obtained from frequency response tests. The main disadvantages are that complexity increases as more terms are considered, and further, the degree of approximation is in doubt unless checked by the exact method.

For the case where $HG_0G_1(s)$ has poles in the right half of the s-plane, we then apply the generalized form of Nyquist criterion and test stability accordingly.

Once stability of the system is determined, we can obtain the response to aperiodic inputs by obtaining the inverse transform of equation (4.45). Again, approximation of the infinite series of the input and denominator ought to be performed to make the analysis practical.

4.11 Analysis of Sampled-Data in the e^{Ts}-Plane

The output of an error-sampled feedback system shown in Fig. 4.10 is given by equation (4.42). Since $HG_0G_1(s)$ and $R(s)$ are rational functions of s, the infinite summations can be represented as a finite summation in terms of e^{Ts}. Thus equation (4.42) can be written as

$$C(s) = R^*(e^{sT}) \frac{G_0G_1(s)}{1 + HG_0G_1{}^*(e^{sT})} \tag{4.49}$$

Similar to the infinite summation case, the stability of the system (assuming $HG_0G_1(s)$ has no poles in the right half of the s-plane) is given if the roots of

$$1 + HG_0G_1{}^*(e^{sT}) = 0 \tag{4.50}$$

are all inside the unit circle in the e^{sT}-plane. This follows from the discussion of Chapter 1 in which it is noted that $e^{Ts} = z$. Analytic tests for stability of equation (4.50) are discussed in detail in that chapter and need no more elaboration. Furthermore, the Nyquist test for stability can also be applied in the e^{Ts}-plane as shown in Chapter 1. These methods of stability tests are exact. However, knowledge of $HG_0G(s)$ is required to determine $HG_0G_1{}^*(e^{sT})$. Since, in most cases, poles and zeros of $HG_0G_1(s)$ are known or can be determined from the frequency response of the continuous system, its z-transform can be determined. This method of frequency response in the e^{Ts}-plane or z-plane is discussed in detail in Chapter 6 and procedures for network compensation are obtained.

To obtain the time function of equation (4.49) we need to evaluate the inverse Laplace transform. Since $C(s)$ is a rational function of both e^{Ts}

and s, the response is given in an infinite series. However, this difficulty is removed if the modified z-transform method is applied to $C(s)$. By the procedure discussed earlier in this chapter, $C(s)$ becomes a rational function of e^{Ts} only, and m is a variable. Thus,

$$C^*(e^{Ts}, m) = \mathfrak{z}_m\,[C(s)] = R^*(e^{sT})\,\frac{G_0G_1^*(e^{Ts}, m)}{1 + HG_0G_1^*(e^{sT})} \tag{4.51}$$

The output $c(t)$ can easily be obtained using the inverse modified z-transform method and is given in a closed form. If the response at the sampling instants is required, the $C(s)$ becomes $C^*(e^{Ts})$, which is given as

$$C^*(e^{Ts}) = R^*(e^{sT})\,\frac{G_0G_1^*(e^{Ts})}{1 + HG_0G_1^*(e^{sT})} \tag{4.52}$$

By partial fraction procedures, we can identify a certain $c(t)$ which satisfies the inverse of equation (4.52) only at the sampling instants.† Further, the inverse z-transform yields the response at the sampling instants nT. Finally, the output can also be obtained by finding the coefficients of the power series expansion of $C^*(e^{Ts})$ in terms of e^{-Ts}.

4.12 Error Coefficients in e^{Ts}-Plane

In Chapter 3 it has been shown that the steady-state error for stable sampled-data feedback system is obtained from the application of the final-value theorem. This gives for the transform of the sampled error:

$$e_{ss} = \lim_{e^{Ts}\to 1} \frac{e^{Ts} - 1}{e^{Ts}}\,E^*(s) \tag{4.53}$$

From equation (4.41) $E^*(s)$ is obtained for unity feedback as

$$E^*(s) = R^*(e^{sT})\,\frac{1}{1 + G_0G_1^*(e^{sT})} \tag{4.54}$$

Certain conditions for zero steady-state error for certain types of inputs are obtained in Chapter 3. In the following the error coefficients are generalized ‡ to yield more information on the steady-state behavior of

† J. R. Ragazzini and L. A. Zadeh, "Analysis of Sampled-Data Systems," *Trans. A.I.E.E.*, Vol. 71, Pt. II, 1952, pp. 225–233.

‡ W. K. Linvill and R. W. Sittler, "Design of Sampled-Data Systems by Extension of Conventional Techniques," *I.R.E. Convention Record*, New York, Pt. I, 1953, pp. 99–104.

sampled systems for more general types of inputs, similar to the continuous case.

For a unity feedback sampled-data system shown in Fig. 4.11, the error transform is given by

$$\frac{E^*(e^{sT})}{R^*(e^{sT})} = \frac{1}{1 + G^*(e^{sT})} \tag{4.55}$$

To obtain information on the steady-state behavior, equation (4.55) can be expanded in a Taylor's series around $e^{Ts} - 1$. Hence equation

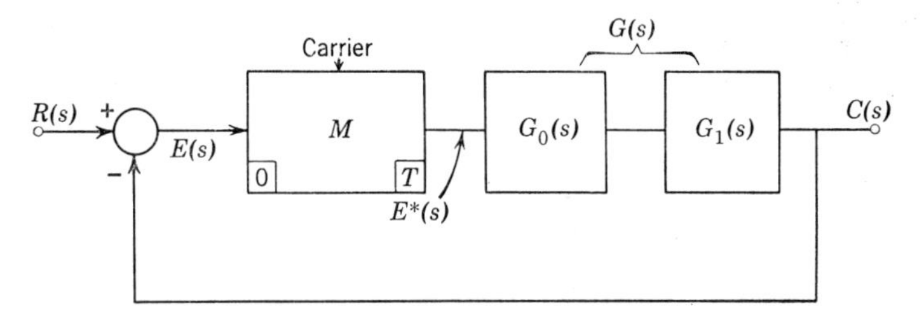

Figure 4.11 Error-sampled feedback system

(4.55) can be expressed as follows:

$$\frac{E^*(e^{sT})}{R^*(e^{sT})} = \sum_{n=0}^{\infty} b_n(e^{sT} - 1)^n \tag{4.56}$$

Where the coefficients b_n are given by

$$b_n = \lim \frac{1}{n!} \frac{d^n}{d(e^{sT})^n} \frac{1}{1 + G^*(e^{sT})}\bigg|_{e^{sT}=1} \tag{4.57}$$

b_n can be easily related to the error coefficients $K_p, K_v, K_a, \cdots$, if the following definitions are observed: †

$$\left.\begin{aligned} K_p &= \lim_{z\to 1} G^*(z) \\ K_v &= \frac{1}{T} \lim_{z\to 1} (z - 1)\, G^*(z) \\ K_a &= \frac{1}{T^2} \lim_{z\to 1} (z - 1)^2\, G^*(z) \end{aligned}\right\} \tag{4.58}$$

† G. V. Lago, "Additions to z-Transformation Theory for Sampled-Data Systems," *Trans. A.I.E.E.*, Vol. 74, Pt. II, 1955, pp. 403–408.

It is noticed that, for instance, K_p and K_v are related to b_0 and b_1 in equation (4.57) as follows:

$$b_0 = \frac{1}{1 + K_p} \tag{4.59}$$

$$Tb_1 = \frac{1}{K_v} \tag{4.60}$$

These error coefficients yield information on the error only at the sampling instants; therefore, it is assumed that no ripple exists between sampling instants. However, to obtain information on the actual behavior between the output and the input the modified z-transform should be applied as discussed briefly at the end of Chapter 3.

4.13 Analysis in the w-plane

This method is based on bilinear transformation from the e^{Ts}-plane or z-plane into the w-plane: †

$$e^{sT} = z = \frac{1 + w}{1 - w} \tag{4.61}$$

This bilinear transformation ‡ preserves $G^*(w)$ as a ratio of two polynomials in w if $G^*(z)$ is also a ratio of two polynomials in z, as is usually the case. The main feature of the transformation indicated in equation (4.61) is the conformal mapping of the inside of the unit circle into the left half of the w-plane as shown in Fig. 4.12. Thus, the w-plane plays the same role as the s-plane for continuous feedback systems. Thus Hurewitz-Routh criterion of stability can be readily applied as discussed in detail in the section on stability in Chapter 1.

From equation (4.61) the bilinear relation between w- and e^{Ts}-plane is given by the following:

$$w = u + jv = \frac{e^{sT} - 1}{e^{sT} + 1} \tag{4.62}$$

where u and v are the real and imaginary values of w.

† It is noted that any bilinear transformation, $z = e^{j\phi} \dfrac{w - \alpha}{w + \alpha}$, ϕ real, ($Re\ \alpha < 0$), is a possible mapping function which can be used.

‡ G. W. Johnson, D. P. Lindorff, and C. G. A. Nordling, "Extension of Continuous Techniques to Sampled-Data Control Systems," *Trans. A.I.E.E.*, Vol. 74, Pt. II, 1955, pp. 252–263.

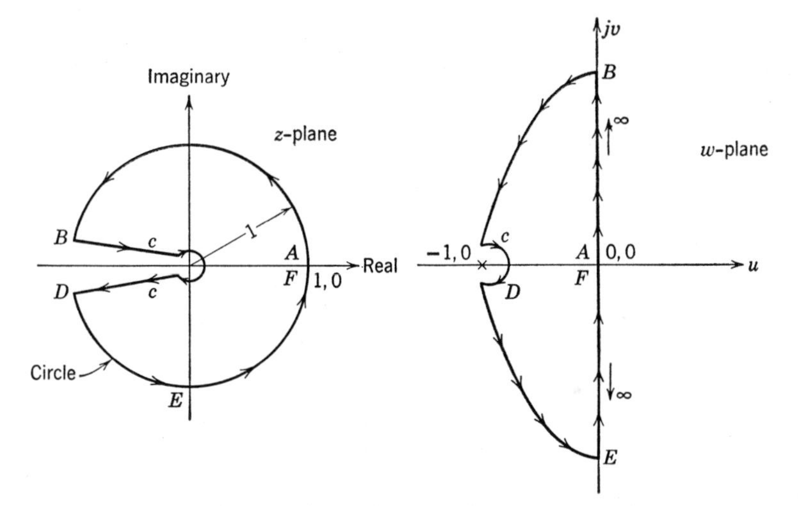

Figure 4.12 Conformal mapping according to relationship (4.61)

For the Nyquist test of stability s assumes the value of $j\omega$ in equation (4.62); thus w can be written as

$$w = u + jv = \frac{e^{j\omega T} - 1}{e^{j\omega T} + 1} \tag{4.63}$$

By using the identity,† $j \tan x = (e^{2xj} - 1)/(e^{2xj} + 1)$, it is noticed that

$$w = jv = j \tan \frac{\omega T}{2} \tag{4.64}$$

and

$$\omega = \frac{2}{T} \tan^{-1} v \tag{4.65}$$

Thus for the frequency response, $G^*(w)$ is replaced by $G^*(jv)$, where v is a dimensionless frequency referred to as a pseudo-frequency and related to ω by equation (4.65).

Therefore, by this transformation, we can make use of asymptotic plotting technique (a Bode diagram method) to obtain a frequency response. Further, this method has the unique advantage of designing discrete compensation in terms of lead and lag network in the w-plane. Gain and bandwidth design criterion can be applied in the pseudo-frequency diagram, which can be transformed by equation (4.65) into the regular frequency ω. Thus, Nichols charts can be advantageously applied in the w-plane to yield useful design values.

† B. O. Pierce, *Short Tables of Integrals*, No. 614, Ginn and Company, New York, 1929.

We can extend this technique to yield information on the total response (instead of only at sampling instants) by applying the modified z-transform method into a typical sampled-data feedback system shown in Fig. 4.11. In this case the output modified z-transform is:

$$C^*(e^{Ts}, m) = \frac{G^*(e^{Ts}, m)}{1 + G^*(e^{Ts})} \tag{4.66}$$

By using the bilinear transformation of equation (4.61), the equation just given is similarly transformed into the w-plane without affecting m. Thus, $C^*(e^{Ts}, m)$ becomes

$$C^*(w, m) = \frac{G^*(w, m)}{1 + G^*(w)} \qquad (4.67)\dagger$$

and for the frequency response $G^*(w) \rightarrow G^*(jv)$; thus

$$C^*(jv, m) = \frac{G^*(jv, m)}{1 + G^*(jv)} \tag{4.68}$$

It should be noted from equation (4.68) that when $m \rightarrow 1$, $G^*(jv, m)$ reduces to $G^*(jv)$ and design information at the sampling instants is obtained. However, to obtain more information on the response between sampling instants, let m vary between zero and unity. This latter procedure is useful for checking the parameters obtained from the design of the response at the sampling instants.

4.14 Frequency Response Example

To illustrate the various methods of frequency response plotting discussed in the preceding sections, a simple second-order sampled-data feedback system is considered. In this sampled-error system shown in Fig. 4.13, the following values are assumed: By using the equivalence of the sampler to an impulse modulator, Fig. 4.13 can be redrawn as shown in Fig. 4.14.

The following methods will now be discussed to illustrate the various alternatives which the designer has at his disposal: (a) frequency analysis in the s-plane; (b) frequency analysis in the e^{Ts}-plane; (c) frequency analysis in the w-plane.

† It should be noted that $C^*(w, m)$ is $C^*(e^{Ts}, m)$ with $\dfrac{e^{sT} - 1}{e^{sT} + 1}$ replaced by w, or e^{Ts} replaced by $\dfrac{1 + w}{1 - w}$.

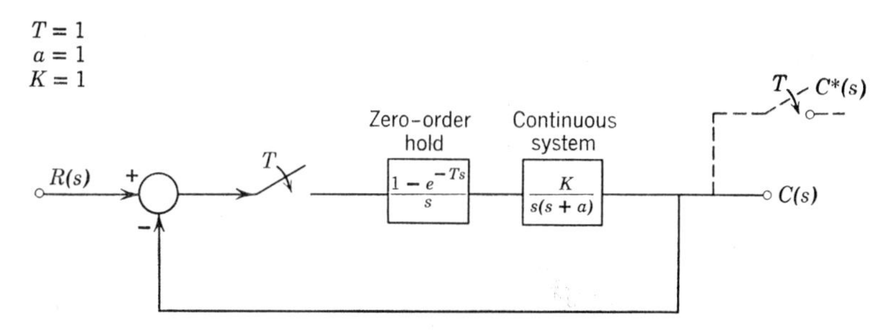

Figure 4.13 Illustrative example

a. Frequency Analysis in the s-Plane

The output transform $C(s)$ for the system shown in Fig. 4.14 can be obtained from equation (4.44) by noting that $H(s)$ equals 1 for this system, giving

$$C(s) = \frac{1}{T} \sum_{k=-\infty}^{k=\infty} R(s + jk\omega_r) \frac{G_0(s)\, G_1(s)}{1 + \frac{1}{T} \sum_{k=-\infty}^{k=\infty} G_0G_1(s + jk\omega_r)} \tag{4.69}$$

The condition for stability is obtained if the roots of the denominator of the equation are in the left half of the s-plane. Since in this example

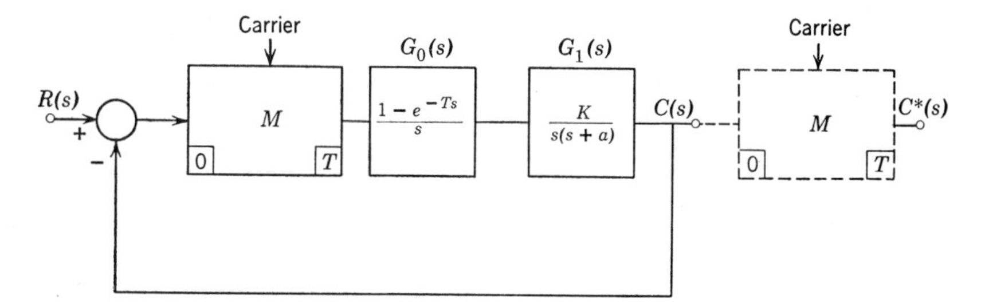

Figure 4.14 Error-sampled feedback system equivalent to Fig. 4.13

the poles of $G_0(s)\, G_1(s)$ are in the left half-plane, or at the origin, we can apply the specialized form of Nyquist criterion to determine stability by plotting the Nyquist locus.

The frequency locus is determined by replacing s by $j\omega$ in the following expression:

$$\frac{1}{T} \sum_{k=-\infty}^{k=\infty} G_0G_1(s + jk\omega_r) \bigg|_{s \to j\omega} \tag{4.70}$$

For the values of T and of $G_1(s)$ assumed in this example, equation (4.70) is approximated by the following terms before plotting:

$$\frac{1}{T}\sum_{k=-\infty}^{k=\infty} G_0G_1(j\omega + jk\omega_r) \cong \frac{1}{T} G_0G_1(j\omega) + \frac{1}{T} G_0G_1(j\omega - j\omega_r) \quad (4.71)$$

For the system under discussion, the following values are inserted in equation (4.71) to give

$$\frac{1}{T}\sum_{k=-\infty}^{k=\infty} \frac{1 - e^{-T(s+jk\omega_r)}}{(s + jk\omega_r)^2(s + jk\omega_r + a)} \cong \frac{1}{T}\frac{1 - e^{-Tj\omega}}{(j\omega)^2(j\omega + a)} + \frac{1}{T}\frac{1 - e^{-T(j\omega - j\omega_r)}}{(j\omega - j\omega_r)^2(j\omega - j\omega_r + a)} \quad (4.72)$$

since $\omega_r = 2\pi/T$ and for this example $T = 1$, therefore $\omega_r = 2\pi$.

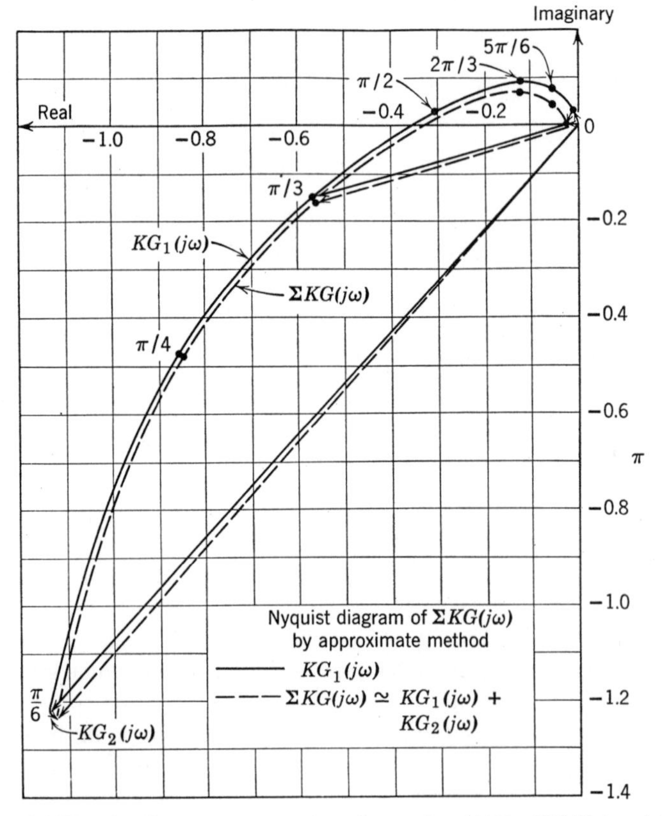

Figure 4.15 Nyquist diagram construction of equation (4.72); $KG_1(j\omega)$ and $KG_2(j\omega)$ are the first and second terms of the right-hand side of equation (4.72)

It is noticed from equation (4.72) that except for T and the zero-order hold, the first term of the right side of the equation is the continuous

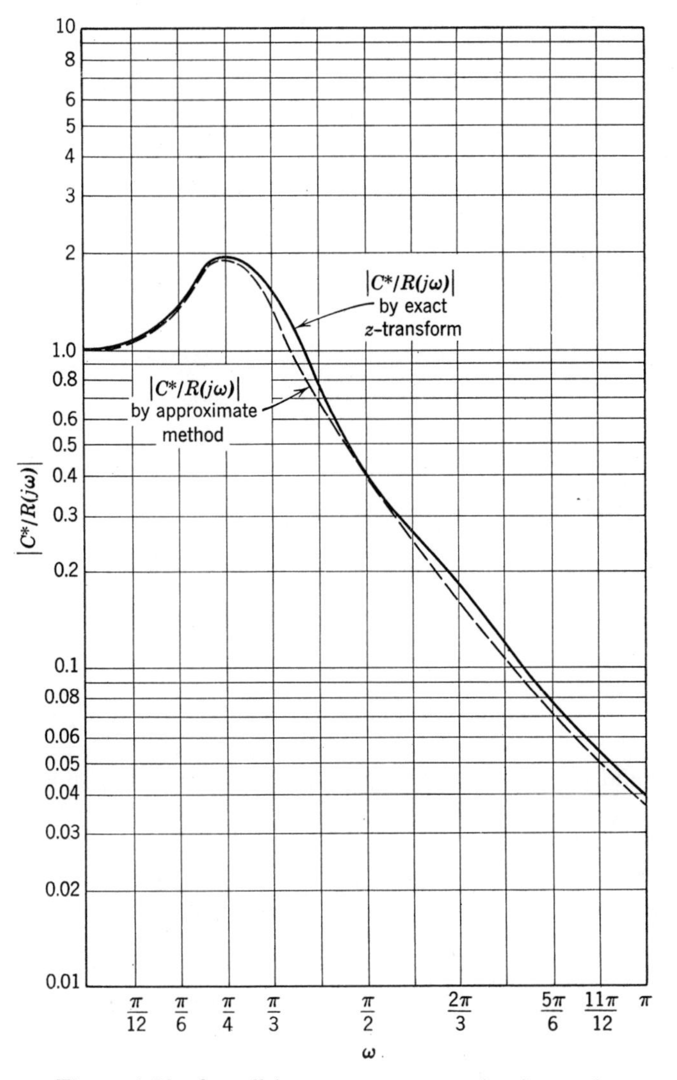

Figure 4.16a Overall frequency response gain of example

frequency locus and the other terms are obtained graphically from the locus of the first term as indicated in Fig. 4.15.

From the Nyquist locus, it is observed that the point $(-1, 0)$ in the s-plane is not enclosed; thus the system is stable. Further, the locus is

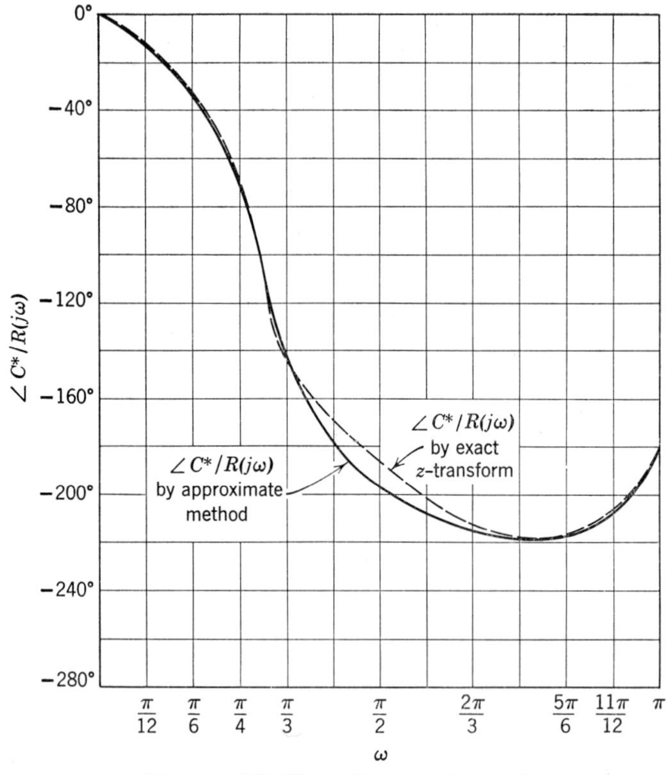

Figure 4.16*b* Phase diagram of example

periodic and symmetric along the real axis. Thus, values of ω from zero to $\omega_r/2$ suffice to plot the Nyquist locus. The overall frequency and phase responses are shown in Figs. 4.16*a* and *b*.

b. Frequency Analysis in the e^{Ts}-Plane

An alternate form for the output in terms of e^{Ts} can be easily obtained from equation (4.69) to yield

$$C(s) = R^*(e^{sT}) \frac{G_0G_1(s)}{1 + G_0G_1^*(e^{sT})} \tag{4.73}$$

Since this equation is of mixed form (i.e., rational in both e^{Ts} and s), the analysis is simplified if the output is first considered at the sampling instants. In this case the sampled output transform is given:

$$C^*(e^{Ts}) = R^*(e^{sT}) \frac{G_0G_1^*(e^{sT})}{1 + G_0G_1^*(e^{sT})} \tag{4.74}$$

Stability can be similarly obtained by plotting the Nyquist locus in the e^{Ts}-plane while s varies along the $j\omega$-axis. In the e^{Ts}-plane the variation of s corresponds to the unit circle as discussed in Chapter 1. Therefore, the Nyquist locus can be easily obtained in the e^{Ts}-plane and needs no more elaboration here, for it is discussed in much detail in Chapter 6.

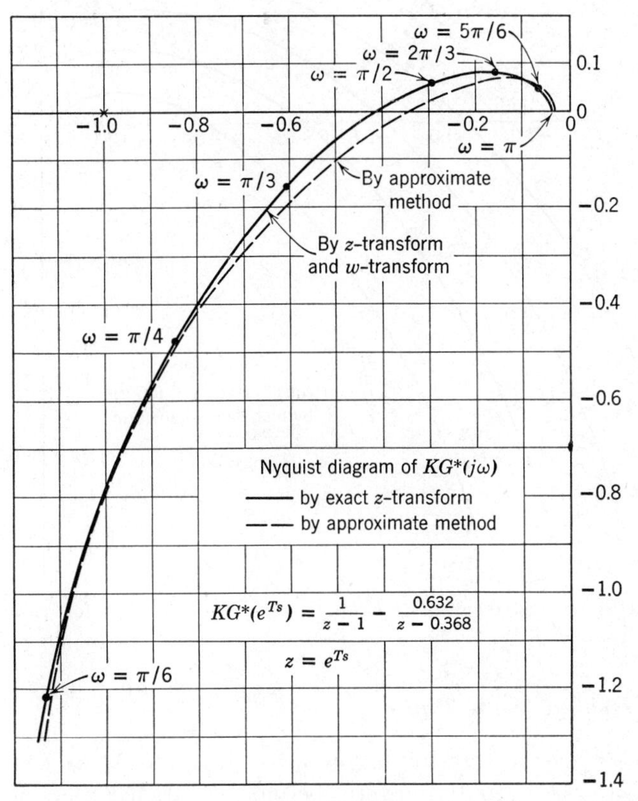

Figure 4.17 Nyquist diagram of $KG^*(e^{Ts}) = G_0G_1{}^*(e^{Ts})$ in example

For this system the Nyquist locus is plotted in Fig. 4.17, which gives an exact check on the accuracy of the approximation assumed in method *a*.

For more critical study on the total system behavior, we can obtain the modified z-transform of equation (4.73) which gives

$$C^*(e^{Ts}, m) = R^*(e^{sT}) \frac{G_0G_1{}^*(e^{Ts}, m)}{1 + G_0G_1{}^*(e^{sT})} \tag{4.75}$$

By varying m from zero to unity, the overall frequency response corresponding to the continuous output can be examined. This method is used in this case for checking the behavior of the system between the sampling instants. Figures 4.18 and 4.19 indicate the frequency response for various values of m.

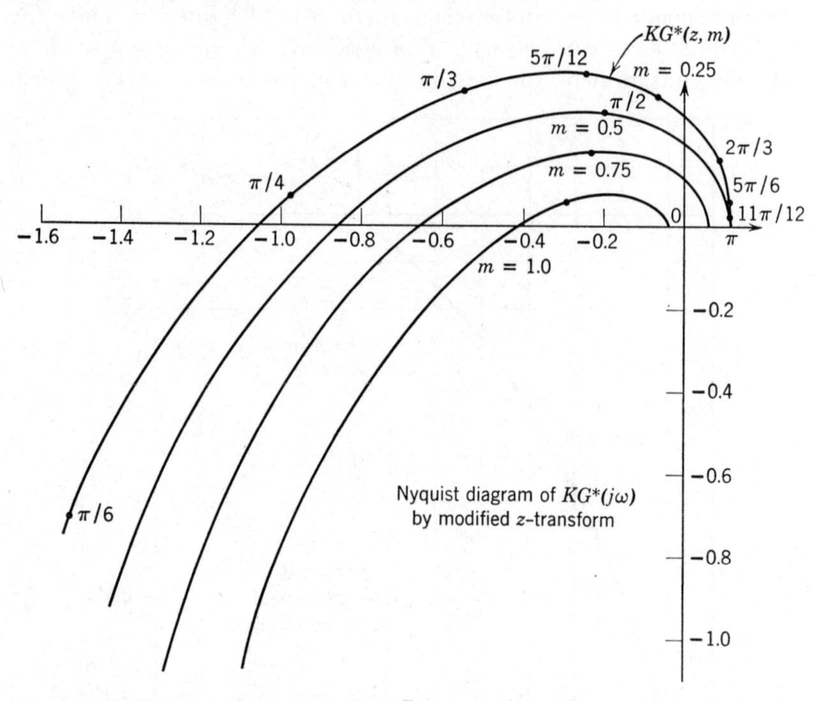

Figure 4.18 Nyquist diagram of $KG^*(e^{Ts}, m) = G_0G_1{}^*(e^{Ts}, m)$ for various values of m

c. *Analysis in the w-Plane*

By inserting the transformation, $e^{Ts} = (1 + w)/(1 - w)$, into equation (4.74), the output transform becomes a rational function of w as follows:

$$C^*(w) = R^*(w) \frac{G_0G_1{}^*(w)}{1 + G_0G_1{}^*(w)} \tag{4.76}$$

For the frequency response w assumes the value of its pseudo-frequency jv; thus equation (4.76) becomes

$$C^*(jv) = R^*(jv) \frac{G_0G_1{}^*(jv)}{1 + G_0G_1{}^*(jv)} \tag{4.77}$$

This equation is rational in the dimensionless frequency jv; therefore the Bode diagram can be used to plot $G_0G_1{}^*(jv)$ in magnitude and phase

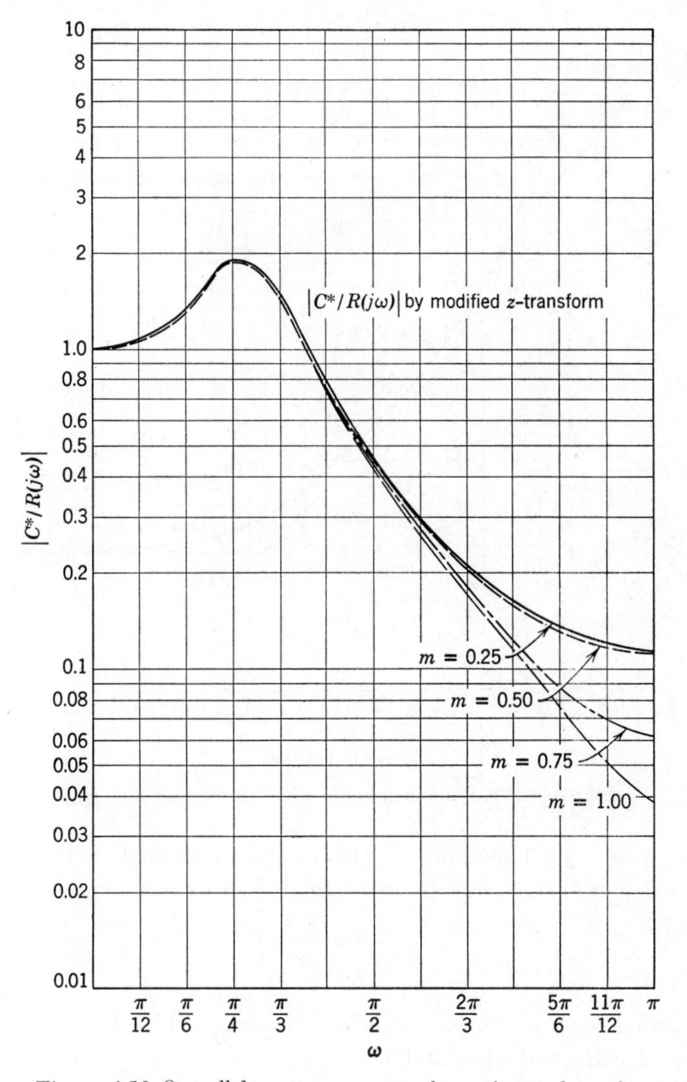

Figure 4.19 Overall frequency response for various values of m

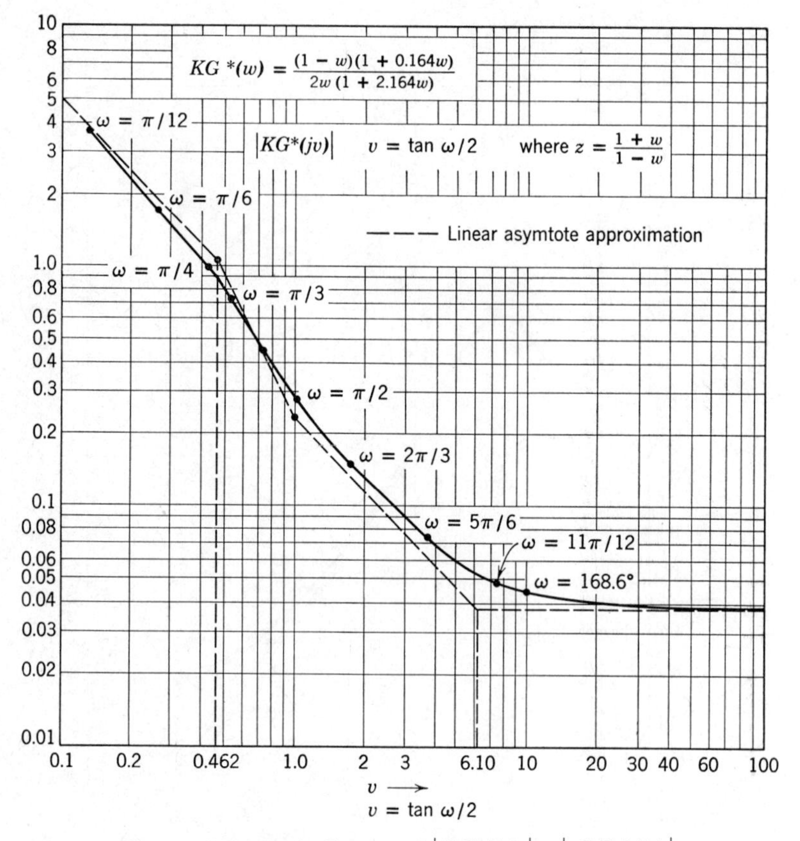

Figure 4.20*a* Bode diagram of $|KG^*(jv)| = |G_0G_1^*(jv)|$

as shown in Figs. 4.20*a* and *b*. This frequency response is transformed to the frequency domain ω by using the following relation:

$$\omega = \frac{2}{T} \tan^{-1} v \tag{4.78}$$

The final form as a function of ω is shown in Fig. 4.17, where it is compared with methods *a* and *b*.

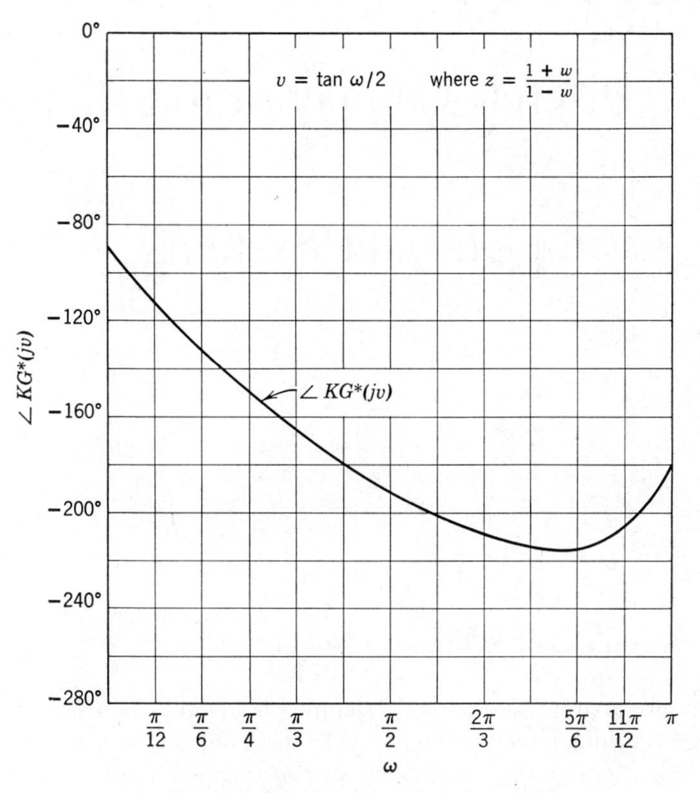

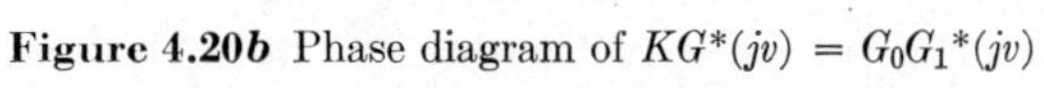
Figure 4.20*b* Phase diagram of $KG^*(jv) = G_0G_1{}^*(jv)$

CHAPTER 5

Discrete-Compensation Methods of Sampled-Data Systems

5.1 Synthesis and Synthesis Criteria

The material of the preceding chapters is mainly concerned with the analysis of sampled-data systems. The main objectives of analysis were stability considerations and system performance when subjected to known inputs or disturbances. The discussions of this and the following chapter deal with synthesis problems and design criteria and the various existing methods of synthesis. Specifically, the material of this chapter deals directly with discrete compensation of fixed linear sampled-data systems. The term "discrete" is chosen to include both digital compensators and continuous compensators consisting of a number of delay elements.†

Synthesis of sampled-data control systems is the art of selecting and combining physically realizable functional devices to perform a specified task. In the design of sampled-data systems we are mainly concerned with synthesis criteria and compensation means which are tractable.

† E. I. Jury and F. W. Semelka, "Time Domain Synthesis of Sampled-Data Control Systems," A.S.M.E.-I.R.D. Conference, April 3, 1958.

Before considering more of the details of sampled-data synthesis, it is worthwhile to discuss the nature of sampled-data control. It is realized that sampling appears in a control system because of physical necessity or for reasons that make this technique of control desirable, such as the use of digital computers in control systems. The purpose of sampled-data systems, as of continuous systems, is to control a physical process which is in most cases a continuous process. Thus, measuring the effectiveness of a sampled-control process only on the basis of system performance at sampling instants of time is quite inadequate. Likewise, design of a system in terms of sampled performance (z-transform technique) cannot be relied upon to yield desirable control, in view of some hidden oscillation phenomena.† The advent of the modified z-transform effectively removed the analysis restriction of determining system behavior between sampling instants, and thus it has been considered in this work as a synthesis tool.

Design of sampled-data control systems similar to the continuous system involves certain steps which are generally followed by the designer. These steps enumerated here, serve as a guide for initial design.

1. Formulate an approach to the system design resulting in a functional block diagram.
2. Decide how to confine the design constraints so that they can be intelligently handled mathematically.
3. Determine preliminary system and component (exclude the unalterable components) specifications from a knowledge of the required physical functions, probable system inputs, acceptable error tolerance, physical constraints, etc.
4. On the basis of step 3, tentatively select or construct the physical components having the required properties, sufficient dynamic range, etc. (The entire aggregation is normally considered the fixed part of the system or plant.)
5. Determine the mathematical characteristics of both the unalterable components and the actual components selected in step 4, and subsequently find a first approximation for the system performance using these components.
6. Finally, the important step of intelligent design is to follow a procedure of iterated analysis and synthesis (stabilization and compensation by introducing minor loop, gain adjustment, compensating networks, digital filters, and delay line) to achieve the required system.

† E. I. Jury, "Hidden Oscillations in Sampled-Data Control Systems," *Trans. A.I.E.E.*, Vol. 75, Pt. II, 1956, pp. 391–395.

Synthesis proper, as followed in this chapter, does not involve steps 1 through 5; in other words, usually certain performance specifications are to be realized using a given plant. Since the designer rarely encounters pure synthesis (a straightforward procedure resulting in the final system), he must necessarily be engaged in all phases of the problem so that he can apply an iterated process to get the required system.

5.2 Criteria for Synthesis

Similar to continuous control systems, sampled-data systems can be synthesized with the following criteria:

1. Frequency domain techniques which include both Nyquist and Bode diagrams
2. Time domain criteria which include
   (*a*) Root-locus and root-contours methods.
   (*b*) Direct time system function approach.

There exist other criteria for design as used in continuous control systems; however, in this work only the criteria listed are discussed in detail, and if specifications are such that other criteria are to be used, the designer has the freedom of choice among all of them.

It will be shown later that under certain conditions, sampled-data systems can be best synthesized in the time domain. Thus, this approach is emphasized here, and consequently the following time domain specifications are imposed.

1. General type of response of aperiodic inputs
   (*a*) Specification of overshoot, peak time, settling time (a measure of speed of response), and steady-state behavior. The type of steady-state behavior possible is particularly dependent on the plant.
   (*b*) Specifications of minimum rise time for specified compensator complexity and tolerable limits of transient performance.
   (*c*) Simultaneous transient and steady-state specifications for step, velocity, and acceleration inputs. (Iterative process of synthesis is necessary and results obtainable are highly dependent on the plant.)
2. Finite settling time types of response for aperiodic inputs
   (*a*) Deadbeat response for either step, velocity, or acceleration inputs.
   (*b*) Finite settling time with peak time, overshoot, and steady-state specifications.

(*c*) Simultaneous specifications for step, velocity, and acceleration inputs. (Iterative process of shaping transient response is necessary.)

3. Response satisfying error criteria for aperiodic inputs

(*a*) Specifications of minimization of the following functions:

$$\text{IE} = \text{Integral error (difference between actual output and input)}$$

$$= \int_0^\infty e(t)\,dt$$

$$\text{ISE} = \text{Integral square error} = \int_0^\infty e^2(t)\,dt$$

5.3 Discussion of the Discrete-Compensation Procedure †

The purpose of compensation is to introduce into the control system the components necessary to force satisfactory feedback control. Of specific interest is the problem of specifying components for sampled-data systems. The choice of components will be limited in this chapter to discrete compensators and zero-order holds. Accordingly, the objectives are to discuss and exemplify the processes of determining transfer functions of discrete compensators which can satisfy a variety of performance specifications.

To be able to discuss the proposed compensation procedure effectively, it is necessary to limit the discussion to a particular type of sampled-data configuration. The type of interest will be the error-sampled system,

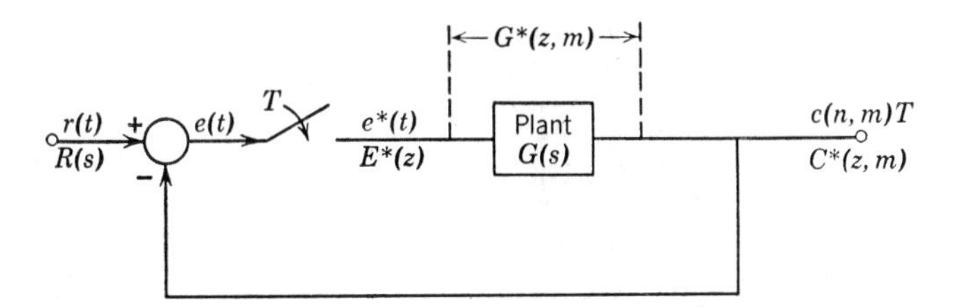

Figure 5.1 Error-sampled feedback system

Fig. 5.1, in which a zero-order hold is considered included with the plant. The extension of the ideas to other sampled-data configurations will then be evident.

† An Appendix has been included at the end of this chapter to familiarize the reader with the matrix notation used herein.

In Fig. 5.2, an error-sampled system with discrete compensator $D_c^*(z)$, the discrete forcing function $E'^*(z)$ is determined by $D_c^*(z)$ and the sampled error $E^*(z)$; that is,

$$E'^*(z) = E^*(z)\, D_c^*(z) \tag{5.1}$$

This discrete forcing function appears at the plant proper as a boxcar or staircase function since a zero-order hold precedes the actual plant.

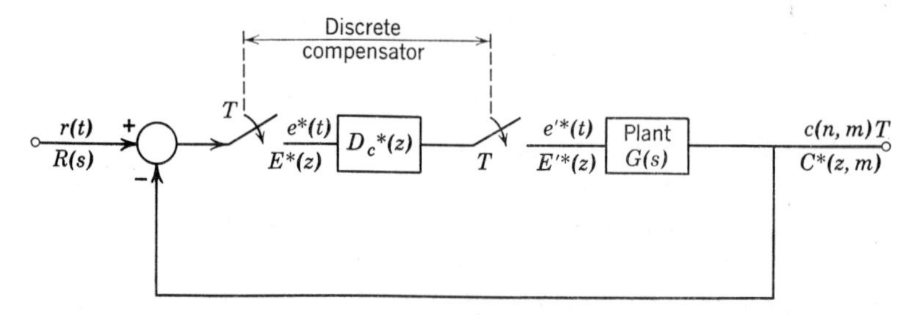

Figure 5.2 Error-sampled system of Figure 5.1 with discrete-compensation component

The values of this forcing function as seen from equation (5.1) can change only at sampling instants and are controllable by choice of $D_c^*(z)$.

The complexity and form allowed for $D_c^*(z)$ determine the number of terms of the output sequence which can be independently specified from any input error sequence. Also the discrete compensator can be a feedback device within itself and can thus have an output for no input in steady state. The control of the plant-forcing function afforded by these unique properties of the discrete compensator suggests the following approach to the synthesis problem.

By using the modified z-transform, the output of the system in Fig. 5.2 is

$$C^*(z, m) = E'^*(z)\, G^*(z, m) \tag{5.2}$$

where

$$E'^*(z) = E^*(z)\, D_c^*(z) = \frac{R^*(z)}{1 + D_c^*(z)\, G^*(z)} D_c^*(z) \tag{5.3}$$

and

$$E^*(z) = R^*(z) - C^*(z) \tag{5.4}$$

In the time domain, by using the matrix representation, the continuous output can be shown (see Appendix) to be:

$$c_n(m)] = [g_n(m)] \times [d_{cn}] \times \{[I] + [g_n(0)] \times [d_{cn}]\}^{-1} \times r_n] \tag{5.5}$$

where $[g_n(m)]$ = continuous-transmission matrix for the plant and zero-order hold;
$[g_n(0)]$ = discrete-transmission matrix for the plant and the included hold;
$[d_{cn}]$ = transmission matrix for the discrete compensator;
$r_n]$ = column matrix representation for the sampled input;
$[I]$ = identity (or unit) matrix.

The output in terms of the discrete forcing function $E'^*(z)$ in the time domain is

$$c_n(m)] = [g_n(m)] \times e'_n] \tag{5.6}$$

Equation (5.6) suggests that we find a forcing function (i.e., a sequence of numbers $e'_0, e'_1, \cdots e'_n, \cdots$) such that a desirable output $c_n(m)]$ results. Equation (5.3) indicates that if such a sequence can be generated from a closed-form function, $D_c^*(z)$ can also be found in a closed form (i.e., the discrete compensator will require a finite number of storage and/or delay units).

The complex relation of the compensator transmission matrix to e'_n when $r_n]$, $[g_n(m)]$, and $[g_n(0)]$ are known, as is seen by comparing equations (5.5) and (5.6), gives a rather dubious outlook for finding a suitable $[d_{cn}]$ to control $e'_n]$ such that a desirable output $c_n(m)]$ results. Fortunately, this difficulty can be easily avoided by considering as an equivalent working model the open-loop configuration of Fig. 5.3.

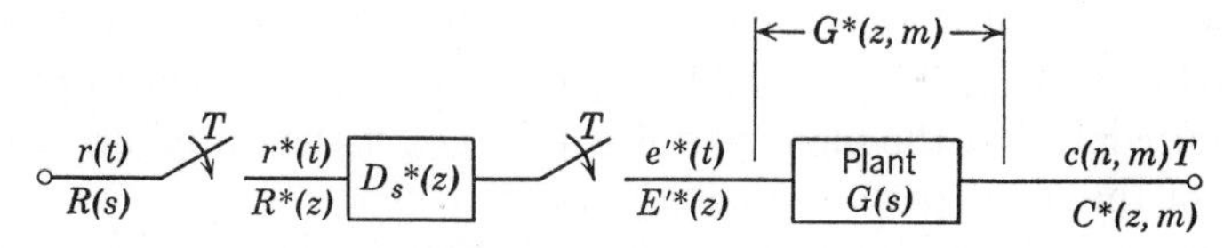

Figure 5.3 Open-loop discrete compensation for plant $G(s)$

The plant and included hold of the feedback system are thus driven from an open-loop compensator $D_s^*(z)$ which has a known input, that is, the actual input of interest. It should be realized, however, that simpler working models may not exist for other configurations. In such cases, the output can be manipulated to achieve the desired response. From the configuration of Fig. 5.3 it becomes very easy to find the closed-loop equivalent system when the satisfactory open-loop system is found.

The modified z-transform for the open-loop configuration of Fig. 5.3 is

$$C^*(z, m) = E'^*(z)\, G^*(z, m) = R^*(z)\, D_s^*(z)\, G^*(z, m) \tag{5.7}$$

or

$$E'^*(z) = R^*(z)\, D_s^*(z)$$

In the time domain the following equation can be written

$$c_n(m)] = [g_n(m)] \times [d_{sn}] \times r_n] \tag{5.8}$$

where

$$e'_n] = [d_{sn}] \times r_n] \tag{5.9}$$

Thus the relation of $e'_n]$ to the discrete-compensator transmission matrix $[d_{sn}]$ becomes very simple.

A little reflection on the required form of e'_n for the type of inputs $1/s^n$ indicates that it should be composed of a transient and a steady-state term with the duration of the transient part not longer than the desired settling time (normally even shorter transient portions suffice). From this we can deduce that an appropriate choice for the form of $D_s{}^*(z)$ is

$$\begin{aligned} D_s{}^*(z) &= D^*(z)\, F_{ss}{}^*(z) \\ &= \frac{z^k + d_1 z^{k-1} + d_2 z^{k-2} + \cdots + d_k}{z^k} F_{ss}{}^*(z) \end{aligned} \tag{5.10}$$

where $F_{ss}{}^*(z)$ is the part of the open-loop compensator which yields the required gain and steady-state forcing function; that is, $F_{ss}{}^*(z)$ is chosen on the basis of steady-state error tolerances. The form of $D^*(z)$ is a finite polynomial in z^{-1}, $D^*(z) = 1 + d_1 z^{-1} + d_2 z^{-2} + \cdots + d_k z^{-k}$. This part of the compensator controls the duration as well as the shape of the transient part of the forcing function. The selection of the number of terms must be judged from the performance specifications (mainly the settling time) and the type of plant. In general, repeated choices will have to be made until it is possible for the open-loop compensator to gain sufficient control of the plant performance (i.e., if the sampling rate and nature of the plant permit adequate control).

The second part of the compensator, $F_{ss}{}^*(z)$, can be found from application of the final-value theorem (assuming the system is stable) to the modified z-transform of the output in Fig. 5.3 when the input is a step. (It is interesting to note that in the steady-state value with a step input and zero-order hold included with the plant this open-loop configuration is equivalent to a continuous system; thus the final value theorem in the s-plane can also be applied.) Therefore, the part $F_{ss}{}^*(z)$ is determined from the steady-state performance specification. For higher-order inputs $F_{ss}{}^*(z)$ will be the same as for a step input.

It is thus seen that the system-forcing function e'_n is specified in terms of a finite number of compensator unknowns. Steady-state behavior for the design input (for no steady-state error) is independent of these unknowns, and thus their choice will be dependent on the desired transient performance.

The system transient output in the time domain is given by equation (5.8). With the aid of this equation the compensator unknowns are related to the continuous output. In this connection, it is realized that synthesis in the time domain is a logical design method, for the transient time domain specifications (peak time, overshoot, settling time, etc.) can be used to select these unknowns of the discrete compensator.

The difficult part of the synthesis problem is thus the selection of a continuous output within the constraints of the plant and the freedom of the compensator. Once the output is chosen, the open-loop compensation is known and the problem of finding the equivalent closed-loop compensator can be easily solved. This is done by equating the expressions for $E'^*(z)$ given by equations (5.3) and (5.7) and solving for $D_c^*(z)$;

$$D_c^*(z) = \frac{D_s^*(z)}{1 - D_s^*(z)\,G^*(z)} \tag{5.11}$$

It is quite apparent that this method allows us to take the plant completely into consideration. The output that can be achieved is certainly dependent on the characteristics of the plant but can be adjusted to optimize the continuous response. Determining the compensation in this way allows the plant a more natural behavior, rather than coercing it to fit a set of points as when a transfer function is specified.

Examples of Discrete Compensation

Three examples are presented which illustrate the essential features of the proposed synthesis technique as well as the types of responses possible with discrete compensation. The first example is a step response design, the second is a ramp response design, and the last one illustrates the design for minimum integral squared error.

Example 1. Step Response Design, Second-Order Plant with Real Poles †

The system for this example is shown in Fig. 5.4. Figure 5.5 gives the continuous uncompensated step response. The severe transient behavior is to be corrected by discrete compensation in tandem with the plant as illustrated in Fig. 5.2. The specifications to be realized for a step input

† F. W. Semelka, "Time Domain Synthesis of Sampled-Data Control Systems," Electronic Research Laboratory Report, Series 60, Issue 175, January 18, 1957, University of California, Berkeley.

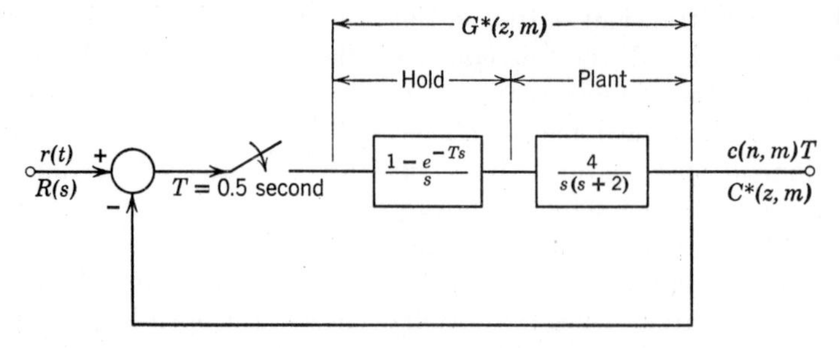

Figure 5.4 Uncompensated system of Example 1

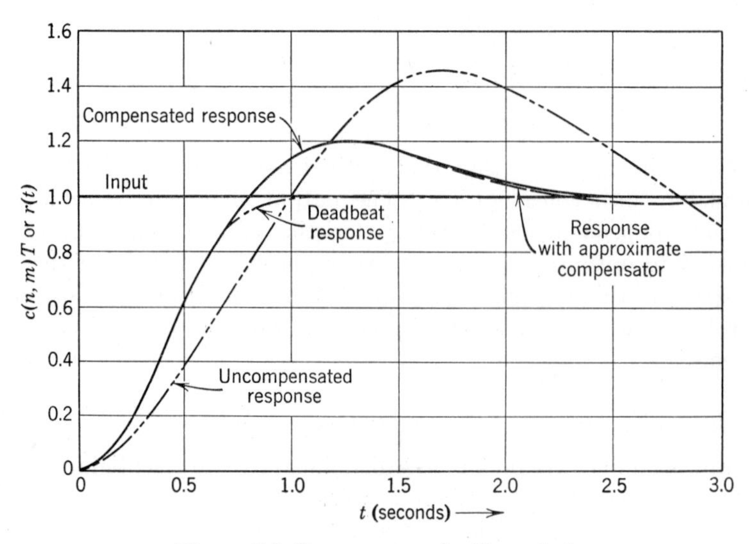

Figure 5.5 Step responses for Example 1

are (in the following $c(n, m)T = c_n(m)$], where T is constant = 0.5 second):

1. Final value: $\lim_{\substack{n\to\infty \\ 0 \le m \le 1}} c(n, m)T = 1.0 = \lim_{z\to 1}\left[\frac{z-1}{z}\, z\, C^*(z, m)\right]$

2. Peak time: $t_p = 1.25$ seconds, $\left.\frac{d}{dm} c_2(m)\right|_{\substack{m=m_p \\ =0.5}} = 0$, and $c''_2(m_p) < 0$

3. Overshoot: $M_p = 20\%$, $\left. c_2(m)\right|_{\substack{m=m_p \\ =0.5}} = 1.2$

The open-loop compensator form is selected as

$$D_s^*(z) = \frac{z^2 + d_1 z + d_2}{z^2} F_{ss}^*(z) \tag{5.12}$$

The minimum number of terms of the compensator, that is, the degrees of freedom, are determined by the number of transient specifications to be met. Depending on the restrictions imposed by the specifications, more than the minimum number of terms may be required. The output for the open-loop configuration is given by

$$C^*(z, m) = R^*(z)\, D_s^*(z)\, G^*(z, m) \tag{5.13}$$

where

$$R^*(z) = \frac{z}{z - 1}$$

and

$$G^*(z, m) = \frac{1}{z}\,\frac{p_0 + p_1 z^{-1} + p_2 z^{-2}}{1 + q_1 z^{-1} + q_2 z^{-2}}$$

$$\begin{aligned} p_0 &= -1 + m + e^{-m} \\ p_1 &= 2 + e^{-1} - m(1 + e^{-1}) - 2e^{-m} \\ p_2 &= -2e^{-1} + me^{-1} + e^{-m} \\ q_1 &= -(1 + e^{-1}) \\ q_2 &= e^{-1} \end{aligned} \tag{5.14}$$

In the time domain the output is represented as follows:

$$c_n(m)] = [g_n(m)] \times [d_{sn}] \times r_n] \tag{5.15}$$

where $[g_n(m)]$ is the transmission matrix of the plant and hold and $[d_{sn}]$ is the transmission matrix of the open-loop compensator. The component $F_{ss}^*(z)$ can be shown to be, by applying the final-value theorem,

$$F_{ss}^*(z) = \frac{1}{(1 + d_1 + d_2)}\,\frac{z - 1}{z} \tag{5.16}$$

Therefore, the open-loop system output for a step input is

$$C^*(z, m) = \frac{1}{(1 + d_1 + d_2)}\,\frac{z}{z - 1}\,\frac{z^2 + d_1 z + d_2}{z^2}\,\frac{z - 1}{z}\,\frac{p_0 + p_1 z^{-1} + p_2 z^{-2}}{z(1 + q_1 z^{-1} + q_2 z^{-2})} \tag{5.17}$$

or

$$c_n(m)] = \left(\frac{1}{1+d_1+d_2}\right)\begin{bmatrix} g_0(m) & 0 & 0 & \cdots & 0 \\ g_1(m) & g_0(m) & 0 & \cdots & 0 \\ g_2(m) & g_1(m) & g_0(m) & \cdots & 0 \\ \cdots & \cdots & \cdots & \cdots & \cdots \\ g_n(m) & g_{n-1}(m) & g_{n-2}(m) & \cdots & g_0(m) \end{bmatrix}$$

$$\times \begin{bmatrix} 1 & 0 & 0 & \cdots & 0 \\ -1 & 1 & 0 & \cdots & 0 \\ 0 & -1 & 1 & \cdots & 0 \\ \cdots & \cdots & \cdots & \cdots & \cdots \\ 0 & 0 & 0 & \cdots & 1 \end{bmatrix}$$

$$\times \begin{bmatrix} 1 & 0 & 0 & 0 & \cdots & 0 \\ d_1 & 1 & 0 & 0 & \cdots & 0 \\ d_2 & d_1 & 1 & 0 & \cdots & 0 \\ 0 & d_2 & d_1 & 1 & \cdots & 0 \\ \cdots & \cdots & \cdots & \cdots & \cdots & \cdots \\ 0 & 0 & 0 & 0 & \cdots & 1 \end{bmatrix} \times \begin{bmatrix} 1 \\ 1 \\ 1 \\ 1 \\ \cdots \\ 1 \end{bmatrix}$$

$$= \left(\frac{1}{1+d_1+d_2}\right)$$

$$\times \begin{bmatrix} g_0(m) & 0 & 0 & \cdots & 0 \\ g_1(m) & g_0(m) & 0 & \cdots & 0 \\ g_2(m) & g_1(m) & g_0(m) & \cdots & 0 \\ \cdots & \cdots & \cdots & \cdots & \cdots \\ g_n(m) & g_{n-1}(m) & g_{n-2}(m) & \cdots & g_0(m) \end{bmatrix} \times \begin{bmatrix} 1 \\ d_1 \\ d_2 \\ 0 \\ \cdots \end{bmatrix} \tag{5.18}$$

Thus, from the last equation,

$$c_2(m) = \frac{1}{(1+d_1+d_2)}\,[g_2(m) + d_1\, g_1(m) + d_2\, g_0(m)] \tag{5.19}$$

$$\frac{d}{dm}c_2(m) = \frac{1}{1+d_1+d_2}\left[\frac{d}{dm}g_2(m) + d_1\frac{d}{dm}g_1(m) + d_2\frac{d}{dm}g_0(m)\right] \tag{5.20}$$

Substituting numerical values (specifications and plant constants) in equations (5.19) and (5.20), we get

$$\frac{0.859 + 0.617d_1 + 0.107d_2}{1 + d_1 + d_2} = 1.2 \tag{5.21}$$

$$\frac{0.141 + 0.383d_1 + 0.394d_2}{1 + d_1 + d_2} = 0 \tag{5.22}$$

The solution of these equations yields

$$d_1 = -0.105$$

$$d_2 = -0.256$$

Therefore,

$$D_s^*(z) = 1.565\frac{(z^2 - 0.105z - 0.256)(z - 1)}{z^3} \tag{5.23}$$

A plot of the resultant output is given in Fig. 5.5. The equivalent closed-loop compensator is found from equation (5.11) as

$$D_c^*(z) = 1.565\frac{z^4 - 1.473z^3 + 0.768z^2 - 0.389z + 0.094}{z^4 - 0.944z^3 - 0.353z^2 - 0.104z - 0.106} \tag{5.24}$$

The completed closed-loop system is shown in Fig. 5.6. Also a check of the derivatives of the output discloses no maxima or minima beyond the first peak. The settling time is uniquely determined by the choice of d_1 and d_2. If the settling time is to be changed, new values of d_1 and d_2 have to be chosen, for the settling time and peak overshoot time are interdependent.

The complexity of the closed-loop compensator is somewhat unfavorable. A little reflection indicates that the forcing function for $n > 3$ is being forced identically to zero at the expense of the closed-loop compensator complexity. It is realized that the forcing function need not be identically zero for $n > 3$ to meet the specifications; that is, it needs to be small and rapidly approaching zero. The following type of approximation gives satisfactory results with this system.

Let an approximate closed-loop compensator be of the form

$$D_{ca}^*(z) = \frac{d_0(z^2 + d_1z + d_2)}{z^2} \tag{5.24a}$$

and consider finding the unknown such that the first three ordinate values of the forcing function, $E'^*(z) = 1.565(1 - 0.105z^{-1} - 0.256z^{-2} +$

$0z^{-3} + \cdots$) are exactly matched. In this way the error sequence is exactly specified for $n < 3$, since the output for $n < 3$ will be the same

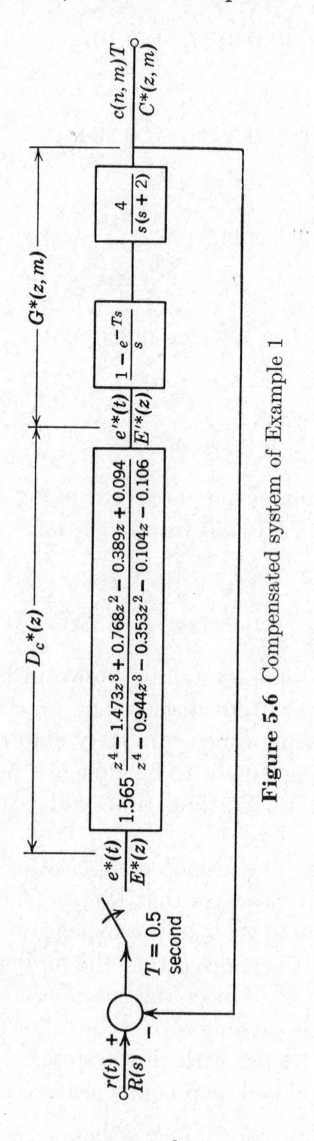

Figure 5.6 Compensated system of Example 1

as with the closed-loop compensator; however, for $n > 3$ the output will deviate, depending on how closely this approximate compensator matches the effect of the accurate closed-loop compensator.

$$E^*(z) = (1 + 0.425z^{-1} - 0.141z^{-2}) \qquad \text{for } n < 3$$

Therefore,

$$E'^*(z) = d_0(1 + d_1 z^{-1} + d_2 z^{-2})\, E^*(z) \tag{5.24b}$$
$$= 1.565(1 - 0.105z^{-1} - 0.256z^{-2}) \qquad \text{for only } n < 3$$

This equation yields

$$d_0 = 1.565$$
$$d_1 = -0.530$$
$$d_2 = +0.110$$
$$D_{ca}^*(z) = 1.565 \frac{(z^2 - 0.530z + 0.110)}{z^2} \tag{5.25}$$

In Fig. 5.5, the system response with the approximate compensator, $D_{ca}^*(z)$, is shown in comparison with the original response. More terms could have been added to this compensator, which would have resulted in a better approximation. This type of approximation is very useful in economizing in the components of the discrete compensator without much loss in performance.

Deadbeat Response

One of the useful features of discrete compensation is that it permits a class of finite settling time responses.† In the following it will be shown that the method discussed earlier yields as a special case the discrete-compensator transfer function for deadbeat response. An illustration of the deadbeat-type step response for the system of this example is given in the following. The conditions under which a true deadbeat response is possible are also given.

The necessary condition for finite settling time response is that the roots of the characteristic equation coincide at the origin in the z-plane.‡ In examining the output function given below for the typical error-

† E. I. Jury, and W. Schroeder, "Discrete Compensation of Sampled-Data and Continuous Control Systems," *Trans. A.I.E.E.*, Vol. 75, Pt. II, 1956.

‡ Deadbeat response occurs when the output equals the input for all time after a given finite time. This happens (*a*) when all the derivatives of the output become identical to those of the input, (*b*) when the d-c gain of the output equals that of the input. Mathematically in the z-domain the conditions above occur if $C^*(z, m)$ is of the following form:

$$C^*(z, m) = \frac{A(z, m)}{z^k} \times R^*(z) \tag{5.25a}$$

It is noticed from this equation that the output equals the input for all time after the kth sampling instant, provided the time contribution of $A(z, m)$ is unity at that instant and thereafter. Further, it is noted that the form of the system characteristic equation for deadbeat response is z^k.

sampled system of Fig. 5.2,

$$C^*(z, m) = R^*(z) \frac{D_c^*(z)}{1 + D_c^*(z)\, G^*(z)} \times G^*(z, m) \tag{5.26}$$

it is noted that $D_c^*(z)$ can always force (provided the plant transfer function has no poles outside the unit circle and at most a single pole on the unit circle) these roots to coincide at the origin. However, the possibility of a true deadbeat response is dependent on the plant transfer function, $G^*(z, m)$, as shown by the following. In this example,

$$z\, G^*(z, m) = \frac{\sum_{k=0}^{2} p_k z^{-k}}{1 + \sum_{k=1}^{2} q_k z^{-k}}. \tag{5.27}$$

where the numerator polynomial coefficients are functions of m. It is thus evident that $D_c^*(z)$ cannot cancel this polynomial for all values of m. Therefore, if a deadbeat response (in this case minimum rise time, T fixed) for a step input is desired, the form of the response function must be

$$z\, C^*(z, m) = \frac{z}{z - 1} \frac{\sum_{k=0}^{2} p_k z^{-k}}{\sum_{k=0}^{2} p_k} \tag{5.28}$$

In the time domain this can be expressed by

$$\left[\; c_n(m) \;\right] = \left(\frac{1}{\sum_{k=0}^{2} p_k}\right) \begin{bmatrix} p_0 & 0 & 0 & 0 & \cdots & 0 \\ p_1 & p_0 & 0 & 0 & \cdots & 0 \\ p_2 & p_1 & p_0 & 0 & \cdots & 0 \\ 0 & p_2 & p_1 & p_0 & \cdots & 0 \\ \cdots & \cdots & \cdots & \cdots & \cdots & \cdots \\ 0 & 0 & 0 & 0 & \cdots & p_0 \end{bmatrix} \begin{bmatrix} 1 \\ 1 \\ 1 \\ 1 \\ \cdots \\ 1 \end{bmatrix}$$

$$= \frac{1}{\sum_{k=0}^{2} p_k} \begin{bmatrix} p_0 \\ p_0 + p_1 \\ \sum_{k=0}^{2} p_k \\ \sum_{k=0}^{2} p_k \\ \cdots \end{bmatrix} \tag{5.29}$$

Since the response is required to be deadbeat at all times, then $\sum_{k=0}^{2} p_k$ must be independent of m, thus a constant. This is a necessary condition for true deadbeat response. The minimum rise time will be $N - 1$ sample periods where N equals the number of p_k in the numerator polynomial of the plant transfer function $G^*(z, m)$.

For this example, the required compensator is found by setting the following equation equal to equation (5.28).

$$z\,C^*(z, m) = R^*(z)\,D_{sc}^*(z) \times z\,G^*(z, m) \tag{5.30}$$

This will yield the form of the series compensator $D_{sc}^*(z)$ from which the closed compensator can be easily obtained using relation (5.11) which gives in this example: †

$$D_c^*(z) = \frac{(z - e^{-1})}{z(1 - e^{-1}) + (1 - 2e^{-1})} \tag{5.31}$$

The deadbeat response is shown in Fig. 5.5.

It is noted that this method of deadbeat compensation does not require that the plant not be saturated. If a system has a sharp saturation characteristic, a deadbeat response is still possible by relaxing the rise time requirement. Thus, if T is not variable, the necessary form for the output (for a step input) should satisfy the following equation:

$$z\,C^*(z, m) = \frac{z}{z-1}\,\frac{1 + \sum_{j=1}^{N} A_j z^{-j} \sum_{k=0}^{n} p_k z^{-k}}{1 + \sum_{j=1}^{N} A_j \quad \sum_{k=0}^{n} p_k} \tag{5.32}$$

where N is chosen in accordance with a rise time which will permit a choice of A_j such that the forcing function is within saturation limits. Once A_j is chosen, the closed-loop compensator is obtained as before.

When considering this system response only in terms of a step input, we would conclude that the deadbeat response is quite good. However, as shown in Fig. 5.7, comparison of the system velocity response for the two compensators is significantly different. As we would expect, a linear system yields a better velocity response at the expense of step overshoot and settling time. Thus, in general, a compromise is necessary. In this connection some authors suggested that design in these cases should force

† E. I. Jury and W. Schroeder, "Discrete Compensation of Sampled-Data and Continuous Control Systems," *Trans. A.I.E.E.*, Vol. 75, Pt. II, 1956, pp. 317–325.

the characteristic equation to have a staleness factor † so that it has the form of $(z - a)^n$ instead of z^n, where a is a staleness factor larger than zero and less than unity. An alternative procedure is to design for higher-order inputs as illustrated in Example 2, or to apply the total square-error criteria as shown in Example 3.

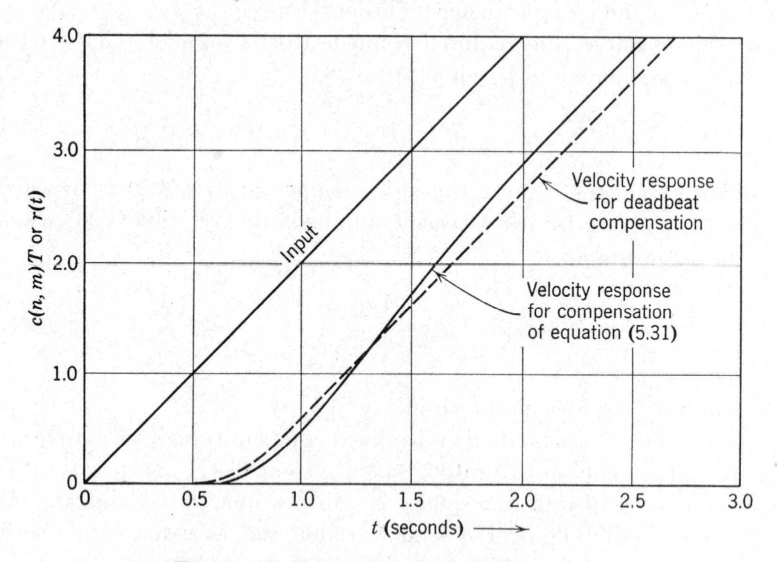

Figure 5.7 Velocity response for Example 1

EXAMPLE 2. RAMP RESPONSE DESIGN, SECOND-ORDER PLANT WITH REAL POLES

This example illustrates a ramp response design without simultaneous step response specifications. However, if such simultaneous specifications are desired, an iterative design procedure is necessary because of the interdependent nature of the performance specifications for the standard inputs.

The same system is utilized as with Example 1, Fig. 5.4. The following ramp response specifications are to be obtained:

1. Final value: Zero steady-state error, $\lim_{z \to 1} \dfrac{z-1}{z} z\, E^*(z, m) = 0$

† C. H. Smith, D. F. Lawden, A. E. Bailey, "Characteristics of Sampling Servo Systems," in *Automatic and Manual Control*, Proceedings of Cranfield Conference, 1951, edited by A. Tustin, Butterworth Scientific Publications, London, 1952, pp. 377–409.

2. Peak time: $t_p = 2.25$ seconds, $\left.\dfrac{dc_4}{dm}\right|_{m=0.5} = 1.0,$

$$\left.\frac{dc_4}{dm}\right|_{m>0.5} < 1.0, \quad \text{and} \quad \left.\frac{dc_4}{dm}\right|_{m<0.5} > 1.0$$

3. Overshoot: $M_p = 2.5\%$, $c_4(0.5) = 4.6125$
4. Settling time (t_s): The approximate minimum for four open-loop compensator variables

The open-loop compensator is selected as stated in the specifications; thus

$$D_s{}^*(z) = \frac{z^4 + d_1z^3 + d_2z^2 + d_3z + d_4}{z^4} F_{ss}{}^*(z) \qquad (5.33)$$

In this equation $F_{ss}{}^*(z)$ is of the same form as the step response of Example 1, except for the two additional compensator variables. Thus,

$$F_{ss}{}^*(z) = \frac{1}{1 + d_1 + d_2 + d_3 + d_4} \frac{z - 1}{z} \qquad (5.34)$$

This form insures that the steady-state output will be coincident with the ramp input. The $(z - 1)/z$ term insures that the steady-state output will be parallel to the ramp input, and the $1/1 + d_1 + d_2 + d_3 + d_4$ term gives the gain required to insure coincidence. This in effect demonstrates the relation of steady-state ramp error to transient response characteristics for the step.

The equivalent open-loop configuration output for the ramp input, $2/s^2$, is given by

$$C^*(z, m) = \frac{1}{1 + d_1 + d_2 + d_3 + d_4} \times \frac{z^4 + d_1z^3 + d_2z^2 + d_3z + d_4}{z^5(z - 1)} \frac{p_0 + p_1z^{-1} + p_2z^{-2}}{1 + q_1z^{-1} + q_2z^{-2}} \qquad (5.35)$$

where the plant constants are given by equation (5.14). The time domain output is obtained as before from the equivalent matrix equation; thus the equations to be satisfied according to the specifications are

$$c_4(m) = \frac{(1 + d_1 + d_2 + d_3)g_0 + (1 + d_1 + d_2)g_1 + (1 + d_1)g_2 + g_3}{1 + d_1 + d_2 + d_3 + d_4} \qquad (5.36)$$

$$\frac{dc_4}{dm} = \frac{1}{1 + d_1 + d_2 + d_3 + d_4}\left[(1 + d_1 + d_2 + d_3)\frac{dg_0}{dm} + (1 + d_1 + d_2)\frac{dg_1}{dm} + (1 + d_1)\frac{dg_2}{dm} + \frac{dg_3}{dm}\right] \tag{5.37}$$

By substituting numerical values, equations (5.36) and (5.37) become

$$3.030d_1 + 3.889d_2 - 4.506d_3 - 4.613d_4 = 2.082$$

$$0.821d_1 + 2.231d_2 - 6.065d_3 - 10d_4 = 0.302$$

Satisfying these equations and the specifications of approximate minimum settling time, we get for the compensator

$$D_s^*(z) = 2.450\,\frac{z - 1}{z}\,\frac{z^4 - 0.182z^3 - 0.493z^2 + 0.0288z + 0.112}{z^4} \tag{5.38}$$

The ramp response with this compensation is shown in Fig. 5.8, and the corresponding step response is also given in the same figure. The

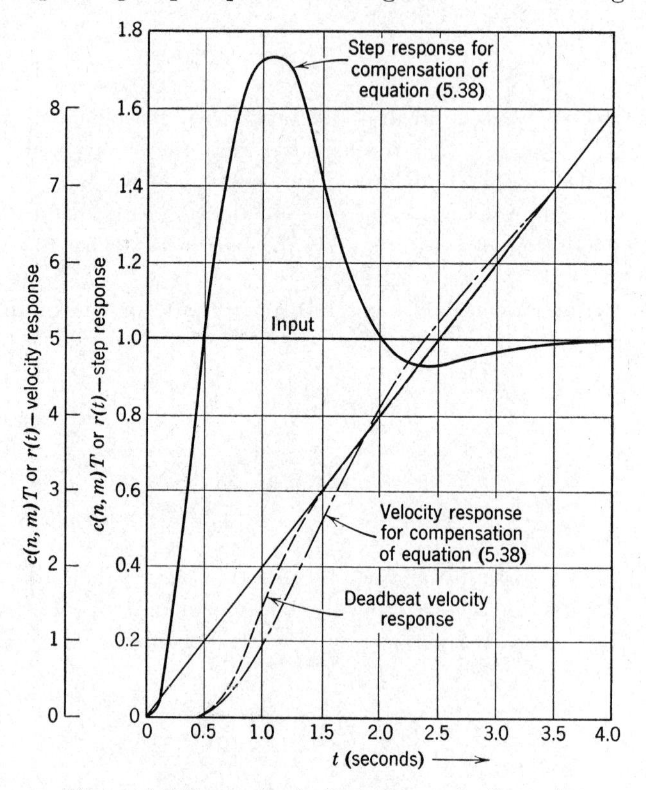

Figure 5.8 Step and velocity responses for Example 2

step overshoot is quite large, as would be expected from the peak time and steady-state ramp specifications. Relaxation of these requirements, especially of the peak time, would permit lowering the step overshoot.

Deadbeat Response

One of the deadbeat-type responses possible with discrete compensation was illustrated in Example 1. A deadbeat ramp response is considered in this example. The deadbeat step response for the system of this example is shown in Fig. 5.5, and the corresponding ramp response is shown in Fig. 5.7. It is evident that the only additional requirement for a deadbeat ramp response with this system would be reducing the velocity error to zero. This can be done only at the expense of step overshoot. A minimum rise time deadbeat ramp response is especially likely to cause excessive step overshoot. Control of this step response characteristic is possible by accepting a reduced ramp rise time (equivalent to poorer acceleration performance). The minimum rise time deadbeat response will be considered first and then a procedure for control of a step response characteristic.

The normalized ramp response for the system-compensated deadbeat step response is found simply by multiplying equation (5.28) by $1/z - 1$. The equivalent time domain response is found by multiplying equation (5.29) by the following transmission matrix $[h_n]$.

$$[h_n] = \begin{bmatrix} 0 & 0 & 0 & \cdots & 0 \\ 1 & 0 & 0 & \cdots & 0 \\ 1 & 1 & 0 & \cdots & 0 \\ \cdots & \cdots & \cdots & \cdots & \cdots \\ 1 & 1 & 1 & \cdots & 0 \end{bmatrix} \tag{5.39}$$

Denoting $c'_n(m)]$ as the ramp response, we obtain

$$\left. c'_n(m) \right] = \frac{1}{\sum_{k=0}^{2} p_k} \begin{bmatrix} 0 \\ p_0 \\ (2p_0 + p_1) \\ (2p_0 + p_1) + \sum_{k=0}^{2} p_k \\ (2p_0 + p_1) + 2\sum_{k=0}^{2} p_k \\ \cdots \end{bmatrix} \tag{5.40}$$

where

$$2p_0 + p_1 = (1 - e^{-1})m + e^{-1} \tag{5.41}$$

and

$$\sum_{k=0}^{2} p_k = 1 - e^{-1} \tag{5.41a}$$

It is evident that for smooth constant velocity error $2p_0 + p_1$ should be linear in m, $\sum_{k=0}^{2} p_k$ should be independent of m, and the constant coefficient of m of the linear term $2p_0 + p_1$ should be equal to $\sum_{k=0}^{2} p_k$. These necessary conditions are indicated by equations (5.41) and (5.41*a*) for this example. In the subsequent equations, it will be evident that these are also *necessary* conditions for deadbeat ramp response. The steady-state error can be reduced to zero in a minimum time as follows.

In equation (5.32), consider limiting N to one, that is, introducing one additional zero into the required form for the output function. Now expanding the resulting form for a ramp input and for $n = 2$ as determined by this example, we obtain the following time domain output:

$$\left[c'_n(m) \right] = \frac{1}{(1 + A_1) \sum_{k=0}^{2} p_k} \begin{bmatrix} 0 \\ p_0 \\ (2p_0 + p_1) + A_1 p_0 \\ (1 + A_1)(2p_0 + p_1) + \sum_{k=0}^{2} p_k \\ (1 + A_1)(2p_0 + p_1) + (A_1 + 1) \sum_{k=0}^{2} p_k + \sum_{k=0}^{2} p_k \\ (1 + A_1)(2p_0 + p_1) + 2(A_1 + 1) \sum_{k=0}^{2} p_k + \sum_{k=0}^{2} p_k \\ \cdots \\ \cdots \\ \cdots \end{bmatrix} \tag{5.42}$$

Since $2p_0 + p_1$ will always be of the form (as indicated earlier) $\sum_{k=0}^{n} p_k m + k_0$ (where k_0 is defined as the constant part of $2p_0 + p_1$), to obtain a deadbeat ramp response the output during the fourth sampling period should be $m + n$, as seen from equation (5.42). Thus A_1 can be obtained by solving the following equation:

$$(1 + A_1)(2p_0 + p_1) + \sum_{k=0}^{2} p_k = [(1 + A_1) \sum_{k=0}^{2} p_k](3 + m), \qquad \text{for all } m \tag{5.43}$$

which yields for A_1 when $m \to 0$ is substituted in this equation:

$$A_1 = \frac{2 \sum_{k=0}^{2} p_k - k_0}{k_0 - 3 \sum_{k=0}^{2} p_k} \tag{5.44}$$

Equation (5.43) is applicable in general to determining the additional zero location for error-sampled type systems when minimum rise time deadbeat velocity responses are desired.

For this example,

$$A_1 = -0.5864$$

The open-loop compensator is thus

$$D_s^*(z) = \frac{1}{(1 + A_1) \sum_{k=0}^{2} p_k} \frac{z + A_1}{z} \frac{z^2 + q_1 z + q_2}{z^2} \tag{5.45}$$

$$= 3.8256 \frac{z - 0.5864}{z} \frac{z^2 - 1.3679z + 0.3679}{z^2} \tag{5.46}$$

If additional freedom is necessary to allow for rise time reduction to gain control of the corresponding step response, the number of A_j in equation (5.32) are chosen consistent with the rise time requirement for the control of the step response. With the aid of this procedure we may have simultaneous control of step and ramp characteristics.†

Furthermore, the ramp deadbeat response is accomplished through cancellation of the undesirable poles, a procedure requiring due caution in shifts in parameters, as will be discussed later.

Example 3. Design for Minimum Integral Squared Error, Second-Order Plant

This example considers a particularly simple problem of minimizing the total squared error for a second-order system with step input. Again the open-loop configuration is chosen as a working model. For the sake of mathematical ease, the number of variables in the compensator will be limited to two. The objectives of this example are to illustrate the basic problems involved and to obtain a solution comparable with that of Example 1.

† E. I. Jury and W. Schroeder, "Discrete Compensation of Sampled-Data and Continuous Control Systems," Electronic Research Laboratory Report, Series 60, Issue 154, December 14, 1955, University of California, Berkeley.

The plant is the same as that of Example 1, Fig. 5.4. Equations (5.13) and (5.14) give the plant constants. Since the open-loop compensator is to be limited to two variables and a final value of unity is necessary because of the previously mentioned error requirements, the compensator has the same form as in Example 1, that is, equations (5.16) and (5.17). The continuous error (for step input) is given by

$$E^*(z, m) = R^*(z, m) - C^*(z, m)$$
$$= \frac{1}{z-1} - \frac{z^2 + d_1 z + d_2}{(1 + d_1 + d_2)z^3} \frac{p_0 z^2 + p_1 z + p_2}{(z-1)(z - e^{-1})} \qquad (5.47)$$

Since the total error squared is desired, it would be convenient to have a closed form for the entire time domain error function. Such a form, when possible, can be obtained with the inversion integral. Owing to the singularities at the origin in $E^*(z, m)$ of equation (5.47), the time inversion is broken into two parts. For $n < 4$, the first three terms of the error, $e_n(m)$], are easily obtained from the coefficients of a series expansion of the integrand; thus

$$e_0(m) = 1 - \frac{p_0}{1 + d_1 + d_2} \qquad (5.48)$$

$$e_1(m) = 1 - \frac{p_0(1 + e^{-1} + d_1) + p_1}{1 + d_1 + d_2} \qquad (5.49)$$

$$e_2(m) = e^{-1} + \frac{p_0(-e^{-1} - e^{-1}d_1 - e^{-2})}{1 + d_1 + d_2} + \frac{p_1(d_2 - e^{-1}) + p_2(d_1 + d_2)}{1 + d_1 + d_2} \qquad (5.50)$$

The remaining portion of error function is found in closed form by evaluation of

$$\frac{1}{2\pi j} \oint_\Gamma \frac{\left\{ \begin{array}{l} z^3(1 + d_1 + d_2 - p_0) \\ \quad + z^2[(1 - e^{-1})(1 + d_1 + d_2) - p_0(1 + d_1) - p_1] \\ \quad + z(p_2 d_1 + p_2 d_2 + p_1 d_2) + p_2 d_2 \end{array} \right\}}{(1 + d_1 + d_2)\, z^3\, (z - e^{-1})} z^{n-1}\, dz \qquad (5.51)$$

This yields

$$e_{n-1}(m) = e^{4-n} \frac{(e^{-1} - p_0 e^{-1} + p_2)(e^{-2} + d_1 e^{-1} + d_2)}{1 + d_1 + d_2} \qquad n \geq 4 \quad (5.52)$$

Squaring in the time domain for a function having a piecewise description is given by

$$c^2(n, m)T = c_n{}^2(m)]$$

$$c_n(m) \quad = \begin{bmatrix} c_0(m) \\ c_1(m) \\ c_2(m) \\ \cdot \\ \cdot \\ \cdot \\ c_n(m) \end{bmatrix} \tag{5.53}$$

Thus the operation of squaring and integrating is given as

$$\int_0^\infty e^2(t)\,dt = T\int_0^\infty [e_0{}^2(m) + e_1{}^2(m) + e_2{}^2(m)]\,dm + T\sum_{n=4}^{\infty}\int_0^1 e_{n-1}^2(m)\,dm \tag{5.54}$$

Performing the above integration and summation and inserting the values of this example yield the following equation for the integral square error:

$$\int_0^\infty e^2\,dt = \frac{1}{2}\left[2.135 + \frac{0.368d_2 - 0.241d_1 - 1.628}{1 + d_1 + d_2} + \frac{(0.0710d_1{}^2 - 0.158d_2 + 0.462d_2{}^2 + 0.203d_1d_2 + 0.198d_1 + 0.458)}{(1 + d_1 + d_2)^2}\right] \tag{5.55}$$

To minimize the total error-squared function (denoting it as F), it is necessary that

$$\frac{\partial F}{\partial d_1} = 0, \qquad \frac{\partial F}{\partial d_2} = 0 \tag{5.56}$$

Thus the equations that must be satisfied are

$$1.331d_2 + 0.669d_1 + 0.253 = 0$$

and

$$1.495d_2 - 1.331d_2{}^2 - 0.669d_1d_2 + 1.331d_1 + 0.669 = 0 \tag{5.57}$$

A solution for these equations is

$$d_1 = -0.745 \qquad d_2 = 0.185 \tag{5.58}$$

The open-loop compensator is

$$D_s^*(z) = 2.273 \frac{z^2 - 0.745z + 0.185}{z^2} \frac{z - 1}{z} \tag{5.59}$$

An equivalent closed-loop compensator can be found as before.

The system output for a step input is shown in Fig. 5.9. Comparison with the compensated response of Example 1 discloses the effect of design

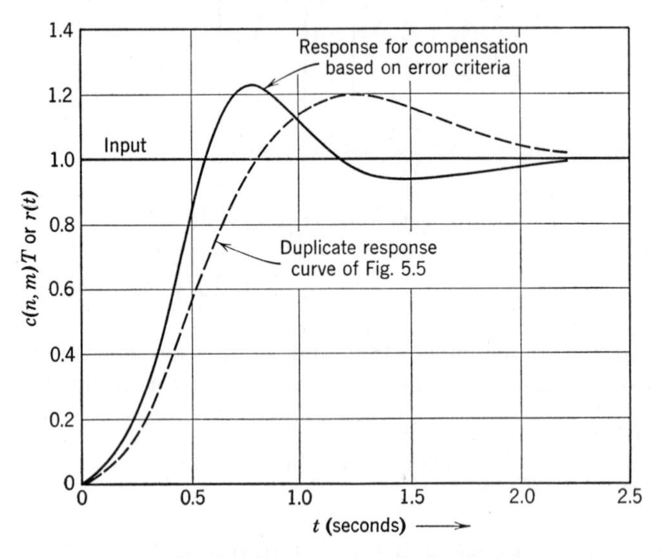

Figure 5.9 Step response for Example 3

for minimum total squared error. As is expected, there is a considerable decrease in rise time since large errors are heavily weighted by this criterion. This result reveals the lack of control the unrestrained criteria afford with the saturation problem. The settling characteristics can be improved by adding more variables in the discrete compensator. A further improvement would be to use the time-weighted error criteria $\left[\int_0^\infty te^2(t)\,dt\right]$ as small errors, for large values of time would then yield an appreciable contribution to the function which is minimized.

5.4 Discussion of Method

The aim with these particularly simple examples of discrete compensation has been to characterize an adaptation of the modified z-transform as a synthesis tool. Thus, many of the possible ramifications are not illustrated in detail; however, the examples do portray the essential ideas of the synthesis technique as well as the flexibility and control of system behavior afforded with discrete compensation. Some of the typical problems that would be encountered—for instance, saturation limits, plants with pure delay, † other system configurations, simultaneous performance specifications for the aperiodic inputs—are quite amenable with this method.

This time domain technique offers a different philosophy of approach to the control synthesis problem. No longer is the designer faced with the trial and error procedures of splicing up the inner loop configuration to obtain a desirable transfer characteristic, nor is he required to concoct a transfer function which insures the desired continuous behavior. One particular advantage of discrete compensation is the achievement of deadbeat response, both for step and higher input accelerations. Therefore, the assumptions underlying synthesis of deadbeat response deserve further clarification as outlined in the next section.

5.5 Discussion of Assumptions for Deadbeat Response

The transfer function of the compensator is chosen so that certain undesirable poles of the original system are canceled. In any physical system it is realized that these poles will never be exactly canceled, and, therefore, an investigation of the effect of imperfect cancellation should be made for each compensated system under consideration. Again, the modified z-transform is a useful tool since the complete response can be found for any pole zero configuration, as explained in detail in Chapter 3.

It has been pointed out in the literature ‡ that imperfect cancellation of a pole outside, on, or near the unit circle in the z-plane can result in an unstable system. Therefore, the compensator should never be required to cancel exactly a pole in this region of the z-plane. If this original plant is stable, as is assumed in the discussion of this chapter, the modified z-transform can have no poles outside the unit circle. However, if the original system has a multiple pole at the origin in the s-plane, $G^*(z, m)$ will have multiple poles at $z = 1 + j0$ in the z-plane. If the procedure for deadbeat response for a step input is applied, at least one of these

† W. Schroeder, "Analysis and Synthesis of Sampled-Data and Continuous Control Systems with Pure Time Delays," Electronics Research Laboratory Report, Series 60, Issue 156, June 8, 1956, University of California, Berkeley.

‡ John E. Bertram, "Factors in the Design of Digital Controllers for Sampled-Data Feedback Systems," *Trans. A.I.E.E.*, Vol. 75, Pt. II, 1956, pp. 151–159.

poles will require cancellation. Cancellation should not be attempted, however, since imperfect cancellation can result in an unstable system. This difficulty can be circumvented in either of the following ways.

1. The order of integration of the original system may be reduced to zero or one with a continuous feedback around the plant. The resulting system must be stable; otherwise there will be a pole outside the unit circle requiring cancellation. A single order of integration gives no difficulty as noticed from Example 1.
2. The multiple integration can be retained and the system compensated for deadbeat ramp response so that the multiple integration is utilized. This will result in an overshoot for step input. This step overshoot can be reduced by adding additional zeros to the compensator, thus increasing the complexity of the compensator.

Imperfect cancellation of poles inside the unit circle in the z-plane can cause undesirable responses, even though the system remains stable. Again the modified z-transform can be used to detect the arising error.

In the examples discussed, it was tacitly assumed that the period T of the sample could be varied. If the period is fixed and the desired response cannot be obtained with the fixed period, it may be possible to reduce the effective order of the system by adding a minor feedback loop around the plant and considering only the dominant pair of poles which would exist by this procedure. Furthermore, multirate controllers † can be applied, which might be useful in reducing the undesirable ripple.

It has also been assumed that the system is linear. Reduction of the rise time by reducing the sampling period or by using multirate ‡ discrete compensators will require higher gain; therefore, saturation will result with smaller signals.

The effect of saturation has not been investigated in detail in this chapter, but saturation and the maximum forcing functions which the system components can withstand will limit the rise times obtainable. In such cases equation (5.32) can be applied for synthesis.

5.6 Root-Locus Method of Synthesis

The root-locus method, as discussed in detail in Chapter 3, for analysis of sampled-data systems can also be applied for synthesis. Its applica-

† G. M. Kranc, "Compensation of an Error-Sampled System by a Multi-rate Controller," *Trans. A.I.E.E.*, Vol. 76, Pt. II, 1957, pp. 149–159.

‡ The sampling rate of the output of a multirate discrete compensator is an integer multiple of its input rate.

tion for synthesis is based on choosing the transfer function of the discrete compensator in terms of poles and zero in the z-plane. An illustrative example has been introduced in Chapter 3 to indicate the principle of this approach. The success of the root-locus method is greatly dependent on the existence of dominant roots of the system transfer function. In view of this the transient response quantities such as peak time and overshoot can easily be correlated to poles and zero location † of the system function in the z-plane. It is realized, however, that the existence of dominant roots is a limitation on the freedom of compensation, and because of its general approach the first method is far superior and more intelligently handled.

Similar to the continuous case, this graphical method of synthesis can be extended to include the root-contours whereby both the gain and one of the time constants can be changed to yield better transient performance.

Deadbeat response can also be achieved with this method by forcing the root-locus to be the real axis and the roots to be at the origin in the z-plane.

In view of the existence of extensive literature of the root-locus and root-contours method, it is not necessary to extend this method beyond what has been discussed in Chapter 3. However, the principle of application of this method to sampled-data is very similar to the use of linear network for compensating continuous control systems with the only restriction that the discrete compensator should be physically realizable, as will be explained in detail in Chapter 7.

5.7 Frequency Response Methods

As in continuous control systems, sampled-data systems are studied in frequency domain as explained in detail in Chapter 4. This was a natural approach because of the existing wealth of sinusoidal theory which can be applied to such systems. Synthesis criteria are stated in frequency domain such as bandwidth, ‡ attenuation characteristics, and phase and gain margins. These resulted in studies of frequency loci and of loci shaping by discrete filters in the $HG^*(e^{sT})$-plane § and the log-frequency

† E. I. Jury, "Correlation between Root-Locus and Transient Response of Sampled-Data Control Systems," *Trans. A.I.E.E.*, Vol. 74, Pt. II, 1955, pp. 427–436.

‡ W. K. Linvill and John M. Salzer, "Analysis of Control Systems Involving Digital Computers," *Proc. I.R.E.*, Vol. 41, No. 7, 1953, pp. 901–908.

§ John M. Salzer, "Systems Compensation with a Digital Computer," *I.R.E. National Convention Record*, Pt. V, March 1954, pp. 179–186.

plane as indicated in Chapter 4. The earliest approach of discrete compensation by frequency loci shaping in the Nyquist diagram was introduced by Linvill and Salzer. In this approach, the Nyquist plot of the uncompensated system was changed by the chosen discrete compensator. This can be done very similarly to the shaping of continuous loci in the $H(s)\,G(s)$-plane, in view of the simple multiplication of the discrete compensator with the z-transform of the uncompensated locus.

Sampled-data systems can be qualitatively compensated with this method; however, the type of transient responses with the use of discrete compensator are not readily revealed. Furthermore, frequency loci shaping is related to the system characteristics only at the sampling instants, which in some cases are not a true representation of the continuous behavior of sampled-data control systems. However, in such cases of severe ripple between sampling instants we can make use of multirate discrete compensators or continuous networks as discussed in Chapter 6, whereby frequency methods can also be applied.

Further significant extension † of the frequency loci shaping method, as discussed in Chapter 4, is the use of the log-frequency coordinate of the Bode diagram, which simplifies the shaping procedures considerably. This has been accomplished as discussed in the preceding chapter by the linear transformation from the $z = e^{Ts}$-plane into the w-plane as follows:

$$z = \frac{1 + w}{1 - w} \tag{5.60}$$

or

$$w = \frac{e^{sT} - 1}{e^{sT} + 1} \tag{5.61}$$

As shown in Chapter 4, by using this transformation, we may utilize the asymptotic plots or Nichols charts, which proved quite convenient as in the continuous case. By this method we can improve the bandwidth and the gain-phase margins by the suitable choice of this discrete compensator. Also by this method we can add lead or lag compensators in the w-plane, very similar to the continuous case, which can be transformed into the z-plane to yield the discrete-compensator transfer function.

To obtain a measure on the system behavior between sampling instants, we may use the modified z-transform transformed into the w-plane where the frequency response for different values of m can be ascertained.

† G. W. Johnson, D. P. Lindorff, C. G. A. Nordling, "Extension of Continuous-Data System Design Techniques to Sampled-Data Control Systems," *Trans. A.I.E.E.*, Vol. 74, Pt. II, 1955, pp. 252–259.

In concluding this section on the frequency response methods, it is important to indicate that these methods can be conveniently applied for the design of discrete compensators where the types of inputs to the systems are not readily defined in terms of step or ramp functions. Under these conditions of arbitrary general input functions, the frequency response method readily yields a qualitative picture of the system degree of stability and of the type of discrete compensators required.

Before concluding this chapter, it is worthwhile to mention a few of the other methods of synthesis which are essentially of the time domain type. For instance, Barker † and Lawden ‡ suggested that the characteristic equation be forced into a desirable form as the method of obtaining the discrete compensator parameters. Of particular significance is the fact that deadbeat response can be achieved by forcing the system characteristic equation to be of the form z^n. This was a sound approach from a steady-state point of view but not sufficient considering transient behavior. Bergen and Ragazzini § presented an interesting discrete-compensation procedure involving digital "processing unit." They set as their objective an idealized transfer function, or the "prototype transfer function"; however, through this transfer function it is a straightforward procedure to obtain the discrete compensator. This prototype transfer function specifies the system behavior only at the sampling instants. In effect, this limits the design procedure to systems whose time constants are large compared with the sample period or whose damping ratio is relatively large. If the procedure were used under other conditions, the intersample response would very likely be undesirable, since the system would be coerced to fit the sample values specified by the transfer function. Bertram, Maitra, and Sarachik || have clarified and extended this method to show the limitations of pole and zero cancellation possible in attempting to get desirable forms of transfer functions. These methods are quite straightforward and have the appeal of working in the time domain; however, the limitations of being able to design only in terms of the sampled response rather than of the continuous limit

† R. H. Barker, "Pulse Transfer Function and its Application to Sampling Servo Systems," *Proc. I.E.E. (London)*, Vol. 99, Pt. IV, 1952.

‡ C. H. Smith, D. F. Lawden, and A. E. Bailey, "Characteristics of Sampling Servo Systems," in *Automatic and Manual Control*, Proceedings of Cranfield Conference, 1951, edited by A. Tustin, Butterworth Scientific Publications, London, 1952, pp. 377–404.

§ A. R. Bergen and J. R. Ragazzini, "Sampled-Data Processing Techniques," *Trans. A.I.E.E.*, Vol. 73, Pt. II, 1954, pp. 236–247.

|| K. K. Maitra and P. E. Sarachik, "Digital Compensation of Continuous Data Feedback Control Systems," *Trans. A.I.E.E.*, Vol. 75, Pt. II, 1956, pp. 107–116. J. E. Bertram, "Factors in the Design of Digital Controllers for Sampled-Data Feedback Control Systems," *Trans. A.I.E.E.*, Vol. 75, Pt. II, 1956, pp. 151–159.

restricts their general applicability for exact synthesis. Design based on this method requires checking the intersample response; if this proves unsatisfactory, in some cases the design procedure is repeated.

Further extension of this method is the use of the multirate controller as a discrete compensator. The controller can reduce the ripple in the output under certain conditions, especially if the sampling period is fixed. The philosophy of approach of this method is again based on the response at the sampling instants similar to the above-mentioned methods.

In conclusion, it is evident that the designer should know all the existing methods and techniques, and certainly no one method is universal for all applications. In certain applications we need to use the frequency, root-locus, and direct time domain synthesis for one particular problem, and thus familiarity with all the existing methods and a knowledge of their limitations and advantages are essential.

APPENDIX

Explanation of Matrix Notations Representation

By referring to Fig. 5.10, the modified z-transform can be written:

$$C^*(z, m) = R^*(z) \times G^*(z, m) \tag{1}$$

or

$$z\,C^*(z, m) = R^*(z) \times z\,G^*(z, m) = \sum_{n=0}^{\infty} r_n z^{-n} \times \sum_{n=0}^{\infty} g_n(m)\, z^{-n} \tag{2}$$

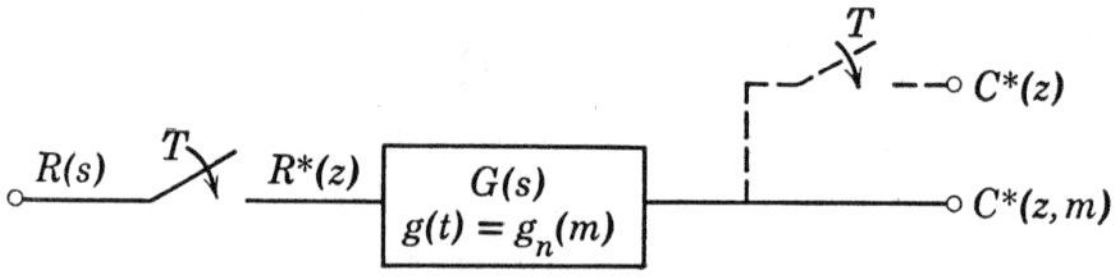

Figure 5.10 A sampled-data system with matrix notations

This equation can be expanded in a series whose coefficients yield the piecewise time response as follows:

$$\begin{aligned} z\,C^*(z, m) &= c_0(m) + c_1(m)\, z^{-1} + c_2(m)\, z^{-2} + \cdots + c_n(m)\, z^{-n} + \cdots \\ &= (r_0 + r_1 z^{-1} + r_2 z^{-2} + \cdots + r_n z^{-n} + \cdots) \\ &\quad \times [g_0(m) + g_1(m)\, z^{-1} + g_2(m)\, z^{-2} + \cdots + g_n(m)\, z^{-n} + \cdots] \end{aligned} \tag{3}$$

Multiplying term by term and equating coefficients of z^{-n} in both sides, we obtain

$$
\begin{aligned}
c_0(m) &= r_0\, g_0(m) \\
c_1(m) &= r_0\, g_1(m) + r_1\, g_0(m) \\
c_2(m) &= r_0\, g_2(m) + r_1\, g_1(m) + r_2\, g_0(m) \\
\cdot\quad & \quad \cdot \\
\cdot\quad & \quad \cdot \\
\cdot\quad & \quad \cdot \\
c_n(m) &= r_0\, g_n(m) + r_1\, g_{n-1}(m) + \cdots r_n\, g_0(m)
\end{aligned}
\tag{4}
$$

By using matrix notation, this set of equations can be conveniently represented as shown below:

$$
\left. c_n(m) \right] = \begin{bmatrix} c_0(m) \\ c_1(m) \\ \cdot \\ \cdot \\ \cdot \\ c_n(m) \end{bmatrix} = \left. [g_n(m)] \times r_n \right] \tag{5}
$$

where $[g_n(m)]$ is a transmission matrix and $r_n]$ is a column matrix represented as follows:

$$
[g_n(m)] = \begin{bmatrix} g_0(m) & 0 & 0 & \cdots & 0 \\ g_1(m) & g_0(m) & 0 & \cdots & 0 \\ \cdot & & & & \\ \cdot & & & & \\ \cdot & & & & \\ g_n(m) & g_{n-1}(m) & g_{n-2}(m) & \cdots & g_0(m) \end{bmatrix}, \qquad \left. r_n \right] = \begin{bmatrix} r_0 \\ r_1 \\ \cdot \\ \cdot \\ \cdot \\ r_n \end{bmatrix} \tag{6}
$$

For the z-transform or the response at sampling instants † this notation can be used provided $m = 0$.

Following the procedure developed for Fig. 5.10, we can apply the same to Fig. 5.2. The z-transform of the error $E^*(z)$ can be expressed

$$
E^*(z) = \frac{1}{1 + D_c{}^*(z)\, G^*(z)} \times R^*(z) \tag{7}
$$

or

$$
R^*(z) = E^*(z)[1 + D_c{}^*(z)\, G^*(z)] \tag{8}
$$

† B. Friedland, "A Technique for the Analysis of Time-Varying Sampled-Data Systems," *Trans. A.I.E.E.*, Vol. 75, Pt. II, 1956, pp. 407–414.

In matrix notation this equation is given as

$$r_n] = \{I + [g_n(0)] \times [dc_n]\} \times e_n] \tag{9}$$

The matrix of e_n in terms of r_n can be obtained as follows:

$$e_n] = \{I + [g_n(0)][dc_n]\}^{-1} \times r_n] \tag{10}$$

where $\{I + [g_n(0)][dc_n]\}^{-1}$ is the inverse matrix of $I + [g_n(0)][dc_n]$.

The output modified z-transform is

$$z\, C^*(z, m) = E^*(z) \times D_c{}^*(z) \times z\, G^*(z, m) \tag{11}$$

In matrix notation this can be represented, by noting equations 7 and 10, as follows:

$$c_n(m)] = [g_n(m)] \times [dc_n] \times \{I + [g_n(0)] \times [dc_n]\}^{-1} \times r_n] \tag{12}$$

where

$$I = \text{unit matrix} = \begin{bmatrix} 1 & 0 & 0 & 0 & 0 & \cdots & 0 \\ 0 & 1 & 0 & 0 & 0 & \cdots & 0 \\ 0 & 0 & 1 & 0 & 0 & \cdots & 0 \\ \cdot & \cdot & \cdot & \cdot & \cdot & \cdots & \cdot \\ \cdot & \cdot & \cdot & \cdot & \cdot & \cdots & \cdot \\ \cdot & \cdot & \cdot & \cdot & \cdot & \cdots & \cdot \\ 0 & 0 & 0 & 0 & 0 & \cdots & 1 \end{bmatrix} \tag{13}$$

If the response at the sampling instants is required, substitute for $m = 0$ in the above expression.

CHAPTER 6

Continuous Network Compensation Method

The preceding chapter was mainly concerned with discrete compensation in which the compensator feed to the plant series of impulses displaced at equal or submultiple values of the sampling time. It has been shown that discrete compensators are flexible enough to achieve all types of responses subject to the plant transfer function; but they are limited in that sometimes ripple between sampling intervals cannot be completely eliminated, although it is reduced by the use of multirate controllers.† Furthermore, the use of discrete compensator may require the use of elaborate equipment, as will be discussed in the next chapter, which might not be necessary for certain types of performance. Thus the method of continuous compensation which involves the use of an ordinary network or, in more complicated cases an analogue computer, might be cheaper than a pulsed network or a digital compensator and have the further advantage of reducing any ripple. The ripple is reduced because the output of the continuous compensator feeds a continuous signal to the plant which monitors its output continuously. The methods of designing the continuous compensator are more elaborate and com-

† G. M. Kranc, "Compensation of an Error-Sampled System by a Multi-Rate Controller," *Trans. A.I.E.E.*, Vol. 76, Pt. II, 1957, pp. 149–159.

plicated than those for the corresponding discrete compensator, but this should not be a deterent factor in its use, as explained in this chapter.

6.1 Description of Method

Continuous-compensation method involves the use of linear networks in either the forward or the feedback path of a sampled-data feedback system.

The input to the network $G_c(s)$ shown in Fig. 6.1 is usually of a staircase type if a hold circuit is used; otherwise it consists of a set of impulses,

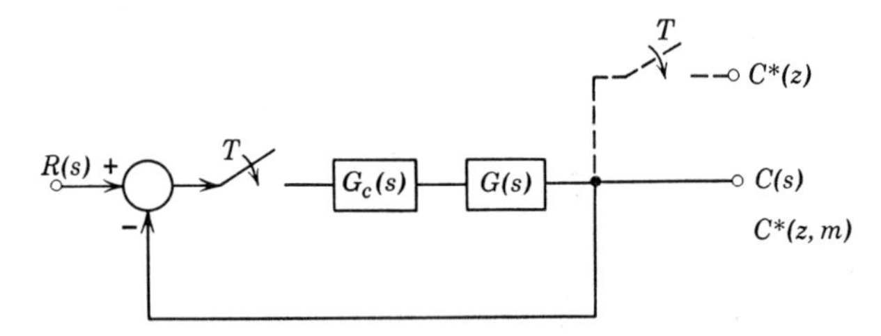

Figure 6.1 Sampled-data control systems with continuous compensator

and its output is continuous and fed continuously to the plant transfer function $G(s)$. The system output as shown in Fig. 6.1 is continuous and can be described using the modified z-transform as follows:

$$C^*(z, m) = \frac{R^*(z)}{1 + G_cG^*(z)} \times G_cG^*(z, m) \tag{6.1}$$

It is noticed from this equation that the system performance depends on the z-transform or the modified z-transform of the product of $G_c(s)$ and $G(s)$. The fact that the z-transform of the product is not equal to the z-transform of each of the terms tends to complicate the procedure for synthesis, in view of the interconnection of the network and the plant in this form. However, this difficulty is not prohibitive for the effective use of the techniques developed in the previous chapter.

6.2 Methods of Synthesis

As with discrete compensation, there exist two main methods, of synthesis, namely, the frequency response and the time response methods.

The frequency response methods can be divided into approximate and exact ones, and both are discussed in this chapter. The time domain methods are also exact and approximate, and these too are discussed herein. One such method is based on approximating the discrete filter with the zero-order hold by linear networks. Thus, the time domain techniques developed in the preceding chapter can be readily applied for the continuous-compensation method.

a. Frequency Response Method Based on the s-Plane Approach

The earliest approach to continuous compensation of sampled-data control systems was performed in the s-plane by Linvill.† This method,

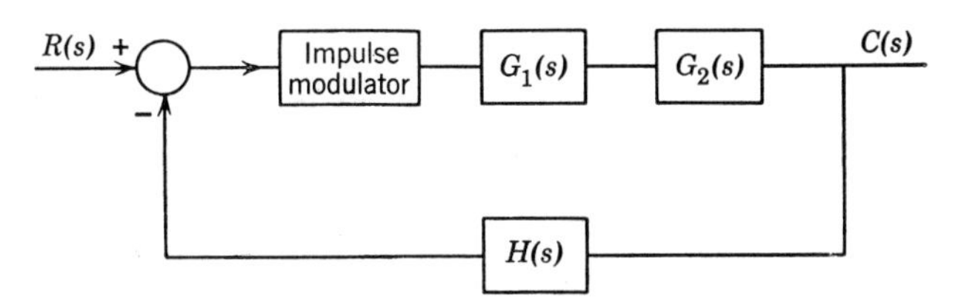

Figure 6.2 Sampled-data control system configuration

which is also referred to as the Poisson sum approximation, is basically an approximate method which neglects the higher harmonics generated by the sampler (impulse modulator) in view of the low-pass characteristics of the controller. By using the concept of representing the sampler by an impulse modulator, the output of a sampled-data control system shown in Fig. 6.2 can be written using the infinite-series summation as

$$C(s) = \frac{\left[\frac{1}{T} \sum_{k=-\infty}^{k=\infty} R(s + jk\omega_r)\right] \times G_1(s)\, G_2(s)}{1 + \frac{1}{T} \sum_{k=-\infty}^{k=\infty} G_1G_2H(s + jk\omega_r)} \tag{6.2}$$

In view of the low-pass characteristics of $G_1(s)$ and $G_2(s)$, the infinite series in the denominator of equation (6.2) can be approximated by a few terms, provided the sampling frequency is high or, alternately, provided the sampled-data system approaches the characteristic of the continuous system. Based on this approximation, synthesis can be attempted in the $G_1G_2H(s)$-plane where the Nyquist locus can be plotted to determine

† W. K. Linvill, "Sampled-Data Control Systems Studied through Comparison of Sampling with Amplitude Modulation," *Trans. A.I.E.E.*, Vol. 70, Pt. II, 1951, p. 1779.

stability. However, the effect of changing poles and zeros of the continuous compensator cannot be readily evaluated, in view of the fact that few terms of the infinite series are needed for the final plot. Thus, shaping the Nyquist locus with this method is more complicated than shaping the corresponding Nyquist locus of the continuous system. Furthermore, exact quantitative relationships between the frequency response quantities and the transient response are not available with this method. However, for quick qualitative design this method can be useful in some cases. The design criteria based on this method can be represented by the following:

1. The system response must be satisfactory; therefore, the frequency response $G_1G_2/(1 + \sum \cdots)$ should have acceptable amplitude and phase characteristics up to $\omega_r/2$.
2. The function $G_1G_2(s)$ should cut off as sharply as practical at $\omega_r/2$ to suppress the ripple produced by the sampling device.

It is further noted that this approximation method is also of value if the frequency responses of the components are given experimentally, which would not require knowledge of poles and zeros for the Nyquist plot. However, for effective design knowledge of transfer function of components in terms of poles and zeros is very important. Since this method is approximate, in some cases the degree of approximation is doubtful unless checked by other exact methods, that is, the z-transform.

b. *Frequency Response Method Based on the z-Plane Approach* †

The significance of the system transfer function $G^*(z)$ locus in the $G^*(z)$ plane is that it relates the steady-state response of the sampled-data control systems to sinusoidal inputs. If the input to a sampled-data system with unity feedback is sinusoidal function,

$$r(nT) = \sin \omega nT \tag{6.3}$$

the steady state output is

$$c(nT) = \frac{G^*(e^{j\omega T})}{1 + G^*(e^{j\omega T})} \sin (\omega nT + \psi) \tag{6.4}$$

where ψ is the angle extended in the $G^*(z)$ plane between $G^*(e^{jT\omega})$ and $1 + G^*(e^{jT\omega})$.

Hence, if the input is a sinusoidal sequence whose envelope is the actual input, the envelope of the output is also a sinusoidal function

† E. I. Jury, "Analysis and Synthesis of Sampled-Data Control Systems," *Trans. A.I.E.E.*, Vol. 73, Pt. II, 1954, pp. 332–346.

of the same frequency and its magnitude and phase equal respectively $\left|\dfrac{G^*(e^{j\omega T})}{1 + G^*(e^{j\omega T})}\right|$, ψ. Therefore, the overall transfer locus in the $G^*(z)$ plane when z describes the unit circle relates the steady-state envelope relationship between input and output. The actual output between the sampling instants is mainly dependent on the transfer function $G(s)$. For instance, in some cases the output between sampling instants can be exponential or sinusoidal in shape, etc.

Synthesis in the $G^*(z)$-plane is based on shaping the frequency locus through the insertion of linear networks in the loop of the system; thus the effect of poles and zeroes of $H(s)\,G(s)$ on $HG^*(z)$ requires extensive discussion.

1. Effect of simple poles of $H(s)\,G(s)$ on $HG^*(z)$. Consider a continuous-loop transfer function which consists of simple poles and zeros cascaded with a zero-order hold circuit, given in the following form:

$$H(s)\,G(s) = \frac{A(1 - e^{-Ts})}{s}\left[\frac{(1 + \tau_1 s)(1 + \tau_3 s)\cdots(1 + \tau_{2m-1}s)}{s(s + a)(1 + \tau_2 s)(1 + \tau_4 s)\cdots(1 + \tau_{2m}s)}\right] \tag{6.5}$$

where $a, \tau_1, \tau_2, \cdots, \tau_{2m}$ are all real and the degree of the denominator in the brackets of equation (6.5) is higher than that of the numerator by at least two. The corresponding z-transform of equation (6.5) can easily be seen to be

$$\begin{aligned}
HG^*(z) = {} & \frac{A}{a}\frac{T}{z-1} - \frac{A}{a^2}\frac{1 - e^{-aT}}{z - e^{-aT}} \\
& \times \frac{(1 - a\tau_1)(1 - a\tau_3)\cdots(1 - a\tau_{2m-1})}{(1 - a\tau_2)(1 - a\tau_4)\cdots(1 - a\tau_{2m})} - \frac{A\tau_2}{a}\frac{1 - e^{-T/\tau_2}}{z - e^{-T/\tau_2}} \\
& \times \frac{(1 - \tau_1/\tau_2)(1 - \tau_3/\tau_2)\cdots(1 - \tau_{2m-1}/\tau_2)}{(1 - 1/\tau_2 a)(1 - \tau_4/\tau_2)\cdots(1 - \tau_{2m}/\tau_2)} \cdots - \frac{A\tau_{2m}}{a}\frac{1 - e^{-T/\tau_{2m}}}{z - e^{-T/\tau_{2m}}} \\
& \times \frac{(1 - \tau_1/\tau_{2m})(1 - \tau_3/\tau_{2m})\cdots(1 - \tau_{2m-1}/\tau_{2m})}{(1 - \tau_1/\tau_{2m}a)(1 - \tau_2/\tau_{2m})\cdots(1 - \tau_{2m-2}/\tau_{2m})}
\end{aligned} \tag{6.6}$$

The first term of $HG^*(z)$ in equation (6.6) is introduced because of a simple pole of $H(s)\,G(s)$ at the origin (excluding the zero-order hold). The frequency locus of this term, as z describes the unit circle, is a straight line (or a circle of infinite radius). This term is characteristic of sampling systems, for as T increases the locus of $HG^*(z)$ is mainly influenced by this term; consequently, the stability of the system is affected. Although T appears in the exponent of other terms, its effect is not substantial. Furthermore, the first term is not affected by the added poles and zeros of $H(s)\,G(s)$ and is consequently indpendent of the τ's.

The loci of the other terms of $HG^*(z)$ are circles with centers on the real axis of the $HG^*(z)$-plane, in view of the fact that the constants a, τ_1,

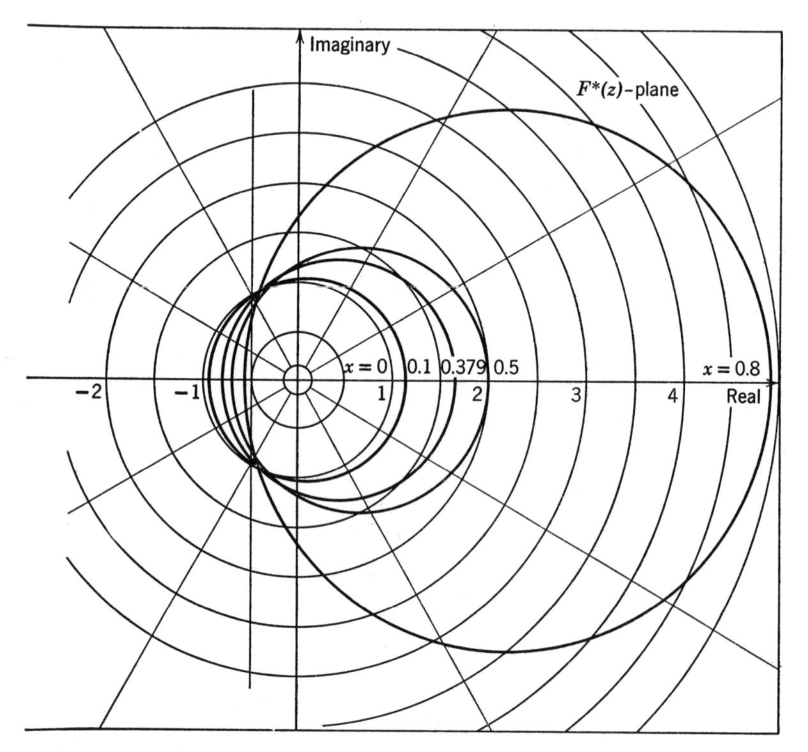

Figure 6.3 Loci of $1/(z - x)$ as z describes the unit circle in the z-plane

$\tau_2, \cdots, \tau_{2m}$ are all real. These circles are shown in Figs. 6.3 and 6.4 for a range of values of each of the varying parameters.

Adding vectorially the corresponding points on various circles and the straight line to obtain the final $HG^*(z)$ locus, we can readily observe the effect of each term of $HG^*(z)$ and its correlation to the location of poles and zeros of $H(s)\,G(s)$. Although the exact shape of $HG^*(z)$ cannot be foreseen before actually plotting $HG^*(z)$ locus point by point, certain characteristics which have significant effects on the final shape of $HG^*(z)$ will be discussed.

1. The locus of $HG^*(z)$ near $z = 1$ can be found, as indicated in chapter 1, by introducing a small semi-circle of radius ρ around the point

$z = 1$ and letting ρ approach zero. At $z = 1$ only the first term of equation (6.6) is significant, and its locus is a straight line or semi-circle of infinite radius in the right half of the $HG^*(z)$-plane.

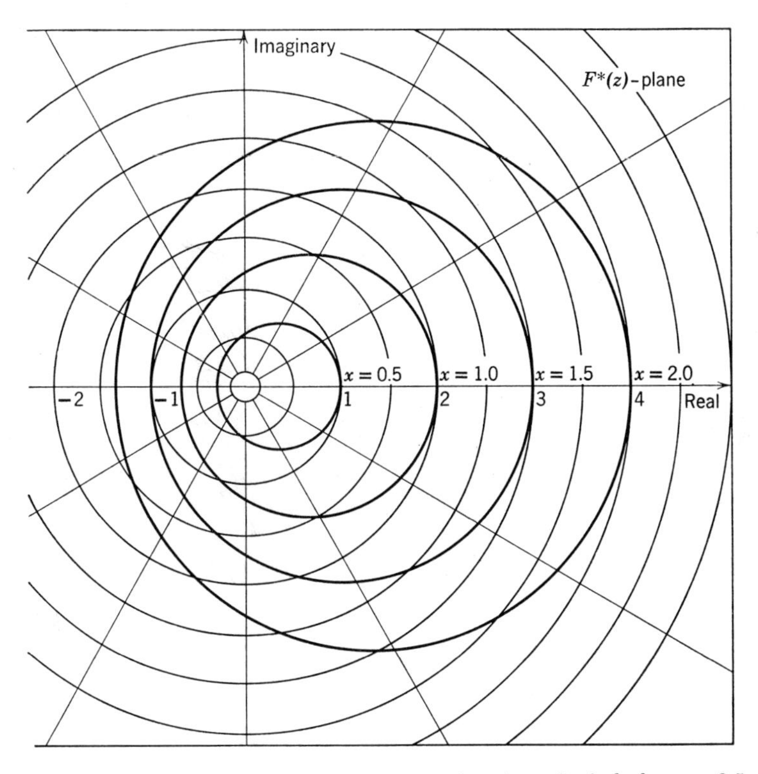

Figure 6.4 Loci plots of $x/(z - a)$ as z describes the unit circle for $a = 0.5$

2. $HG^*(z)$ is always real at $z = -1$, as indicated in chapter 1, and its magnitude at this point can be easily obtained by substituting $z = -1$ into equation (6.6). This magnitude value can be positive or negative, depending on the system parameters.

3. To determine whether $HG^*(z)$ locus will or will not intersect the real axis of $HG^*(z)$ plane at more than one finite point besides $z = -1$, $HG^*(z)$ of equation (6.6) is written as follows:

$$HG^*(z) = \frac{kT}{z - 1} - \frac{\alpha_1}{z - e^{-aT}} - \frac{\alpha_2}{z - e^{-T/\tau_2}} \cdots - \frac{\alpha_n}{z - e^{-T/\tau_{2m}}} \quad (6.7)$$

where k, α_1, α_2, $\cdots$, α_n represent their respective values in equation

(6.6). Since for the frequency locus z describes the unit circle in $HG^*(z)$ locus,

$$z = \cos\phi + j\sin\phi \tag{6.8}$$

Substituting for z in equation (6.7), we obtain the imaginary part:

$$I_m[HG^*(z)] = \sin\phi\left[\frac{-kT}{2(1-\cos\phi)} + \frac{\alpha_1}{(1+e^{-2aT}) - 2\cos\phi\, e^{-aT}} + \cdots + \frac{\alpha_n}{(1+e^{-2T/\tau_{2m}}) - 2\cos\phi\, e^{-T/\tau_{2m}}}\right] \tag{6.9}$$

Equation (6.9) is zero when $\phi = \pi$ or $z = -1$, as indicated earlier. If the constants $\alpha_1, \alpha_2, \cdots, \alpha_n$ are all negative, equation (6.9) is always

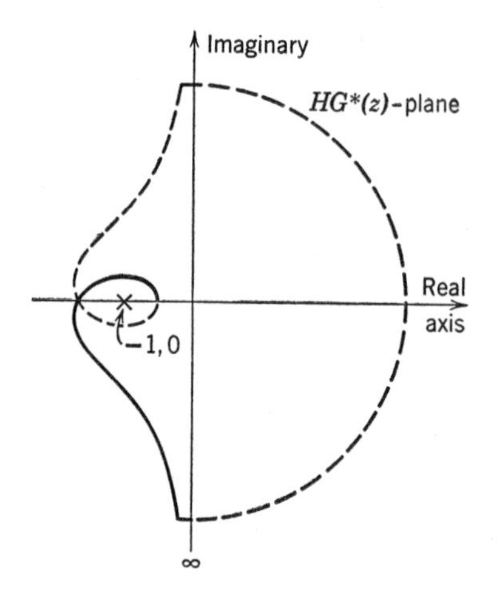

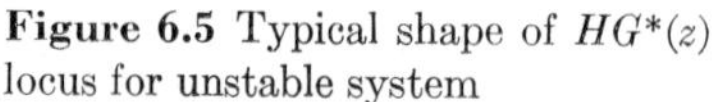
Figure 6.5 Typical shape of $HG^*(z)$ locus for unstable system

Figure 6.6 Typical shape of $HG^*(z)$ locus for stable system

negative as ϕ varies from zero to π, because all the terms in the brackets will remain negative and never become zero or positive. In this case $HG^*(z)$ locus has only one real value at $z = -1$.

Evidently when the real numbers $\alpha_1, \alpha_2, \cdots \alpha_n$ have any sign, it is not possible to predict the exact zeros of equation (6.9), unless it is solved for the constants given. However, we may conclude that if $HG^*(z)$ has an n degree denominator in z, the maximum number of time the locus crosses the real axis for $0 < \phi < \pi$ is only $n - 1$ times.

If T is large compared to the linear system time constants, it can be shown that the locus of $HG^*(z)$ will be mainly limited to one of the two shapes shown in Figs. 6.5 and 6.6.† Furthermore, when T is small compared to the linear system time constants, the shape of $HG^*(z)$ will approach that of $H(s)\,G(s)$ where the latter is described extensively in the literature.

2. Effect of complex zeros and poles of $H(s)\,G(s)$ on $HG^*(z)$. Since in physical systems complex zeros and poles appear in conjugate pairs, the numbers τ_2 and τ_4 are conjugate pairs; so are τ_1 and τ_3 and all other pairs of zeros and poles of $H(s)\,G(s)$ in equation (6.5). The corresponding $HG^*(z)$ in this case is as given in equation (6.6), from which the following remarks are important.

1. The first term of $HG^*(z)$ in equation (6.6) is unaffected by the complex zeros and poles of $H(s)\,G(s)$; hence its frequency locus is fixed, irrespective of the variation of complex zeros and poles of $H(s)\,G(s)$.
2. The second term of $HG^*(z)$ in equation (6.6) represents a locus of a circle whose center lies on the real axis of the $HG^*(z)$-plane. This is because the product $(1 - a\tau_1)(1 - a\tau_3) \cdots (1 - a\tau_{2m-1})$ as well as $(1 - a\tau_2)(1 - a\tau_4) \cdots (1 - a\tau_{2m})$ are all real numbers in view of conjugate zeros and poles.
3. The loci of third and fourth terms in equation (6.6) represent circles of center not lying on the real axis. The vector addition of these two loci circles yields real values for the point $z = 1$ and $z = -1$. Similarly, each pair of the remaining terms of $HG^*(z)$ in equation (6.6) has a similar locus.

Since, in this case, the closure of $HG^*(z)$ locus at $z = 1$, as well as the crossover condition of the real axis, follows closely the $HG^*(z)$ locus discussed in equation (6.6), the asymptotic shapes of $HG^*(z)$ are similar to the loci represented in Figs. 6.5 and 6.6.

3. Effect of multiple poles at the origin of $H(s)\,G(s)$ on $HG^*(z)$. Suppose that $H(s)\,G(s)$ is given as follows:

$$H(s)\,G(s) = \frac{1 - e^{-Ts}}{s} \times \left[\frac{(1 + \tau_1 s)(1 + \tau_2 s) \cdots (1 + \tau_{2m-1} s)}{s^k (s + a)(1 + \tau_2 s) \cdots (1 + \tau_{2m} s)}\right] \tag{6.10}$$

where k is an integer and $\tau_1, \tau_2, \cdots, \tau_{2m}$ are either real or complex. Equation (6.10) can be written

$$H(s)\,G(s) = \frac{1 - e^{-Ts}}{s^n}\left(\frac{A_0}{s + a} + \frac{B_0}{s + 1/\tau_2} + \frac{C_0}{s + 1/\tau_4} + \cdots \frac{M_0}{s + 1/\tau_{2m}}\right) \tag{6.11}$$

† E. I. Jury, "Analysis and Synthesis of Sampled-Data Control Systems," Doctorate of Engineering Science Thesis, Columbia University, New York, April 1953.

where $n = k + 1$, and A_0, B_0, C_0, $\cdots$, M_0 are the residues of equation (6.10) at their respective poles. To obtain the z-transform of equation (6.11), it is necessary to know the z-transform of $1/s^n$. This can be found from tables or from equation (1.39). For discussing the critical behavior of the locus $HG^*(z)$ of equation (6.11), it is necessary to obtain the z-transform of the term corresponding to $1/s^n$ because it has the highest degree of z in its denominator. It can easily be shown that the first term of z-transform of

$$\frac{1 - e^{-Ts}}{s^n} \tag{6.12}$$

equals

$$\frac{T^{n-1}}{2} \frac{z + 1}{(z - 1)^{n-1}} \tag{6.13}$$

To obtain the locus of $HG^*(z)$ about $z = 1$, substitute for

$$z = \lim_{\rho \to 0} (1 + \rho e^{j\theta})$$

in equation (6.13). The locus of relation (6.13) is infinity at an angle $-(n - 1)\pi/2$ when $\theta = \pi/2$ and at an angle $(n - 1)\pi/2$ when $\theta = -\pi/2$. At $z = -1$, the z-transform of equation (6.11) is real, as discussed previously. The significance of higher-order poles at $z = 1$ of $HG^*(z)$ in sampled-data control systems lies in the fact that the steady-state sampled-error vanishes when certain input functions are fed to the system, as explained in Chapter 3.

4. *Effect of lead and lag networks on shaping $HG^*(z)$ loci.* When lead or lag networks are inserted to shape the continuous transfer locus $H(s)\,G(s)$ in continuous control systems, the asymptotic values of the transfer loci usually do not change for $\omega = 0$ and $\omega = \infty$, but the effect of such networks lies primarily in shaping $H(s)\,G(s)$ between these two frequencies. In contrast to this, the effect of inserting lead or lag networks in sampled-data control systems would change the asymptotic value of $HG^*(z)$ at $z = -1$; consequently, the entire shape of $HG^*(z)$ is altered. Under certain conditions, the $HG^*(z)$ locus may cross the real axis at one or two points, depending on the values of lead or lag introduced and on the system constants; the system might therefore be unstable because of the insertion of either lead or lag networks. The effect of networks on a general-order sampled-data control system can be deduced from their effect on a second-order system containing a zero-order hold. Suppose that

$$H(s)\,G(s) = \frac{A(1 - e^{-Ts})}{s} \frac{1}{s(s + a)} \tag{6.14}$$

The corresponding z-transform, utilizing Table 1.1, is

$$HG^*(z) = \frac{AT}{a(z-1)} - \frac{A}{a^2}\frac{1-e^{-aT}}{z-e^{-aT}} \tag{6.15}$$

To test whether $HG^*(z)$ locus would cross the real axis of $HG^*(z)$-plane at points other than at $z = -1$, equate the imaginary part of equation (6.15) to zero. Since $z = \cos\phi + j\sin\phi$, then

$$\frac{-AT/a}{2(1-\cos\phi)} + \frac{A(1-e^{-aT})}{a^2[(1+e^{-2aT}) - 2e^{-aT}\cos\phi]} = 0 \tag{6.16}$$

Since equation (6.16) is of first degree in $\cos\phi$, there exists at most one value of ϕ in the range $0 < \phi < \pi$ that satisfies it. Therefore, the locus of $HG^*(z)$ given in equation (6.15) may be either one of the shapes shown in Figs. 6.5 and 6.6.

A network with transfer function $(1+\tau_1 s)/(1+\tau_2 s)$, where τ_1 and τ_2 are real, may be lead or lag, depending on whether $\tau_1 > \tau_2$ or $\tau_1 < \tau_2$. By inserting such a typical network into the system described by equation (6.14), the loop transfer function becomes

$$H(s)\,G(s) = \frac{A(1-e^{-Ts})}{s} \times \frac{1}{s(s+a)}\frac{1+\tau_1 s}{1+\tau_2 s} \tag{6.17}$$

The corresponding z-transform of equation (6.17) can be obtained using Table 1.1 as follows:

$$HG^*(z) = \frac{AT}{a(z-1)} - \frac{A}{a^2}\frac{1-e^{-aT}}{z-e^{-aT}}\frac{1-\tau_1 a}{1-\tau_2 a} - \frac{A\tau_2}{a}\frac{1-e^{-T/\tau_2}}{z-e^{-T/\tau_2}}\frac{1-\tau_1/\tau_2}{1-1/\tau_2 a} \tag{6.18}$$

To compare equation (6.18) with (6.15), the following remarks are important in the shaping of $HG^*(z)$ locus.

1. The first term of equation (6.18) is the same as that of equation (6.15), which indicates that this term is not influenced by one or n number of networks. The transfer locus contributed by this term is a straight line, as indicated earlier.

2. The second term of equation (6.18) is of the same form as the corresponding term of equation (6.15), except for a multiplying factor which is called *contraction factor*, the effect of which is to magnify or nullify the circle locus of the second term of equation (6.15), depending on τ_1 and τ_2.

In this connection it is important to mention that only the magnitude of the circle locus of equation (6.15) is changed, and not its shape.

3. A new term is added by equation (6.18), the locus of which is a circle whose center is a real axis and whose radius depends on τ_1/τ_2 and τ_2. This new circular locus is introduced through the pole $1/\tau_2$; the effect is partially to compensate for the effect of the circle of the second term. The final shape of $HG^*(z)$ depends on τ_1/τ_2 and τ_2, and by varying these values the shaping of $HG^*(z)$ can be effected. Although shaping is done by trial and error, the shapes of $HG^*(z)$ are limited to those shown in Figs. 6.5 and 6.6. In consequence, by plotting a few points of the $HG^*(z)$ locus, the final shape can be estimated.

The insertion of n networks of the type $(1 + \tau_1 s)/(1 + \tau_2 s)$ in equation (6.17) will introduce n additional terms in $HG^*(z)$ as shown in equation (6.6). The locus of each term is a circle whose magnitude and shape depend on the network constants. The final expected shape of $HG^*(z)$ was discussed in a previous section.

As an illustration, the transfer locus of equation (6.18) is plotted in the $HG^*(z)$-plane for the following values:

$$\left.\begin{aligned} A &= 1 \\ a &= 1 \\ T &= 1 \\ \tau_2 &= 0.2 \\ \tau_1/\tau_2 &= 0.5,\ 1,\ 2,\ 3,\ 4,\ 10 \end{aligned}\right\} \tag{6.19}$$

The various plots are shown in Fig. 6.7. It is observed that when the lead as measured by the ratio τ_1/τ_2 is small, the locus of $HG^*(z)$ crosses the real axis at two distinct points. As the lead is further increased, the crossover converges into one point only, that is, when $z = -1$. When further lead is introduced, the crossover point will be nearer the point $(-1, 0)$ and the system will tend to be unstable. Furthermore, when lag is introduced, that is, when $\tau_1/\tau_2 = 0.5$, the system will also tend to be less stable because the $HG^*(z)$ locus will cross the real axis at two distinct points where one of these points will be near the point $(-1, 0)$. Thus, there exists a certain value of lead that can be applied to this particular system below and above which the system will be less stable. Sampled-data control systems of this type will generally start to oscillate at one of two frequencies $\omega_r/2$ for $z = -1$, or at less than $\omega_r/2$ for complex value of z on the unit circle. This conclusion has been indicated in the discussion of the root-locus in Chapter 3.

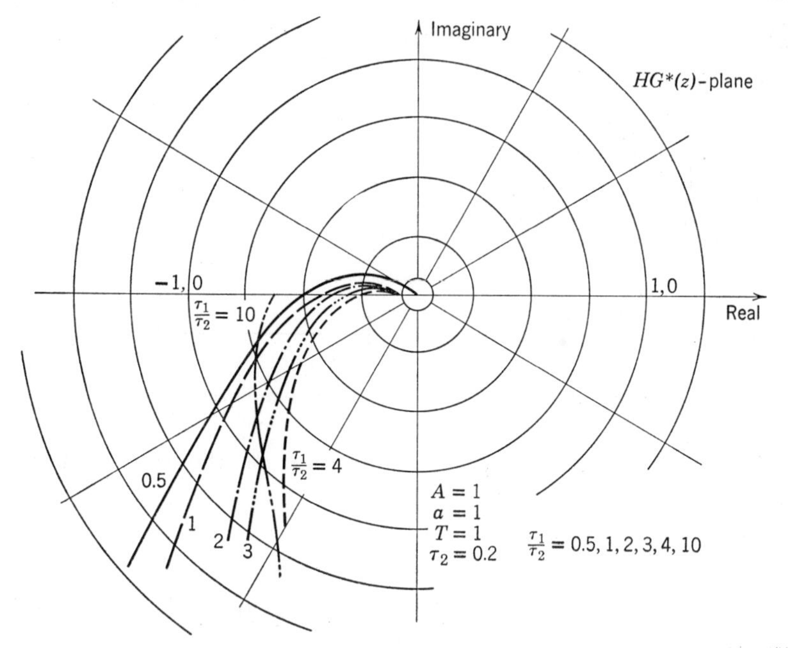

Figure 6.7 Locus plot of $HG^*(z)$ in example

6.3 Design Criterion for Sampled-Data Control Systems

The purpose of this section is to correlate the graphical-mathematical relationship between the shape of the system loci and the transient response of a second-order sampled-data control system subjected to step. Generalization to higher-order systems is indicated. Contours of constant gain and phase margins are plotted in $G^*(z)$-plane whereby shapes of transfer loci can be made to tally with design requirements as illustrated in a simple example.

6.4 General Relationship between Transient and Frequency Response of Second-Order Sampled-Data Systems †

Assume $G_2(s)$, for a system shown in Fig. 6.8, with unity feedback, given as

$$G_2(s) = \frac{{\omega_0}^2}{s(s + 2\omega_0\eta)} \tag{6.20}$$

† E. I. Jury, "Analysis and Synthesis of Sampled-Data Control Systems," Doctor of Engineering Science Thesis, Columbia University, New York, April 1953.

where ω_0 = undamped natural frequency of the second-order system;
η = damping ratio of the same system.

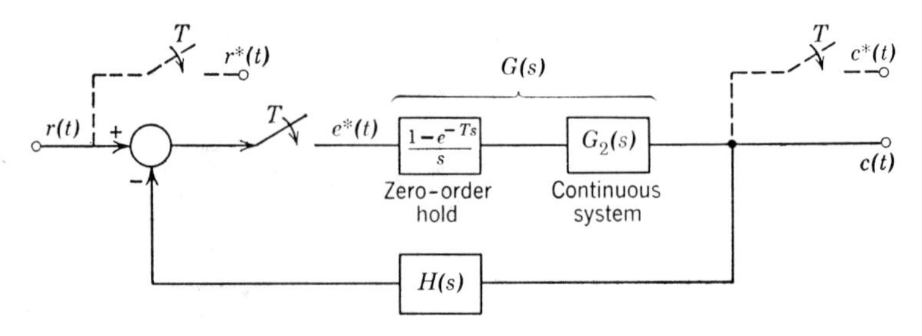

Figure 6.8 Sampled-data feedback system of second order

By utilizing Table 1.1, the z-transform of the system function $\frac{1 - e^{-Ts}}{s} G_2(s)$ can be written

$$\frac{G^*(z)}{1 + G^*(z)} = \frac{Az + B}{z^2 + Cz + D} \tag{6.21}$$

where

$$A = K_v \left(\frac{1}{2\omega_0 \eta T} e^{-2\omega_0 \eta T} + 1 - \frac{1}{2\omega_0 \eta T} \right) \tag{6.22}$$

$$B = K_v \left[1 - \frac{1}{\omega_0 \eta T} e^{-2\omega_0 \eta T} - \left(1 - \frac{1}{2\omega_0 \eta T} \right) (1 + e^{-2\omega_0 \eta T}) \right] \tag{6.23}$$

$$C = K_v - 1 - e^{-2\omega_0 \eta T} - K_v \frac{1}{2\omega_0 \eta T} (1 - e^{-2\omega_0 \eta T}) \tag{6.24}$$

$$D = e^{-2\omega_0 \eta T}(1 - K_v) + \frac{1}{2\omega_0 \eta T} K_v (1 - e^{-2\omega_0 \eta T}) \tag{6.25}$$

$$K_v = \frac{\omega_0 T}{2\eta} = \text{system velocity constant} \tag{6.26}$$

It is noticed that A, B, C, and D are constants depending on K_v and $1/2\omega_0 \eta T$ or on η and $\omega_0 T$. For the frequency response, let z describe the unit circle; then

$$z = e^{jT\omega} = \cos \phi + j \sin \phi \tag{6.27}$$

where ϕ needs to vary only from 0 to π.

By substituting for z in equation (6.21), the magnitude M is

$$M = \left| \frac{G^*(z)}{1 + G^*(z)} \right| = \frac{(B^2 + A^2 + 2AB\cos\phi)^{1/2}}{\left\{ \begin{array}{l} [C^2 + 2C(\cos\phi\cos 2\phi + \sin\phi\sin 2\phi) \\ \quad + 1 + D^2 + 2D(\cos 2\phi + C\cos\phi)]^{1/2} \end{array} \right\}} \tag{6.28}$$

Differentiate equation (6.28) with respect to ϕ to obtain the angle $\phi_{\max}$ for maximum M as follows:

$$\cos\phi_{\max} = -\frac{A^2 + B^2}{2AB} \pm \sqrt{\left(\frac{A^2 + B^2}{2AB}\right)^2 - \frac{\left\{ \begin{array}{l} C(A + B)(D + 1) + 2ABD \\ \quad - AB(C^2 + D^2 + 1) \end{array} \right\}}{4ABD}} \tag{6.29}$$

By substituting equation (6.29) into equation (6.28), it is observed that the $M_{\max}$ is a function of A, B, C, and D or alternately of η and $\omega_0 T$.

Having thus obtained the condition for $M_{\max}$, the transient response for a step of the same system can be readily derived. The modified z-transform † of the output can be formed using equation (2.43) as follows:

$$C^*(z, m) = \frac{z}{z - 1} \times \frac{G^*(z, m)}{1 + G^*(z)} \tag{6.30}$$

or

$$C^*(z, m) = \frac{K_v}{z} \frac{az^2 + bz + c}{z^2 + \alpha z + \beta} \times \frac{z}{z - 1} \tag{6.31}$$

where

$$\left. \begin{array}{l} a = u'e^{-m/u'} + m - u' \\ b = [1 - 2u'e^{-m/u'} - (m - u')(1 + e^{-1/u'})] \\ c = [u'e^{-m/u'} - (1 + u')e^{-1/u'} + me^{-1/u'}] \\ \alpha = K_v - (1 + e^{-1/u'}) - K_v u'(1 - e^{-1/u'}) \\ \beta = e^{-1/u'} - K_v e^{-1/u'} + u' K_v(1 - e^{-1/u'}) \\ u' = \dfrac{1}{2\omega_0 \eta T}, \qquad K_v = \dfrac{\omega_0 T}{2\eta} \end{array} \right\} \tag{6.32}$$

The output equals

$$c(n, m)T = \frac{1}{2\pi j} \int_\Gamma \frac{K_v(az^2 + bz + c)}{(z - 1)(z^2 + \alpha z + \beta)} z^{n-1}\, dz \tag{6.33}$$

† E. I. Jury, "Synthesis and Critical Study of Sampled-Data Control Systems," *Trans. A.I.E.E.*, Vol. 75, Pt. II, 1956, pp. 141–151.

where Γ is a path of integration in the z-plane that encloses all the singularities of the integrand in equation (6.33). The output can be of two forms, depending on whether the roots are real or complex. For real roots it can be easily shown that the continuous output is

$$c(n, m)T = 1 + \frac{K_v}{\alpha_1 - \alpha_2}\left[\frac{(a\alpha_1^2 + b\alpha_1 + c)}{\alpha_1 - 1}\alpha_1^{n-1} - \frac{(a\alpha_2^2 + b\alpha_2 + c)}{\alpha_2 - 1}\alpha_2^{n-1}\right], \; t = (n - 1 + m)T \quad (6.34)$$

where

$$\left.\begin{aligned} \alpha_1 &= -\frac{\alpha}{2} + \sqrt{\left(\frac{\alpha}{2}\right)^2 - \beta} \\ \alpha_2 &= -\frac{\alpha}{2} - \sqrt{\left(\frac{\alpha}{2}\right)^2 - \beta} \end{aligned}\right\} \quad (6.35)$$

For complex roots the continuous output

$$c(n, m)T = 1 + \frac{K_v}{\beta_1}\left[\frac{(a\alpha_1^2 - a\beta_1^2 + b\alpha_1 + c)^2 + \beta_1{}^2(2a\alpha_1 + b)^2}{(\alpha_1 - 1)^2 + \beta_1{}^2}\right]^{1/2}$$

$$\times (\alpha_1{}^2 + \beta_1{}^2)^{\frac{n-1}{2}} \sin[(n - 1)\theta + \lambda + \psi] \quad (6.36)$$

where

$$\left.\begin{aligned} \theta &= \tan^{-1}\frac{\beta_1}{\alpha_1} \\ \alpha_1 &= \frac{-\alpha}{2} \\ \beta_1 &= \sqrt{\beta - (\alpha/2)^2} \\ \lambda &= \tan^{-1}\frac{\beta_1(2a\alpha_1 + b)}{a(\alpha_1{}^2 - \beta_1{}^2) + b\alpha_1 + c} \\ \psi &= -\tan^{-1}\frac{\beta_1}{\alpha_1 - 1} \end{aligned}\right\} \quad (6.37)$$

The maximum response for both cases can be obtained as shown in Chapter 3, in which it can be observed that the total response or the overshoot is also a function of $(\omega_0 T)$ and η. Hence, a simple relationship between the maximum of frequency response and the maximum of

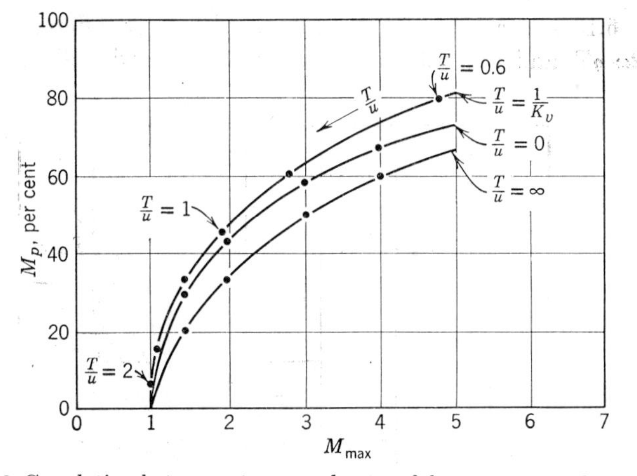

Figure 6.9 Correlation between step overshoot and frequency overshoot for second order system; the curve $T/u = 0$ represents the continuous system, and the curve $T/u = \infty$ represents an error-sampled system with purely integrating $G_2(s)$

TABLE 6.1

Correlation between $\mathbf{M}_p$ and $\mathbf{M}_{max}$

The correlation between M_p and M_{max}, as follows, has been obtained from †

If $\omega_0 T = 1$

$K_v = 1/T/u$, where $T/u = 2\omega_0 \eta T$

η	$\frac{T}{u}$	K_v	M_{max}	M_p, %
0.3	0.6	1.67	4.85	80
0.4	0.8	1.25	2.80	60
0.5	1.0	1.0	1.96	45
0.6	1.2	0.833	1.50	33
0.7	1.4	0.714	1.20	23
0.8	1.6	0.625	1.12	16
0.9	1.8	0.555	1.06	10
1.0	2.0	0.500	1.01	4.6

† E. I. Jury, "Analysis and Synthesis of Sampled-Data Control Systems," *Trans. A.I.E.E.*, Vol. 73, Pt. I, 1954, pp. 332–346, Figure 18.

transient response is established. Table 6.1 represents this relationship for different values of K_v as plotted in Fig. 6.9 and compared with the continuous system and the error-sampled system with purely integrating plant.†

† J. Sklansky, Network Compensation of Error-Sampled Feedback Systems," Technical Report No. T-11/B, April 1955, Columbia University, New York.

Figure 6.10 relates K_v versus peak overshoot for different values of $T/u = 2\omega_0\eta T$, and Fig. 6.11 relates the peak time with different values of T/u.

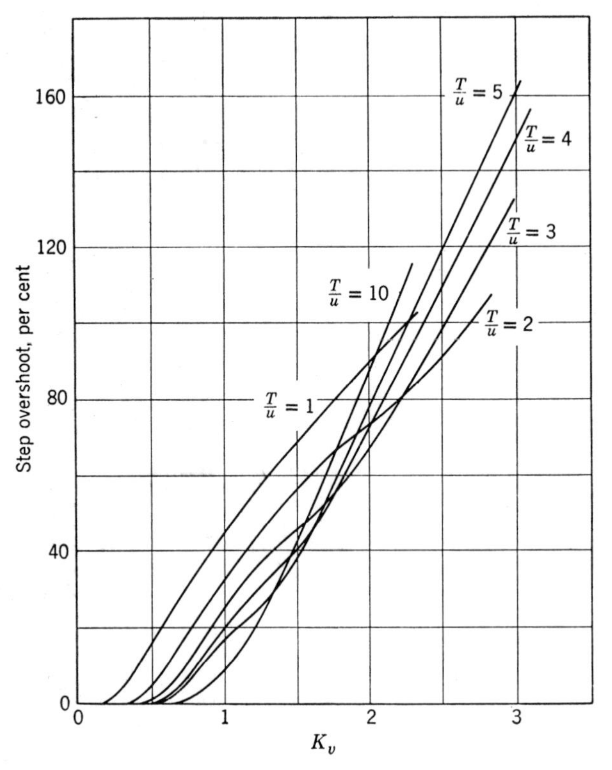

Figure 6.10 Correlation between step overshoot and K_v for second-order system

To obtain constant magnitude M and constant phase N contours, write for $G^*(z)$ the following:

$$G^*(z) = x^*(z) + j\, y^*(z) \tag{6.38}$$

constant magnitude M can be shown to fulfill the following

$$y^2 + \left(x + \frac{M^2}{M^2 - 1}\right)^2 = \frac{M^2}{(M^2 - 1)^2} \tag{6.39}$$

Equation (6.39) is a family of circles in the $HG^*(z)$-plane whose centers and radii are given by

$$x_0 = -\frac{M^2}{M^2 - 1}$$

$$y_0 = 0 \tag{6.40}$$

$$\text{Radius} = \frac{M}{M^2 - 1}$$

For constant phase N, write

$$\text{ang}\frac{C^*(z)}{R^*(z)} = \tan^{-1}\frac{y}{x} - \tan^{-1}\frac{y}{1+x} \tag{6.41}$$

By putting

$$\tan \text{ang}\frac{C^*}{R^*}(z) = N \tag{6.42}$$

equation (6.41) becomes

$$\left(x + \frac{1}{2}\right)^2 + \left(y - \frac{1}{2}N\right)^2 = \frac{1}{4}\left(\frac{N^2 + 1}{N^2}\right) \tag{6.43}$$

The contours of constant M and N are shown in Fig. 6.12.

An identical treatment for shaping $G^*(z)$ can be prepared for shaping $G^{-1}*(z)$ or the inverse $G^*(z)$ locus. The use of the locus leading to

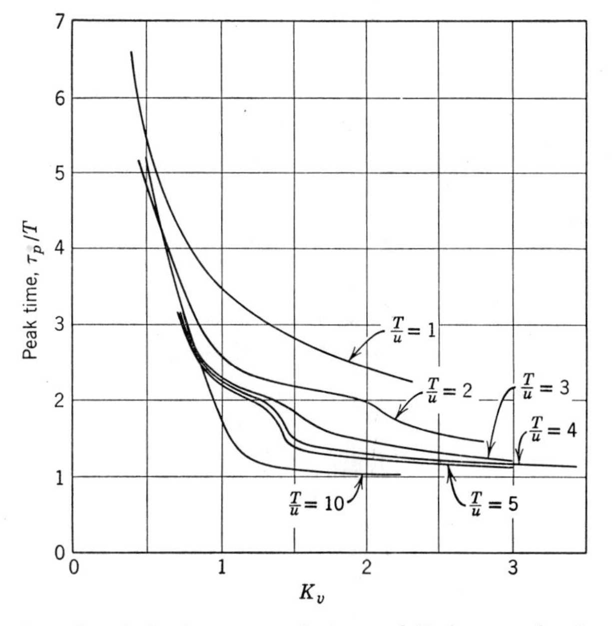

Figure 6.11 Correlation between peak time and K_v for second-order system

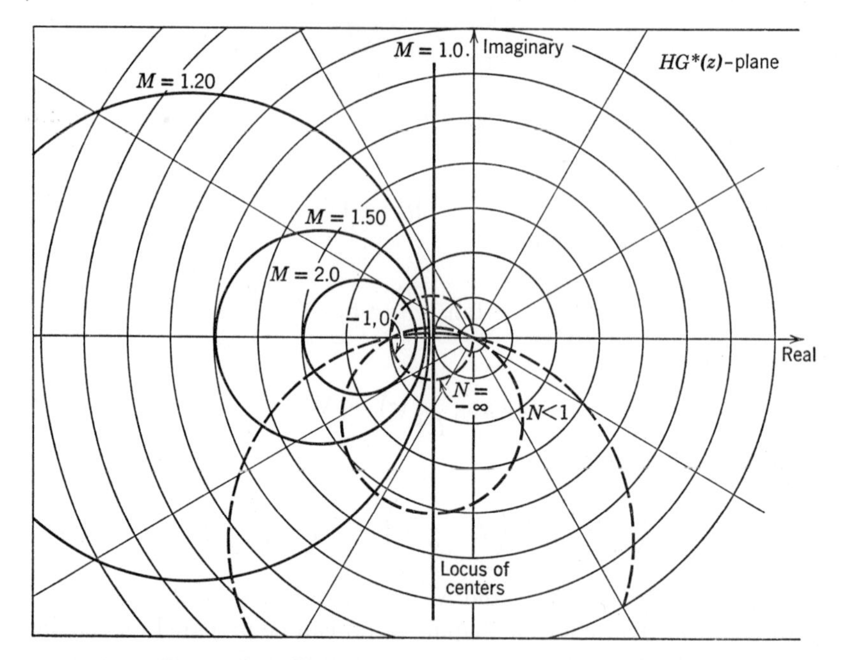

Figure 6.12 Constant M-N contours in $HG^*(z)$-plane

response $G^{-1*}(z)$ often simplifies studies which involve certain types of sampled-data control systems or the use of digital computers in stabilizing such systems.

Contours of constant magnitude M and constant phase N in the inverse plane can readily be deduced following the same procedure used in the $G^*(z)$-plane. It can easily be noted that the constant M contours have the following equation:

$$\frac{1}{M^2} = (1 + x)^2 + y^2 \tag{6.44}$$

equation (6.44) is a family of circles [as shown in Fig. (6.13)] of center and radii given by

$$\text{Center} = (-1, 0)$$

$$\text{Radius} = 1/M \tag{6.45}$$

Similarly for constant phase N

$$y + N(x + 1) = 0 \tag{6.46}$$

Equation (6.46) is represented by the family of radial lines in Fig. 6.13 emanating from the center of the constant M circles.

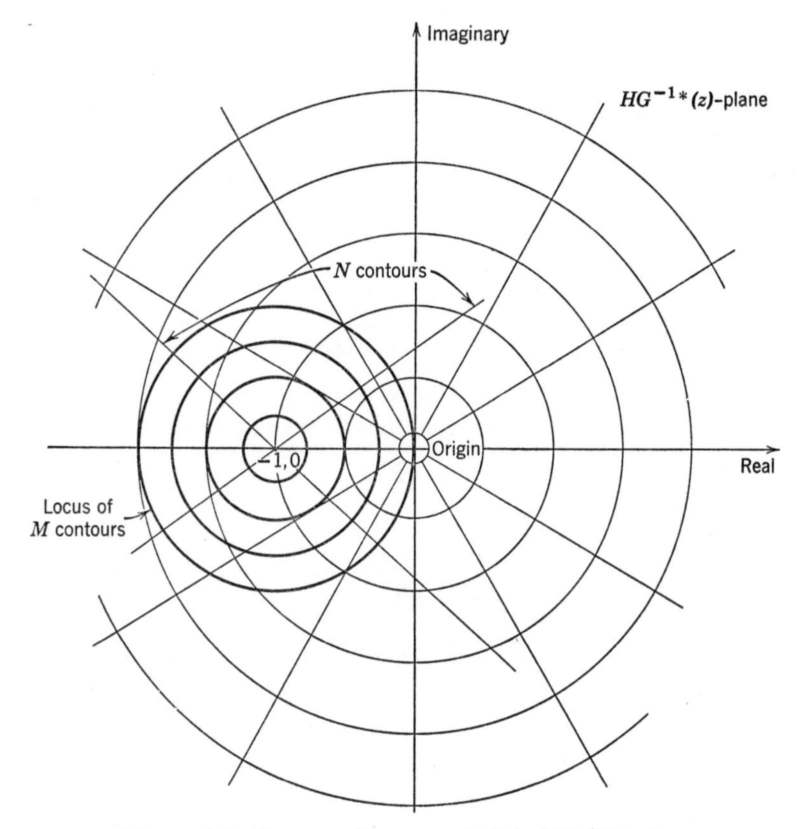

Figure 6.13 Contours of constant M-N in $HG^{-1*}(z)$-plane

ILLUSTRATIVE EXAMPLE

To illustrate a synthesis procedure based on the preceding material, an error-sampled data shown in Fig. 6.14 is analyzed and synthesized according to the following:

1. To obtain the value of gain K for $M_{\max} = 1.2$, when $k_0 = 0$.
2. To obtain $\omega_s T$ for $M_{\max} = 1.2$ ($\omega_s T$ = Resonant angle).
3. To obtain values of k_0 and τ that gives a resonant angle $\omega_s T \cong 75°$ for the same $M_{\max}$.

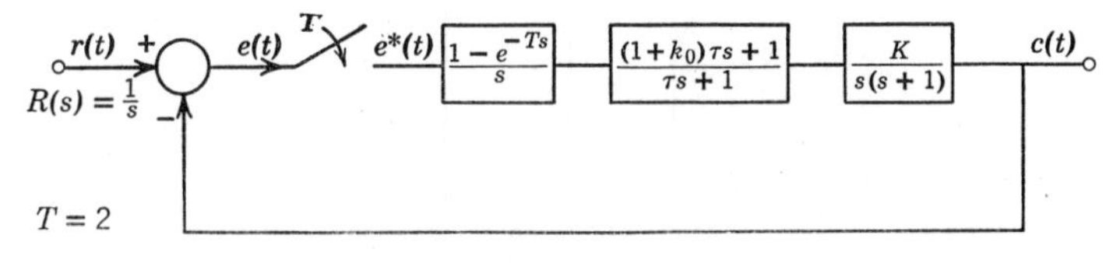

Figure 6.14 Sampled-data feedback system of example

4. To compare the compensated and uncompensated responses for a step input.

Solution

1. To obtain the value K required, first $KG^*(z)$ is found from tables:

$$KG^*(z) = K\left[\frac{T}{z-1} - \frac{1-e^{-T}}{z-e^{-T}}\right], \qquad \text{when } k_0 = 0 \tag{6.47}$$

For $T = 2$,

$$KG^*(z) = K\left[\frac{2}{z-1} - \frac{0.865}{z-0.135}\right] \tag{6.48}$$

The Nyquist plot of $KG^*(z)$ can be drawn for $K = 1$. The circle for $M_{\max} = 1.2$ can be found from equations (6.39) and (6.40) to have radius and center of:

$$\begin{aligned} \text{Radius} &= 2.73 \\ \text{Center} &= (0, -3.27) \end{aligned} \tag{6.49}$$

By locating a few points on the locus and its distances to the circle of $M_{\max}$, we find that the gain should be

$$K \cong 0.37 \tag{6.50}$$

The locus for this value of gain is shown in Fig. 6.15.

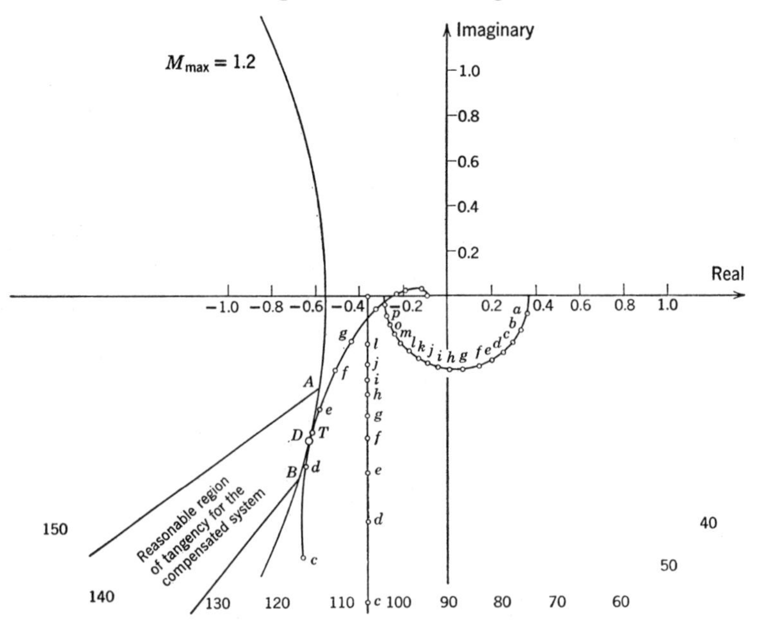

Figure 6.15 Nyquist plot of uncompensated system $k_0 = 0$

1. From the new locus it is found that

$$\omega_s T \cong 45^\circ \tag{6.51}$$

2. The pulsed transfer function for any value of k_0 can be found by obtaining the z-transform of $KG(s)$ including the network. This yields

$$KG^*(z) = \left[\frac{0.74}{z-1} + \frac{0.37k_0\tau}{(1-1/\tau)}\frac{1-e^{-2/\tau}}{z-e^{-2/\tau}} + \frac{[1-(1+k_0)\tau]0.37}{\tau-1}\frac{1-e^{-T}}{z-e^{-T}}\right] \tag{6.52}$$

since the period T is fixed at $T = 2$ seconds. Therefore, equation (6.52) can be written as

$$KG^*(z) = \left(\frac{0.74}{z-1} + \frac{k_1}{z-e^{-2/\tau}} + \frac{k_2}{z-0.135}\right) \tag{6.53}$$

$$\left.\begin{aligned} k_1 &= \frac{0.37k_0\tau}{\left(\dfrac{\tau-1}{\tau}\right)}(1-e^{-2/\tau}) \\ k_2 &= \frac{0.37[1-(1+k_0)\tau]}{\tau-1}(1-0.135) \end{aligned}\right\} \tag{6.54}$$

Before proceeding in choosing τ and k_0 to fulfill the design requirement, it is important to indicate the following points.

1. In equation (6.53) $KG^*(z)$ is composed of three vectors which assume certain magnitude and phase as z traverses the unit circle. For a fixed z in equation (6.53) the phase angle is fixed but the magnitude of the vectors changes. Therefore, k_1 and k_2 affect only the magnitude of the vectors but not the phase. The angular contribution of $(z - 0.135)$ as z varies is shown in Fig. 6.16. The reciprocal of this vector has the same angle but with a negative sign. For the design requirements $KG^*(z)$ should be tangential to $M_{\max} = 1.2$ when $z = e^{j75^\circ}$, or when z has an angle of 75° which corresponds to point g' in Fig. 6.16.

2. From Fig. 6.15 it is seen that a reasonable point of tangency to $M_{\max} = 1.2$ is between A and B. Any point higher than A or lower than B will let the locus $KG^*(z)$ cut into the M circle, either after or before the tangent point. Therefore, a point D is selected at which the locus of the compensated locus is to be tangent to $M_{\max}$ circle.

Figure 6.17 shows the tangency point D and the locus of $0.74/(z-1)$ and also the *locus-amplitude* of $k_2/(z - 0.135)$ at $z = e^{j75^\circ}$. A little trial shows that one of the terms of $KG^*(z)$ has to be negative so that the sum of all the vectors at $z = e^{j75^\circ}$ will be at the point D. In order to get a

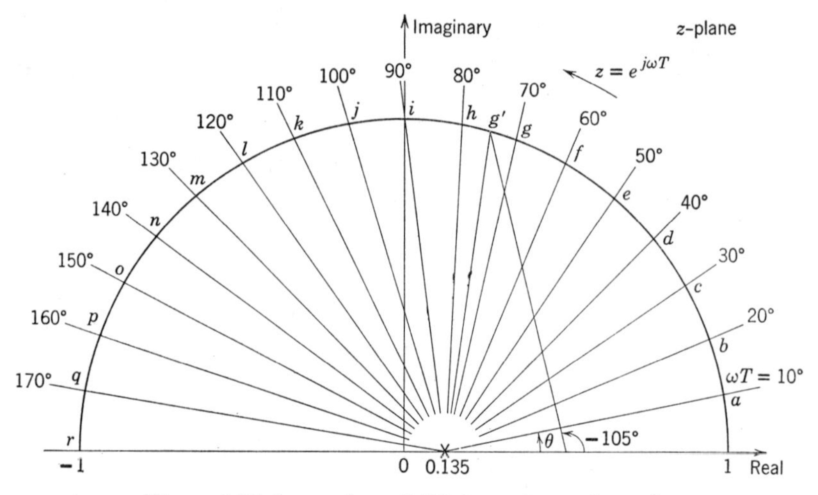

Figure 6.16 Locus of $z - 0.135$ for various values of z

compensator having a pole at the positive real axis, the negative term is chosen to be the third term of the right side of equation (6.53).

To obtain a reasonable range for the vector $k_2/(z - 0.135)$, it is estimated in Fig. 6.17 to be from $\mathbf{Og'}_1$ to $\mathbf{Og'}_2$ when $z = e^{j75°}$. By taking

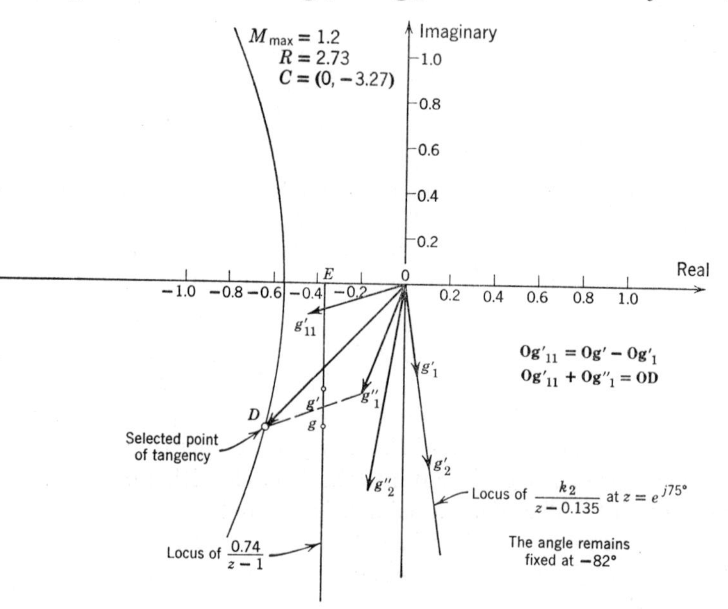

Figure 6.17 Graphical construction of data using the network compensated parameter

$\mathbf{Og'}_1$ vector first, the following vector equation can be written:

$$\mathbf{OD} = \mathbf{Og'} - \mathbf{Og'}_1 + \mathbf{Og''}_1 \tag{6.55}$$

Knowing $\mathbf{OD}$, $\mathbf{Og'}$, $\mathbf{Og'}_1$, we can calculate $\mathbf{Og''}_1$, and similarly we can also obtain $\mathbf{Og''}_2$ for the second range of the vector $k_2/(z - 0.135)$ as indicated in Fig. 6.17. Also, it is noticed from the same figure that the third vector to be calculated, that is, either $\mathbf{Og''}_1$ or $\mathbf{Og''}_2$ must have an angular contribution of approximately $-100°$ to $-112°$. By referring to Fig. 6.16 it is seen that a pole at $z = 0.5$ contributes an angle of $-105°$ when $z = e^{j75°}$ which is approximately the average of these two limits. Therefore, we can choose that compensator pole at $z = 0.5$; thus $KG^*(z)$ from equation (6.53) becomes:

$$KG^*(z) = \frac{0.74}{z-1} + \frac{k_1}{z-0.5} - \frac{k'_2}{z-0.135} \tag{6.56}$$

It follows from equations (6.53) and (6.54) that

$$\left.\begin{aligned} \tau &= 2.86 \\ k_1 &= 0.815k_0 \\ k_2 &= -k'_2 = -0.172(1.86 + 2.86k_0) \end{aligned}\right\} \tag{6.57}$$

Thus, equation (6.56) becomes

$$KG^*(z) = \left[\frac{0.74}{z-1} + \frac{0.815k_0}{z-0.5} - \frac{0.172(1.86 + 2.86k_0)}{z-0.135}\right] \tag{6.58}$$

3. To obtain the second parameter k_0 we can fix the value of $KG^*(z)$ at some value of z, which can conveniently be at ($z = -1$). Hence, equation (6.58) becomes

$$KG^*(z)\,|_{z=-1} = -0.085 - 0.11k_0 \tag{6.59}$$

If the locus is not to cut into the $M_{\max}$ circle, it should start fairly close to the origin on the negative real axis. The uncompensated locus starts at -0.04. In this case a point -0.16 is chosen. Substituting this value into equation (6.59), we obtain the value of k_0 as:

$$k_0 \cong 0.682 \tag{6.60}$$

The compensated locus finally becomes:

$$KG^*(z) = \frac{0.74}{z-1} + \frac{0.555}{z-0.5} - \frac{0.655}{z-0.135} \tag{6.61}$$

This locus is plotted in Fig. 6.18 where it is seen that the curve is tangent at point T when $z = e^{j72°}$, which is very close to the design requirements. More trials will bring the tangency point at $\omega_s T = 75°$. However, this is not needed in a way of illustration.

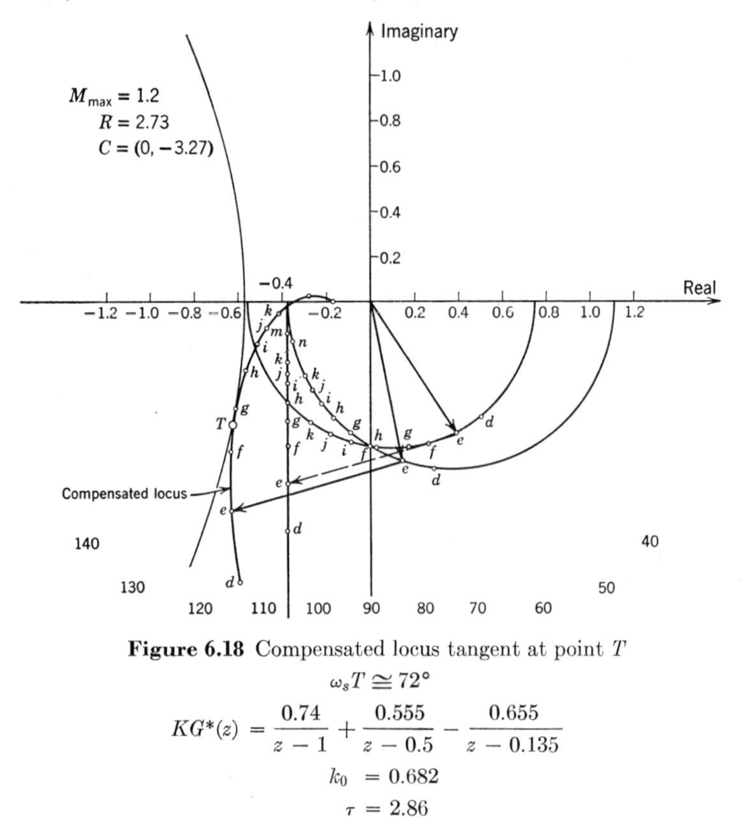

Figure 6.18 Compensated locus tangent at point T

$$\omega_s T \cong 72°$$

$$KG^*(z) = \frac{0.74}{z-1} + \frac{0.555}{z-0.5} - \frac{0.655}{z-0.135}$$

$$k_0 = 0.682$$

$$\tau = 2.86$$

4. The modified z-transform of the output is obtained for both the compensated and the uncompensated system responses, and this is plotted in Fig. 6.19. It is noticed that the rise time is considerably improved as expected, and the overshoot is about the same in view of the same requirement on $M_{\max}$.

It is seen from this example that the procedure is straightforward in the choice of parameters for one network. Furthermore, it can also be applied for compensation of more than one network. However, the trial and error procedures become more involved because of the increasing number of choices required. Thus a recourse to approximation could be helpful as discussed in the next sections.

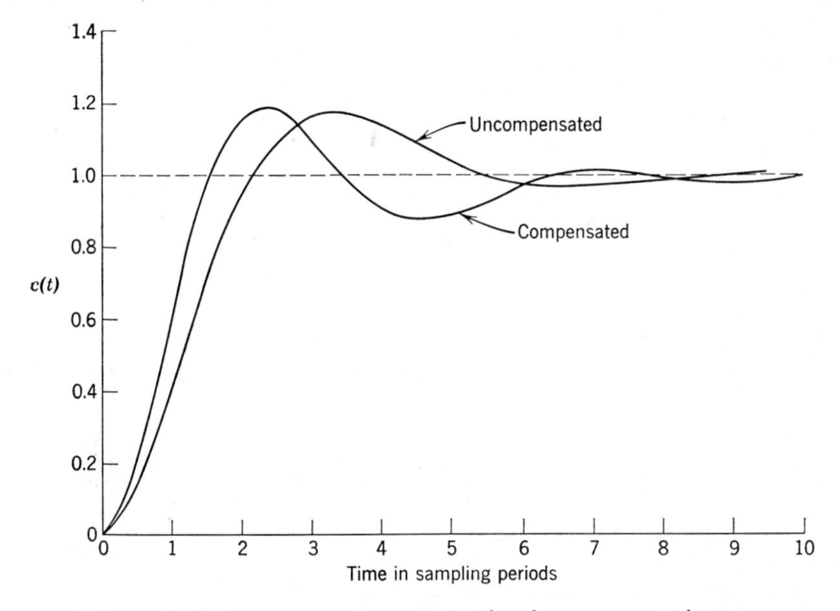

Figure 6.19 Step response of compensated and uncompensated system

6.5 The z-s Approximation Method of Synthesis †

The preceding method is an exact procedure for plotting and shaping the Nyquist locus in the $KG^*(z)$ plane. It has been indicated that shaping is based on trial and error procedure and sometimes can be quite involved if more than one or two networks are desired for compensation.

In the following, an approximate procedure derived by Sklansky † is presented. Although useful under certain conditions, the procedure does not remove completely the network restrictions discussed in the earlier method.

This approximate procedure, which is also called the z-s approximation method, is based on fictitiously sampling the output plant with multiple values of the sampling frequency and introducing a mathematical hold to reconstruct the sampled information. This is indicated in approximat-

† The z-s approximation method discussed in this chapter is obtained from parts of a Doctor of Engineering Science Thesis by Dr. J. Sklansky, published in a report entitled, "Network Compensation of Error-Sampled Feedback Systems," Technical Report No. T-11/B, April 1955, Columbia University, New York. The author is grateful to Dr. J. Sklansky for permitting the inclusion of part of his thesis in the discussion of this section.

ing the system of Fig. 6.20a by an equivalent system shown in Fig. 6.20b.

It is noted that $\hat{c}(t)$ is an approximation of $c(t)$ the actual output.

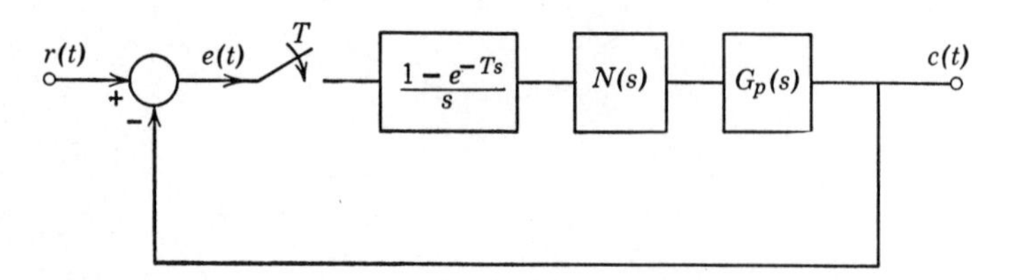

Figure 6.20*a* Network compensated sampled-data feedback system

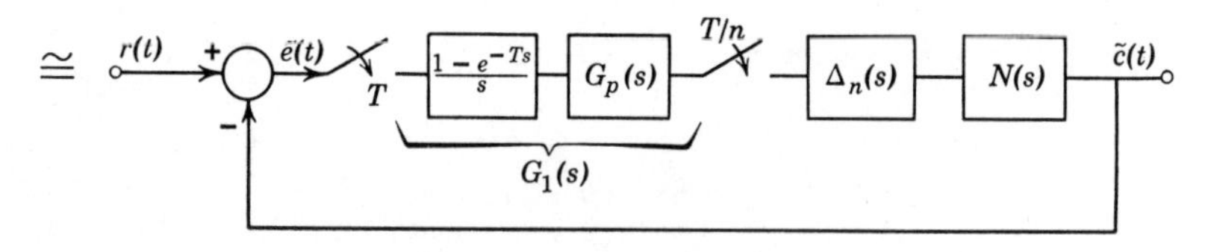

Figure 6.20*b* The z-s approximation of Fig. 6.20a

This approximation depends on n and $\Delta_n s$ and the larger n is the closer the approximation, but unfortunately the shaping procedure becomes more involved as n increases.

The type of computational hold used in this approximation is called bandwidth-limited hold as shown in Fig. 6.21. At this point it is worth-

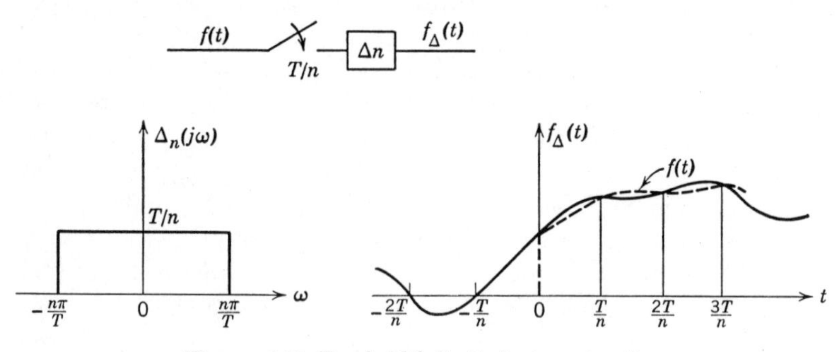

Figure 6.21 Bandwidth-limited approximation

while to mention that we may use other types of holds such as boxcar or triangle holds. However, the choice of the former in this system has proved to be convenient.

6.6 Mathematical Formulation

To calculate the effect of the network compensation, we have to decide on what value of n is to be used. For instance, for $n = 1$,

$$G_1N^*(z) \cong G_1{}^*(z) \times \Delta_1 N^*(z) \tag{6.62}$$

where

$$\Delta_1 N^*(z) = \mathfrak{z}\,[\Delta_1(s)\,N(s)] \tag{6.63}$$

It is seen from equation (6.62) that with introduction of the fictitious sampler the effect of the compensating network is untangled from $G_1N^*(z)$, which simplifies the procedure of shaping when $n = 1$.

For the case $n = 2$, the reader is referred to the material at the beginning of Chapter 2 where the submultiple method of obtaining the response between sampling instants is discussed. The output z-transform is given

$$\tilde{C}^*(z_2) = \left\{\sum_{k=0}^{\infty} [r(kT) - \tilde{c}(kT)]\, z_2{}^{-2k}\right\} G_1{}^*(z_2) \times \Delta_2 N^*(z_2) \tag{6.64}$$

where

$$z_2 = e^{sT/2}, \qquad \text{by definition } z_2\text{-transform of } \tilde{c}(t) = \tilde{C}^*(z_2) \tag{6.65}$$

Also

$$\tilde{C}^*(z_2) = \tilde{c}(0) + \tilde{c}\left(\frac{T}{2}\right) z_2{}^{-1} + \tilde{c}(T)\, z_2{}^{-2} + \tilde{c}\left(\frac{3T}{2}\right) z_2{}^{-3} + \cdots \tag{6.66}$$

Thus

$$\sum_{k=0}^{\infty} \tilde{c}(kT)\, z_2^{-2k} = \text{Even part of } \tilde{C}^*(z_2) = \text{Odd part of } z_2^{-1}\,\tilde{C}^*(z_2) \tag{6.67}$$

Furthermore,

$$\sum_{k=0}^{\infty} r(kT)\, z_2^{-2k} = \mathfrak{z}\,[R(s)]_{z=z_2^2} = R^*(z_2^2) \tag{6.68}$$

Therefore,

$$\tilde{C}^*(z_2) = [R^*(z_2{}^2) - \mathcal{P}\,\tilde{C}^*(z_2)]\,\Delta_2 N^*(z_2)\,G_1{}^*(z_2) \tag{6.69}$$

where

$$\mathcal{P}\,[\tilde{C}^*(z_2)] = \text{Even part of } \tilde{C}^*(z_2)$$

Taking the even part of both sides of equation (6.69) we obtain

$$\mathcal{P}\,[\tilde{C}^*(z_2)] = [R^*(z_2{}^2) - \mathcal{P}\,\tilde{C}^*(z_2)]\,\mathcal{P}\,[\Delta_2 N^*(z_2)\,G_1{}^*(z_2)] \tag{6.70}$$

or

$$\mathcal{P}\,[\tilde{C}^*(z_2)] = \frac{R^*(z_2{}^2)\,\mathcal{P}\,[G_1{}^*(z_2)\,\Delta_2 N^*(-z_2)]}{1 + \mathcal{P}\,[G_1{}^*(z_2)\,\Delta_2 N^*(z_2)]} \tag{6.71}$$

Now, taking the odd part of equation (6.69), we get

$$\mathcal{O}\,\tilde{C}^*(z_2) = R^*(z_2{}^2)\,\mathcal{O}\,[\Delta_2 N^*(z_2)\,G_1{}^*(z_2)] - \mathcal{P}[\tilde{C}^*(z_2)]\,\mathcal{O}\,[\Delta_2 N^*(z_2)\,G_1{}^*(z_2)] \tag{6.72}$$

Substituting for $\mathcal{P}\,[\tilde{C}^*(z_2)]$ from equation (6.71) into the above we obtain for $\mathcal{O}\,[\tilde{C}^*(z_2)]$ the following:

$$\left\{R^*(z_2{}^2) - \frac{R^*(z_2{}^2)\,\mathcal{P}\,[G_1{}^*(z_2)\,\Delta_2 N^*(z_2)]}{1 + \mathcal{P}\,[G_1{}^*(z_2)\,\Delta_2 N^*(z_2)]}\right\}\mathcal{O}\,[\Delta_2 N^*(z_2)\,G_1{}^*(z_2)] \tag{6.73}$$

Simplifying this expression, we get

$$\mathcal{O}\,[\tilde{C}^*(z_2)] = \frac{R^*(z_2{}^2)\,\mathcal{O}\,[\Delta_2 N^*(z_2)\,G_1{}^*(z_2)]}{1 + \mathcal{P}\,G_1{}^*(z_2)\,\Delta_2 N^*(z_2)} \tag{6.74}$$

It is seen from equations (6.71) and (6.74) that, for the total respon e,† the even part of $G_1{}^*(z_2)\,\Delta_2 N^*(z_2)$ is important for synthesis and shaping. Note that

$$G_1{}^*(z) = \text{Even part of } G_1{}^*(z_2) \equiv \tfrac{1}{2}[G_1{}^*(z_2) + G_1{}^*(-z_2)] \tag{6.76}$$

Thus, for $n = 2$,

$$G_1 N^*(z) \cong \tfrac{1}{2}[G_1{}^*(z_2)\,\Delta_2\,N^*(z_2) + G_1{}^*(-z_2)\,\Delta_2 N^*(-z_2)] \tag{6.77}$$

Similarly for larger n,

$$G_1 N^*(z) \cong \frac{1}{n}\sum_{k=0}^{n-1} G_1{}^*(z_n e^{j2\pi k/n})\,\Delta_n N^*(z_n e^{j2\pi k/n}) \tag{6.78}$$

The preceding equation can be easily derived by showing the identity of the following relation,

$$C^*(z) = \frac{1}{n}\sum_{k=0}^{n-1} C^*(z_n e^{j2\pi k/n}) \qquad (6.79)\ ‡$$

To show the identity of this equation, expand the right side as follows:

$$\sum_{k=0}^{n-1} C^*(z_n e^{j2\pi k/n}) = C^*(z_n) + C^*(z_n e^{j2\pi/n}) + C^*(z_n e^{j4\pi/n}) + \cdots + C^*(z_n e^{j2\pi\frac{n-1}{n}}) \tag{6.80}$$

† The total response transform can be obtained by using the following identity:

$$\tilde{C}^*(z_2) = \mathcal{P}\,[\breve{C}^*(z_2)] + \mathcal{O}\,[\breve{C}^*(z_2)] \tag{6.75}$$

‡ This expression is identical to equation (2.55), where z_n, z, and n are substituted for $z_{T2} = e^{sT_1/n}$, $z_{T1} = e^{sT_1}$, and T_1/T_2 respectively.

$C^*(z_n)$ can be expanded in power series as follows:

$$C^*(z_n) = c(0)\, z_n{}^{-0} + c\left(\frac{T}{n}\right) z_n{}^{-1} + c\left(\frac{2T}{n}\right) z_n{}^{-2} + \cdots + c\left(\frac{kT}{n}\right) z_n{}^{-k} + \cdots + c(T)\, z_n{}^{-n} + \cdots \tag{6.81}$$

Similarly, $C^*(z_n e^{j2\pi/n})$ and other terms can be expanded to yield

$$C^*(z_n e^{j2\pi/n}) = c(0)\, z_n{}^{-0} + c\left(\frac{T}{n}\right) z_n{}^{-1} e^{-j2\pi/n} + c\left(\frac{2T}{n}\right) z_n{}^{-2} e^{-j4\pi/n} + \cdots + c(T)\, z_n{}^{-n} e^{-j2\pi} + \cdots$$

$$\vdots$$

$$C^*(z_n e^{j2\pi(n-1)/n}) = c(0)\, z_n{}^{-0} + c\left(\frac{T}{n}\right) z_n{}^{-1} e^{-j2\pi(n-1)/n} + c\left(\frac{2T}{n}\right) z_n{}^{-2} \times e^{-j4\pi(n-1)/n} + \cdots + c(T)\, z_n{}^{-n} e^{-j2\pi(n-1)} + \cdots \tag{6.82}$$

Add equations (6.81) and (6.82) and note that

$$c(T/n)\, z_n{}^{-1} + c(T/n)\, z_n{}^{-1}\, e^{-j2\pi/n} + c(T/n)\, z_n{}^{-1}\, e^{-j4\pi/n} + \cdots + c(T/n)\, z_n{}^{-1}\, e^{-j2\pi(n-1)/n} = 0 \tag{6.83}$$

and that similar other terms also equal zero. Thus,

$$\sum_{k=0}^{n-1} C^*(z_n e^{j2\pi k/n}) = n[c(0)\, z_n^{-0} + c(T)\, z_n^{-n} + c(2T)\, z_n^{-2n} + \cdots] = n[c(0) + c(T)\, z^{-1} + c(2T)\, z^{-2} + \cdots] \tag{6.84}$$

which is equal to

$$\sum_{k=0}^{n-1} C^*(z_n e^{j2\pi k/n}) = n\, C^*(z) \tag{6.85}$$

6.7 The z-s Approximation

If we choose $\Delta_n(s)$ to be a rectangular frequency characteristic indicated in Fig. 6.21, the following relation can easily be noted:

$$\Delta_n N^*(z_n) = \frac{n}{T} \sum_{k=-\infty}^{k=\infty} \Delta_n(s + jkn\omega_r)\, N(s + jkn\omega_r) \tag{6.86}$$

$$= N(s), \qquad \text{for } s = j\omega,\ |\omega| < \frac{n\omega_r}{2}$$

This equation is recognized as the infinite summation of the z-transform (also called the Poisson's summation), which is equal to $N(s)$ because

$$\Delta_n(s)\big|_{s=j\omega} = \begin{Bmatrix} T/n \text{ for } |\omega| < n\omega_r/2 \\ 0 \text{ elsewhere} \end{Bmatrix} \tag{6.87}$$

Therefore, equations (6.62), (6.76), and (6.77) become: For $n = 1$,

$$G_1N^*(z) \cong G_1^*(z)\, N(s) \tag{6.88}$$

For $n = 2$,

$$G_1N^*(z) \cong \tfrac{1}{2}[G_1^*(z_2)\, N(s) + G_1^*(-z_2)\, N(s - j\omega_r)] \tag{6.89}$$

For n = any positive integer,

$$G_1N^*(z) \cong \frac{1}{n} \sum_k G_1^*(z_n e^{j2\pi k/n}) N(s + jk\omega_r) \tag{6.90}$$

$$k = \underbrace{0,\ -1,\ 1,\ -2,\ 2 \cdots + \frac{n-1}{2} \text{ if } n \text{ is odd, } \frac{-n}{2} \text{ if } n \text{ is even}}_{n \text{ elements}}$$

This z–s approximation is valid for $0 \leq \omega \leq \omega_r/2$ when n is odd and for $0 \leq \omega \leq \omega_r$ when n is even.

6.8 Design Procedure Using the z-s Approximation

The following steps can be initially applied for design using this method.

1. Starting with the locus

$$\mathfrak{z}_2 \left[\frac{1 - e^{-sT}}{s} G_p(s) \right]_{z_2 = e^{j\omega T/2}} \tag{6.91}$$

obtain $G_1^*(z)$, using the relation

$$G_1^*(z) = \text{Even part of } G_1^*(z_2) = \tfrac{1}{2}[G_1^*(z_2) + G_1^*(-z_2)] \tag{6.92}$$

A convenient geometric technique can be applied to this identity. The points

$$G_1^*(z_2)\big|_{z_2 = e^{j\omega T/2}} \quad \text{and} \quad G_1^*(z_2)\big|_{z_2 = e^{j(\omega T - 2\pi)/2}} \tag{6.93}$$

are joined by a straight-line segment, and the midpoint of this line is a point on the locus $G_1^*(z)$.

From $G_1^*(z)$ we can determine the uncompensated $M_{\max}$ and ω_s from M-N circles in $G_1^*(z)$-plane.

2. Choose a structure of $N(s)$ usually based on experience.
3. Choose parameters of $N(s)$ such as the locus for $n = 2$.

$$\tfrac{1}{2}[G_1^*(z_2)\, N(s) + G_1^*(-z_2)\, N(s - j\omega_r)] \tag{6.94}$$

will have the desired $M_{\max}$ and ω_s (compensated parameters).

The first term of this equation can be used as a rough approximation, and the second term can be used as a correction locus. Furthermore, this second locus is a measure of the error.

4. Compute

$$G_1N^*(z) = \mathfrak{z}\left[\frac{1 - e^{-sT}}{s} N(s)\, G_p(s)\right] \tag{6.95}$$

To obtain the exact locus of the response quantities, this locus will serve as a final check on the previous approximation.

Illustrative Example

To illustrate the design procedures for the z–s approximation method, the same system designed in the previous example is to be checked with this procedure.

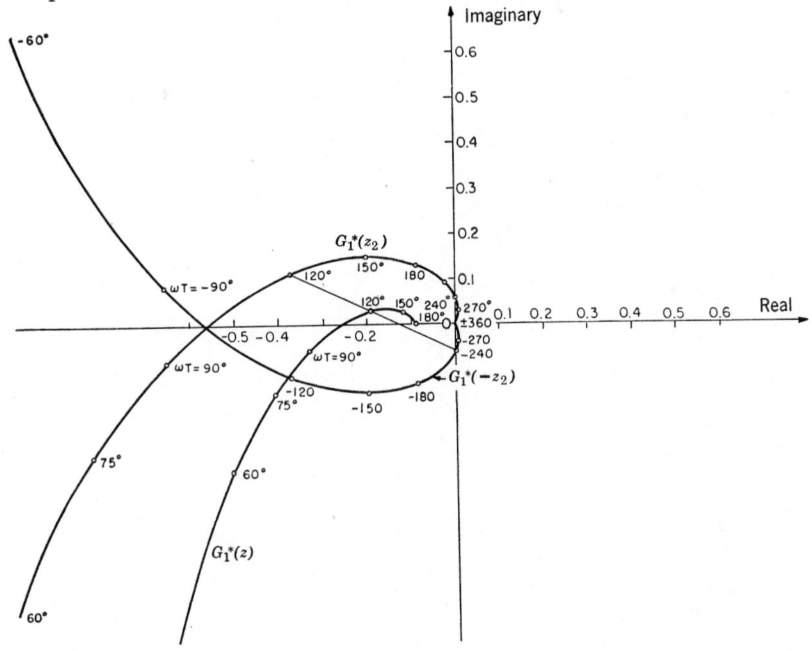

Figure 6.22 Construction of $G_1^*(z)$ from $G_1^*(z_2)$

The $G_1^*(z_2)$ of $G_1(s)$ is found as follows:

$$\mathfrak{z}_2\,[G_1(s)] = \mathfrak{z}_2\left[\frac{0.37}{s^2(s+1)}\right]\frac{z_2^{\,2}-1}{z_2^{\,2}} = \frac{0.136(z_2^{\,1}+0.718)}{(z_2-1)(z_2-0.368)}(1+z_2^{\,-1}),$$

$$T_2 = 1 = T/2 \qquad (6.96)$$

$G_1^*(z)$ is obtained from $G_1^*(z_2)$ graphically as shown in Fig. 6.22.

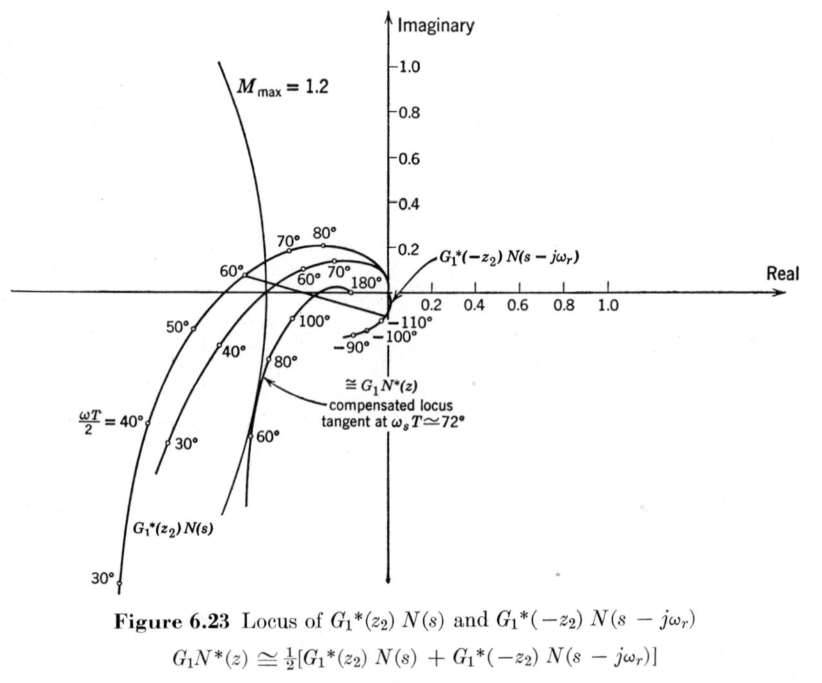

Figure 6.23 Locus of $G_1^*(z_2)\,N(s)$ and $G_1^*(-z_2)\,N(s-j\omega_r)$

$$G_1N^*(z) \cong \tfrac{1}{2}[G_1^*(z_2)\,N(s) + G_1^*(-z_2)\,N(s-j\omega_r)]$$

$$\omega_r = \frac{2\pi}{T} = \pi$$

The network compensator is assumed the same as found in the previous example. Thus:

$$N(s) = 1.682\,\frac{s+0.208}{s+0.35} \qquad (6.97)$$

The compensated locus for $n = 2$ as given in equation (6.98) is plotted in Fig. 6.23.

$$G_1N^*(z) \cong \tfrac{1}{2}[G_1^*(z_2)\,N(s) + G_1^*(-z_2)\,N(s-j\omega_r)] \qquad (6.98)$$

It is noticed that this locus is tangent to $M_{\max} = 1.2$ at $\omega_s T = 70°$.

For this system the locus matches the exact locus very closely, which indicates that for a second-order system $n = 2$ in the z–s approximation is justified.

Furthermore, we can also obtain $N(s)$ directly from the z–s approximation method which requires trial and error not simpler than the exact procedure discussed in the preceding method.

Similar to the exact method the z–s approximation can be very useful in obtaining the parameters of a simple network as discussed in the example. However, for a general-order network and for $n > 2$ in the z–s method, the design procedure becomes more involved and trial and error procedures become more emphasized. If the order of the system is more than two, Linvill's procedure, which is also called the Poisson sum approximation, is useful in obtaining rough engineering criteria for the network compensator parameters.

The w-transform † method as applied for discrete compensation can also be applied in network compensation, in which case the Nyquist plot is superseded by the Bode diagram. This extension might prove of some value; however, the degrees of approximation discussed earlier still exist.

6.9 Extension to General-Order Systems

The correlation between frequency response quantities and transient response is obtained for the most part for second-order sampled-data control systems. However, it is difficult to extend the correlation for any order system similar to the continuous feedback systems. The general effect of the location of the poles and zeros of the transfer function of a sampled-data system on the step response quantities has been investigated.‡ In the mentioned reference, theorems are given relating to the necessary conditions for the production of monotonic and non-monotonic time response expressed in terms of pole and zero location in the z-plane. It is shown that, under certain conditions of pole and zero locations, the normalized time sequence response may well be approximated by a single dominant time term. A method is presented of ascertaining from the pole and zero location whether these conditions exist.

On the basis of dominant-term approximation,‡ the methods of synthesis and design charts obtained earlier for second-order systems can also

† G. W. Johnson, E. P. Lindorff, and C. G. A. Nordling, "Extension of Continuous-Data Design Technique to Sampled-Data Control Systems," *Trans. A.I.E.E.*, Vol. 74, Pt. II, 1955, pp. 252–263.

‡ E. I. Jury, "The Effect of Pole and Zero Location on the Transient Response of Sampled-Data Systems," *Trans. A.I.E.E.*, Vol. 74, Pt. II, 1955, pp. 41–48.

be applied with approximation to general-order systems. For instance, if a general-order system has the first pair of complex poles near the unit circle and all other complex and real poles are concentrated near the origin of the unit circle, the transient behavior of this system is well approximated by that of a second-order system. The effect of other poles and zeros on the dominant term approximation is discussed in detail in Chapter 3.

6.10 Time Domain Methods of Continuous Network Compensation

In the preceding sections, frequency response methods are introduced whereby the system frequency locus is shaped to tally with design requirement in the frequency domain. Similar to continuous feedback systems, sampled-data systems can be designed in time domain whereby the continuous network compensator can be determined from the time response quantities.

There exist several approaches for the synthesis problem using the continuous compensator. The promising approach as discussed in detail in this chapter is based on the discrete-compensation method. The philosophy of this approach is to approximate the impulsive response of the discrete compensator plus the zero-order hold by linear networks. The degree of approximation depends for the most part on the complexity of the network desired. In this manner the methods of discrete compensation discussed in the preceding chapter can be applied to this approach, which simplifies considerably the synthesis procedure.

In addition to the aforementioned method, there are several alternative procedures which are based on design of sampled-data systems at the sampling instants. One of the procedures, for instance, is to describe a continuous output whose sampled value coincides with the sampled response of the sampled-data control system. The second procedure is to consider the sampled-data system as a predictor with certain degree of prediction such as linear, quadratic, cubic, etc. The third approach, due to Linvill and Sittler,† is to design the linear networks through specifications of the error coefficients signal. All these methods will be discussed in various degrees of detail in this chapter, and the limitations and advantages of each will be indicated.

† W. K. Linvill and R. W. Sittler, "Extension of Conventional Techniques to the Design of Sampled-Data Systems," *I.R.E. Convention Record,* New York, Pt. I, 1953, pp. 95–104.

6.11 Network Compensation †

Practical realizability of compensating components cannot be overlooked in any design problem. Economic and physical situations always demand the simplest system. There are many cases in which network compensation (which is easy to realize) can be inserted in the system instead of the discrete compensator. Thus synthesis of such continuous compensators should not be overlooked and indeed warrants extensive investigation. This section is mainly concerned with a synthesis procedure whereby linear networks can be designed to yield a prescribed response of a sampled-data system.

The technique of network compensation proposed herein attempts to circumvent by time domain methods of approximation the multitude of difficulties encountered by network synthesis procedures in the frequency domain. The basis of the technique is the recognition that, for a particular input, certain characteristics of the plant-forcing function (transient nature and low-frequency content) must be preserved reagrdless of the type of compensation, whether discrete or continuous, in order to get similar performance. The detailed structure of the plant-forcing function (corresponding to the high-frequency content) is of little significance because of the low-pass characteristics of the normal plant.

The data-processing properties of a discrete compensator followed by a hold circuit are completely specified by the response to a unit impulse. With a zero-order hold, these properties result in a transfer characteristic which, from a mathematical point of view, converts impulses arriving at sampling instants into a boxcar function having a definite amplitude relation to the area of the incoming impulses. In order that a network possess a transfer characteristic at all similar for impulse inputs at sampling instants, it follows that the network impulse response must at least crudely approximate the discrete compensator and zero-order hold combined impulse response. It is also evident that the discrete compensator and zero-order hold combination impulse response must have some semblance of overall continuity or smoothness (excluding the sharp discontinuities) to allow any sort of reasonable approximation with a lumped constant network of tolerable complexity. Whenever these conditions of continuity of smoothness do not exist (for example, with rigid specifications of deadbeat response, whenever a plant has abnormally poor characteristics, when the sampling rate is very slow, etc.), we would

† E. I. Jury and F. W. Semelka, "Time-Domain Synthesis of Sampled-Data Control Systems," A.S.M.E. Transactions Paper No. 58-IRD-8, presented in Newark, Del., April 3, 1958.

tend to doubt the feasibility of network compensation. In any case, a few design attempts will readily disclose, either by analytical or by analogue computational means, both the feasibility and quality of the approximations.

At least intuitively it is apparent that in some cases approximating the impulse response characteristics of the discrete compensator and associated hold with a network may result in good approximation for the forcing function obtained with discrete compensation. To be able to study the effects of network approximations with ease, it is necessary to find a straightforward means of approximating these impulse response characteristics. Certain time domain approximation techniques of network theory lend themselves advantageously to this problem, as will be shown by the following.

6.12 Mathematics of the Approximation

The design of lumped constant networks producing a specified output when excited by a prescribed input is time domain synthesis. Ba Hli † has developed a method for handling this type of synthesis problem.

In the normal process with this method, part of the designer's task is to find a time sequence representation for the impulse response of the network which is to have the desired transfer characteristic. This time sequence representation is formed by a process of synthetic division of periodically sampled values of the output function by the corresponding sampled values of the input function. The result of this synthetic division is actually a sequence of areas which in time sequence generates a stairstep function approximating the smooth impulse response characteristic of the required network. In this compensation problem, this part of the task is already accomplished since an exact stairstep function of time representing the impulse response of the discrete compensator and hold is already known (from the coefficients of the series expansion of the discrete-compensator transfer function obtained from the synthesis method of Chapter 5). Thus, it is only necessary to find the function

$$N(s) = \frac{P(s)}{Q(s)} = \frac{p_0 + p_1 s + p_2 s^2 + \cdots + p_n s^n}{q_0 + q_1 s + q_2 s^2 + \cdots + q_m s^m} \tag{6.99}$$

which has an impulsive time response approximating that of the discrete compensator and zero-order hold. From Ba Hli's method, the approxi-

† F. Ba Hli, "A General Method for Time Domain Network Synthesis," *I.R.E. Trans. on Circuit Theory*, Vol. CT-1, No. 3, September 1954, pp. 21–28.

mation is a time moments matching technique stemming from the definition of Laplace transform. The factor e^{-st} within the integrand of the transformation is replaced by a power series; thus,

$$
\begin{aligned}
\mathcal{L}[f(t)] &= \int_0^\infty f(t)\, e^{-st}\, dt \\
&= \int_0^\infty f(t)\, dt - \frac{s}{1!}\int_0^\infty t\, f(t)\, dt + \frac{s^2}{2!}\int_0^\infty t^2 f(t)\, dt + \cdots \qquad (6.100) \\
&= b_0 + b_1 s + b_2 s^2 + \cdots
\end{aligned}
$$

where b_0 is the area of the impulse response and b_n, $n \geq 1$, are recognized as the time moments.

The coefficients of a series expansion of equation (6.99) must match $m + n + 2$ of the b_n terms in order that the impulsive responses of $N(s)$ have approximately the same shape as the function from which the b_n were derived. Therefore, $m + n + 2$ of the following equations must be satisfied (since one of the constants can be normalized, actually $m + n + 1$ equations must be solved):

$$
\begin{aligned}
p_0 &= b_0 q_0 \\
p_1 &= b_1 q_0 + b_0 q_1 \\
&\cdots \qquad (6.101) \\
p_n &= b_n q_0 + b_{n-1} q_1 + b_{n-2} q_2 + \cdots + b_0 q_n \\
0 &= b_{n+1} q_0 + b_n q_1 + b_{n-1} q_2 + \cdots + b_1 q_n + b_0 q_{n+1}
\end{aligned}
$$

These equations place in evidence the fact that better approximations are in general acquired with greater network complexity.

In an error-sampled type system where the output of the network compensator is required to begin with a large discontinuity, the relative order in equation (6.99) is given by $m = n + 1$ since the input is considered mathematically to be a sequence of impulses when a hold does not precede the network.

Owing to the staircase nature of the impulse response of the discrete compensator and zero-order hold, the moments are easily evaluated without any approximation other than neglecting small values of the impulsive response corresponding to large values of time (where the error goes to zero). The decision about what part of the impulse response is significant in evaluating the moments requires some judgment, as does a choice of m which governs the complexity allowed for the network compensator. In general, terminating the moments computation to about

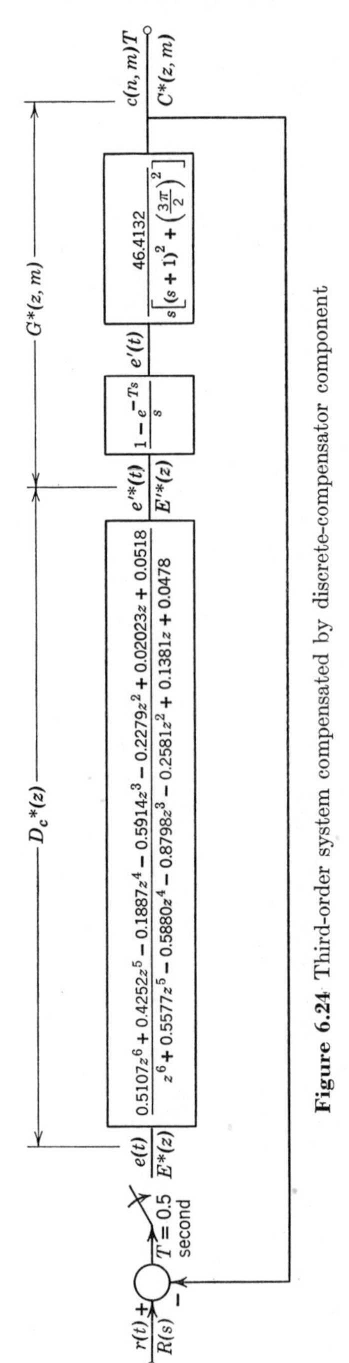

Figure 6.24 Third-order system compensated by discrete-compensator component

10 per cent of the initial value of the impulse response yields a satisfactory engineering approximation. The error of the approximation can be successively reduced by increasing the labor of calculations.

Before proceeding with examples of this method, it is worthwhile to mention the need for an analogue computer with this synthesis procedure. Even though the problem of inversion is immensely simplified with the series expansion method, analysis with higher-order feed forward functions is still a tedious task. A system analogue is comparatively easy to set up, and the results of these network approximations can thus be readily found.

Illustrative Example

To illustrate the method of network compensation of a sampled-data system, an approximate network substitute will be found for the discrete compensator and zero-order hold of a certain system as shown in Fig. 6.24. The actual effects of the approximating networks on performance can be checked by theoretical and analogue computational methods.†

The first step in finding the approximating networks is an area and moments evaluation. As a starting point, the impulsive response of the discrete compensator and hold circuit is arbitrarily terminated at $n = 4$ (Fig. 6.25), which results in the following constants:

$$\begin{aligned} b_0 &= 0.3077 \\ b_1 &= -0.0770 \\ b_2 &= -0.0089 \\ b_3 &= 0.0191 \end{aligned} \tag{6.102}$$

necessary to obtain a second-order network approximation. Thus to obtain the second-order network (where q_0 is normalized to unity), the following set of equations must be satisfied:

$$\begin{aligned} p_0 &= 0.3077 \\ p_1 &= -0.0770 + 0.3077q_1 \\ 0 &= -0.0089 - 0.0770q_1 + 0.3077q_2 \\ 0 &= 0.0191 - 0.0089q_1 - 0.0770q_2 \end{aligned} \tag{6.103}$$

† E. I. Jury and F. W. Semelka, "Time-Domain Synthesis of Sampled-Data Control Systems," A.S.M.E. Transactions Paper No. 58-IRD-8, presented in Newark, Del., April 3, 1958.

Solution of these equations yields

$$N(s) = 0.3077 \frac{0.3487s + 1}{0.1788s^2 + 0.5990s + 1}$$

or

$$= 0.6001 \frac{s + 2.8677}{(s + 1.6751)^2 + (1.6695)^2} \tag{6.104}$$

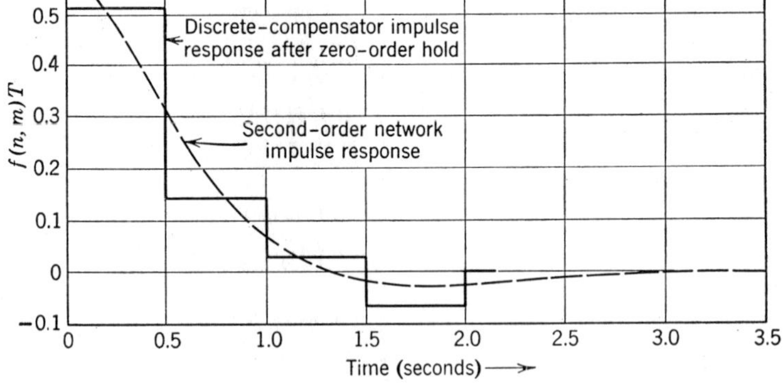

Figure 6.25 Unit impulse responses of comparison in example

The impulsive response of this network is shown for comparison in Fig. 6.25. The compensated system for this initial trial approximation is shown in Fig. 6.26. The modified z-transform of the output can be found, and the time domain response can be easily calculated from the power

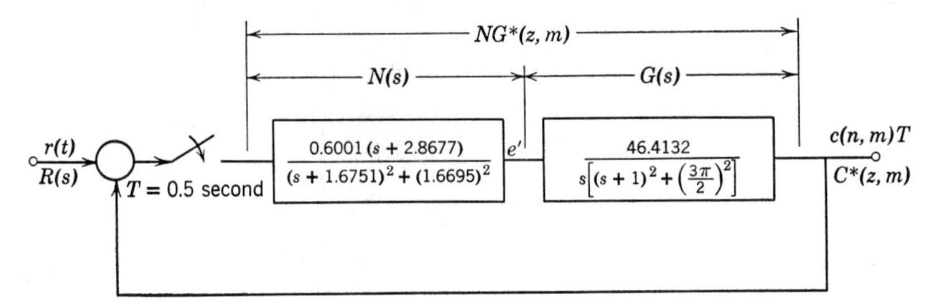

Figure 6.26 System of Fig. 7.24 with second-order network compensation

series expansion of the output modified z-transform. A plot of this output is shown in Fig. 6.27; also the discrete-compensation response is duplicated on the same graph for comparison. As is seen from this figure, the principle deviation in this approximation is the settling characteristic which appears to be mainly due to the approximation of terminating the impulse response of the discrete compensator and hold at $n = 4$ in the moments and area calculations. The need for using a larger portion of this impulse response in the approximation is also indicative of the

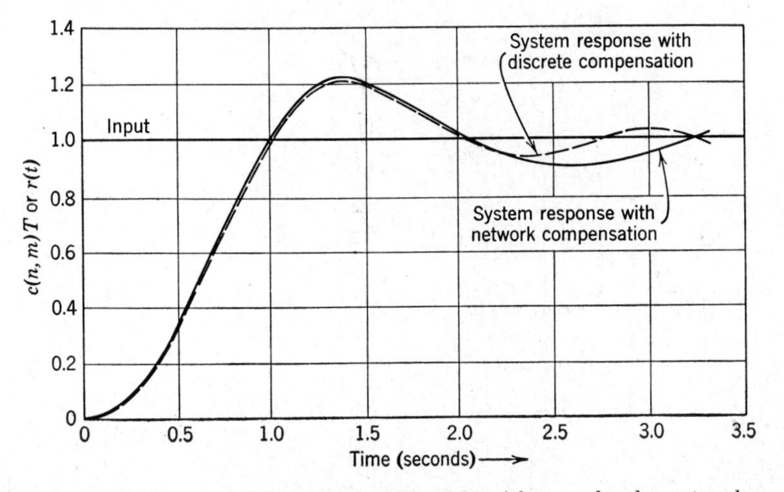

Figure 6.27 Step responses for system of Fig. 6.24 with second-order network compensation and discrete compensation

necessity for greater network complexity. Thus the subsequent approximations will proceed in that direction.

To find a better network approximation for the discrete compensator and hold circuit, a new set of constants (area of moments) is calculated for the impulse response arbitrarily terminated at $n = 7$, (Fig. 6.28). These are

$$\begin{aligned} b_0 &= 0.3384 \\ b_1 &= -0.1510 \\ b_2 &= 0.08780 \\ b_3 &= -0.07233 \\ b_4 &= 0.05878 \\ b_5 &= -0.04065 \\ b_6 &= 0.02371 \\ b_7 &= -0.01186 \\ b_8 &= 0.005178 \\ b_9 &= -0.002001 \end{aligned} \tag{6.105}$$

The constants of this equation determine the p's and q's using equation (6.101), which permits approximations inclusive of a fifth-order network.

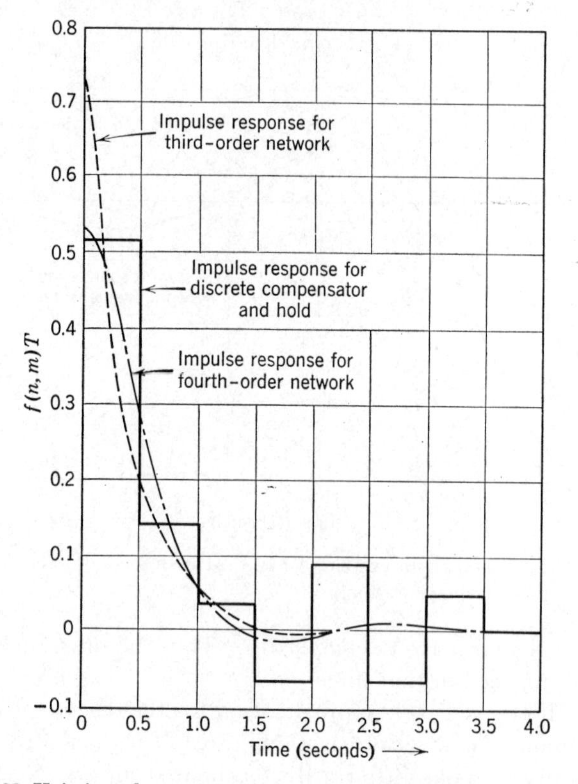

Figure 6.28 Unit impulse response for compensation components of Fig. 6.24

Solving the equations for p's and q's for a third-order network approximation, we find

$$N(s) = 0.7560 \frac{s^2 + 2.1741s + 2.4459}{(s + 1.6597)[(s + 1.2059)^2 + (1.3558)^2]} \tag{6.106}$$

For a fourth-order network approximation, we obtain, as indicated in Fig. 6.29, the following:

$$N(s) = 0.5279 \frac{(s + 5.9669)[(s + 1.1268)^2 + (1.0275)^2]}{[(s + 2.0881)^2 + (0.4065)^2][(s + 1.5792)^2 + (1.5127)^2]} \tag{6.107}$$

Figure 6.28 shows the impulsive response of the third- and fourth-order networks for comparison with the impulsive response of the dis-

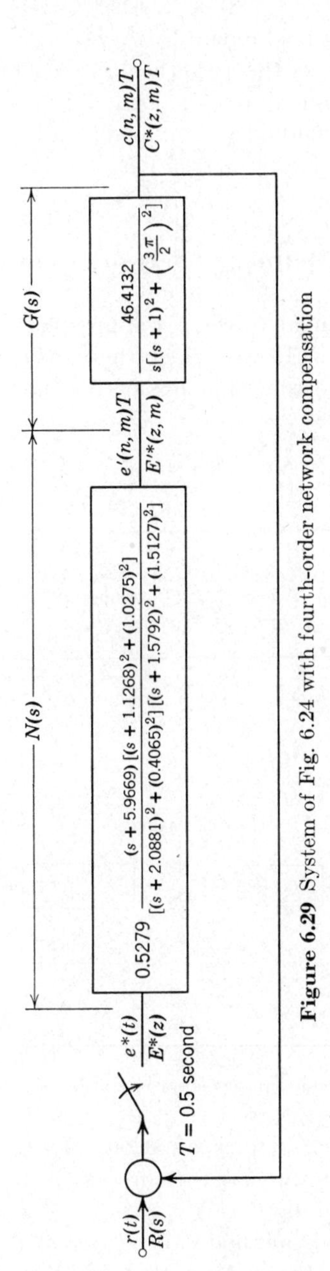

Figure 6.29 System of Fig. 6.24 with fourth-order network compensation

crete compensator and hold circuit. It is seen that the higher the order of the network, the better the fit to the discrete compensator. Thus this procedure yields an approximate analogue representation to the discrete compensator. Other methods are available, and these are discussed in the remainder of this chapter and in Chapter 7.

6.13 Approximate Method of Network Compensation

This method † is similar to the z–s approximation discussed in detail earlier in this chapter. However, synthesis using this method can be performed through the time domain method instead of the frequency

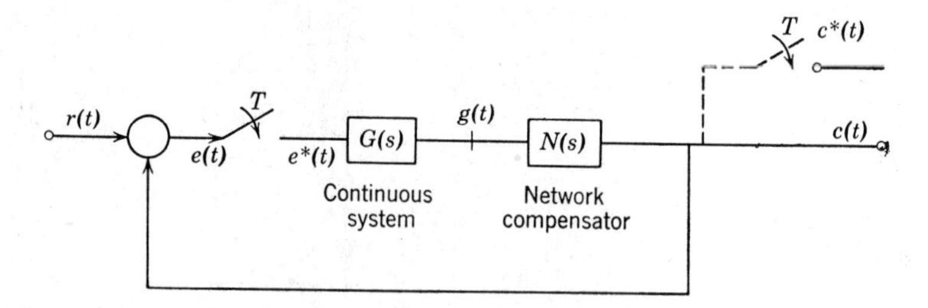

Figure 6.30*a* Error-sampled feedback system with a network compensator

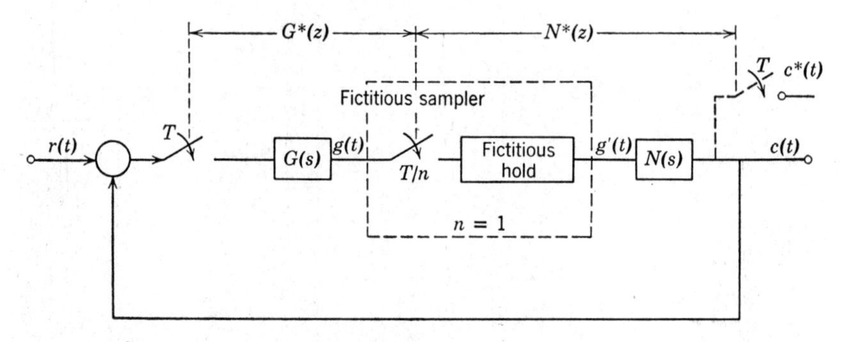

Figure 6.30*b* Multiple sampler approximation of system in Fig. 6.30*a*

domain method of the z–s approximation. Furthermore, the fictitious interpolator (or hold) in this case is to produce a straight-line approximation of the continuous function.

The basic idea of this method can be best illustrated by comparing Figs. 6.30*a* and 6.30*b*. It is noticed that Fig. 6.30*b* is an approximation

† R. F. Nease, "Analysis and Design of Non-linear Sampled-Data Control Systems," W.A.D.C. Technical Note 57–162, M.I.T., June 1957.

of Fig. 6.30a. However, the signal $g'(t)$ is a good approximation to $g(t)$, as long as $G(s)$ has the property of being lower-pass filter. This approximation is a time domain, and the accuracy is readily determined by observing the discrepancy between the actual $g(t)$ and its linear straight-line approximation between successive sampling instants.

The interpolator or fictitious hold transfer function is obtained as the transform of triangle pulse † and is

$$B(s) = \frac{e^{sT} - 2 + e^{-sT}}{Ts^2} \tag{6.108}$$

The correspondence between $N^*(z)$ indicated in Fig. 6.30b and $N(s)$, the compensating network for $n = 1$, is shown in Fig. 6.31.

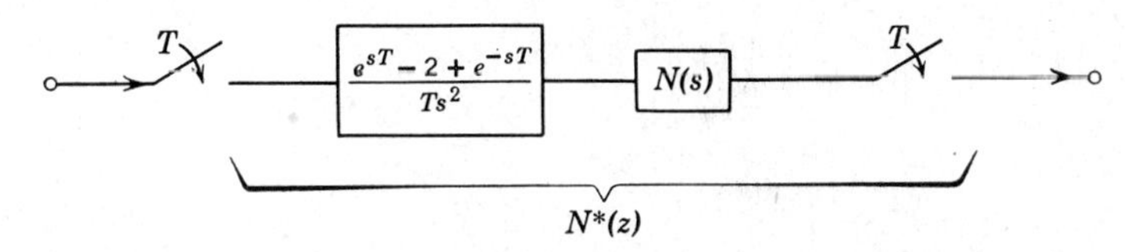

Figure 6.31 The continuous network representation of $N^*(z)$

With this equivalence, we may tabulate certain approximate relationships between $N(s)$ and $N^*(z)$, which can be used for design. These relationships are given in Table 6.2.

6.14 Discussion of Method

This method is based on the fact that $G(s)$ has an impulse response which is well represented by straight lines between sampling instants. However, if such is not the case, this approximation is not expected to give good results. But, in such cases, we can still use these techniques provided the fictitious sampler shown in Fig. 6.30b can be made to sample at a higher rate. Furthermore, the output design for such a case should take into account the response between sampling instants, as in the design of multirate controllers.‡

Another possibility for improving the approximation is to use second- or higher-degree interpolators which will give better smoothing properties. Thus, the choice between the fictitious sampling rate and the degree of the fictitious hold depends on the system and the design requirements.

† See equation (8.6) and Fig. 8.4.

‡ G. M. Kranc, "Compensation of an Error-Sampled System by a Multi-Rate Controller," *Trans. A.I.E.E.*, Vol. 76, Pt. II, 1957, pp. 149–159.

TABLE 6.2

Relationship between $N(s)$ and $N^*(z)$ †

$N(s)$	$N^*(z)$
$\dfrac{T_1 s + 1}{s}$	$\dfrac{z(T/2 + T_1) + (T/2 - T_1)}{z - 1}$
$\dfrac{(T_2 s + 1)}{(T_1 s + 1)}$	$\dfrac{z[T + (T_1 - T_2)(D - 1)] + [-TD - (T_1 - T_2)(D - 1)]}{T(z - D)}$ $\quad D = e^{-T/T_1}$
$\dfrac{K_1 s^2 + K_2 s + 2\left(\alpha^2 + \dfrac{\pi^2}{T^2}\right)}{[(s + \alpha)^2 + \pi^2/T^2]}$	$\dfrac{z[T - A(1 + D)] + [TD + A(1 + D)]}{T(z + D)}$ $A = \dfrac{2\alpha - K_2}{\alpha^2 + \pi^2/T^2}, \quad B = -1 + K_1 + \alpha A, \quad D = e^{-\alpha T}$
$\dfrac{K_1 s^3 + K_2 s^2 + K_3 s}{s[(s + \alpha)^2 + \pi^2/T^2]} + \dfrac{2(\alpha^2 + \pi^2/T^2)}{s[(s + \alpha)^2 + \pi^2/T^2]}$	$\dfrac{z^2[T(A + T) - B(D + 1)] + z[T^2(D + 1) + AT(D - 1) + 2B(D + 1)] + TD(T - A) - B(D + 1)}{T(z - 1)(z + D)}$ $A = \dfrac{K_3 - 4\alpha}{\alpha^2 + \pi^2/T^2}, \quad B = \dfrac{2(1 + \alpha A) - K_2}{\alpha^2 + \pi^2/T^2}, \quad C = \dfrac{K_3 + \alpha(K_2 - 6 - 2A)}{\alpha^2 + \pi^2/T^2} - K_1, \quad D = e^{-\alpha T}$

$\dfrac{1+T_1s}{1+T_2s}\times\dfrac{1+T_3s}{1+T_4s}$	$\dfrac{(z-1)^2}{Tz}\left\{\dfrac{T_2(1-T_1/T_2)(1-T_3/T_2)}{(1-T_4/T_2)}\dfrac{z}{z-e^{-T/T_2}} + \dfrac{T_4(1-T_1/T_4)(1-T_3/T_4)}{Tz/T_4}\dfrac{z}{z-e^{-T/T_4}} + z\dfrac{\{(z-1)[(T_1+T_3)-(T_2+T_4)]+T\}}{(z-1)^2}\right\}$
$\dfrac{1+T_1s}{1+T_2s}\times\dfrac{1+T_3s}{1+T_4s}\cdots\times\dfrac{1+T_{2n-1}s}{1+T_{2n}s}$	$\dfrac{(z-1)^2}{Tz}\left\{\dfrac{T_2(1-T_1/T_2)(1-T_3/T_2)\cdots(1-T_{2n-1}/T_2)}{(1-T_4/T_2)\cdots(1-T_{2n}/T_2)}\times\dfrac{z}{z-e^{-T/T_2}} + \dfrac{T_4(1-T_1/T_4)(1-T_3/T_4)\cdots(1-T_{2n-1}/T_4)}{(1-T_2/T_4)(1-T_6/T_4)\cdots(1-T_{2n}/T_4)}\cdot\dfrac{z}{z-e^{-T/T_4}} + \cdots + T_{2n}\dfrac{(1-T_1/T_{2n})(1-T_3/T_{2n})\cdots(1-T_{2n-1}/T_{2n})}{(1-T_2/T_{2n})\cdots(1-T_{2n-2}/T_{2n})}\cdot\dfrac{z}{z-e^{-T/T_{2n}}} + z\dfrac{\{(z-1)[(T_1+T_3+\cdots+T_{2n-1})-(T_2+T_4+\cdots+T_{2n})]+T\}}{(z-1)^2}\right\}$

† This table is a further extension of the table in R. F. Nease "Analysis and Design of Non-linear Sampled-Data Control Systems," W.A.D.C. Technical Note 57–162, M.I.T., June 1957.

The main feature of this method is that the approximation depends on the form of $G(s)$ or $g(t)$, and this is usually given for it refers to the unalterable part of the system. Therefore, a measure of errors involved may be obtained without assuming any particular $N(s)$, since it is calculated from the known value of $G(s)$.

6.15 Other Time Domain Procedures

As indicated earlier, a few authors have attempted the continuous network compensation method following the same principles applied in continuous feedback systems. Pertinent among these methods is the Lago † approach. This philosophy of design is the choice of $C(s)$, the transform of a continuous output. From $C(s)$ we can obtain its z-transform or $C^*(z)$. Since the input is known, we can evaluate $G^*(z)$. With the use of table or partial fraction expansion, the corresponding $G(s)$ can be obtained. There are two limitations to this method. The first is that only the response at the sampling instants is specified, and secondly, it is not always simple to obtain a linear network for any $G^*(z)$. Furthermore, the plant transfer function cannot be directly connected with the type $G(s)$ chosen. Thus poles and zeros of the plant should be canceled, which in some cases is impractical.

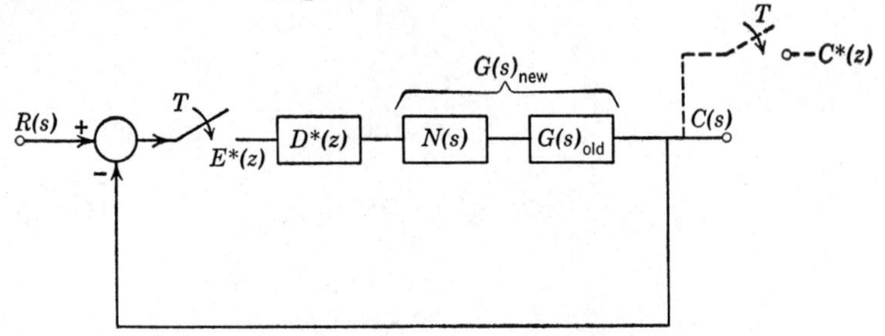

Figure 6.32 Compensation of sampled-data feedback system

The second pertinent approach is due to Linvill and Sittler.‡ This method is based on specifying the error coefficients of $E^*(z)$ for the system shown in Fig. 6.32.

$$\frac{E^*(z)}{R^*(z)} = \frac{1}{1 + P^*/Q(z)} \tag{6.109}$$

† G. V. Lago, "Additions to z-Transform Theory for Sampled-Data Systems," *Trans. A.I.E.E.*, Vol. 74, Pt. II, 1955, pp. 403–408.

‡ W. Linvill and R. W. Sittler, "Extension of Conventional Techniques to the Design of Sampled-Data Systems," *I.R.E. Convention Record*, New York, Pt. I, 1953, pp. 99–104.

or

$$E^*(z) = R^*(z) \times \frac{1}{1 + P^*/Q(z)} \tag{6.110}$$

The z-transform of open-loop system $P^*/Q(z)$ can be obtained from the specifications of $\frac{1}{1 + P^*/Q(z)}$; that is

$$P^*/Q(z) = \frac{1 - \dfrac{1}{1 + P^*/Q(z)}}{\dfrac{1}{1 + P^*/Q(z)}} \tag{6.111}$$

or

$$G^*(z)_{\text{new}} = P^*/DQ \tag{6.112}$$

and

$$G(s)_{\text{new}} = \mathcal{L}\,[g(t)] \tag{6.113}$$ †

Thus the compensating network is given by

$$N(s) = \frac{G(s)_{\text{new}}}{G(s)_{\text{old}}} \tag{6.114}$$

This method has the same limitations as the previous one, with the main difference that the error coefficients are specified instead of the sampled output.

The third method is based on the choice of the linear network so that the characteristic equation of the system is forced to be of the form $(z - a)^n$. This has been discussed in the preceding chapter. The realization of the compensator, often referred to as the operational instruction of the network, is achieved by use of hold circuit and linear networks.‡

Finally the linear compensator can also be obtained by considering the sampled-data system as a predictor.§ Then by using this procedure $C^*(z)$ can be written as

$$C^*(z) = (a_0 + a_1/z + a_2/z^2 + \cdots)\, R^*(z) \tag{6.115}$$

From the relation $\frac{G^*(z)}{1 + G^*(z)} = \frac{C^*(z)}{R^*(z)}$, which requires values of a_n corresponding to the degree of prediction desired, $G^*(z)$ can be obtained. From $G^*(z)$ we can obtain a corresponding $G(s)$ as indicated earlier.

† In this equation $G(s)_{\text{new}}$ indicates the Laplace transform of a continuous time function $g(t)$ whose sampled values coincide with $\mathfrak{Z}^{-1}[G^*(z)_{\text{new}}$.

‡ For a complete discussion see Chapter 7.

§ C. H. Smith, D. F. Lawden, and A. E. Bailey, "Characteristics of Sampling Servo Systems," in *Automatic and Manual Control*, Proceedings of Cranfield Conference, 1951, edited by A. Tustin, Butterworth Scientific Publications, London, 1952, pp. 377–404.

CHAPTER 7

Physical Realization of Discrete Compensators

In the preceding two chapters methods of synthesis have been discussed which yield the form of the discrete-compensator transfer function. In this chapter several methods are discussed for the realization of the obtained transfer function. These realization methods or techniques can be generally divided into four categories, namely, *programming, delay elements procedure pulsed R-C network method*, and *computer operational-instruction method*. The mentioned methods offer a wide variety of physical realization of the discrete compensator, and furthermore, each method of the group can also be implemented in a variety of ways. The choice of one of these methods depends on economy, accuracy, simplicity, and procedures. In the following section these four general methods are discussed in detail, and the advantages and disadvantages of each are enumerated.

7.1 Programming †

Because the field of digital computers is growing day by day and various components are being developed in this area, the control engineer

† John M. Salzer, "Frequency Analysis of Digital Computers Operating in Real Time," *Proc. I.R.E.*, Vol. 42, No. 2, 1954, pp. 457–466.

has a particular advantage in using digital computers in the realization of discrete compensators. The choice of the method of programming depends on the number of storage registers, the computing time required, and the value of accumulation of round-off errors. In view of these factors there are three methods of programming, namely, direct, cascade, and parallel programming, and finally a combination of two, cascade-parallel programming.

a. Direct Programming

The discrete transfer function which must be realized by this method can be in general written as

$$D^*(z) = \frac{C^*(z)}{R^*(z)} = \frac{a_0 + a_1 z^{-1} + a_2 z^{-2} + \cdots + a_m z^{-m}}{1 + b_1 z^{-1} + b_2 z^{-2} + \cdots + b_n z^{-n}}, \quad m \leq n - 1 \tag{7.1}$$

The difference equation which is described by this program can be easily obtained in the following:

$$c^*(t) = \sum_{k=0}^{m} a_k \, r^*(t - kT) - \sum_{k=1}^{n} b_k \, c^*(t - kT) \tag{7.2}$$

The program required to solve this equation has two distinct tasks. The first, the arithmetic task, requires the multiplications and additions as indicated in equation (7.2). In this case, $m + n + 1$ multiplications and $m + n$ additions are required, since there are $m + n + 1$ terms in the right side of equation (7.2). The second operation is the task of the program to bring the data up to date. The sample $r^*(t)$ of the present calculation becomes $r^*(t - T)$ in the next one, and therefore the present $r^*(t)$ must be manipulated into the storage location associated with $r^*(t - T)$. Similar manipulations take account of the aging of other input and output data and are carried out by means of storage transfer operations. If all the constants in equation (7.2) are different and non-zero, the storage for direct programming is

Constants		$m + n + 1$
Data		$m + n$
Multiplications	$m + n + 1$	
Additions	$m + n$	
Transfers	$m + n$	
	Total operation	$3m + 3n + 1$
	Total	$5m + 5n + 2$

The operations required to perform the mentioned task are within the capabilities of most conventional computers. A schematic diagram of the programming is shown in Fig. 7.1. Figure 7.2 shows a block diagram of direct programming.

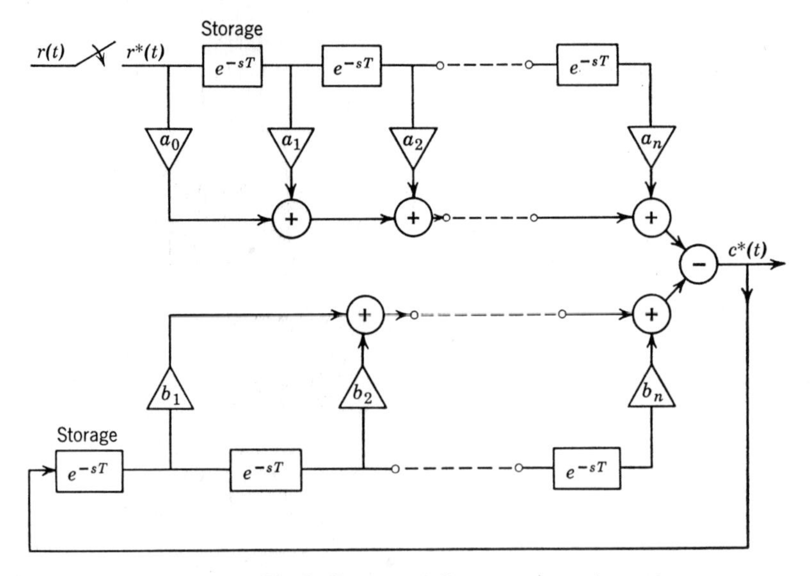

Figure 7.1 Block diagram of direct programming unit

This method is preferred when several of the constants in $D^*(z)$ are zero because factorization involved in the next two methods reproduces all the constants. The delay due to computation with this method is minimized.

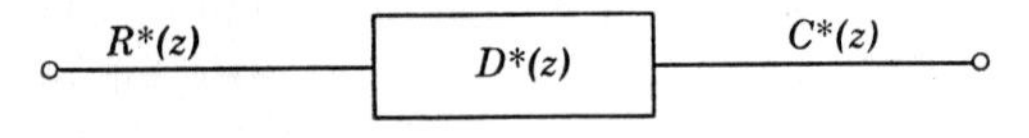

Figure 7.2 Direct programming

b. *Cascade Programming*

Programming with this method requires rewriting equation (7.1) in the following form:

$$D^*(z) = \frac{a_0}{1 + d_1 z^{-1}} \frac{1 + e_2 z^{-1}}{1 + d_2 z^{-1}} \cdots \frac{1 + e_n z^{-1}}{1 + d_n z^{-1}} \tag{7.3}$$

where $-1/e_k$ and $-1/d_k$ are zeros of the numerator and denominator respectively (some of the e_n's can be zero). With this procedure the direct program of Fig. 7.2 is replaced by Fig. 7.3 where the output of one block is the input to the next one; thus,

$$\frac{C^*(z)}{R^*(z)} = \frac{C_1^*(z)}{R^*(z)} \cdot \frac{C_2^*(z)}{C_1^*(z)} \cdot \cdots \cdot \frac{C^*(z)}{C_{n-1}^*(z)} \tag{7.4}$$

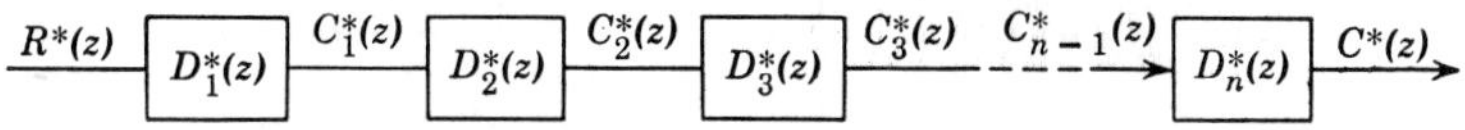

Figure 7.3 Cascade programming

Identifying the corresponding factors in equations (7.3) and (7.4) and performing the inverse transformation, we obtain:

$$\begin{aligned}
c_1^*(t) &= a_0\, r^*(t) & & - d_1\, c_1^*(t-T) \\
c_2^*(t) &= c_1^*(t) & + e_2\, c_1^*(t-T) & - d_2\, c_2^*(t-T) \\
&\vdots & \vdots & \vdots \\
c^*(t) &= c_{n-1}^*(t) & + e_n\, c_{n-1}^*(t-T) & - d_n\, c^*(t-T)
\end{aligned} \tag{7.5}$$

Counting the terms of equation (7.5) yields the following total of operations required for storage for cascade programming:

Constants	$m + n + 1$	
Data	n	
Transfers	n	(7.6)
Multiplications	$m + n + 1$	
Additions	$m + n$	
Total	$3m + 5n + 2$	

This figure favors cascade programming over direct method. Furthermore, with this method synthesis can be performed experimentally by changing the poles and zeros of the discrete transfer function. Furthermore, intermediate results when needed can be obtained by this method. However, the computation time is more than that for the direct method.

c. *Parallel Programming*

This is based on the partial-fraction expansion of $D^*(z)$, which can be written as

$$D^*(z) = \frac{f_1}{1 + d_1 z^{-1}} + \frac{f_2}{1 + d_2 z^{-1}} + \cdots + \frac{f_n}{1 + d_n z^{-1}} \tag{7.7}$$

where f_k are the residues of $D^*(z)$ at its respective poles. As shown in Fig. 7.4, the input-output relation can be expressed as

$$\frac{C^*(z)}{R^*(z)} = \frac{C_1{}^*(z)}{R^*(z)} + \frac{C_2{}^*(z)}{R^*(z)} + \cdots + \frac{C_n{}^*(z)}{R^*(z)} \tag{7.8}$$

This equation leads to the following set of difference equations: †

$$\begin{aligned} c_1{}^*(t) &= f_1\, r^*(t) - d_1\, c_1{}^*(t - T) \\ c_2{}^*(t) &= f_2\, r^*(t) - d_2\, c_2{}^*(t - T) \\ &\;\;\vdots \\ c_n{}^*(t) &= f_n\, r^*(t) - d_n\, c_n{}^*(t - T) \\ c^*(t) &= c_1{}^*(t) + c_2{}^*(t) + \cdots + c_n{}^*(t) \end{aligned} \tag{7.9}$$

The total operations required by parallel programming are as follows:

Constants	$2n$	
Data	n	
Multiplications	$2n$	(7.10)
Additions	$2n - 1$	
Transfers n	n	
Total	$8n - 1$	

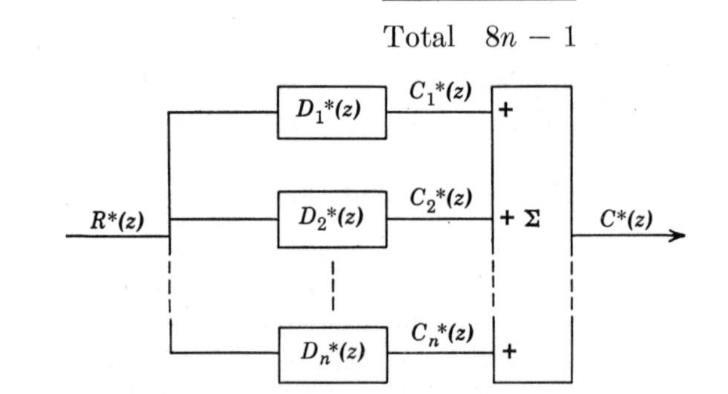

Figure 7.4 Parallel programming

Parallel programming occupies a position in between the other two methods as far as efficiency is concerned.

When a program is to be designed or improved by experimental methods this scheme offers a particular advantage. For instance, each constant in parallel programming has a relation with either a pole or a

† It is to be noted that the outputs $C_1{}^*(z)$, $C_2{}^*(z)$, $\cdots$, $C_n{}^*(z)$ in equation (7.8) are not the same as those in equation (7.4).

residue of the discrete transfer function. For a desired effect, a particular constant needs to be changed.

In some cases, we may combine some of the advantages of cascade and parallel programming and design the computer according to cascade-parallel programming. In other cases combinations of the mentioned three methods can be applied. From the discrete design procedure discussed in Chapter 5, it appears that the direct programming is the logical one, for the transfer functions obtained are not given in terms of poles and zeros. However, if design is effected through the root-locus method discussed in Chapter 3, cascade and parallel programmings are of advantage.

7.2 Delay Elements Method †

This method indicates that any transfer function whose numerator and denominator is a rational polynomial in z, with the denominator of equal or higher order than the numerator, can be realized with pure-delay elements, voltage dividers, two algebraic summing devices, and two amplifiers. If the sampler and hold are considered as a part of the compensator, these elements will also be required. However, if the original system is sampled, these elements will be required or present even if the system is not compensated. The configuration and the value of the elements are apparent if the output of the compensator is equated to the algebraic sum of previous outputs and inputs. As an example, consider the following:

$$D^*(z) = \frac{C^*(z)}{R^*(z)} = \frac{a_0 + a_1 z^{-1} + a_2 z^{-2} + a_3 z^{-3} + a_4 z^{-4}}{b_0 + b_1 z^{-1} + b_2 z^{-2} + b_3 z^{-3} + b_4 z^{-4}}$$

$$= \frac{k_1}{b_0} \frac{\dfrac{a_0}{k_1} + \dfrac{a_1}{k_1} z^{-1} + \dfrac{a_2}{k_1} z^{-2} + \dfrac{a_3}{k_1} z^{-3} + \dfrac{a_4}{k_1} z^{-4}}{1 + \dfrac{b_1}{b_0} z^{-1} + \dfrac{b_2}{b_0} z^{-2} + \dfrac{b_3}{b_0} z^{-3} + \dfrac{b_4}{b_0} z^{-4}} \tag{7.11}$$

where k_1 is the largest of a_i. Solving for $C^*(z)$ yields

$$C^*(z) = \frac{k_1}{b_0}\left(\frac{a_0}{k_1} + \frac{a_1}{k_1} z^{-1} + \frac{a_2}{k_1} z^{-2} + \frac{a_3}{k_1} z^{-3} + \frac{a_4}{k_1} z^{-4}\right) R^*(z)$$

$$- \frac{k_2}{b_0}\left(\frac{b_1}{k_2} z^{-1} + \frac{b_2}{k_2} z^{-2} + \frac{b_3}{k_2} z^{-3} + \frac{b_4}{k_2} z^{-4}\right) C^*(z) \tag{7.12}$$

† E. I. Jury and W. Schroeder, "Discrete Compensation of Sampled-Data and Continuous Control Systems," *Trans. A.I.E.E.*, Vol. 75, Pt. II, 1956, pp. 317–325.

where k_2 is the largest of the b_i. By factoring out the largest coefficients k_1 and k_2, all others are less than unity and therefore only two amplifiers are required. One configuration is then as shown in Fig. 7.5. The samplers may be placed on either end. If it is in the input, the delay must be nearly exact integers of the sampling period T since the pulses

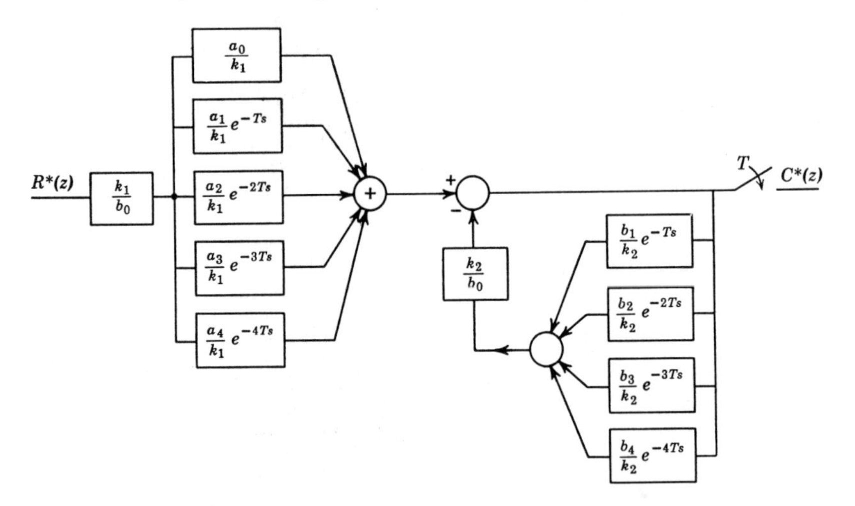

Figure 7.5 Realization of discrete compensator with pure delays

must be synchronized upon arrival at the summing devices. Likewise the amplifiers may be altered in position, depending on the desired summing level. This approach is not restricted to electric systems, and the delays may, of course, be realized in either digital or analogue method or a combination of both.

7.3 Pulsed *R-C* Networks Procedures †

This method utilizes *R-C* networks whose output is sampled in synchronism with its sampled input, as shown in Fig. 7.6. Their performance is similar to that of linear digital computers, discussed earlier, but at a considerable reduction in cost. However, this reduction is paid for by their lack of flexibility. In some applications the discrete-compensator transfer function is simple so that pulsed *R-C* networks may be used instead of digital computers. This method offers various alternatives for realization and characterization. It also offers alternatives for con-

† J. Sklansky, "Pulsed R-C Networks for Sampled-Data Systems," *I.R.E. Convention Record*, Pt. II, 1956, pp. 81–99.

figurations, namely, cascade, feedback, and parallel, as will be discussed.

Characterization of pulsed *R-C* networks assumes different forms, namely, basic series, basic feedback, and the cascaded series-feedback network.

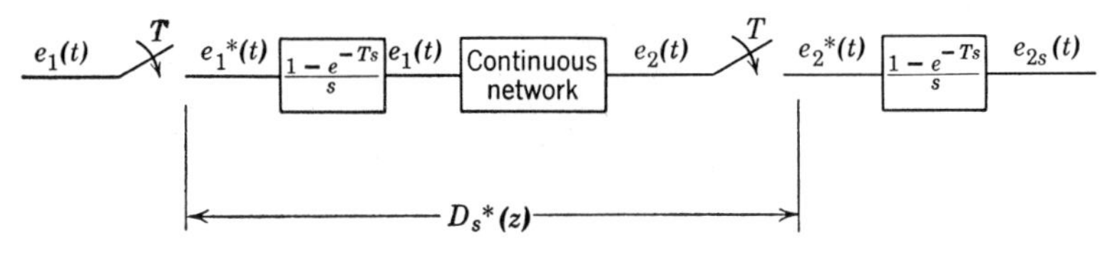

Figure 7.6 Pulsed network

a. Basic Series Network

The form of the pulsed transfer function of a network such as the one shown in Fig. 7.7 can be written

$$D_s^*(z) \triangleq \frac{\mathcal{L}\,[e_2^*(t)]}{\mathcal{L}\,[e_1^*(t)]} = \mathfrak{z}\left[\frac{1 - e^{-sT}}{s}\,P(s)\right] \qquad (7.13)$$

$$= (1 - z^{-1})\,\mathfrak{z}\left[\frac{P(s)}{s}\right]$$

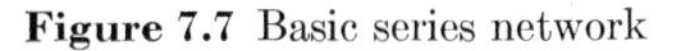

Figure 7.7 Basic series network

The assumed restrictions on $P(s)$ to be relizable by *R-C* network can be expressed as follows:

1. $P(s)$ is a ratio of polynomials in s.
2. The degree in s of the numerator of $P(s)$ does not exceed that of its denominator.
3. The poles of $P(s)$ are all real, non-positive and simple.

Since the operator $\mathfrak{z}$ is linear, $\mathfrak{z}\left[\frac{P(s)}{s}\right]$ may be evaluated by expanding $P(s)/s$ into its partial fractions. From the definition of the z-transform the following can be written

$$\mathfrak{z}\left(\frac{1}{s + a}\right) = \frac{1}{1 - e^{-aT}z^{-1}} \qquad (7.14)$$

The partial fraction expansion of $\frac{P(s)}{s}$ will be $\sum_i \frac{k_i}{s - s_i}$ and therefore

$$\mathfrak{Z}\left[\frac{P(s)}{s}\right] = \sum_i \frac{k_i}{1 - z_i z^{-1}}, \qquad z_i = e^{s_i T} \tag{7.15}$$

Since all the poles of $P(s)$ are negative (assuming no pole at origin), $D_s^*(z)$ has no pole at $z = 1$, and all the poles z_i are inside the unit circle, that is, $0 < z_i < 1$. In view of the form of equation (7.15), it is noted from equation (7.13) that the degree of the numerator in z^{-1} does not exceed that of the denominator. Since all the poles of $P(s)$ are simple and real negative, it follows from (7.15) that all the poles of $D_s^*(z)$ are simple and fall in the intervals $0 < z < 1$.

Thus, if $P(s)$ is the transfer function of the continuous portion of a basic series network, and if it satisfies these restrictions, the pulsed transfer function $D_s^*(z)$ must be of the form

$$D_s^*(z) = \frac{c_0 + c_1 z^{-1} + \cdots + c_p z^{-p}}{(1 - z_1 z^{-1})(1 - z_2 z^{-1}) \cdots (1 - z_q z^{-1})} \tag{7.16}$$

where the c_i and z_i are all real, $0 < z_i < 1$ for every i and $p \leq q$.

If $P(s)$ has a pole at $s = 0$, the only change in the previous equation is that one of the poles is equal to unity, the others being positive and less than unity.

From the preceding discussion it follows that if the discrete compensator transfer function is given in the form of equation (7.16), we can readily obtain from partial fraction expansion the form of $P(s)/s$. Summarizing this discussion we can characterize the basic series structure as follows: A necessary and sufficient condition that $P(s)$ be a rational fraction in s whose poles, s_i, are all non-infinite, non-positive, real, and simple is that $D_s^*(z)$ be a rational fraction in z^{-1}, all of whose poles are simple and in the real interval $0 < z_i \leq 1$.

b. Basic Feedback Structure

By referring to Fig. 7.8, the pulsed transfer function of the basic feedback network is

$$D_f^*(z) = \frac{\mathfrak{L}\,[e_2^*(t)]}{\mathfrak{L}\,[e_1^*(t)]} = \frac{1}{1 + (1 - z^{-1})\,\mathfrak{Z}\left[\frac{Q(s)}{s}\right]} \tag{7.17}$$

from this

$$\frac{1}{D_f^*(z)} - 1 = (1 - z^{-1})\, \mathfrak{Z}\left[\frac{Q(s)}{s}\right] \tag{7.18}$$

By comparing equations (7.18) and (7.13), it is noted that the right-hand members are exactly the same in form; therefore, the left-hand members must correspond to one another.

Owing to this correspondence, the constraints of equation (7.16) on the poles of $D_s^*(s)$ may be replaced by the same constraints on the zeros of

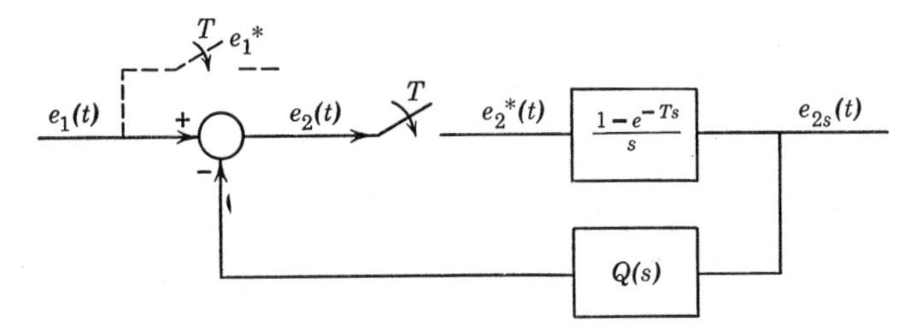

Figure 7.8 Basic feedback network

$D_f^*(z)$, since the latter are the poles of $1/D_f^*(z) - 1$. Therefore, the characterization of the basic feedback networks follows: A necessary and sufficient condition that $Q(s)$ be a rational fraction in s whose poles, s_i, are all non-infinite, non-positive, real, and simple is that $D_f^*(z)$ be a rational fraction in z^{-1}, all of whose zeros are simple and lie in the real interval $0 < z_i \leq 1$ where $z_i \triangleq e^{s_i T}$. As a corrollary from the characterization of the basic series and basic feedback structure, we note: If a pulsed transfer function, $D^*(z)$, is known to be realizable by a basic series structure, then as a consequence the reciprocal, $1/D^*(z)$, must be realizable by a basic feedback structure and vice versa.

c. *Cascaded Series-Feedback Networks*

By considering the cascaded-feedback network of Fig. 7.9 and defining $D_s^*(z)$ and $D_f^*(z)$ as the pulsed transfer functions of the basic series and feedback networks, it can be easily seen that the pulsed transfer function of any of the configurations of Fig. 7.9 is the product $D_f^*(z)\, D_s^*(z)$.

Thus the cascaded series-feedback network can realize any pulsed transfer function as long as it is rational in z and physically realizable. The characterization of the basic series-feedback network is: A necessary and sufficient condition that $P(s)$ and $Q(s)$ of Fig. 7.9 be rational fractions in s with poles which are non-infinite, non-positive, real, and simple is that the overall pulsed transfer function $D^*(z)$ be rational in z.

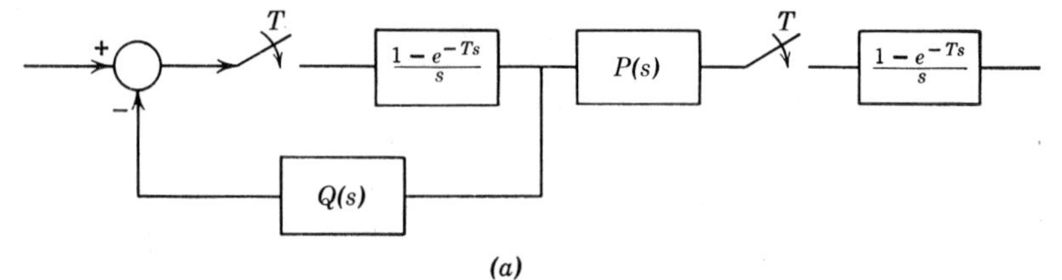

(a)

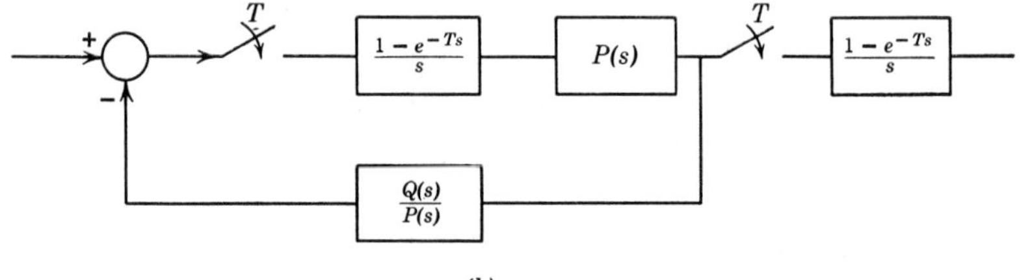

(b)

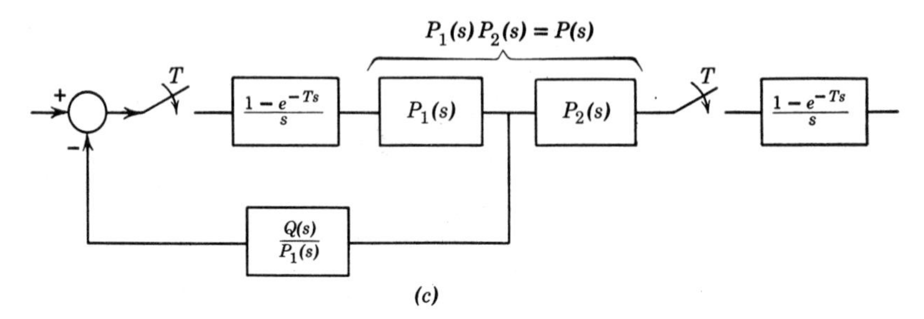

(c)

Figure 7.9 Cascaded series–feedback network

d. Realization Techniques

There are three techniques for realizing $D^*(z)$, namely, cascade, feedback, and parallel realizations. It is assumed that $D^*(z)$ is rational in z and physically realizable. These techniques will be discussed in detail.

1. Cascade realization. In this technique any $D^*(z)$ can be realized by the cascaded series-feedback network as shown in Fig. 7.9.

The first step in the realization is to determine all the zeros and poles of $D^*(z)$ in the real interval z. By so doing $D^*(z)$ can be factored into two parts:

$$D^*(z) = A^*(z)\,B^*(z) \tag{7.19}$$

The forms of $A^*(z)$ and $B^*(z)$ are determined by the following rules:

1. All the zeros of $D^*(z)$ outside the real interval $0 < z \leq 1$ are assigned to $A^*(z)$; all the poles of $D^*(z)$ outside that interval are assigned to $B^*(z)$.

2. The poles and zeros of $D^*(z)$ inside the real interval $0 < z \leq 1$ are free and can be assigned either to $A^*(z)$ or to $B^*(z)$, in such a way insuring that $A^*(z)$ and $B^*(z)$ will contain only simple poles and zeros.

3. Sufficient number of free poles should be assigned to $A^*(z)$ so that the degree in z^{-1} of the numerator of $A^*(z)$ will not exceed that of its denominator, thus making $A^*(z)$ realizable as a basic series network. Similarly, sufficient free poles and zeros should be assigned to $B^*(z)$ for the same reason in order to make $B^*(z)$ realizable as a basic feedback network.

4. Let $A^*(z) = D_s^*(z)$, $B^*(z) = D_f^*(z)$ and obtain $P(s)$ and $Q(s)$ corresponding to the basic series and basic feedback network as follows:

$$\mathfrak{z}\left[\frac{P(s)}{s}\right] = \frac{D_s^*(z)}{1 - z^{-1}} \tag{7.20}$$

$$\mathfrak{z}\left[\frac{Q(s)}{s}\right] = \frac{1}{1 - z^{-1}}\left[\frac{1}{D_f^*(z)} - 1\right] \tag{7.21}$$

From tables or partial fraction expansion, $P(s)$ and $Q(s)$ are determined.

5. $P(s)$ and $Q(s)$ can be synthesized as *R-C* networks following the techniques available in the literature for this purpose.

2. Feedback realization. In this case $D^*(z)$ will be realized by the configuration of Fig. 7.10; $D^*(z)$ can be written as ratio of two polynomials in z^{-1} as

$$D^*(z) = \frac{E^*(z)}{F^*(z)} = \frac{E^*(z)}{F_1^*(z) + F_2^*(z)} \tag{7.22}$$

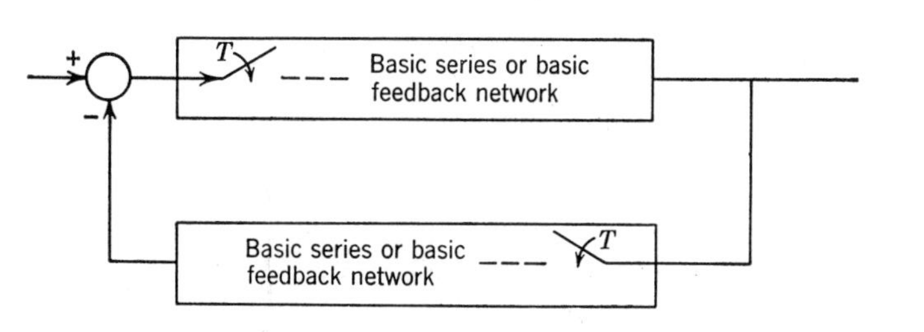

Figure 7.10 Feedback realization

The feedback realization is to find two polynomials in z^{-1}, $F_1^*(z)$ and $F_2^*(z)$, such that

$$\frac{E^*(z)}{F_1^*(z)} \quad \text{and} \quad \frac{F_2^*(s)}{E^*(z)} \tag{7.23}$$

satisfy either the basic series or basic feedback networks. Equation (7.22) can also be written as

$$D^*(z) = \frac{\dfrac{E^*(z)}{F_1^*(z)}}{1 + \dfrac{F_2^*(z)}{F_1^*(z)}} \tag{7.24}$$

The above is also deduced from Fig. 7.10. To realize each of the blocks in that figure, we let $E^*(z)/F_1^*(z)$ and $F_2^*(z)/E^*(z)$ be equal to the right side of (7.20) or (7.21) to obtain $P(s)$ or $Q(s)$, depending on which is appropriate. It can be seen that when $E^*(z) = F_1^*(z)$, and $F_2^*(z)/E^*(z)$ is realizable by a basic series network, the network of Fig. 7.10 reduces to the basic feedback network.

3. ***Parallel Realization.*** The pulsed network to be realized by this method is shown in Fig. 7.11. In this procedure $D^*(z)$ is written as the sum of two functions:

$$D^*(z) = D_s^*(z) + D_f^*(z) \tag{7.25}$$

where $D_s^*(z)$ and $D_f^*(z)$ satisfy the characterization of the basic series and the basic feedback respectively; $P(s)$ and $Q(s)$ can be obtained as outlined in the earlier techniques.

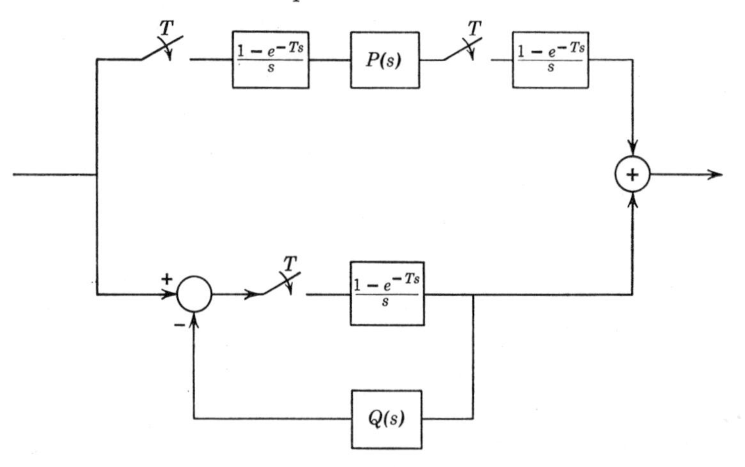

Figure 7.11 Parallel realization

Cascade, feedback, and parallel realization techniques may be combined in numerous ways, depending on the advantages and use of each of the techniques.

ILLUSTRATIVE EXAMPLE

In this example we wish to realize a pulsed *R-C* network whose pulsed transfer function is z^{-1} by the discussed three methods.

Cascade Realization

$$D^*(z) = z^{-1} = \frac{z^{-1}}{1 - \alpha z^{-1}}(1 - \alpha z^{-1}), \qquad 0 < \alpha \leq 1 \tag{7.26}$$

Then

$$D_s^*(z) = \frac{z^{-1}}{1 - \alpha z^{-1}} \tag{7.27}$$

$$D_f^*(z) = 1 - \alpha z^{-1} \tag{7.28}$$

From equation (7.20),

$$\mathfrak{z}\left[\frac{P(s)}{s}\right] = \frac{Ds^*(z)}{1 - z^{-1}} = \frac{1}{1 - \alpha}\left(\frac{1}{1 - z^{-1}} - \frac{1}{1 - \alpha z^{-1}}\right) \tag{7.29}$$

Thus

$$\frac{P(s)}{s} = \frac{1}{1 - e^{-aT}}\left(\frac{1}{s} - \frac{1}{s + a}\right) = \frac{a}{1 - e^{-aT}}\frac{1}{s + a}\frac{1}{s} \tag{7.30}$$

where $\alpha = e^{-aT}$. From equation (7.21) follows

$$\mathfrak{z}\left[\frac{Q(s)}{s}\right] = \frac{\alpha z^{-1}}{(1 - z^{-1})(1 - \alpha z^{-1})} \tag{7.31}$$

or

$$Q(s) = \frac{a}{e^{aT} - 1}\frac{1}{s + a} \tag{7.32}$$

and

$$\frac{Q(s)}{P(s)} = e^{-aT}$$

The final pulsed network is shown in Fig. 7.12*a*.

Feedback Realization

In this case $D^*(z)$ can be written

$$z^{-1} = \frac{z^{-1}}{1 - \alpha z^{-1} + \alpha z^{-1}} = \frac{\dfrac{z^{-1}}{1 - \alpha z^{-1}}}{1 + \dfrac{\alpha z^{-1}}{1 - \alpha z^{-1}}} \tag{7.33}$$

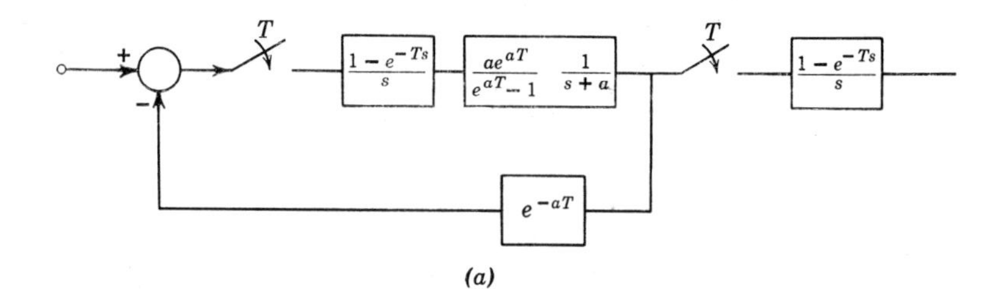

(a)

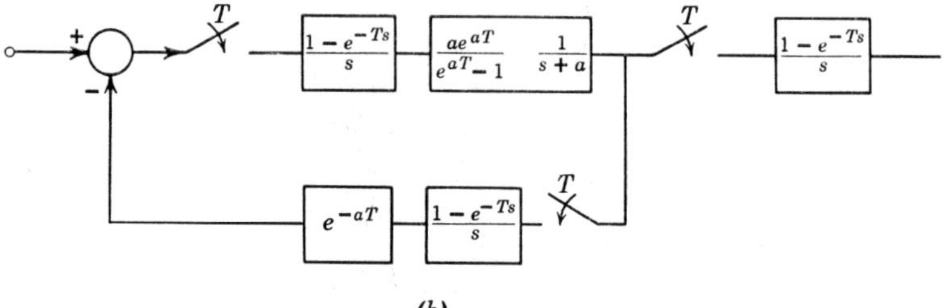

(b)

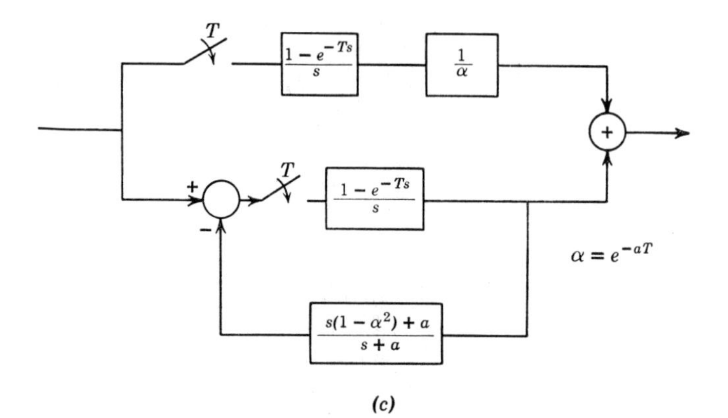

(c)

Figure 7.12 Realization of the illustrative example: (*a*) cascade realization, (*b*) feedback realization, (*c*) parallel realization

where $0 < \alpha \leq 1$. This equation represents the transfer function of a pulsed feedback system in which the forward pulsed transfer function is $z^{-1}/(1 - \alpha z^{-1})$ and the feedback pulsed transfer function is α. The resulting network is shown in Fig. 7.12*b*.

Parallel Realization

In this case, we can represent $D^*(z) = z^{-1}$ in the following form:

$$z^{-1} = \frac{1}{\alpha} - \frac{1}{\alpha}(1 - \alpha z^{-1}) \tag{7.34}$$

Thus,

$$D_s^*(z) = \frac{1}{\alpha} \tag{7.35}$$

$$D_f^*(z) = -\frac{1}{\alpha}(1 - \alpha z^{-1}) \tag{7.36}$$

From equations (7.20) and (7.21) it follows that

$$P(s) = \frac{1}{\alpha} \tag{7.37}$$

$$Q(s) = \frac{1}{\alpha - 1} \frac{s(1 - \alpha^2) + a}{s + a}, \qquad \alpha = e^{-aT} \tag{7.38}$$

The resulting network is shown in Fig. 7.12*c*.

7.4 Operational-Instruction Method †

The realization of the discrete compensator $D^*(z)$ using the pulsed *R*-*C* network requires in most cases a sampler and a zero-order hold as noticed from the discussions indicated earlier. In some cases this added sampler and hold can be removed. A special case of the preceding section is the feedback realization method whereby we utilize the sampled information and hold to perform the discrete compensation. In some cases the discrete compensator can be approximately realized by linear network whereby analogue components can be used. This method of realization is called the operational-instruction method,‡ which can in general be divided into two classes: (*a*) the approximate network realization of discrete compensator and (*b*) the exact network realization of the discrete compensator.

† R. H. Barker, "The Pulse Transfer Function and Its Application to Sampling Servo Systems," *Proc. I.E.E. (London)*, Vol. 99, Pt. IV, 1952, pp. 302–307.

‡ R. H. Barker, "A Servo System for Digital Data Transmission," *Proc. I.E.E. (London)*, Part B, Vol. 103, 1956, pp. 52–64.

a. Approximate Method of Network Compensation †

This method, as discussed in detail in the preceding chapter, is based on approximating the discrete-compensator transfer function plus the zero-order hold by a linear network, not necessarily R-C, such that the more terms of linear networks introduced the closer the approximation.

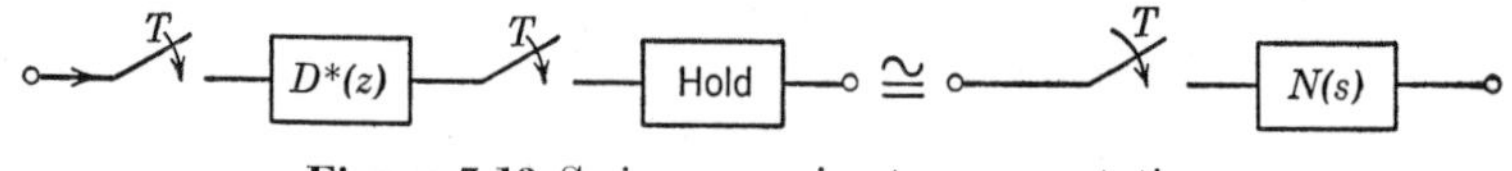

Figure 7.13 Series approximate representation

This can be done either by series approximation as shown in Fig. 7.13, or series-feedback approximation as shown in Fig. 7.14. This method is used as an aid in the analogue computer study of sampled-data with a discrete compensator and has the advantage that an extra sampler and

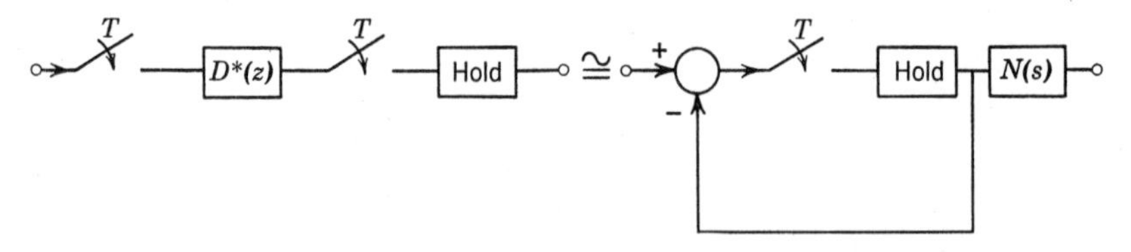

Figure 7.14 Series-feedback approximate representation

hold are not required. The procedure for such synthesis and approximation is discussed in the preceding chapter.

b. Exact Network Realization Method

In certain cases where $D^*(z)$ is of simple form, we may use the basic feedback realization discussed in the preceding sections, thus eliminating

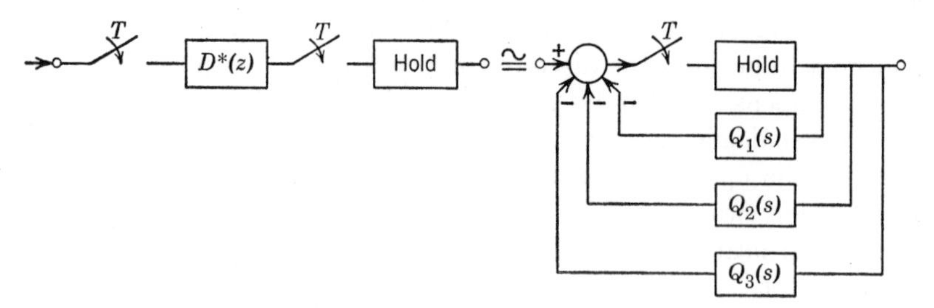

Figure 7.15 Feedback exact representation

† E. I. Jury and F. W. Semelka, "Time Domain Synthesis of Sampled-Data Control Systems," *A.S.M.E. Transactions* Paper No. 58-IRD-8, presented at Newark, Del., April 3, 1958.

the introduction of a sampler and a hold. This method can be further extended to include more than one feedback path as shown in Fig. 7.15. In this procedure we may realize a larger class of $D^*(z)$ and at the same time the requirement of extra sampler and hold can be removed. Furthermore, we can also use more general networks other than R-C to obtain more flexibility on the form of $D^*(z)$.

Illustrative Example

To illustrate the last method, assume $D^*(z)$ given as:

$$D^*(z) = \frac{1 - B_2 z^{-1}}{1 + bz^{-1}}, \qquad \text{where } B_2 < 1, b > 0 \tag{7.39}$$

In view of the fact that $B_2 < 1$, we can realize $D^*(z)$ as a feedback network in the following procedure:

$$D_f^*(z) = \frac{1 - B_2 z^{-1}}{1 + bz^{-1}} \tag{7.40}$$

From equation (7.21) we obtain

$$\mathfrak{z}\left[\frac{Q(s)}{s}\right] = \frac{1}{1 - z^{-1}}\left[\frac{1 + bz^{-1}}{1 - B_2 z^{-1}} - 1\right] \tag{7.41}$$

Finding the partial fraction of the above equation yields

$$\mathfrak{z}\left[\frac{Q(s)}{s}\right] = \frac{b + B_2}{1 - B_2}\frac{1}{1 - z^{-1}} - \frac{b + B_2}{1 - B_2}\frac{1}{1 - B_2 z^{-1}} \tag{7.42}$$

From tables, $Q(s)/s$ yields

$$\frac{Q(s)}{s} = \frac{b + B_2}{1 - B_2}\frac{1}{s} - \frac{b + B_2}{1 - B_2}\frac{1}{s + \beta} \tag{7.43}$$

where $B_2 = e^{-\beta T}$. Finally,

$$Q(s) = \frac{b + e^{-\beta T}}{1 - e^{-\beta T}}\frac{\beta}{s + \beta} \tag{7.44}$$

The feedback realization of $D^*(z)$ is shown in Fig. 7.16; $Q(s)$ can be easily realized by an R-C network with certain gain adjustments.

More complicated forms of $D^*(z)$ can be similarly realized by one or more feedback paths; this procedure utilizes the sampled-data sampler and its hold circuit plus the necessary network components.

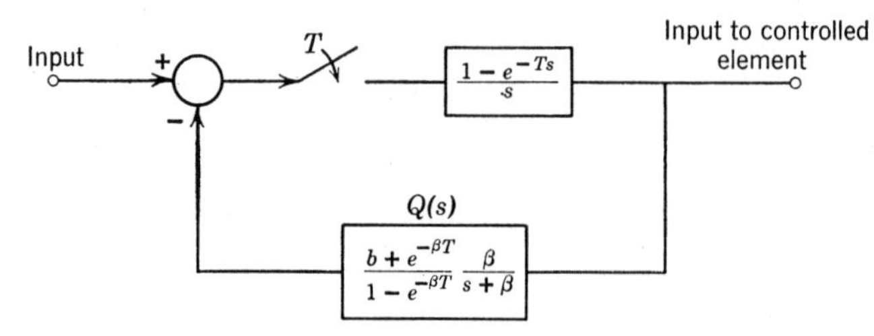

Figure 7.16 Feedback network realization

CHAPTER 8

Approximate Analysis of Continuous Control Systems

The application of the modified z-transform to sampled-data control systems yields the system response without evaluating the roots of the characteristic equations. This feature of the method makes the analysis of sampled-data systems easier than the corresponding continuous systems. The power series method of obtaining the response is readily applicable to obtaining the important response quantities of stable sampled-data control systems.

In order to apply the numerical technique developed in the modified z-transform to continuous control systems, the latter are purposely sampled either in the feedback path or in the forward path by inserting a fictitious sampler followed by a fictitious hold. This technique basically approximates the linear differential equation that describes the continuous output by a corresponding linear difference equation. In the literature, there exist several methods of such an approximation, widely known as numerical analysis technique. In this chapter it is shown that the z-transform method is but one of the several techniques used in such an approximate analysis of continuous control systems. The fictitious sampler and hold and their functions are discussed thoroughly, and a measure of the error of approximations is outlined. This technique is applicable to linear feedback control systems with and without pure delay and can be extended to non-linear and time-varying systems.

8.1 Approximate Systems

The mathematical approximation of a feedback control system by a corresponding sampled-data system † can best be visualized by noting

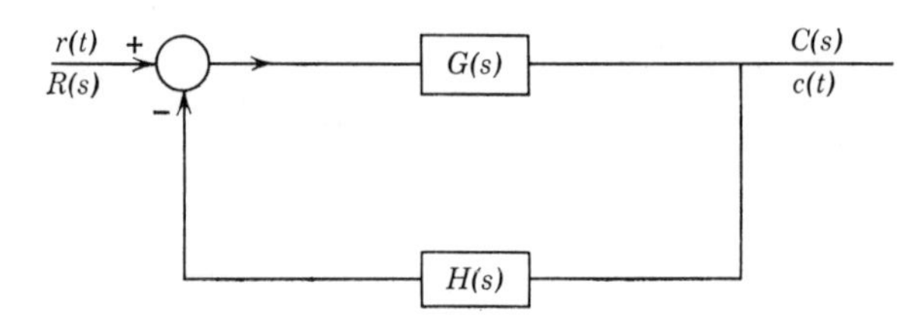

Figure 8.1 Continuous feedback control system

Figs. 8.1 and 8.2. It is noticed that Fig. 8.2 represents a sampled-data control system, and therefore the z-transform and the modified z-transform discussed in detail in the previous chapters are readily applicable.

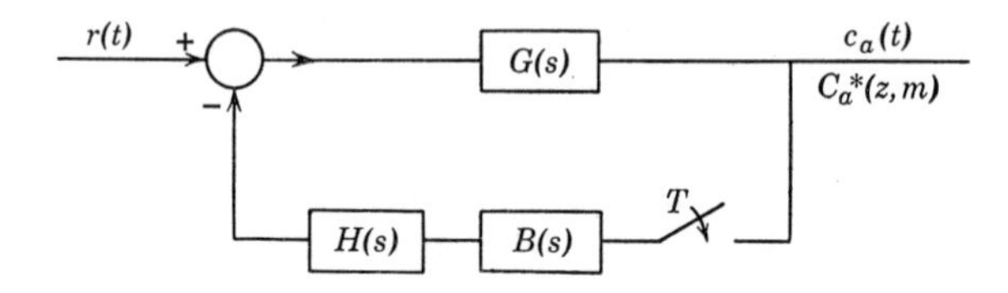

Figure 8.2 Sampled-data approximation of system in Fig. 8.1 with a fictitious (mathematical) sampler and hold $B(s)$

The modified z-transform of the output in Fig. 8.2 can be written readily as: ‡

$$C_a^*(z, m) = RG^*(z, m) - \frac{RG^*(z)\, HBG^*(z, m)}{1 + HBG^*(z)} \tag{8.1}$$

The approximate output can be obtained by the power series method indicated in Chapter 2. Thus, the roots of $1 + HG^*(z)$ need not be obtained if the system is stable as is assumed in this chapter.

† J. R. Ragazzini and A. R. Bergen, "A Mathematical Technique for the Analysis of Linear Systems," *Proc. I.R.E.*, Vol. 42, November 1954, pp. 1645–1651.

‡ E. I. Jury, "Additions to the Modified z-Transform Method," *I.R.E. Wescon Convention Record*, Pt. 4, August 20, 1957, pp. 136–156.

The output $c_a(t)$ is an approximation to the output $c(t)$ of the actual system, which when evaluated exactly requires the solution of the following complex integral:

$$c(t) = \mathfrak{L}^{-1}[C(s)] = \frac{1}{2\pi j}\int_{c-j\infty}^{c+j\infty} R(s)\frac{G(s)}{1 + G(s)H(s)}e^{ts}\,ds \tag{8.2}$$

To evaluate this integral, the roots of $1 + G(s)H(s) = 0$ need be obtained, which requires long computation if the system is of higher order.

The error between the actual and the approximated output mainly depends on the following three factors, namely:

1. The location of the fictitious sampler.
2. The frequency of the sampling.
3. The form of the fictitious hold circuit.

8.2 Location of the Sampler

Since the output element of a feedback control system is usually a low-pass filter or the output transform has a denominator of much higher order in s than the numerator, the frequency component of the signal is

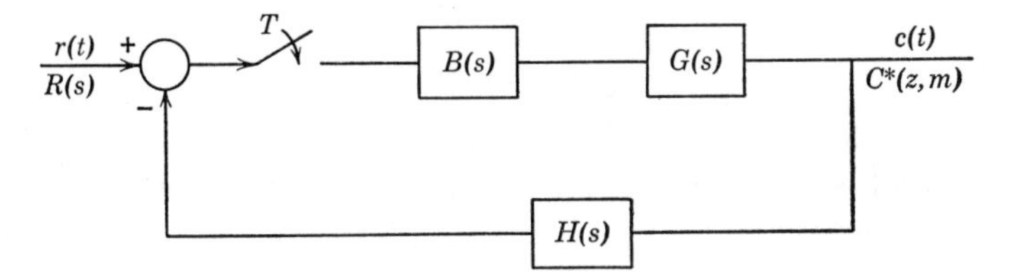

Figure 8.3 Error-sampled feedback system with a fictitious (mathematical) sampler and hold $B(s)$

filtered considerably; therefore it is only logical to sample the output or insert the sampler in the feedback path as shown in Fig. 8.2. However, if the input is given only in an experimental curve, it is necessary to insert the sampler † in the forward path as shown in Fig. 8.3. This is due to the form of equation (8.1) which requires that $R(s)$ be given in order to obtain $RG^*(z, m)$.

† J. R. Ragazzini and A. R. Bergen, "A Mathematical Technique for the Analysis of Linear Systems," *Proc. I.R.E.*, Vol. 42, November 1954, pp. 1645–1651.

The modified z-transform of the output in Fig. 8.3 is

$$C^*(z, m) = R^*(z) \times \frac{BG^*(z, m)}{1 + HBG^*(z)} \tag{8.3}$$

Thus, it is noticed from this equation that the input can be presented from experimental data in time.

8.3 The Choice of the Sampling Period

The error of approximation depends mainly on the sampling period. For instance, if the sampling period T is zero in the limit, the approximate system is exactly equivalent to the original system. On the other hand if T is large, the error of approximation is increased. However, the number of computations in obtaining the output is considerably less than for small T, and in the limit where $T \to 0$ the number of computations is infinite. Thus, the choice of the sampling period T requires a compromise between the error of approximation and the number of computations required on the desk calculator.

There are several criterion for the choice of T, and the one considered in this work is based on the frequency response of the output. For instance, if the output magnitude as a function of real frequency is written as

$$|(C(j\omega))| = \left|\frac{HG(j\omega)}{1 + HG(j\omega)}\right| \tag{8.4}$$

then we can choose a value of frequency, ω_k, that gives a small value of $|C(j\omega)|$, that is around 0.01. By obtaining such a frequency, the value of the sampling period is given by

$$T = \frac{\pi}{\omega_k} \tag{8.5}$$

To obtain an approximate value of ω_k, $|C(j\omega)|$ is approximated by its highest frequency, which avoids any exact calculations. Furthermore, the choice of the sampling period is also effected to a certain extent by the complexity of the fictitious hold that follows the sampler.

8.4 The Fictitious-Hold Form

The function of the fictitious hold is to reconstruct as much as possible the continuous function being sampled. Thus its form can be of several types, for example, staircase approximation, straight-line approximation, parabolic approximation, and higher powers of time hold. If $B(s)$ is chosen so that its output is a straight-line approximation of $c(t)$ between the sampling points, $c_a(t)$ will be very nearly $c(t)$. The transfer function of such a hold, shown in Fig. 8.4, is

$$B(s) = \frac{(1 - e^{-sT})^2 \, e^{sT}}{s^2 T} \tag{8.6}$$

This function is not physically realizable since it is only a mathematical model. The choice of a more complicated hold might effect the choice of the sampling period; then the sampler and the hold should be considered jointly in determining the initial value of the sampling frequency. Figure 8.5 indicates the polygonal approximation of the output function.

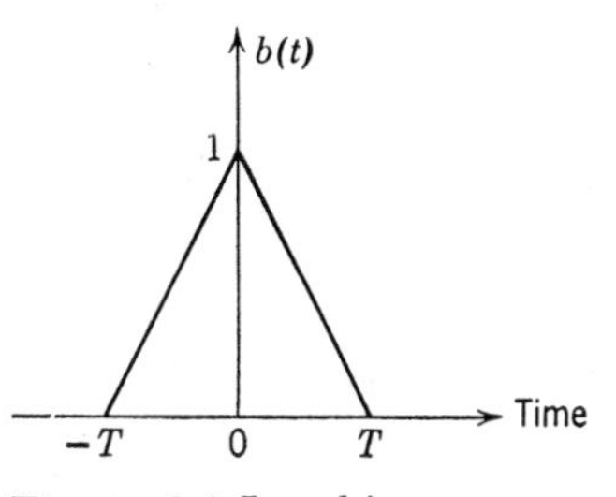

Figure 8.4 Impulsive response of a triangle hold

It is indicated that the output $c_a(t)$ can be obtained from the modified z-transform by power series expansion which involves the evaluation of the coefficients of the modified z-transform. This can be done by regular division or using a simplified formula, developed in the Appendix, which is of considerable help in the calculation of the approximate response.

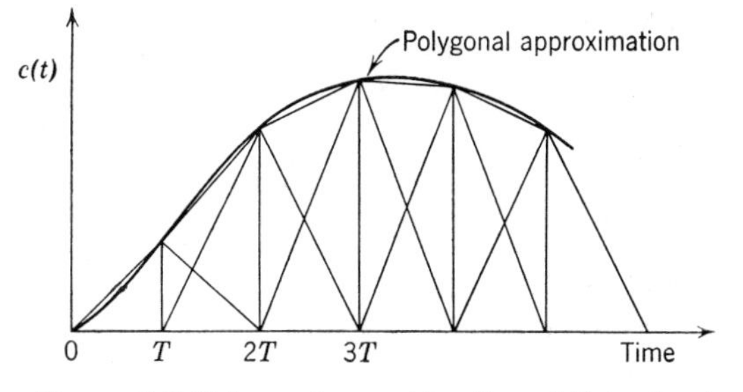

Figure 8.5 Polygonal approximation of the output

8.5 Analysis of the Error

The error entailed in such an analysis cannot be formulated exactly. The determination of the error bound is generally more elaborate than the actual procedure. The error bound becomes significant only when many samples are considered, as is done in the analysis using digital computers. However, the error can be readily estimated if the sampling period is halved or subdivided to calculate a few transient terms. The method of determining the modified z-transform coefficients described earlier is very convenient for such a procedure. If by so changing the sampling period the original solution is essentially unchanged or the change is small for engineering approximation, the original solution is satisfactory. Otherwise, the sampling period has to be changed to obtain better approximation.

Before concluding the discussion of this method, it must be mentioned that we can determine the initial sampling period from the frequency characteristics of the continuous-system open-loop transfer function in the same way, as has been done earlier in equation (8.4) for the frequency response of the output. This procedure is especially advantageous if the input is given only from experimental data in time.

8.6 z-Form and Modified z-Form Methods of Analysis †

In the previous section it has been shown how the modified z-transform method can be applied for approximate analysis of continuous feedback systems. It was indicated that to obtain the modified z-transform of the output, as noticed from equation (8.1), we must first obtain the z-transform and the modified z-transform of the open-loop components. This requires first the evaluation of the poles of the transfer function of such components, which may be quite laborious if only the frequency response is given. Therefore, approximate relations for the z-transform and the modified z-transform have been proposed by Boxer and Thaler; these approximate relations do not require the evaluation of the poles of the open-loop system and are called the z-forms and the modified z-forms. They are based on the following discussion.

a. *z-Forms Relations*

The inverse Laplace transform of a rational function of s is given by the following integral:

$$f(t) = \mathcal{L}^{-1}[F(s)] = \frac{1}{2\pi j}\int_{c-j\infty}^{c+j\infty} F(s)\, e^{ts}\, ds \tag{8.7}$$

† R. Boxer and S. Thaler, "A Simplified Method of Solving Linear and Non-Linear Systems," *Proc. I.R.E.*, Vol. 44, No. 1, 1956, pp. 89–101.

For simplicity c is assumed to be zero [that is, all poles of $F(s)$ lie in the left half plane], and the integration can then be performed along the imaginary axis in the s-plane as shown in Fig. 8.6.

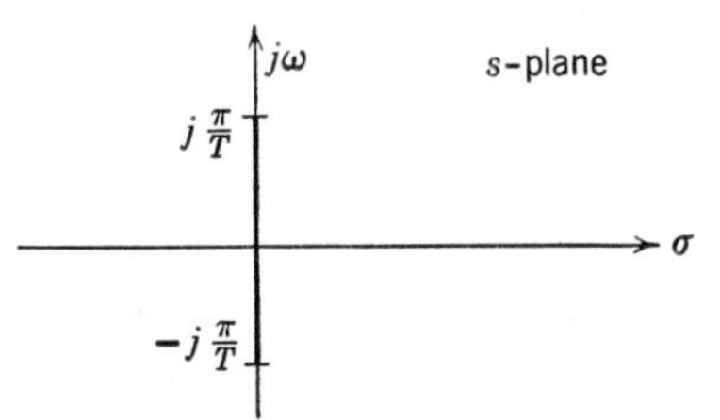

Figure 8.6 Path of integration in s-plane

Equation (8.7) can be written as the sum of the following integrals:

$$f(t) = \frac{1}{2\pi j}\int_{-j\pi/T}^{j\pi/T} F(s)\, e^{ts}\, ds + \frac{1}{2\pi j}\int_{j\pi/T}^{j\infty} [F(s)\, e^{st} + F(-s)\, e^{-st}]\, ds \tag{8.8}$$

If T is chosen small enough, then

$$f(t) \simeq f_A(t) = \frac{1}{2\pi j}\int_{-j\pi/T}^{j\pi/T} F(s)\, e^{ts}\, ds \tag{8.9}$$

The error is given by the following integral:

$$\text{Error} = \frac{1}{2\pi j}\int_{j\pi/T}^{j\infty} [F(s)\, e^{st} + F(-s)\, e^{-st}]\, ds \tag{8.10}$$

It is noticed that the error is zero if $T \to 0$. Let $t = nT$ in equation (8.9):

$$f_A(nT) = \frac{1}{2\pi j}\int_{-j\pi/T}^{j\pi/T} F(s)\, e^{snT}\, ds \tag{8.11}$$

Now $s = \dfrac{1}{T}\ln e^{Ts} = \dfrac{1}{T}\ln z$; thus equation (8.11) becomes

$$f_A(nT) = \frac{1}{2\pi j}\int_{\Gamma} \frac{1}{T} F\left(\frac{1}{T}\ln z\right) z^{n-1}\, dz \tag{8.12}$$

The contour Γ is the unit circle in the z-plane. The function $F\left(\dfrac{1}{T}\ln z\right)$ is a transcendental equation in z; thus a polynomial approximation for

$T/\ln z$ is affected:

$$\ln z = 2\left[\frac{1 - z^{-1}}{1 + z^{-1}} + \frac{1}{3}\left(\frac{1 - z^{-1}}{1 + z^{-1}}\right)^3 + \frac{1}{5}\frac{(1 - z^{-1})^5}{1 + z^{-1}} + \cdots\right] \tag{8.13}$$

$$\frac{1}{s} = \frac{T}{\ln z} = \frac{\dfrac{T}{2}}{\left(\dfrac{1 - z^{-1}}{1 + z^{-1}}\right) + \dfrac{1}{3}(u)^3 + \dfrac{1}{5}(u)^5 + \cdots} \tag{8.14}$$

$$= \frac{T}{2}\frac{1}{\left(\dfrac{1 - z^{-1}}{1 + z^{-1}}\right)} - \frac{1}{3}(u) - \frac{4}{45}(u^3) - \cdots$$

$$u = \frac{1 - z^{-1}}{1 + z^{-1}} \tag{8.15}$$

or

$$s^{-k} = \frac{N_k(z^{-1})}{(1 - z^{-1})^k} = F_k(z^{-1}) \tag{8.16}$$

and $F_k(z^{-1})$ is called the z-form of s^{-k}.

By retaining only the principal part and the constant term of the Laurent series in equation (8.14), a table of z-forms can be obtained (Table 8.1).

TABLE 8.1

z-Forms †

s^{-k}	$F_k(z^{-1})$
s^{-1}	$\dfrac{T}{2}\dfrac{1 + z^{-1}}{1 - z^{-1}}$
s^{-2}	$\dfrac{T^2}{12}\dfrac{1 + 10z^{-1} + z^{-2}}{(1 - z^{-1})^2}$
s^{-3}	$\dfrac{T^3}{2}\dfrac{z^{-1} + z^{-2}}{(1 - z^{-1})^3}$
s^{-4}	$\dfrac{T^4}{6}\dfrac{z^{-1} + 4z^{-2} + z^{-3}}{(1 - z^{-1})^4} - \dfrac{T^4}{720}$
s^{-5}	$\dfrac{T^5}{24}\dfrac{z^{-1}(z^{-1} + 11z^{-2} + 11z^{-3} + z^{-4})}{(1 - z^{-1})^5}$

† R. Boxer and S. Thaler, "A Simplified Method of Solving Linear and Non-linear Systems," *Proc. I.R.E.*, Vol. 44, No. 1, 1956, pp. 89–101.

Similar relations are obtained when $s \rightarrow j\omega$, where z is in this case $e^{Tj\omega}$.

b. Modified z-Forms †

As with the z-forms, we can obtain approximate relations to the modified z-transforms; these relations are called modified z-forms. By assuming the Laplace transform of a continuous output,

$$F(s) = \frac{c_0 + c_1 s + c_2 s^2 + \cdots + c_n s^n}{d_0 + d_1 s + d_2 s^2 + \cdots + d_k s^k} \tag{8.17}$$

If this equation is multiplied by e^{smT}, the inverse Laplace transform will be $f(t + mT)$. By letting m vary between zero and unity, we obtain the total response between the sampling instants if $f(t)$ is approximated by $f_A(nT)$ as discussed earlier.

The use of these relations requires rewriting equation (8.17) in the following form:

$$F(s) = \frac{c\left(\frac{1}{s^k}\right) + c_1\left(\frac{1}{s^{k-1}}\right) + \cdots + c_n\left(\frac{1}{s^{n-k}}\right)}{d_0\left(\frac{1}{s^k}\right) + d_1\left(\frac{1}{s^{k-1}}\right) + \cdots + d_k} \tag{8.18}$$

The numerator of equation (8.94) is multiplied by the Taylor series expansion of e^{smT}; that is,

$$e^{msT} = 1 + smT + \frac{(smT)^2}{2!} + \frac{s^3m^3T^3}{3!} + \cdots \tag{8.19}$$

If each term in the numerator is multiplied by the series and carrying terms that yield only the principal part plus a constant term, then

$$F(s)\, e^{smT} = \frac{c_0\left(\frac{1}{s^k}, s, mT\right) + c_1\left(\frac{1}{s^{k-1}}, s, mT\right) + \cdots\; c_n\left(\frac{1}{s^{n-k}}, s, mT\right)}{d_0\left(\frac{1}{s^k}\right) + d_1\left(\frac{1}{s^{k-1}}\right) + \cdots + d_k} \tag{8.20}$$

Substituting the z-forms of $1/s^k$, we obtain the modified z-forms. These modified z-forms are tabulated in Table 8.2.

† R. Boxer and S. Thaler, "Extensions of Numerical Transform Theory," Rome Air Development Center Technical Report, RADC-TR-56-115, November 1956.

TABLE 8.2

Modified z-Forms †

$\frac{1}{s^n}$	$F(m,z)$
$\frac{1}{s}$	$\frac{T}{2}\frac{(1+2m)z+(1-2m)}{(z-1)}$
$\frac{1}{s^2}$	$\frac{T^2}{12}\frac{\left\{(1+6m+6m^2)z^2+(10-12m^2)z+(1-6m+6m^2)\right\}}{(z-1)^2}$
$\frac{1}{s^3}$	$\frac{T^3}{12}\frac{\left\{(m+3m^2+2m^3)z^3+(6+9m-3m^2-6m^3)z^2+(6-9m-3m^2+6m^3)z+(-m+3m^2-m^3)\right\}}{(z-1)^3}$

† R. Boxer and S. Thaler, "Extensions of Numerical Transform Theory," Rome Air Development Center Technical Report, RADC-TR-115, November 1956.

If $m \to 0$, the modified z-forms reduce to the z-forms. The accuracy of the calculations is improved if m is allowed to vary in the range $-\frac{1}{2} \leq m \leq \frac{1}{2}$, to obtain the total response.

The procedures to be followed using the modified z-forms are:

1. The modified z-forms are substituted into the numerator of the Laplace transform expression.
2. The z-forms are substituted into the denominator of the Laplace transform expression.
3. Divide the resulting ratios of polynomials in z^{-1} by T. To obtain the time function carry on the synthetic division method by first choosing a particular value of T.

8.7 Discussion of the z-Form and the Modified z-Form Methods

This approximate method of analysis can be directly applied to the output transform $C(s)$ of a continuous feedback system. This assumes that $C(s)$ is the ratio of rational polynomials in s which may include transportation lag.† If the latter exists, this lag should be an integer value of the sampling period. The initial sampling period T can be determined exactly as in the first method, and the error of approximation can be considered if T is halved and a few terms of the calculations are repeated.

† The word transportation lag means the same as pure delay in this textbook.

In this method there exists no formula for upper bounds of the error of approximation. If the z-forms are used throughout the analysis, we obtain the response only at the sampling instants. However, if both the z-forms and the modified z-forms are used, we obtain the complete response at all instants of time.

Furthermore, this method can also be used in combination with the previous one by obtaining approximate relations for the modified z-transform and the z-transform of the system components. By so doing we can obtain the response of continuous system with transportation lags that are non-integer values of the sampling period. Thus by combination of the two approximate methods of analysis presented, we can solve a variety of systems and improve the degree of accuracy in some cases.

Illustrative Example

To illustrate the application of the z-transform method to the approximate analysis of continuous control systems, consider the system shown in Fig. 8.7 where

$$G(s)\, e^{-\Delta s} = \frac{s + 0.3}{s^2}\, e^{-s} \tag{8.21}$$

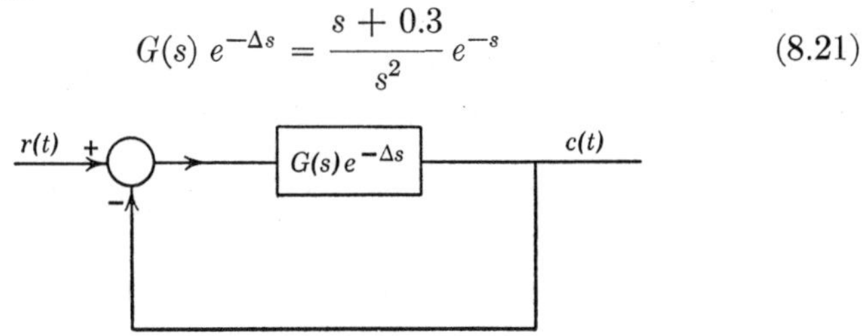

Figure 8.7 Continuous closed-loop system with delay

This example has been analyzed with the root-locus method.† The overall transfer function is

$$\frac{C(s)}{R(s)} = \frac{(s + 0.3)\, e^{-s}}{s^2 + (s + 0.3)\, e^{-s}} \tag{8.22}$$

and the roots were found to be

$$s = -0.41,\ -0.17 \pm j1.17,\ -2.06 \pm j7.56,\ -2.65 \pm j13.9, \cdots \tag{8.23}$$

All other roots are complex conjugates with larger negative real parts. Only the predominant first three roots were considered, and the approximate transient response to a ramp input was therefore found to be

$$c(t) = t - 1.17e^{-0.41t} + 1.35e^{-0.17t} \cos\,(1.17t + 0.61) \tag{8.24}$$

† Yaohan Chu, "Feedback Control Systems with Dead-time Lag or Distributed Lag by Root-Locus Method," *Trans. A.I.E.E.*, Vol. 71, Pt. II, 1952, pp. 291–296.

If the ramp response is determined by analyzing the sampled-data system shown in Fig. 8.8, the first step is to choose an appropriate sampling period T. The Laplace transform of the output is $R(s)$ times the

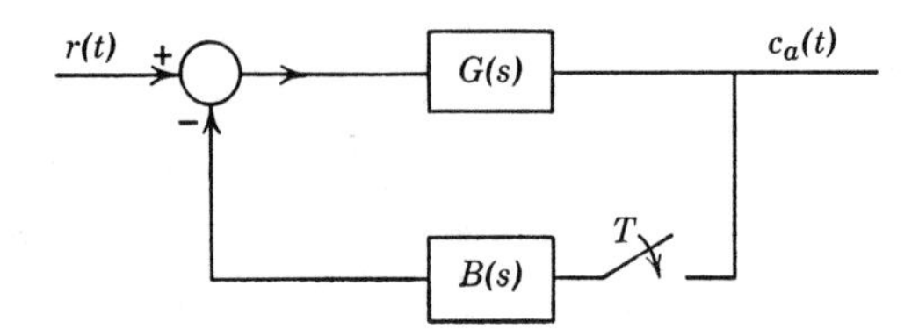

Figure 8.8 Sampled-data system approximation of Fig. 8.7

overall transfer function; therefore, for a unit ramp input,

$$C(s) = \frac{(s + 0.3)\, e^{-s}}{s^2[s^2 + (s + 0.3)\, e^{-s}]} \tag{8.25}$$

The relative real-frequency composition of the output can be obtained by replacing s with $j\omega$ in equation (8.25), which yields

$$C(j\omega) = \frac{(j\omega + 0.3)e^{-j\omega}}{-\omega^2[-\omega^2 + (j\omega + 0.3)e^{-j\omega}]} \tag{8.26}$$

Equating the absolute amplitude of $C(j\omega)$ to 0.01 yields

$$|C(j\omega)| = \frac{|j\omega + 0.3| \times |e^{-j\omega}|}{|\omega^2|\,|-\omega^2 + (j\omega + 0.3)e^{-j\omega}|} = 0.01 \tag{8.27}$$

An exact solution of equation (8.27) could be difficult, especially in more complicated systems. Fortunately, an exact solution is not necessary since any convenient ω yielding an absolute value near 0.01 will be satisfactory. Such an ω can be obtained by recognizing that for large ω equation (8.27) becomes approximately

$$|C(j\omega)| \simeq \frac{1}{\omega^3} = 0.01 \tag{8.28}$$

from which an upper frequency limit of 4.64 radians per second is obtained. Evaluation of equation (8.27) for ω equal to 4.64 yields an absolute value for $C(j\omega)$ of 0.012, and therefore the approximation made in equation (8.28) is satisfactory. A sampling frequency of twice 4.64

radians per second (twice because of sampling theorem) corresponds to a sampling period of 0.675 second. This sampling period can be used, but a T of 0.5 second is more convenient (also more accurate) since the delay is 1 second. It is not necessary for the delay to be an integer value of the sampling period, since a sampled-data system can be analyzed for any arbitrary delay.

With a period of 0.5 second, the approximate transient response at the sampling instants to a ramp input can be found from expression (8.1). The Laplace transform of the input times $G(s)$ is

$$R(s)\,G(s) = \frac{1}{s^2} \times \frac{(s+0.3)\,e^{-sT}}{s^2} \tag{8.29}$$

and from tables,

$$RG^*(z) = \frac{0.125(2.1z^2 + 0.4z - 1.9)}{2z(z-1)^4} \tag{8.30}$$

From equation (8.6),

$$H(s)\,B(s)\,G(s) = \frac{(1-e^{-sT})^2 e^{sT}}{Ts^2} \times \frac{(s+0.3)e^{-2sT}}{s^2} \tag{8.31}$$

and therefore

$$HBG^*(z) = \frac{(z-1)^2}{Tz} \times RG^*(z) = \frac{0.25(2.1z^2 + 0.4z - 1.9)}{2z^2(z-1)^2} \tag{8.32}$$

Substitution of equations (8.30) and (8.32) into (8.1) when m equals unity yields

$$C^*(z) = \frac{0.125(2.1z^2 + 0.4z - 1.9)z}{2z^2(z-1)^4 + 0.25(2.1z^2 + 0.4z - 1.9)(z-1)^2} \tag{8.33}$$

and simplification yields

$$C^*(z) = \frac{(1.05z^2 + 0.2z - 0.95)z}{(z-1)^2(8z^4 - 16z^3 + 10.1z^2 + 0.4z - 1.9)} \tag{8.34}$$

Long division of the denominator into the numerator yields the power series †

$$C^*(z) = 0.131z^{-3} + 0.550z^{-4} + 1.26z^{-5} + 2.18z^{-6} + 3.17z^{-7} + 4.10z^{-8} + 4.86z^{-9} + 5.41z^{-10} + 5.78z^{-11} + 6.05z^{-12} + \cdots \tag{8.35}$$

† W. I. Schroeder, "Analysis and Synthesis of Sampled-Data and Continuous Control Systems with Pure Time Delays," Electronics Research Laboratory Report, Series 60, Issue 156, June 1956, University of California, Berkeley.

The response at the sampling instants is given by the coefficients of equation (8.35) and is plotted in Fig. 8.9. The values at the sampling instants obtained from equation (8.24) are also shown for comparison.

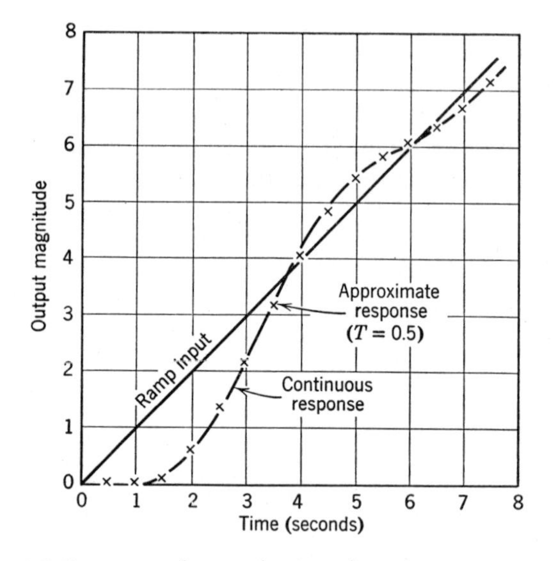

Figure 8.9 Responses of approximate and continuous-system example

The maximum difference between the two approximate responses is only 0.05, which occurs at t equal to 3.9. As a percentage this difference is only 1.5 per cent, all of which could be due to the accuracy of the calculations. This difference in magnitude is plotted in Fig. 8.10.

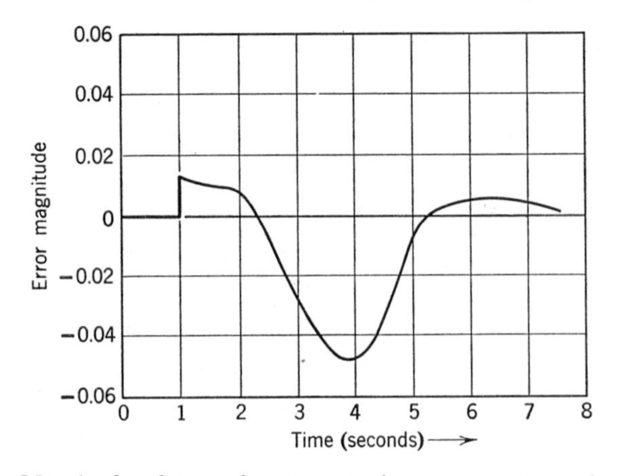

Figure 8.10 Magnitude of error between continuous response and approximate response

The procedure is quite simple; and the labor required for the long division is reduced by using the power series method of expanding $C^*(z)$ as follows:

$$C^*(z) = c_0 + c_1z^{-1} + c_2z^{-2} + \cdots \qquad (8.36)$$

The coefficients $c_0, c_1, \cdots, c_n$ can be easily obtained by using the relations developed in the Appendix.

The same procedure may also be used to evaluate the continuous time function from the modified z-transform, only in this case the coefficients $c_0, c_1, \cdots$ are functions of m instead of constants. Thus we may readily obtain the continuous response as well as that at the sampling instants. The accuracy may be increased by changing T and repeating the process. A negligible error between the first and second choice of T makes certain that the result is within engineering approximation.

8.8 z-Transform Method of Solution of Difference Equations

In the preceding discussion it has been shown that the z-transform can be applied for the approximate analysis of continuous systems. Mathematically, this indicates that the z-transform can be applied to the solution of the linear difference equations which approximate the differential equations that describe the continuous system. The process of approximation has been carried from the s-domain to the z-domain directly without having to obtain the approximate difference equations. In this section, it is shown how the z-transform can be applied directly to the solution of linear difference equations whose coefficients are constant or periodic. Furthermore, it is shown that a sampled-data system can be described by difference equations where the z-transform method for obtaining the system response is applied.

Transform techniques for the solution of difference equations are not new. Gardner and Barnes † have used the jump function and the Laplace transform. Fort ‡ has used the Dirichlet series transform whereas Neufeld § has solved linear mixed difference-differential equations with a transform method. Stone || has used the generalized Laplace transform,

† M. F. Gardner and J. L. Barnes, *Transients in Linear Systems*, Vol. 1, John Wiley & Sons, New York, 1942, Chapter 9.

‡ T. Fort, "Linear Difference Equations of the Dirichlet Series Transform," *Am. Math. Monthly*, November 1955, p. 641.

§ J. Neufeld, "On the Operational Solution of Linear Mixed Difference Differential Equations," *Cambridge Phil. Soc.*, Vol. 30, 1934, p. 289.

|| W. M. Stone, "A List of Generalized Laplace Transforms," *Iowa State Coll. J. Sci.*, Vol. 22, 1948, p. 215.

and Brown † has discussed the theoretical considerations of the method suggested by Tustin ‡ for solving linear differential equations. Thus the use of operators and transform method for solving difference equations is not new, and the z-transform method can be considered an extension of these ideas.

8.9 Solution of Linear Difference Equations with Constant Coefficients

Consider the following form of linear difference equation:

$$\sum_{i=0}^{p} a_i x_{n+i} = \sum_{i=0}^{q} b_i y_{n+i} \tag{8.37}$$

In this equation a_i and b_i are constants, y_n is the forcing function, known for all values of n, and it is desired to obtain x_n; x_n and y_n are functions of the parameter t but are defined only for $t = n$, where n is an integer equal to or greater than zero. Let x_n and y_n be represented by impulses occurring at $t = n$; using this representation for x_n and y_n and assuming zero initial conditions, we can take the z-transform of equation (8.37) and solve for $X^*(z)$.§ Then x_n can be obtained by performing the inverse contour integration in the z-plane or with the power series expansion method or through the use of tables as discussed in Chapter 1.

Following this procedure, we obtain

$$X^*(z) = Y^*(z) \frac{\sum_{i=0}^{q} b_i z^i}{\sum_{i=0}^{p} a_i z^i} \tag{8.38}$$

and $x(n)$ equals

$$x(n) = \frac{1}{2\pi j} \int_{\Gamma} X^*(z)\, z^{n-1}\, dz \tag{8.39}$$

If initial conditions are not zero, they are considered in the z-trans-

† B. M. Brown, *Automatic and Manual Control,* edited by A. Tustin, Butterworth Scientific Publications, London, 1951.

‡ A. Tustin, "A Method of Analyzing the Behavior of Linear Systems in Terms of Time Series," *J.I.E.E.* (London), Vol. 94, Pt. II, No. 1, 1947, pp. 130–142.

§ It should be noted that $X^*(z) = \sum_{k=0}^{\infty} x_k z^{-k}$.

formation process by noting that

$$\mathfrak{z}\,[x(n+k)] = z^k \left[X^*(z) - \sum_{n=0}^{k-1} x(n)\, z^{-n} \right] \tag{8.40}$$

where k is a non-negative integer. This equation only modifies the form of equation (8.38); however, the solution process is not changed. Since most sampled-data systems are described by difference equations with zero initial conditions, these are not considered in detail in this section.†

8.10 Solution of Difference Equations Whose Coefficients Are Periodic Functions

In the early discussion of this chapter and in the earlier chapters, it has been shown how to apply the modified z-transform to obtain the total response. The total response of a sampled-data system can be described by a difference equation whose coefficients are periodic functions; thus, the application of the modified z-transform for solving such equations will be discussed.

Consider the following type of difference equation:

$$x(t) = \sum_{i=0}^{p} f_i(t)\, x_{n+i} + \sum_{i=0}^{q} g_i(t)\, y_{n+i} \tag{8.41}$$

$$(n+p) \leq t \leq (n+p+1)$$

where $f_i(t)$ and $g_i(t)$ are arbitrary periodic functions of the independent variable t with periods equal to one: $x_n = x(t)\,|_{t=n}$ and y_n is a known function of t but is defined only for $t = n$ where n is an integer equal to or greater than zero. Let x_n and y_n be represented by impulses occurring at $t = n$. Because of the periodicity of $f(t)$ and $g(t)$, we may replace $f(t)$ and $g(t)$ by $f(m)$ and $g(m)$ where m is a parameter which varies from zero to one. With this change of variable the actual time scale becomes $t = n + p + m$ and equation (8.41) becomes

$$x(n+p+m) = \sum_{i=0}^{p} f_i(m)\, x_{n+i} + \sum_{i=0}^{q} g_i(m)\, y_{n+i} \tag{8.42}$$

† E. I. Jury and F. J. Mullin, "A Note on the Operational Solutions of Difference Equations," Electronics Research Laboratory Report, Series 60, Issue 199, January 1958, University of California, Berkeley; also *Journal Franklin Inst.*, Vol. 266, No. 3, 1958, p. 189.

If we take the modified z-transform of equation (8.42), there results

$$z^{p+1} X^*(z, m) = X^*(z) \left[\sum_{i=1}^{p} f_i(m) z^i \right] + Y^*(z) \left[\sum_{i=1}^{q} g_i(m) z^i \right] \quad (8.43)$$

in which both $X^*(z, m)$ and $X^*(z)$ are undetermined. However, $X^*(z)$ can be easily found by noting $x_n = x(n - 1 + m)|_{m=1}$. Thus, substituting $m = 1$ into equation (8.42) gives a difference equation with constant coefficients from which $X^*(z)$ can be determined as discussed in the preceding section. This expression for $X^*(z)$ can be substituted into equation (8.43), which then can be solved for $X^*(z, m)$. Following this procedure gives

$$X^*(z, m) = \frac{Y^*(z)}{z^{p+1}} \left[\frac{\left(\sum_{i=0}^{p} f_i(m) z^i \right) \left(\sum_{i=0}^{q} g_i(1) z^i \right)}{z^{p+1} - \sum_{i=0}^{p} f_i(1) z^i} + \sum_{i=0}^{q} g_i(m) z^i \right] \quad (8.44)$$

In this equation $x(n - 1 + m)$ or $x(t)$ can be found by using the contour integration, in which m is a constant during the integration process; this process can be represented by

$$x(n - 1 + m) = \frac{1}{2\pi j} \int_{\Gamma} X^*(z, m) z^{n-1} dz \quad (8.45)$$

The inverse can also be conveniently obtained with the aid of tables in Chapter 1, or using the power series expansion as follows:

$$X^*(z, m) = x_0(m) + x_1(m) z^{-1} + \cdots + x_n(m) z^{-n} + \cdots \quad (8.46)$$

The coefficients of z^{-k} represent $x(t)$ for $k \leq t \leq k + 1$ when m is varied from 0 to 1. The advantage of the power series expansion method is that knowledge of the roots of the characteristic equation is not necessary to obtain the solution. The stability requirements for this type of equation are the same as those for equations with constant coefficients.†

Illustrative Example 1

To illustrate the methods just given, a second-order sampled-data feedback system is chosen as shown in Fig. 8.11. The output of this system can be obtained through the use of difference equations. The differential equation which relates the output $c(t)$ to the output of

† E. I. Jury and F. J. Mullin, "A Note on the Operational Solutions of Difference Equations," Electronics Research Laboratory Report, Series 60, Issue 199, January 1958, University of California, Berkeley.

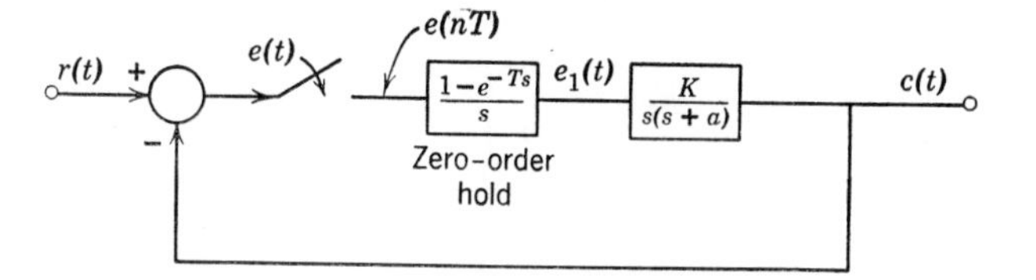

Figure 8.11 A second-order sampled-data feedback system

the zero-order hold $e_1(t)$ can be written as follows:

$$\frac{d^2c}{dt^2} + a\frac{dc}{dt} = K\,e_1(t) \tag{8.47}$$

It is noted that $e_1(t)$, the output of the hold, is constant except for sudden changes that occur at the sampling instants.† If equation (8.47) is integrated once and applied to the interval beginning at $(n-1)T$, we can write

$$\frac{dc}{dt} + ac = K\int_0^{(n-2)T} e_1(t)\,dt + K\int_{(n-1)T}^{nT} e_1(t)\,dt \tag{8.48}$$

but

$$K\int_0^{(n-2)\text{ interval}} e_1(t)\,dt = KT\sum_{k=0}^{n-2} e_1(kT) \tag{8.49}$$

Thus, equation (8.48) becomes

$$\frac{dc}{dt} + ac = KT\sum_{k=0}^{n-2} e_1(kT) + Kt'\,e_1(n-1)T, \qquad 0 \le t' \le 1 \tag{8.50}$$

The solution of this equation, which can be written in the following form,

$$\frac{dc}{dt} + ac = k_1 + k_2t, \qquad c(0^+) = c(n-1)T \tag{8.51}$$

is as follows:

$$c(t) = e^{-at'}\,c(n-1)T + \frac{Kt'}{a}\,e_1(n-1)T$$
$$+ (1 - e^{-at'})\left[\frac{KT}{a}\sum_{k=0}^{n-2} e_1(kT) - \frac{K}{a^2}\,e_1(n-1)T\right] \tag{8.52}$$
$$t' = mT,\ (n-1)T \le t \le nT$$

† R. H. Barker, "The Pulse Transfer Function and Its Application to Sampling Servo Systems," *Proc. I.E.E. (London)*, Vol. 99, Pt. IV, 1952, pp. 302–317.

It is noted that $e_1(n-1)T = e\,(n-1)T$; thus

$$c(t) = e^{-at'}\,c(n-1)T + \frac{Kt'}{a}\,e(n-1)T$$
$$+ (1 - e^{-at'})\left[\frac{KT}{a}\sum_{k=0}^{n-2} e(kT) - \frac{K}{a^2}\,e(n-1)T\right] \quad (8.53)$$
$$(n-1)T \le t \le nT, \quad t' = mT$$

This equation is similar to equation (8.42); thus we may apply the modified z-transform to the equation to obtain

$$C^*(z, m) = e^{-amT}z^{-1}\,C^*(z) + mT\frac{K}{a}\,z^{-1}\,E^*(z)$$
$$+ (1 - e^{-amT})\left[\frac{KT}{a}\frac{z}{z-1}\,z^{-2}\,E^*(z) - \frac{K}{a^2}\,E^*(z)\,z^{-1}\right] \quad (8.54)$$

We can obtain the response at the sampling instants by letting $t' = T$ in equation (8.53); thus

$$c(nT) = e^{-aT}\,c(n-1)T + T\frac{K}{a}\,e(n-1)T$$
$$+ (1 - e^{-aT})\left[\frac{KT}{a}\sum_{k=0}^{n-2} e(kT) - \frac{K}{a^2}\,e(n-1)T\right] \quad (8.55)$$

Taking the z-transform of this difference equation, we obtain

$$C^*(z) = e^{-aT}z^{-1}\,C^*(z) + T\frac{K}{a}\,z^{-1}\,E^*(z)$$
$$+ (1 - e^{-aT})\left(\frac{KT}{a}\frac{z}{z-1}\,z^{-2} - \frac{K}{a^2}\,z^{-1}\right)E^*(z) \quad (8.56)$$

or

$$C^*(z) =$$
$$\left(\frac{1}{1 - e^{-aT}z^{-1}}\right)\left[T\frac{K}{a}\,z^{-1} + (1 - e^{-aT})\,\frac{K}{a}\left(\frac{T}{z-1} - \frac{1}{a}\right)z^{-1}\right]E^*(z)$$
$$= G^*(z)\,E^*(z) \quad (8.57)$$

Substituting $C^*(z)$ in equation (8.54), we obtain the modified z-transform of the transfer function $G^*(z, m)$ as follows:

$$G^*(z, m) = \frac{C^*(z, m)}{E^*(z)} = \frac{K}{az}\left[\frac{(z-1)}{z-e^{-aT}} \cdot \frac{e^{-amT}}{a} + \frac{T}{z-1} + \left(mT - \frac{1}{a}\right)\right] \tag{8.58}$$

The other equation which relates the output to the input can be written

$$e(nT) = r(nT) - c(nT) \tag{8.59}$$

or, taking the z-transform of this equation, we obtain

$$E^*(z) = R^*(z) - C^*(z) \tag{8.60}$$

From equations (8.57) and (8.60) or (8.54), we obtain the z-transform or the modified z-transform of the output as

$$C^*(z, m) = R^*(z)\frac{G^*(z, m)}{1 + G^*(z)} \tag{8.61}$$

where

$$G^*(z) = \lim_{m \to 1} G^*(z, m)$$

From equation (8.61) the output can be obtained using the inverse modified z-transform or the power series method as discussed in Chapter 2.

Illustrative Example 2

In this example the z-transform method is applied to obtain the transfer function of a magnetic amplifier.† Under certain conditions the dynamic operation of a typical magnetic amplifier shown in Fig. 8.12 is

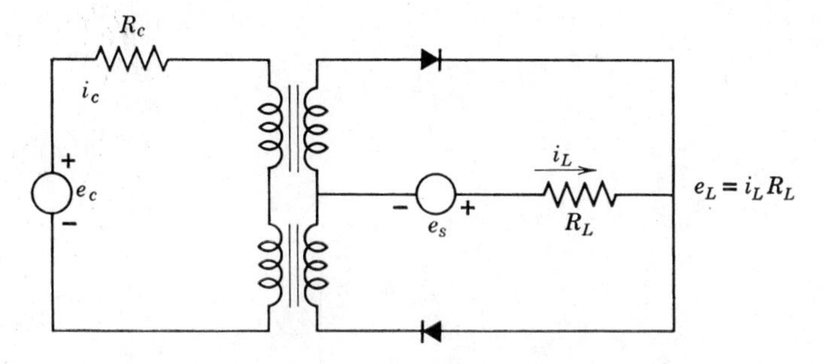

Figure 8.12 Typical magnetic amplifier circuit

† T. Kadota and H. C. Bourne, "Operational Magnetic Amplifiers with Multiple Control Windings," *Trans. A.I.E.E.*, Vol. 76, Pt. I, 1957, pp. 515–520.

described by the following linear first-order difference equation:

$$e_L(n+1) = k_1\, e_c(n+1) + k_2\, e_c(n) + k_3\, e_L(n) + k_4 \qquad (8.62)$$

in which $e_c(n)$ and, $e_c(n+1)$, $e_L(n)$, and $e_L(n+1)$ are half-cycle average values of control and output voltages for the nth and $(n+1)$th half-cycles respectively. The constants k_1, k_2, k_3, and k_4 are functions of the supply voltages, the magnetizing currents, and the circuit parameters and configurations.

Applying the z-transform into equation (8.62), we obtain

$$z[E_L^*(z) - E_L(0)] = k_1 z[E_c^*(z) - e_c(0)] + k_2\, E_c^*(z) + k_3\, E_L^*(z) + k_4 \frac{z}{z-1} \qquad (8.63)$$

or

$$E_L^*(z) = \frac{k_1 z + k_2}{z - k_3} E_c^*(z) + \frac{k_4}{z - k_3}\frac{z}{z-1} + \frac{z}{z-k_3}[e_L(0) - k_1\, e_c(0)] \qquad (8.64)$$

If the magnetic amplifier is assumed to be initially in steady state with no control voltage applied, that is, $e_c(n) = 0$ for $n < 0$, the initial conditions are obtained by substituting $n = -1$ into equation (8.62) to yield:

$$e_L(0) = k_1\, e_c(0) + k_3\, e_L(-1) + k_4 \qquad (8.65)$$

The output voltage $e(-1) = e(-2) = e(n < 0) = k_4/(1 - k_3)$ † together with equation (8.65) are substituted into equation (8.62) to obtain

$$E_L^*(z) = \frac{k_1 z + k_2}{z - k_3} E_c^*(z) + \frac{k_4}{1 - k_3}\frac{z}{z-1} \qquad (8.66)$$

The incremental transfer function is:

$$G^*(z) = \frac{k_1 z + k_2}{z - k_3} \qquad (8.67)$$

The block diagram representation of equation (8.66) is given in Fig. 8.13.

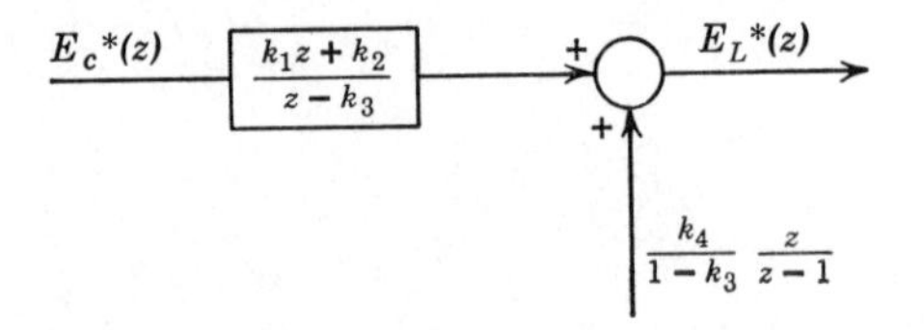

Figure 8.13 Block diagram of magnetic amplifier

† T. Kadota and H. C. Bourne, "Operational Magnetic Amplifiers with Multiple Control Windings," *Trans. A.I.E.E.*, Vol. 76, Pt. I, 1957, pp. 515–520.

Application of two theorems of the z-transform method to equation (8.67) gives the following conclusions.

1. Stability condition is $|k_3| < 1$
2. Final-value theorem gives the steady-state gain as:

$$K = \lim_{z \to 1} G^*(z) = \frac{k_1 + k_2}{1 - k_3} \tag{8.68}$$

It should be remarked in this example that a magnetic amplifier is not a sampled-data system, but through the impulse function representation, treatment as a sampled-data system is applicable if proper interpretation of the results is made.

When a magnetic amplifier is used as a compensating device (or pulse width modulating circuit) in a continuous control system, its transfer function in terms of z cannot be used directly, since neither the input nor its output are true impulses. However, if the components before and after the magnetic amplifier are low-pass filters with respect to the supply voltage frequency, the z-transform method can be (with its modification) extended to the whole system which contains the magnetic amplifier as a compensating device.

Illustrative Example 3. Application of Sampled-Data Control Theory to Inventory Control †

In this example the z-transform technique is applied to an economic problem often encountered in industry. It is intended to obtain a criterion for "reorder rule" whereby the cost of operation is minimized. The conditions of the operations are:

1. The system operates on a fixed interval, that is, stocks are reviewed and data taken periodically at equal intervals.
2. The "lead time" is fixed. The lead time is defined as the elapsed time between the issuance of an order to replenish stocks and the arrival of the order into stock. For convenience this lead time is measured in number of review intervals.
3. Orders for shipment out of stocks (e.g., customer orders) are filled immediately.

Under these conditions, the difference equation which describes the variation of inventory from a fixed quantity is as follows:

$$c_k = c_{k-1} + \theta_{k-(L+1)} - r_k \tag{8.69}$$

† Herbert J. Vassian, "Application of Discrete Variable Servo Theory to Inventory Control," *J. Operation Research Soc. Am.*, Vol. 3, No. 3, August 1955, pp. 272–282.

where c_k = variation of inventory from a fixed quantity, at the end of the kth period;
θ = recorder quantity, that is, the order placed for replenishment stock;
r_k = cumulative customer orders received during the kth period;
L = lead time.

In order to complete the description of an automatically controlled inventory system, a rule determining the quantity to be ordered is needed in addition to equation (8.69). Evidently, this reorder quantity is dependent on the past history of both the customer orders and the inventories. In this example the reorder rule is considered to be a linear combination of past customer orders and inventories. Thus, for this analysis, the general reorder rule is of the form:

$$\theta_k = \sum_{j=0}^{k} g_j r_{k-j} + \sum_{j=0}^{k} h_j c_{k-j} \tag{8.70}$$

where g_j and h_j are sequence constants which are chosen to suit any particular system.

The objective of this discussion is to obtain the particular set of values of the sequence constants that yields the most profitable specific reorder rule.

The system of equations (8.69) and (8.70) represents the basic form of a feedback system. This can be easily seen since the order quantity θ is the controlling function the input, and the inventory c is the output, the quantity to be controlled.

The corresponding z-transform of equations (8.69) † and (8.70) yields

$$C^*(z)(1 - z^{-1}) = z^{-(L+1)}\,\Theta^*(z) - R^*(z) \tag{8.71}$$

$$\Theta^*(z) = G^*(z)\,R^*(z) + H^*(z)\,C^*(z) \tag{8.72}$$

where $G^*(z)$ and $H^*(z)$ are the z-transforms of the sequences g_k and h_k, respectively. Eliminating $\Theta^*(z)$, we obtain

$$C^*(z) = R^*(z)\left[\frac{z^{-(L+1)}\,G^*(z) - 1}{1 - z^{-1} - z^{-(L+1)}\,H^*(z)}\right] \tag{8.73}$$

The sampled-data system representation of equations (8.71) and (8.72) is shown in Fig. 8.14. Block diagram reduction or transformation can be applied to Fig. 8.14 to yield the equivalent shown in Fig. 8.15. It is

† Note that for zero initial conditions

$$z^{-n}\,Y^*(z) = \sum_{k=0}^{\infty} y_{k-n} z^{-k}.$$

noticed that this block diagram transformation is equivalent to defining a new variable—in this case $E^*(z)$—and eliminating the former variable $\Theta^*(z)$.

The transformed sampled-data feedback block diagram reveals that the problem of minimizing inventory variations divides into two distinct

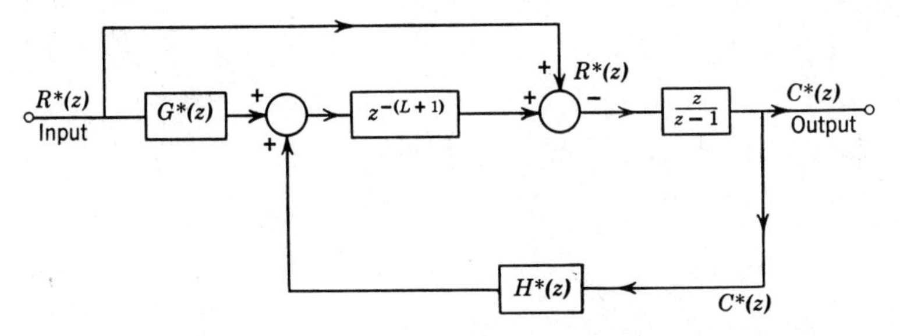

Figure 8.14 Sampled-data representation of equations (8.71) and (8.72)

parts: (*a*) choosing $G^*(z)$ to give the best possible forecast of customer orders; and (*b*) choosing $H^*(z)$ to minimize inventory variations resulting from forecast errors.

The choice of $G^*(z)$ depends on the statistical nature of customer order data; thus, no unique $G^*(z)$ exists. On the other hand, the choice

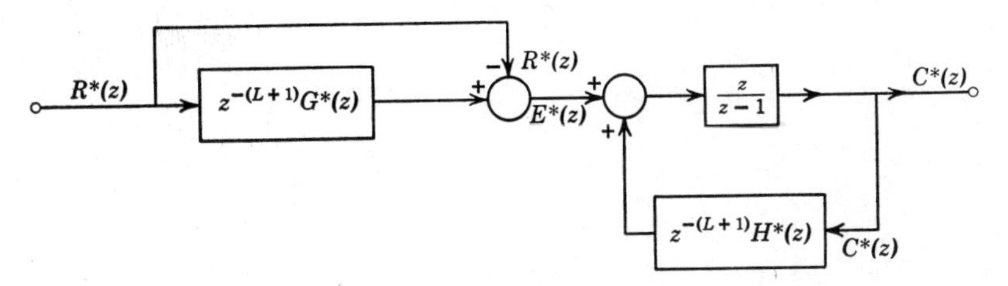

Figure 8.15 Equivalent sampled-data block diagram of Fig. 8.14

of $H^*(z)$ is common to all reorder systems, independent of the particular customer order statistics. Inventory variations are minimized by choosing $H^*(z)$ to provide the deadbeat response or minimum transient. This condition requires that all the roots of the characteristic equation be at the origin in the z-plane. A condition stemming from deadbeat response is discussed in Chapter 5. Thus, from equation (8.73), all poles of $C^*(z)$ will be at the origin in the z-plane if the following condition is satisfied:

$$H^*(z) = -\frac{1 - z^{-1}}{1 - z^{-(L+1)}} \tag{8.74}$$

From Fig. 8.15 it is noticed that for this choice of $H^*(z)$ we obtain

$$C^*(z) = \frac{1 - z^{-(L+1)}}{1 - z^{-1}} E^*(z) \tag{8.75}$$

And from equation (8.73) we find

$$C^*(z) = \frac{z^{-(L+1)}G^*(z)\, R^*(z)[1 - z^{-(L+1)}]}{1 - z^{-1}} - \frac{R^*(z)[1 - z^{-(L+1)}]}{1 - z^{-1}} \qquad (8.76)\dagger$$

For simplicity we make the following definitions,

$$R^{*\prime}(z) = \frac{z^{-(L+1)}\, G^*(z)\, R^*(z)[1 - z^{-(L+1)}]}{1 - z^{-1}} \tag{8.77}$$

and

$$R^{*\prime}(z) = a_0 + a_1 z^{-1} + a_2 z^{-2} + \cdots \tag{8.78}$$

We also note that

$$\frac{1 - z^{-(L+1)}}{1 - z^{-1}} = 1 + z^{-1} + z^2 + \cdots + z^{-L} = \sum_{k=0}^{L} z^{-k} \tag{8.79}$$

and

$$R^*(z) \frac{1 - z^{-(L+1)}}{1 - z^{-1}} = \sum_{k=0}^{\infty} (r_k + r_{k-1} + \cdots + r_{k-L}) z^{-k} \tag{8.80}$$

Then, from equations (8.76), (8.77), (8.78), and (8.80), we may deduce, by equating coefficients, the following:

$$c_k = a_k - (r_k + r_{k-1} + \cdots + r_{k-L}) \tag{8.81}$$

where c_k is the fluctuation of inventory about the prescribed level (at the end of the kth period). Since we desire c_k to be zero for all k, then a_k should be chosen as a forecast of total customer orders over the periods $k, k - 1, \cdots, k - L$; that is,

$$a_k = r'_{k-(L+1)}(L + 1) \tag{8.82}$$

where

$r'_{k-(L+1)}(L + 1) =$ forecast of total customer orders during periods $k - L$ through k

Thus,

$$R^{*\prime}(z) = \sum_{k=0}^{\infty} r'_{k-(L+1)}(L + 1) z^{-k} \tag{8.83}$$

† Also note that $C^*(z) = \sum_{k=0}^{\infty} c_k z^{-k}$.

To determine the reorder rule, equation (8.74) is substituted into the expression for $\Theta^*(z)$ in equation (8.72), giving

$$\Theta^*(z) = G^*(z)\,R^*(z) - \frac{1 - z^{-1}}{1 - z^{-(L+1)}}\,C^*(z) \tag{8.84}$$

By substituting for $G^*(z)\,R^*(z)$ from equation (8.77) in the above and noting equation (8.79), we finally obtain the z-transform equation of the reorder rule,

$$\Theta^*(z) \sum_{k=0}^{L} z^{-k} = \frac{1}{z^{-(L+1)}}\,R^{*\prime}(z) - C^*(z) \tag{8.85}$$

The corresponding difference equation is obtained by noting equation (8.83) to give

$$\theta_k = r'_k(L+1) - \sum_{j=1}^{L} \theta_{k-j} - c_k \tag{8.86}$$

where $r'_k(L + 1)$ = forecast of total customer orders during periods $k + 1$ through $k + L + 1$. This cumulative forecast is made during the kth period and is a function of $L + 1$.

CHAPTER 9

Analysis of Sampled-Data Systems with Finite† Pulse Width

9.0 Introduction

The methods of the z-transform and the modified z-transform discussed in the earlier chapters are mainly applicable to the analysis of sampled-data systems, assuming *zero* pulse width. Essentially the solutions are exact only if (*a*) the sampler transforms the finite amplitude of input signal to *true* impulses of equivalent area (physically impossible); or (*b*) the sampler is followed by an ideal hold circuit.

It was indicated previously, in Chapters 1 and 2, that with a finite pulse width and with the use of a hold circuit the z-transform or the modified z-transform can be used to obtain an approximate solution. This method is based on the assumption that the pulse width is small compared to the time constants of the system.

In this chapter, the degree of approximation involved using the z-transform is investigated, and a method for determining the response

† Dr. Farmanfarma has generously permitted the inclusion of certain material from his Doctor of Philosophy thesis in this chapter. The thesis investigation of Dr. Farmanfarma under the supervision of the author was conducted at the University of California in Berkeley, 1957.

when the pulse width is comparable to the system time constant is determined.

Investigating the effects of pulse width is of considerable importance in view of its engineering applications. For instance, a pulsed network in a servoloop might provide a desirable method of compensating the system. Also, techniques developed for the analysis of finite pulsed systems might eventually be applied to the analysis of relay servomechanisms and other servo systems employing various linear and nonlinear pulse-generating devices.

9.1 *p*-Transform Method of Analysis

Assume an ideal periodic sampler with period T and uniform pulse width h as shown in Fig. 9.1. To determine the relation between the Laplace transform of the input and output of the sampler, the following procedure is introduced.

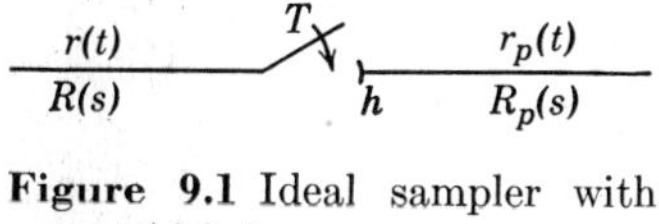

Figure 9.1 Ideal sampler with pulse width h

Let $r(t)$ in Fig. 9.2*a* be an arbitrary input to the sampler; then the corresponding output of an ideal periodic sampler is the time function shown in Fig. 9.2*c*. It is evident that we can reconstruct $r_p(t)$, by multiplying the input $r(t)$ by a time function $u_p(t)$ as shown in Fig. 9.2*b*, where

$$
\begin{aligned}
u_p(t) &= 1 \quad \text{for} \quad nT < t < nT + h \\
u_p(t) &= 0 \quad \quad nT + h < t < (n+1)T \\
& \quad n = 0, 1, 2, 3, \cdots, \infty
\end{aligned}
\tag{9.1}
$$

Figure 9.2 shows that when $r(t)$ is multiplied (or modulated) by the unit pulse function $u_p(t)$, the resultant time function $r_p(t)$ is the sampler output. Thus, in effect, the sampler may be regarded as a multiplier in the time domain, multiplying its input by the unit pulse function $u_p(t)$. Therefore, the relation between input and output in the time domain may be written as:

$$r_p(t) = r(t) \times u_p(t) \tag{9.2}$$

The Laplace transform of equation (9.2) can be obtained using the complex convolution theorem as follows:

$$R_p(s) = \mathfrak{L}\,[r_p(t)] = \frac{1}{2\pi j}\int_{c-j\infty}^{c+j\infty} R(\nu)\, u_p(s-\nu)\, d\nu \tag{9.3}$$

where

$$\mathcal{L}\,[r(t)] = R(s) \tag{9.3a}$$

$$\mathcal{L}\,[u_p(t)] = U_p(s) = \frac{1 - e^{-hs}}{s(1 - e^{-Ts})} \tag{9.4}$$

Substituting equations (9.3a) and (9.4) in (9.3), we obtain

$$R_p(s) = \frac{1}{2\pi j} \int_{c-j\infty}^{c+j\infty} R(\nu) \frac{1 - e^{-h(s-\nu)}}{(s - \nu)[1 - e^{-T(s-\nu)}]} \, d\nu \tag{9.5}$$

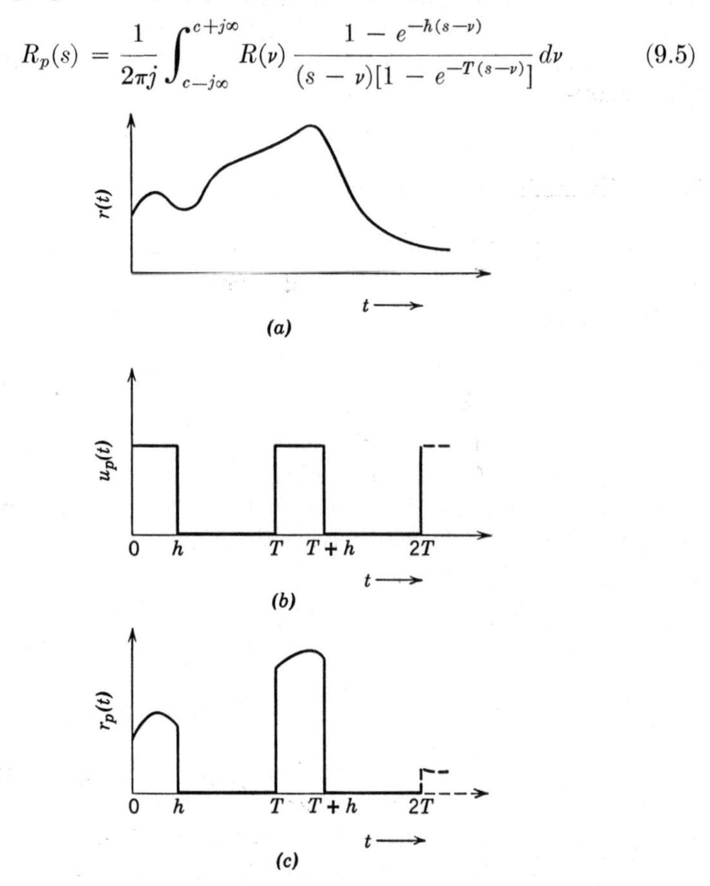

Figure 9.2 (a) Input signal to sampler, (b) unit pulse function, (c) sampler output constructed by multiplying input by unit pulse function

The line integral $(c - j\infty)$ to $(c + j\infty)$ can be evaluated either in the right or left half-plane of the complex plane ν.

Evaluating the integral in the left half-plane which encloses all the poles of $R(\nu)$ as shown in Fig. 9.3, we find that equation (9.5) becomes

$$R_p(s) = \frac{1}{2\pi j} \oint R(\nu) \frac{1 - e^{-h(s-\nu)}}{(s - \nu)[1 - e^{-T(s-\nu)}]} \, d\nu \tag{9.6}$$

where

$$R(\nu) = R(s)\big|_{s=\nu} \tag{9.7}$$

Equation (9.6) expresses the Laplace transform of the sampler output in terms of the Laplace transform of its input. Hence, the sampler can be regarded as an operator in the s-plane transforming the input $R(s)$ ac-

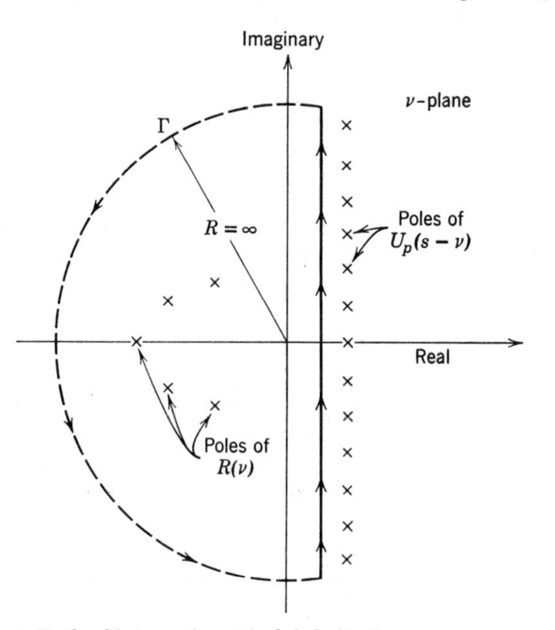

Figure 9.3 Path of integration Γ in left half-plane of complex variable ν

cording to equation (9.6) to yield the output $R_p(s)$. This is called p-transformation and is denoted by

$$R_p(s) = \mathsf{P}\,[R(s)] \tag{9.8}$$

and its inverse is denoted by

$$r_p(t) = \mathsf{P}^{-1}\,[R_p(s)] \tag{9.9}$$

It is evident from the preceding equations that the p-transform is only a particular form of the Laplace transform.

Equation (9.6) can be readily evaluated by the sum of the residue if $R(s)$ has no branch points and consists of poles and zeros.

If we assume that

$$R(s) = \frac{A(s)}{B(s)} \tag{9.10}$$

where $A(s)$ and $B(s)$ are polynomials in s, then $R_p(s)$ can be expressed as

$$R_p(s) = \sum_{\substack{\text{roots of}\\ B(\nu)}} \text{Residue of} \left\{ \frac{A(\nu)}{B(\nu)} \frac{1 - e^{-h(s-\nu)}}{(s-\nu)[1 - e^{-T(s-\nu)}]} \right\} \begin{array}{l}\text{at the}\\ \text{roots of } B(\nu)\end{array} \tag{9.11}$$

A special case arises when $R(s)$ has simple poles only; then equation (9.11) reduces to

$$R_p(s) = \sum_{n=1}^{N} \frac{A(\nu_n)}{B'(\nu_n)} \frac{1 - e^{-h(s-\nu_n)}}{(s-\nu_n)[1 - e^{-T(s-\nu_n)}]} \tag{9.12}$$

where

$$B'(\nu_n) = \left. \frac{dB(\nu)}{d\nu} \right|_{\nu=\nu_n}$$

and $\nu_1, \nu_2, \cdots, \nu_N$ are the simple roots of $B(\nu)$. Equations (9.11) and (9.12) indicate that the p-transform of the input functions is composed

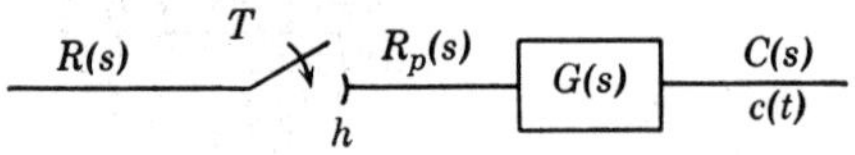

Figure 9.4 Finite pulsed sampled-data system

of functions of e^{-hs}, e^{-Ts}, and s, and the finite summation indicates that it is given in a closed form.

The output transform of the sampled-data system with finite pulse width shown in Fig. 9.4 can be obtained using the regular Laplace transform multiplication:

$$C(s) = R_p(s) \times G(s) \tag{9.13}$$

Table 9.1 (page 378) gives the p-transform of various functions of s. This table with the aid of partial fraction expansion can be used to determine the p-transform of the most encountered functions.

Alternately, evaluating $R_p(s)$ by integrating in the right half of the ν-plane † shown in Fig. 9.5, we obtain

$$R_p(s) = \frac{1}{2\pi j} \oint R(\nu) \frac{1 - e^{-h(s-\nu)}}{(s-\nu)[1 - e^{-T(s-\nu)}]} d\nu \tag{9.14}$$

Equation (9.14) is equal to

$$R_p(s) = -\sum \text{Residue of integrand at the poles of} \frac{1 - e^{-h(s-\nu)}}{(s-\nu)[1 - e^{-T(s-\nu)}]} \tag{9.15}$$

† E. I. Jury, "Progress in Sampled-Data Systems," A.I.E.E. Transaction Paper No. CP58-1182, presented at the Fall General Meeting, Pittsburgh, Pa., October 26–31, 1958.

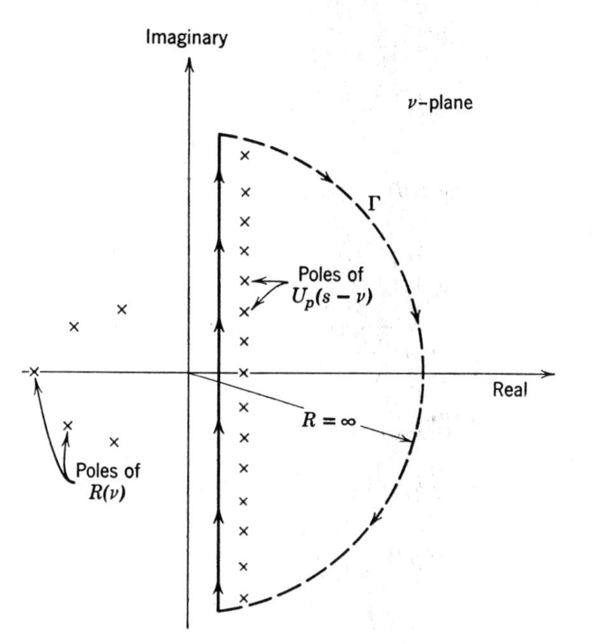

Figure 9.5 Path of integration Γ in right half-plane of complex variable ν

This has simple poles at

$$\nu = s \quad \text{and} \quad \nu = s + \frac{2\pi jk}{T}, \qquad -\infty < \underset{k\neq 0}{k} < \infty \tag{9.15a}$$

Let $\omega_r = 2\pi/T$. Then

$$R_p(s) = -\sum_{\substack{k=-\infty \\ k\neq 0}}^{k=\infty} \frac{1}{2\pi j} R(s + j\omega_r k) \frac{1 - e^{jhk\omega_r}}{k} + R(s)\frac{h\omega_r}{2\pi} \tag{9.16}$$ †

Figure 9.6 indicates the complementary frequency components of the sampler output for various values h/T. It is seen that as h/T becomes larger, the complementary frequency components reduce in magnitude. Therefore, less filtering of these components at the sampler output is required.

It can easily be noted that when $h \to T$, then $R_p(s)$ becomes

$$R_p(s) = R(s) \tag{9.17}$$

Also when $h \to 0$ and the pulse function shown in Fig. 9.2*b* approach

† This equation indicates that the effect of the finite pulse width sampler is to introduce high-frequency components (complementary components) at its output.

unit impulses, $R_p(s)$ becomes

$$R_p(s) = \frac{1}{T} \sum_{k=-\infty}^{k=\infty} R(s + jk\omega_r) = R^*(s) \tag{9.18†}$$

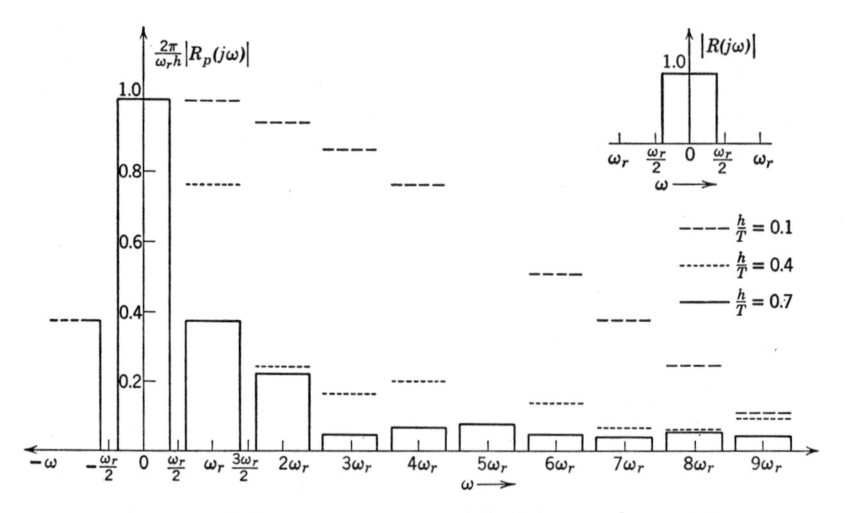

Figure 9.6 Frequency spectrum of the finite sampler output

9.2 Inverse *p*-Transform Method

It is evident from equation (9.13) that the output $C(s)$ is usually composed of rational function of e^{-Ts} and s and furthermore that the poles of $C(s)$ are infinite in number in the s-plane. Because of these infinite poles attempts to use the inverse Laplace integral results in time function of an infinite series form.

To obtain the time solution $c(t)$ in a closed form, we may use the inverse modified z-transform, that is,

$$c(t) = \mathcal{L}^{-1}[C(s)] = \mathfrak{z}_m^{-1}[C^*(z, m)]_{t=(n-1+m)T} \tag{9.19}$$

where $C^*(z, m)$ is the modified z-transform of $C(s)$.

Thus equation (9.19) provides an alternative method for evaluating the inverse Laplace through the use of the modified z-transform.

† This expression can easily be obtained by multiplying equation (9.16) by K and taking the limit as $h \rightarrow 0$ and $hK \rightarrow 1$.

The inverse p-transform is defined in the following relation

$$c(t) = \mathsf{P}^{-1}[C(s)] = \mathfrak{z}_m^{-1}[C^*(z, m)]_{t=(n-1+m)T} = \frac{1}{2\pi j}\int_{\Gamma} C^*(z, m)z^{n-1}\,dz$$

$$t = (n - 1 + m)T \qquad (9.20)$$

where "Γ" is a path of integration in the z-plane that encloses all the singularities of $C^*(z, m)$. Most common inverse p-transforms are tabulated in Table 9.2 (page 380).

From Table 9.2 it is noticed that the inverse p-transform is expressed as a function of t, n, m, T and $d(-h)$, where $d(-h)\,k\,f(t)$ denotes a delay of h seconds along the positive time axis operating on the function $k\,f(t)$. Its meaning is further illustrated in Fig. 9.7. The time t is related to n, m, and T by equation

$$t = (n - 1 + m)T \qquad (9.21)$$

where $t > 0$

T = sampling period in seconds;

n = 1, 2, 3, $\cdots$ = the number of sampling period from zero time; n can be zero if $m = 1$ as seen from equation (9.21);

m = a numeric such that at all times $0 \leq m \leq 1$.

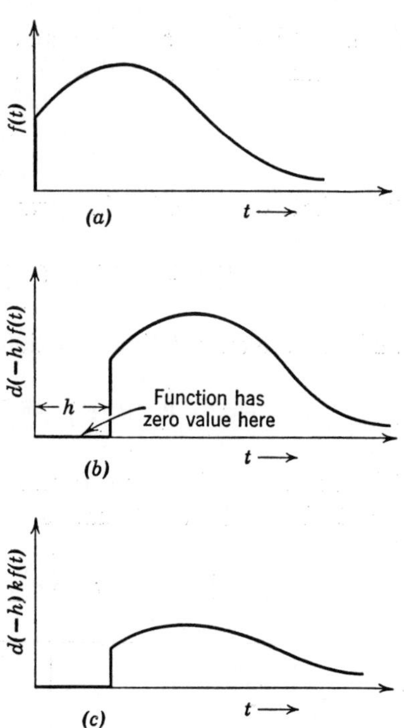

Figure 9.7 Illustrating meaning of $d(-h)\,f(t)$

Equation (9.20) indicates that $c(t)$, the output, can be obtained either by evaluating the residues of $C^*(z, m)\,z^{n-1}$ in the z-plane, or by using the power series method as discussed in Chapter 2.

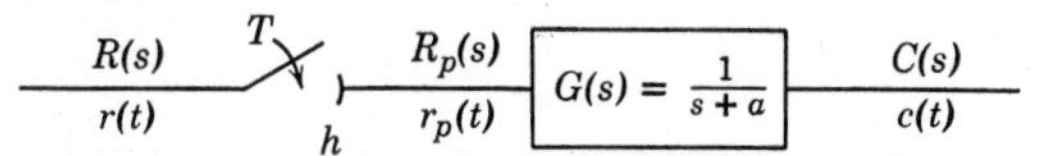

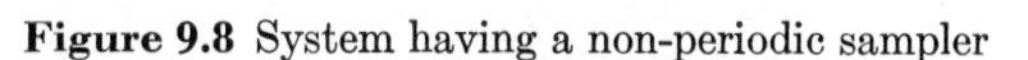

Figure 9.8 System having a non-periodic sampler

To illustrate, consider the system shown in Fig. 9.8. Let the input be

$$r(t) = u(t)\text{(unit step)} \qquad (9.22)$$

whose transform is

$$R(s) = \frac{1}{s} \tag{9.23}$$

Then the p-transform of $R(s)$ is given by

$$R_p(s) = \mathsf{P}\left[\frac{1}{s}\right] = \frac{1}{2\pi j}\int_{\Gamma}\frac{1}{\nu}\,\frac{1 - e^{-h(s-\nu)}}{(s-\nu)[1 - e^{-T(s-\nu)}]}\,d\nu \tag{9.24}$$

Because the integrand in equation (9.25) has simple poles, equation (9.12) can be used to find $R_p(s)$ as

$$R_p(s) = \frac{1 - e^{-hs}}{s(1 - e^{-Ts})} \tag{9.25}$$

Therefore, $C(s)$, the Laplace transform of the output, is

$$C(s) = R_p(s) \times G(s) = \frac{1 - e^{-hs}}{1 - e^{-Ts}} \times \frac{1}{s(s+a)} \tag{9.26}$$

and $c(t)$, the output time function, is given by

$$c(t) = \mathsf{P}^{-1}[C(s)] = \mathsf{P}^{-1}\left[\frac{1 - e^{-hs}}{1 - e^{-Ts}} \times \frac{1}{s(s+a)}\right] \tag{9.27}$$

The output can be found from relation 5 of Table 9.2. For the values $a = 1$, $T = 0.5$, it is equal to

$$c(t) = [1 - d(-h)]\left\{n - \frac{1}{e^{0.5} - 1}\,[e^{-0.5(m-1)} - e^{-t}]\right\} \tag{9.28}$$

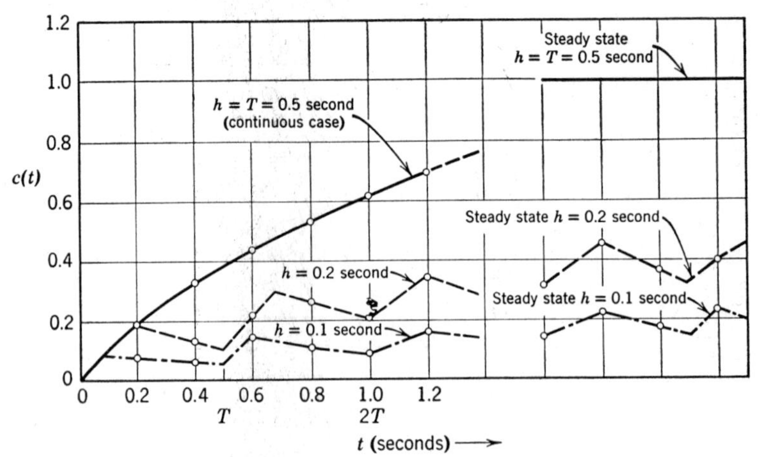

Figure 9.9 Exact response for finite pulsed system shown in Fig. 9.8: $R(s) = 1/s$, $a = 1$, and $T = 0.5$ second

The time function $c(t)$ is plotted in Fig. 9.9 for various values of h including $h = T = 0.5$ the continuous case.

Furthermore, the output can also be obtained by the power series method, that is by expanding $\mathfrak{z}_m\left[\frac{1-e^{-hs}}{1-e^{-Ts}}\frac{1}{s(s+a)}\right]$ in powers of z^{-1} and noting that e^{-hs} introduces only delay in the time function obtained.

9.3 Limiting Cases of p-Transform and Limitations of the z-Transform Method

The p-transform must satisfy certain known limiting conditions. It is interesting to study these limiting cases and compare the results with

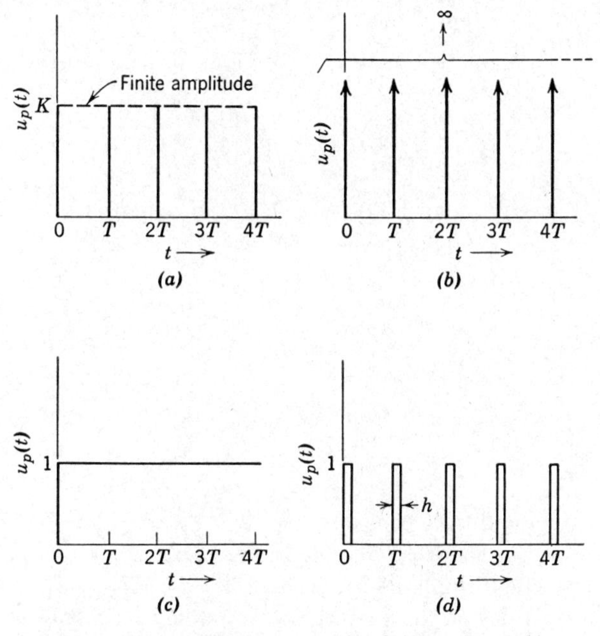

Figure 9.10 Limiting cases of pulse function $u_p(t)$

those physically expected. There are four possible limits:

1. $h = 0$ with $u_p(t)$ having any *finite* amplitude K (Fig. 9.10a).
2. $h = 0$ but $u_p(t)$ becomes unit impulses (i.e., has infinite amplitude and area = unity) (Fig. 9.10b).
3. $h = T$, $u_p(t)$ becomes unit step (Fig. 9.10c).
4. h is small compared to time constants of the system (Fig. 9.10d).

a. Case 1

In Fig. 9.10*a*, h equals 0 and $u_p(t)$ has finite amplitude K. This is a trivial case. Under these conditions, the Laplace transform of the pulse function can be written as

$$\mathcal{L}\,[u_p(t)] = \frac{\int_0^0 Ke^{-st}\,dt}{1 - e^{-Ts}} = 0 \tag{9.29}$$

Thus the sampler output is zero, and the system remains at rest. This is to be expected since under these conditions the system does not receive any energy to cause a change.

b. Case 2

In Fig. 9.10*b*, h equals 0 and $u_p(t)$ becomes unit impulses (unit area). Then

$$\mathcal{L}\,[u_p(t)] = \frac{1}{1 - e^{-Ts}} \tag{9.30}$$

Substitution of equation (4.30) for $\mathcal{L}\,[u_p(t)]$ in equation (4.3) gives

$$R_p(s) = \frac{1}{2\pi j} \oint R(\nu) \frac{1}{1 - e^{-T(s-\nu)}}\, d\nu \tag{9.31}$$

which is the relation used to determine the z-transform of the function $R(\nu)$. Therefore

$$\lim_{\substack{h \to 0 \\ K \to \infty \\ hK \to 1}} R_p(s) = R^*(z)\,\big|_{z=e^{sT}} \tag{9.32}$$

where K is the amplitude of $u_p(t)$.

This case occurs in problems where mathematically the behavior of the system can be formulated in terms of *true* impulses (see also case 4). In such cases tables of z-transform and modified z-transform and their inverse together with Table 9.2 are suitable for finding a solution.

c. Case 3

In Fig. 9.10 *c*, h equals T and $u_p(t)$ has unit amplitude. From Table 9.1 and equation (9.5) it is readily seen that

$$\lim_{h \to T} R_p(s) = R(s) \tag{9.33}$$

This is clearly an expected result. From equations (9.33) and (9.20) it follows that

$$\lim_{h \to T} \mathsf{P}^{-1} [R_p(s)] = \mathfrak{L}^{-1} [R(s)] \tag{9.34}$$

This, although true, is not obvious from the inverse tables because of the particular method used to evaluate the inverse p-transform. However, it is possible to show both analytically and numerically that relation (9.34) is satisfied by any one of the p-transform pairs listed in Table 9.2.† For example, by referring to Fig. 9.8 and from equations (9.25) and (9.28) it is to be expected that

$$c(t) = [1 - d(-T)] \left\{ n - \frac{1}{e^{0.5} - 1} [e^{-0.5(m-1)} - e^{-t}] \right\}$$

$$= \mathfrak{L}^{-1} \left[\frac{1}{s(s+1)} \right] \tag{9.35}$$

Figure 9.9 shows that this identity is satisfied for the assumed value of $T = 0.5$ second. This property of the p-transformation provides a valuable check for numerical calculations.

d. Case 4

In Fig. 9.10*d*, h is small compared to the time constants of the system. This case can be best illustrated by means of an example. Consider the system shown in Fig. 9.8, with a single time constant $\tau = 1/a$. Assuming a step input, the output can be written as

$$C(s) = \frac{1 - e^{-hs}}{(1 - e^{-Ts})s} \frac{1}{s + a} \tag{9.36}$$

For $t > h$, the numerator can be expanded in powers of hs, and if (for the time being) h is sufficiently small so that $(h^2 s^2)$ and higher powers can be neglected, $C(s)$ may be closely approximated by

$$C_1(s) = \frac{h}{1 - e^{-Ts}} \frac{1}{s + a} = \left(\frac{hz}{z - 1} \frac{1}{s + a} \right)_{z = e^{sT}} \tag{9.37}$$

where $C_1(s)$ is an approximate transform. Equation (9.37) is the z-transform approximation used for solving such a system. Comparison of equations (9.36) and (9.37) shows that, effectively, the finite pulses in equation (9.36), with an area $hK(k = 1$, unit step input), have been

† See note at end of table 9.2.

replaced by impulses of equal area and then multiplied by system transfer function to obtain the approximate transform $C_1(s)$. It is the purpose of the following section to derive the inverse of equation (9.36) in order to compare it with the approximate inverse obtained from equation (9.37) and hence show the extent of the approximation caused by the use of equation (9.37).

For clarity it is advisable to divide the time axis into four regions corresponding to the four operations of the sampler during each cycle. Let these be

(i) $t = nT, \quad n = 0, 1, 2, 3, 4, \cdots$ The actual sampling instants.

(ii) $nT < t < nT + h$ The time during which the sampler is *definitely* closed.

(iii) $t = nT + h$ The actual instants at which the sampler is transferred from closed to open position.

(iv) $nT + h < t < (n + 1)T$ The time during which the sampler is definitely open.

Regions (i) and (iii) are the boundary points.

Equation (9.36) for the exact transform of the output may be written as

$$C(s) = \frac{1 - e^{-hs}}{s(s + a)} (1 + e^{-Ts} + e^{-2Ts} + \cdots) \tag{9.38}$$

Let

$$\mathcal{L}^{-1} [R(s)\, G(s)] = \mathcal{L}^{-1} \left[\frac{1}{s(s + a)}\right] = c(t) = \frac{1}{a} (1 - e^{-at}) \tag{9.39}$$

From these the inverse time function can be evaluated term by term as

$$c(t) = \frac{1}{a} (1 - e^{-at}), \qquad \text{for } 0 \leq t \leq h \tag{9.40}$$

$$c(t) = \frac{1}{a} (e^{ah} - 1)e^{-at}, \qquad \text{for } h \leq t \leq T \tag{9.41}$$

These may be generalized as follows: for $nT \leq t \leq nT + h$ [i.e., Regions (i), (ii), and (iii)],

$$c(t) = \left\{\frac{e^{ah} - 1}{a} [1 + e^{aT} + e^{2aT} + \cdots + e^{(n-1)aT}]e^{-at} + \frac{1}{a} [1 - e^{-a(t-nT)}]\right\} \tag{9.42}$$

and for $nT + h \leq t \leq (n + 1)T$ [i.e., Regions (i), (iii), and (iv)],

$$c(t) = \frac{e^{ah} - 1}{a}(1 + e^{aT} + e^{2aT} + \cdots + e^{anT})e^{-at} \tag{9.43}$$

The output at the sampling instants $t = nT$ can be obtained from equation (9.42) and is

$$c(nT) = \frac{e^{ah} - 1}{a}(e^{-aT} + e^{-2aT} + \cdots + e^{-anT}) + c(0) \qquad (9.44)\dagger$$

where $c(0) = c(t)\big|_{t=0}$ [see equation (9.39)].

Equation (9.44) gives the true output at the sampling instants $t = nT$, since it is derived from the exact transform. When the ratio $ah = h/\tau(\tau =$ time constant) is small so that a^2h^2 and higher powers can be neglected, then $(e^{ah} - 1)/a$ can be closely approximated by

$$\frac{e^{ah} - 1}{a} \simeq h \tag{9.45}$$

By substituting equation (9.45) in (9.44), a *true* approximation for the output at times $t = nT$ is obtained. This is

$$c_2(nT) = h(e^{-aT} + e^{-2aT} + \cdots + e^{-anT}) + c(0) \tag{9.46}$$

Similarly, substitution of relation (9.45) in equations (9.42) and (9.43) results in a true approximation for the output at the corresponding time intervals. These may be written as: for $nT \leq t \leq nT + h$ [i.e., Regions (i), (ii), and (iii)],

$$c_2(t) = h[1 + e^{aT} + \cdots + e^{(n-1)aT}]e^{-at} + \frac{1}{a}[1 - e^{-a(t-nT)}] \tag{9.47}$$

and for $(nT + h) \leq t \leq (n + 1)T$, [i.e., Regions (i), (iii), and (iv)],

$$c_2(t) = h(1 + e^{aT} + e^{2aT} + \cdots + e^{anT})e^{-at} \tag{9.48}$$

Equations (9.46), (9.47), and (9.48) are valid approximations derived from equations (9.42), (9.43), and (9.42) for the exact response.

Now consider equation (9.37) for the approximate transform $C_1(s)$. This can be expanded as follows:

$$C_1(s) = \frac{h}{s + a}[1 + e^{-Ts} + e^{-2Ts} + \cdots + e^{-nTs} + \cdots) \tag{9.49}$$

† It should be noted that $c(0)$ in this example is zero.

The impulse response of the system is

$$\mathcal{L}^{-1}[G(s)] = \mathcal{L}^{-1}\left(\frac{1}{s+a}\right) = g(t) = e^{-at} \tag{9.50}$$

Thus the inverse transform of equation (9.49) representing the approximate inverse time function is

$$c_1(t) = h[1 + u(t - T) + u(t - 2T) + \cdots]\, e^{-at} \tag{9.51}$$

From this, the output at the sampling instants $t = nT$ may be written as

$$c_1(nT) = h[g(0) + e^{-aT} + e^{-2aT} + \cdots + e^{-anT}] \tag{9.52}$$

where

$$g(0) = g(t)\big|_{t=0} = 1 \text{ (in this case)}$$

Similarly the output at any other time $nT < t < (n+1)T$ [i.e., Regions (ii), (iii), and (iv)] can be written as

$$c_1(t) = h(1 + e^{aT} + e^{2aT} + \cdots + e^{anT})e^{-at} \tag{9.53}$$

Equations (9.52) and (9.53) are the resulting time functions when equation (9.36) is approximated by equation (9.37).

It is known that z-transform can only give information at sampling instants $t = nT$. Hence, if the z-transform is applied to equation (9.37) to evaluate the response of the system at these instants, the results obtained will be identical to that given by equation (9.52).

By comparing the approximate solution of equation (9.52) obtained when using the z-transform to the true approximation given by equation (9.46), it is seen that the error at the sampling instants $t = nT$ is

$$\text{Error}\big|_{t=nT} = h\,g(0) - c(0) = c_1(nT) - c_2(nT) \tag{9.54}$$

From equations (9.39) and (9.50) it is evident that if $g(0)$ is zero, for any finite input $R(s)$ or an impulse function $c(0)$ is also zero. Thus when $g(0)$ is zero, no error exists at $t = nT$. But if $g(0)$ is not zero, for a finite input there exists an error at the sampling instant $t = nT$. Hence, it can be stated that the use of z-transform [equation (9.37)] for determining the solution of a finitely pulsed system at sampling instants $t = nT$ is not correct, leading to wrong results, unless the system transfer function $G(s)$ has a continuous impulse response, that is, the degree of its denominator in s is two or more higher than the degree of its numerator.

Comparison of equation (9.53) with equations (9.47) and (9.48) also shows that the time domain solution derived from the approximate transform does not correspond with the true approximation during the interval $nT < t < nT + h$ [i.e., Region (ii)]. This applies to a general system of any order and can be proved by use of partial fraction expansion. It is a simple matter to show this for the duration of the first pulse.

For example, consider a general transfer function,

$$\frac{1 - e^{-h(s+a)}}{[1 - e^{-T(s+a)}](s + a)} G(s) \tag{9.55}$$

where $G(s)$ can be of any order. The approximate transform of equation (9.55) reduces to

$$\frac{h}{1 - e^{-T(s+a)}} G(s) = \left[\frac{hz}{z - e^{-aT}} G(s)\right]_{z=e^{sT}} \tag{9.56}$$

It is clear that equation (9.56), and hence its inverse, is a valid approximation of equation (9.55) only for $t \geq h$, irrespective of the order of $G(s)$ and the method used to evaluate the inverse. From these considerations a statement can be formulated as follows.

Consider a system with transfer function $G(s)$, the input to which is a sequence of finite pulses of width h and period T. When h is small compared to the time constants of the systems, the output can be approximated by replacing the finite pulses by impulses of equivalent area. In general two cases arise.

1. $G(s)$ has a discontinuous impulse response. In this case the solution is only a true approximation for the time duration $nT + h \leq t < (n + 1)T$ [i.e., Regions (iii) and (iv)]. This does *not* include the sampling instants $t = nT$. Hence the z-transform approximation fails completely. However, the modified z-transform can be used to obtain the output over the duration $nT + h \leq t < (n + 1)T$, and in the limiting process at $(n + 1)T$.
2. $G(s)$ has a continuous impulse response. In this case the approximate solution is valid for the time duration $nT + h \leq t \leq (n + 1)T$ [i.e., Region (iii) (iv) and (i)]. This includes the sampling instants $t = nT$. Here both the z-transform and modified z-transform can be used to obtain a true approximate solution.

From these it is seen that the solutions derived from the approximate transforms [equations (9.37) and (9.56)] are not a true approximation of the system output during the interval $nT < t < nT + h$ [i.e., Region (ii)], irrespective of the order of $G(s)$ and the method used to evaluate the inverse. Thus, when the z-transform approximation is used, the true behavior of the system during the interval $nT < t < nT + h$ is not known. This, however, can have negligible effect when h is sufficiently small and $G(s)$ has a continuous impulse response. In both these cases,

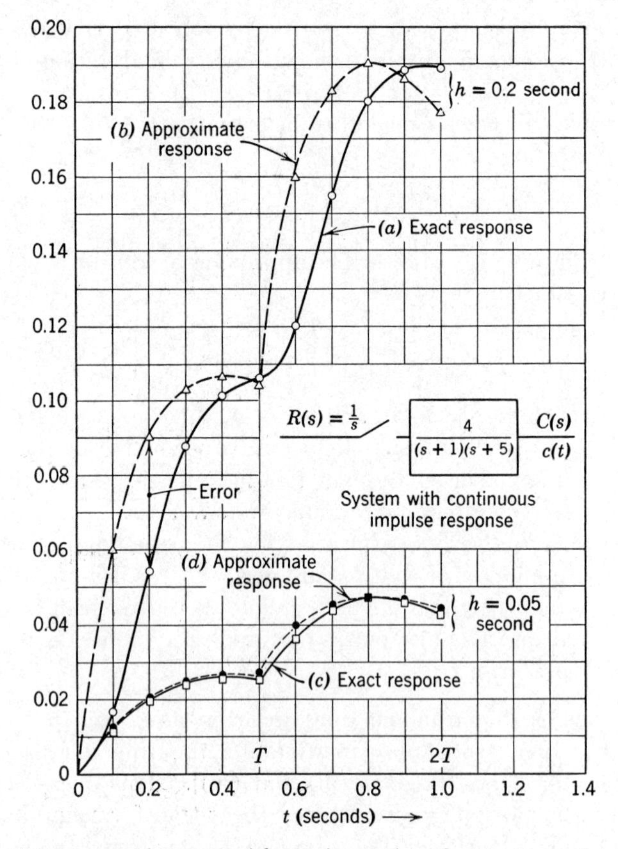

Figure 9.11 Response of system with continuous impulse response; plot shows that errors are small for sufficiently small h

the p-transform can be applied to obtain the exact response for all values of time.

Figure 9.11 shows a system with a continuous impulse response. The output $c(t)$ for a step input is plotted on the same figure. Curves c and d show that the errors are negligible for a sufficiently small h.

$R(s) = \frac{1}{s}$, $r(t)$ — T, h — $R_p(s)$, $r_p(t)$ — $\frac{2.5}{s + 0.5}$ — $C(s)$, $c(t)$

Figure 9.12 Example of finite pulsed system with discontinuous impulse response

Figure 9.12 shows a system with a discontinuous impulse response. The output is plotted in Fig. 9.13 for a unit step input and assumed values of $h = 0.2$ second and $T = 0.5$ second. Curve a is the exact time function calculated from the inverse p-transform. Curve b is the approximate response calculated from the approximate transform. Comparison of the two curves shows the extent of the error which can be caused both at the sampling instants and for the duration $nT < t < nT + h$ where the approximate transform is not valid.

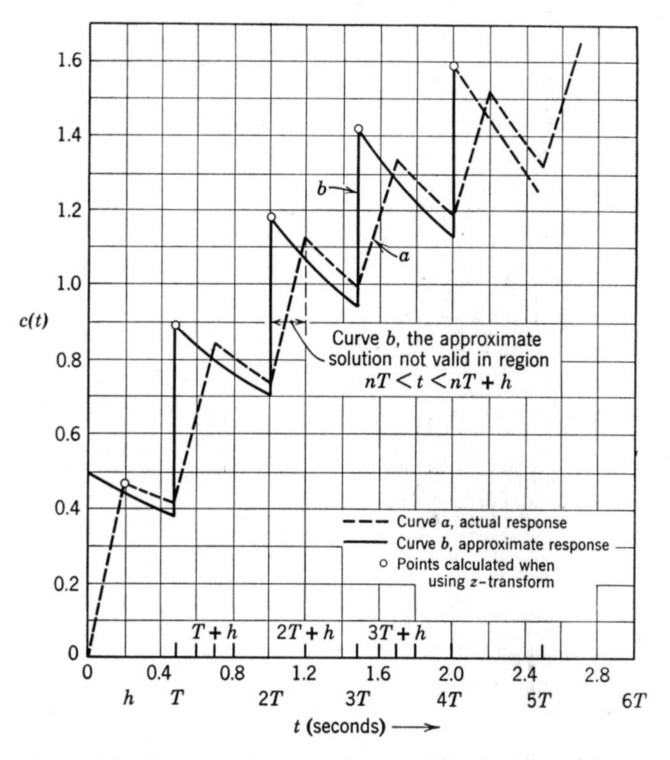

Figure 9.13 Response of system shown in Fig. 9.12 to step input

In the above the degree of approximation depends on the ratio of h to the time constants of the system. From equations (9.43), (9.45), and (9.48) it is seen that for the single time constant system of Fig. 9.12, with unit step input, the approximations are due to substitution of

$$\frac{e^{ah} - 1}{a} = h \tag{9.45}$$

From this the percentage error can be expressed as

$$\text{Per cent of error} = \left(1 - \frac{ah}{e^{ah} - 1}\right) \times 100 \tag{9.57}$$

Equation (9.57) shows that for a step input the percentage error is fixed, independently of sampling period T and time t. For a stable system (poles in the negative half of s-plane),

$$\frac{e^{ah} - 1}{a} > h \tag{9.58}$$

Therefore the approximate solution is always less than the actual values. Figure 9.14 shows the percentage error for a system with single time constant $\tau = 1/a$ and a step input as a function of ah. It is seen that

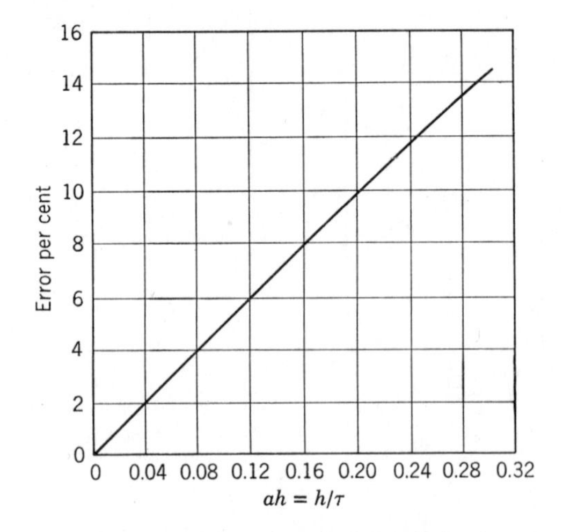

Figure 9.14 Percentage error as function of ah for single-time constant system

for an *error of less than* 5 *per cent ah must be less than or equal to one-tenth.* For systems with more than one time constant the total error varies with time as shown in Fig. 9.11.

Figure 9.12 shows a single time constant system with $\tau = 2$ seconds. Its output is plotted in Fig. 9.13, assuming a pulse width $h = 0.2$, $T = 0.5$ and a unit step input. Inspection shows that in its region of validity, $nT + h \leq t < (n + 1)T$, the approximate solution is less than the actual output and the percentage error is nearly 5 per cent corresponding to $ah = \frac{1}{10}$.

9.4 Initial and Final Values

Since p-transform is only a particular form of the Laplace transform, all operations valid for the Laplace transformation are equally applicable to p-transform. For example, given a function

$$C_p(s) = \frac{1 - e^{-h(s+a)}}{1 - e^{-T(s+a)}} \frac{G(s)}{s + a} \tag{9.59a}$$

its initial value is given by

$$C_p(0) = \lim_{s \to \infty} \frac{s[1 - e^{-h(s+a)}]}{1 - e^{-T(s+a)}} \frac{G(s)}{s + a} = \lim_{s \to \infty} \frac{s\,G(s)}{s + a} \tag{9.59b}$$

Similarly, if the limit exists, the final-value theorem can be applied to obtain the steady state as

$$\lim_{t \to \infty} c_p(t) = \lim_{s \to 0} \frac{s[1 - e^{-h(s+a)}]}{1 - e^{-T(s+a)}} \frac{G(s)}{s + a} \tag{9.60}$$

In most open-loop systems the steady state is oscillating (see Fig. 9.9) and the final-value theorem is not applicable.

Also, when the equations are expressed in terms of their z-transforms or the modified z-transforms, the corresponding theorems of the z-transformation may be used to find the initial and final values.†

9.5 Practical Realization of the Sampler

In order to correlate the theoretical calculations with practical results it is necessary that elements of the system be closely approximated by their idealized mathematical descriptions.

In the preceding discussion an ideal sampler has been assumed. As such, the sampler can make or break instantly with no sparking. Further, it is assumed that the output of the sampler is zero for the time duration $(nT + h) < t < (n + 1)T$; see Fig. 9.2. Consider the case where the input to the sampler is voltage; then it follows that the output voltage is zero for duration $nT + h < t < (n + 1)T$. In effect, this means that the sampler (or sampling equipment) must act as a short circuit for this duration, providing a short-circuited path for the elements of the following block. It is clear that unless this condition is satisfied the calculated values will not correspond with the experimental results.

In general, the input is not limited to voltages but can be any quantity. Hence, it is necessary to determine the exact interpretations of these assumptions in terms of the quantities being sampled and a method must be found for their practical realization.

† E. I. Jury, "Additions to the Modified z-Transform Method," I.R.E. Wescon Convention Record, Pt. IV, August 21, 1957, pp. 136–156.

9.6 General-Sampler Output and Multiple-Sampler Systems

Figure 9.15 shows an open-loop system with an ideal sampler. Assume that the sampler is arbitrarily closed at instants T_0, T_1, $\cdots$, T_n and opened at instants $(T_0 + h_1)$, $(T_1 + h_2)$, $\cdots$, $(T_n + h_{n+1})$, etc.

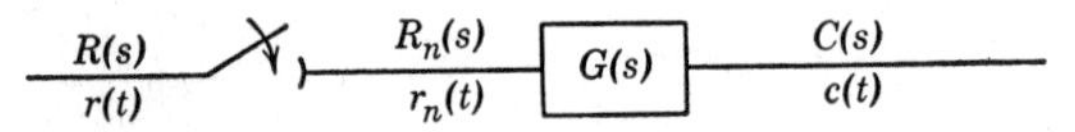

Figure 9.15 Finite pulsed system with ideal sampler

If $r(t)$ in Fig. 9.16*a* is the input to the sampler, the corresponding output of an ideal sampler is the time function $r_n(t)$ indicated in Fig. 9.16*b*. Inspection shows that $r_n(t)$ can be obtained by multiplying the input

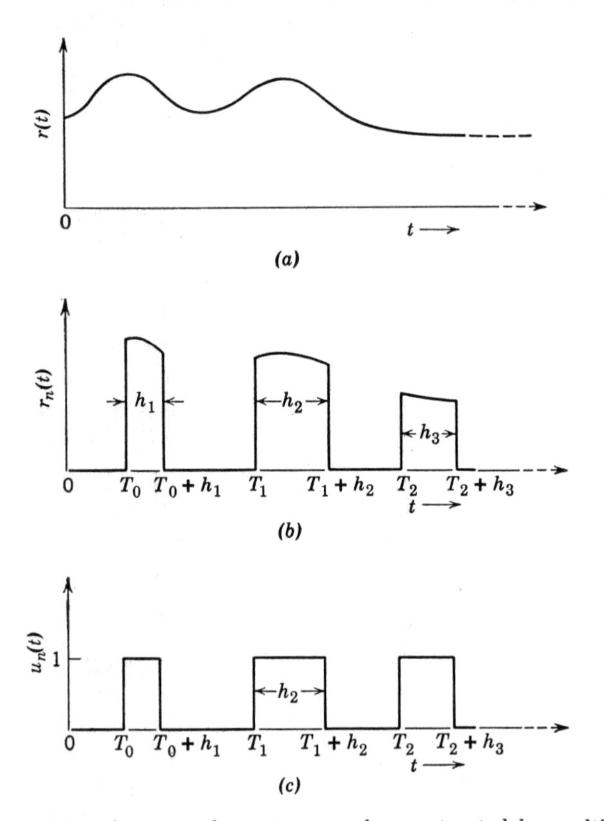

Figure 9.16 Showing how sampler output can be constructed by multiplying its input by the pulse function $u_n(t)$: (*a*) input to sampler, (*b*) output of ideal sampler, (*c*) pulse function $u_n(t)$

$r(t)$ by a time function $u_n(t)$ shown in Fig. 9.16c where

$$u_n(t) = 1, \qquad \text{for } T_n < t < T_n + h_{n+1} \tag{9.61}$$

and

$$u_n(t) = 0 \qquad \text{at all other times}$$

Similar to the uniform pulse width case discussed earlier, the sampler can be regarded as a multiplier in the time domain, multiplying its input $r(t)$ by a time function $u_n(t)$ to give its output $r_n(t)$; thus

$$r_n(t) = r(t)\, u_n(t) \tag{9.62}$$

The Laplace transform of equation (9.62) may be evaluated by applying equation (9.3) as follows:

$$R_n(s) = \frac{1}{2\pi j} \int_{\Gamma} R(\nu)\, U_n(s - \nu)\, d\nu \tag{9.63}$$

where

$$R_n(s) = \mathfrak{L}\,[r_n(t)] \tag{9.64}$$

$$R(\nu) = \mathfrak{L}\,[r(t)]_{s=\nu} \tag{9.65}$$

$$U_n(s) = \mathfrak{L}\,[u_n(t)] \tag{9.66}$$

and Γ is in the path of integration enclosing all the poles of $R(\nu)$ to its left. But the Laplace transform of $u_n(t)$ is

$$\mathfrak{L}\,[u_n(t)] = \sum_{n=0}^{\infty} [e^{-T_n s} - e^{-(T_n + h_{n+1})s}]\, \frac{1}{s} \tag{9.67}$$

Hence $R_n(s)$, the transform of the sampler output, can be written as:

$$R_n(s) = \frac{1}{2\pi j} \int_{\Gamma} R(\nu) \sum_{n=0}^{\infty} \frac{e^{-T_n(s-\nu)} - e^{-(T_n + h_{n+1})(s-\nu)}}{s - \nu}\, d\nu \tag{9.68}$$

It is seen from Fig. 9.16b that, by a step by step superposition, $R_n(s)$ can also be written as

$$R_n(s) = \sum_{n=0}^{\infty} \frac{1}{2\pi j} \int_{\Gamma} R(\nu)\, \frac{e^{-T_n(s-\nu)} - e^{-(T_n + h_{n+1})(s-\nu)}}{s - \nu}\, d\nu \tag{9.69}$$

In the special case where the sampler is synchronized (i.e., $T_0 = 0$) and periodic, as discussed earlier, $U_n(s)$ can be written as

$$U_n(s) = U_p(s) = \frac{1 - e^{-hs}}{1 - e^{-Ts}}\, \frac{1}{s} \tag{9.70}$$

where T is the period of the sampler and h its pulse width. Equation (9.69) then becomes

$$R_p(s) = \frac{1}{2\pi j}\int_\Gamma R(\nu)\frac{1 - e^{-h(s-\nu)}}{(s-\nu)[1 - e^{-T(s-\nu)}]}\,d\nu \tag{9.71}$$

which is identical to equation (9.6). Equations (9.69) and (9.71) and hence $R_n(s)$ and $R_p(s)$ can be evaluated by the residue method.

The integral equations (9.69) and (9.71) can be written in a more simplified form by employing the following p-notations. Let

$$\frac{1}{2\pi j}\int_\Gamma R(\nu)\frac{[e^{-T_n(s-\nu)} - e^{-(T_n+h_{n+1})(s-\nu)}]}{s-\nu}\,d\nu = \underset{T_n}{\overset{T_n+h_{n+1}}{\mathsf{P}}}[R(s)] \tag{9.72}$$

Then equation (9.69) for the non-periodic case becomes

$$R_n(s) = \sum_{n=0}^{\infty}\underset{T_n}{\overset{T_n+h_{n+1}}{\mathsf{P}}}[R(s)] \tag{9.73}$$

Similarly, equation (9.71) for the periodic case may be denoted by

$$R_p(s) = \underset{h,T}{\mathsf{P}}[R(s)] \tag{9.74}$$

9.7 Delayed Functions

Essentially, the main interest at any stage is the relation between the Laplace transform of the sampler input and that of its output. When this is known, it can be multiplied by the transfer function of the following block to obtain the Laplace transform of the output. In linear systems under consideration, that is, systems described by linear differential equations with constant coefficients, it is found that the primitive form of the input at any stage is limited to a function in the form of

$$B(s) = e^{-\sigma s}F(s) \tag{9.75}$$

where $\sigma \geq 0$ is a time delay measured in seconds and $F(s)$ is a polynomial in s. All other forms of input can be obtained by a finite or infinite summation of this primitive form. Therefore, an important basic step is to obtain the sampler output, assuming its input is the primitive function given by equation (9.75). Knowing this, we can obtain the sampler output for any input by a summation process.

Let $f(t)$ denote the inverse Laplace of $F(s)$ as given by equation (9.75) so that

$$f(t) = \mathcal{L}^{-1}[F(s)] \tag{9.76}$$

Now let $f(t)$ be the arbitrary time function shown in Fig. 9.17*a*; then $b(t)$, the inverse of equation (9.75), is represented by the same function

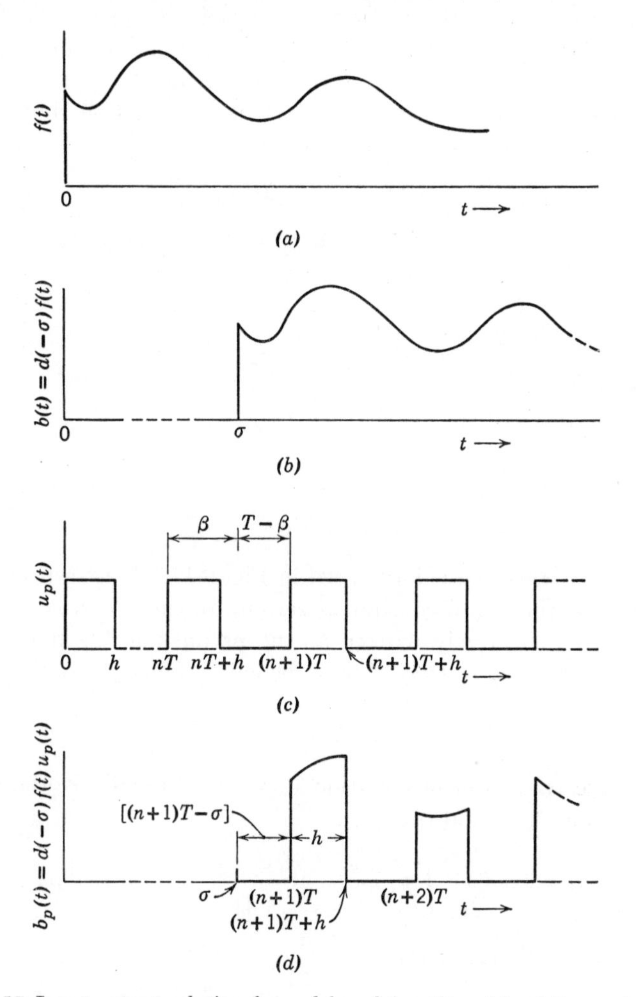

Figure 9.17 Input-output relation for a delayed function: (*a*) arbitrary time function $f(t)$; (*b*) $f(t)$ delayed by σ seconds, considered as the input to the periodic sampler; (*c*) unit pulse function u_p; (*d*) output of periodic sampler

delayed by σ seconds along the positive time axis as indicated in Fig. 9.17*b*. Thus, $b(t)$ can be written as

$$\begin{aligned} b(t) &= d(-\sigma)\, f(t) \\ &= \mathfrak{L}^{-1}\,[e^{-\sigma s}\, F(s)] \end{aligned} \tag{9.77}$$

where $d(-\sigma)$ is the notation used to express a delay of σ seconds along the positive time axis.

Assume that $b(t)$ is the input to a periodic sampler; then the corresponding sampler output will be the time function shown in Fig. 9.17*d*. This can, however, be constructed by multiplying the sampler input by the unit pulse function $u_p(t)$ where $u_p(t)$ is the function shown in Fig. 9.17*c*. Hence the sampler output can be written as

$$b_p(t) = d(-\sigma)\, f(t)\, u_p(t) \tag{9.78}$$

The Laplace transform of equation (9.78) now depends on the relation between σ, T, and h. Let

$$\sigma = nT + \beta \tag{9.79}$$

where $n = 0, 1, 2, \cdots$ positive integers and $0 \le \beta \le T$. In general, three cases arise depending on whether

$$\begin{aligned} &\text{(i)} \quad h \le \beta \le T \\ &\text{(ii)} \quad 0 < \beta \le h \\ &\text{(iii)} \quad \beta = 0 \end{aligned} \tag{9.80}$$

Consider case (i) which is illustrated in Fig. 9.17. It is seen that under this condition the sampler output is zero up to time $t = (n + 1)T$, and that it can be effectively written as the product of $f(t)$ and $d[-(T - \beta)]\, u_p(t)$, all of which is delayed by σ seconds. Thus, the output may be written as

$$b_p(t) = d(-\sigma)\{f(t)\, d[-(T - \beta)]\, u_p(t)\} \tag{9.81}$$

The Laplace transform of equation (9.81) is obtained by the complex convolution integral and is

$$B_p(s) = \frac{e^{-\sigma s}}{2\pi j} \int_\Gamma F(\nu)\, \frac{e^{-(T-\beta)(s-\nu)}[1 - e^{-h(s-\nu)}]}{(s - \nu)[1 - e^{-T(s-\nu)}]}\, d\nu \tag{9.82}$$

which may also be written as

$$B_p(s) = \frac{e^{-(n+1)Ts}}{2\pi j} \int_\Gamma F(\nu)\, e^{(T-\beta)\nu}\, \frac{[1 - e^{-h(s-\nu)}]}{(s - \nu)[1 - e^{-T(s-\nu)}]}\, d\nu \tag{9.83}$$

Equation (9.83) is similar in form to equation (9.71). By employing the same notations, the output may be written as

$$B_p(s) = e^{-(n+1)Ts} \underset{h,T}{\mathsf{P}} [F(s)\, e^{(T-\beta)s}] \tag{9.84}$$

Thus, when $h \le \beta \le T$, equation (9.84) expresses the Laplace transform of the sampler output; similar results can be obtained for the other two cases. These are given by relation 2 in Table 9.3 (page 382).

Consider the special cases where $\beta = T$; then

$$\sigma = (n + 1)T \tag{9.85}$$

The input is thus

$$B(s) = e^{-(n+1)Ts} F(s) \tag{9.86}$$

and the corresponding output given by equation (9.84) becomes

$$B_p(s) = e^{-(n+1)Ts} \underset{h,T}{\mathsf{P}} [F(s)] \tag{9.87}$$

In other words, delays equal to integer multiples of the sampler period can be factored out directly.

Now suppose that the sampler input $b(t)$ is a periodic time function with period T equal to the sampler period. Then $B(s)$, the Laplace transform of the sampler input, is in general in the form of

$$B(s) = \frac{F(s)}{1 - e^{-T(s+a)}} = \sum_{n=0}^{\infty} e^{-nT(s+a)} F(s) \tag{9.88}$$

where all n's are positive integers. By assuming a synchronized sampler and utilizing relation (9.87), the corresponding sampler output becomes

$$\begin{aligned} B_p(s) &= \sum_{n=0}^{\infty} e^{-nT(s+a)} \underset{h,T}{\mathsf{P}} [F(s)] \\ &= \frac{1}{1 - e^{-T(s+a)}} \underset{h,T}{\mathsf{P}} [F(s)] \end{aligned} \tag{9.89}$$

Generalizing, we may state this as follows: If the input to a synchronized, periodic sampler can be expressed in terms of delayed functions with delays equal to integer multiples of the sampler period T, such that the Laplace transform of the input is in the form of

$$B(s) = \frac{F(s)}{[1 - e^{-k_1T(s+a_1)}][1 - e^{-k_2T(s+a_2)}] \cdots [1 - e^{-k_iT(s+a_i)}]} \tag{9.89a}$$

where all k_i's are integers and $F(s)$ is a polynomial in s, then the corresponding sampler output is

$$B_p(s) = \frac{1}{[1 - e^{-k_1T(s+a_1)}][1 - e^{-k_2T(s+a_2)}] \cdots [1 - e^{-k_iT(s+a_i)}]} \underset{h,T}{\mathsf{P}} [F(s)] \tag{9.89b}$$

Relations (9.88) and (9.89) are of utmost importance in the solution of multiple-sampler systems. Tables 9.3 and 9.4 (pages 382 and 384) show additional input-output relations for delayed periodic inputs and delayed samplers.

9.8 Delayed Functions and Delayed Samplers

Consider the case where the sampler has a fixed operating delay of δ seconds with respect to the $t = 0$ time axis, that is, the first closure of the sampler occurs at $t = \delta$ seconds, after which it continues to operate normally. The effective result of such a fixed delay is to displace the unit pulse function $u_p(t)$ by δ seconds along the time axis.

Let the input to a periodic sampler be the primitive function:

$$b(t) = d(-\sigma)\, f(t) \tag{9.90}$$

Then by constructions similar to Fig. 9.17 it can be seen that the corresponding sampler output is

$$b_p(t) = [d(-\sigma)\, f(t)][d(-\delta)\, u_p(t)] \tag{9.91}$$

assuming in this particular case that

$$\delta \geq \sigma \tag{9.92}$$

Then $b_p(t)$ may be written as

$$b_p(t) = d(-\sigma)[f(t)\, d[-(\delta - \sigma)]\, u_p(t)] \tag{9.93}$$

The Laplace transform of equation (9.93) is

$$B_p(s) = \frac{e^{-\sigma s}}{2\pi j} \int_\Gamma F(\nu) \frac{e^{-(\delta-\sigma)(s-\nu)}[1 - e^{-h(s-\nu)}]}{(s - \nu)[1 - e^{-T(s-\nu)}]}\, d\nu \tag{9.94}$$

which may be written as

$$B_p(s) = \frac{e^{-\delta s}}{2\pi j} \int_\Gamma F(\nu)\, e^{(\delta-\sigma)\nu} \frac{1 - e^{-h(s-\nu)}}{(s - \nu)[1 - e^{-T(s-\nu)}]}\, d\nu \tag{9.95}$$

By using previous notations this may be written as

$$B_p(s) = e^{-\delta s} \underset{h,T}{\mathsf{P}} [F(s)\, e^{(\delta-\sigma)s}] \tag{9.96}$$

Equation (9.96) expresses the sampler output when $\delta \geq \sigma$. Other relations can be derived in a similar manner.

Table 9.4 (page 384) shows the relation between input and output of a delayed, periodic sampler for various input functions.

When the sampler is not periodic, a step by step procedure must be used to obtain the output in the form of an infinite series. For example, Fig. 9.16 shows a function $r_n(t)$ being sampled by a non-periodic sampler with an operating delay of $\delta = T_0$ seconds. The sampler output is in this case expressed by equation (9.69). Similar relations can be obtained for other forms of input.

This discussion has described the fundamental steps necessary for the solution of multiple-sampler systems. Repeated application of these steps can be used to find the solution of any given open-loop system.

9.9 Periodic Samplers with the Same Periods

Under this heading are discussed systems having periodic samplers with the same period T. It is assumed that the samplers have uniform pulse widths h_1 and h_2, etc. These need not be equal. Samplers with fixed delays are also considered.

A simple example can best illustrate the procedure.† Figure 9.18 shows a two-sampler system. It is assumed that they have the same periods

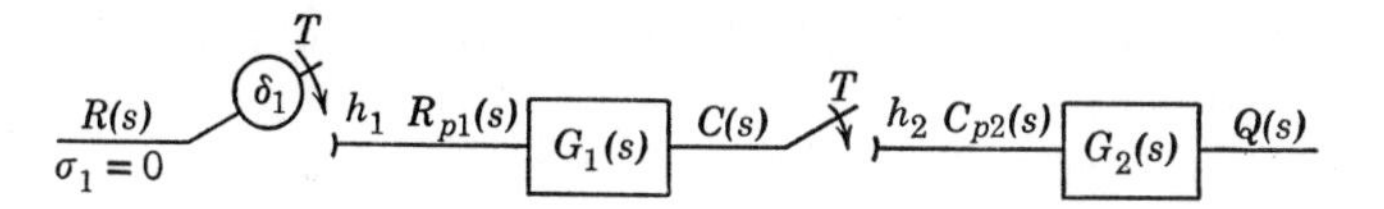

Figure 9.18 System with two samplers having equal periods T and pulse widths h_1, h_2, with the first sampler delayed by δ_1 seconds

T but different pulse widths h_1 and h_2 respectively. In addition, the first sampler is assumed to have an operating delay of δ_1 seconds. Let

$$R(s) = \frac{1}{s+a}$$

$$G_1(s) = \frac{1}{s+\gamma} \tag{9.97}$$

Here σ_1 is zero, and therefore $\delta_1 \geq \sigma_1$. Thus the output of the first sampler is given by equation (9.96) as

$$R_{p1}(s) = e^{-\delta_1 s} \underset{h_1, T}{\mathsf{P}} \left[\frac{e^{\delta_1 s}}{s+a} \right] \tag{9.98}$$

† In this example the subscripts 1 and 2 are used for the various quantities related to the first and second sampler respectively.

$R_{p1}(s)$ can now be obtained from relation 16 of Table 9.1 and is

$$R_{p1}(s) = e^{-\delta_1 s} \frac{e^{-\delta_1 a}[1 - e^{-h_1(s+a)}]}{(s+a)[1 - e^{-T(s+a)}]} \tag{9.99}$$

Therefore,

$$C(s) = R_{p1}(s)\, G_1(s) = e^{-\delta_1 s} \frac{e^{-\delta_1 a}[1 - e^{-h_1(s+a)}]}{1 - e^{-T(s+a)}} \frac{1}{(s+a)(s+\gamma)} \tag{9.100}$$

which can be written as

$$C(s) = \frac{e^{-\delta_1(s+a)}}{1 - e^{-T(s+a)}} \frac{1}{(s+a)(s+\gamma)} - \frac{e^{-(h_1+\delta_1)(s+a)}}{1 - e^{-T(s+a)}} \frac{1}{(s+a)(s+\gamma)} \tag{9.101}$$

Note that $C(s)$ is composed of two periodic functions, both with period T but one having a delay of δ_1 seconds and the other a delay of $h_1 + \delta_1$ seconds. The second sampler, which is assumed to have no operating delay, has the input $C(s)$. The output $C_{p2}(s)$ of this sampler now depends on the relation between the delays δ_1 and $h_1 + \delta_1$, the pulse width h_2, and period T of the sampler. (See relation 3 of Table 9.3.) Now suppose that

$$\delta_1 < T \qquad (\text{i.e., } n_1 = 0 \text{ and } \beta_1 = \delta_1) \tag{9.102}$$

and

$$\delta_1 > h_2$$

Then the output of the sampler from the first component of $C(s)$ can be written from relation $3a$, Table 9.3, as

$$C_{p21}(s) = \frac{e^{-\delta_1 a} e^{-Ts}}{1 - e^{-T(s+a)}} \underset{h_2,T}{\mathsf{P}} \left[\frac{e^{(T-\delta_1)s}}{(s+a)(s+\gamma)} \right] \tag{9.103}$$

Now $C_{p21}(s)$ can be obtained from relation 13 of Table 9.1:

$$C_{p21}(s) = \frac{e^{-Ts}}{1 - e^{-T(s+a)}} \left\{ \frac{1}{\gamma - a} \left[\frac{e^{-Ta}(1 - e^{-h_2(s+a)})}{1 - e^{-T(s+a)}} \frac{1}{s+a} - \frac{e^{-T\gamma} e^{-\delta_1(a-\gamma)}[1 - e^{-h_2(s+\gamma)}]}{[1 - e^{-T(s+\gamma)}](s+\gamma)} \right] \right\} \tag{9.104}$$

From the last term of equation (9.101), it is assumed that

$$h_1 + \delta_1 = T + \beta_2 \qquad (\text{i.e., } n_2 = 1,\ \beta_2 = h_1 + \delta_1 - T) \tag{9.105}$$

and that

$$\beta_2 > h_2$$

Then, relation $3a$ of Table 9.3 together with relation 13 of Table 9.1 can again be used to write the contribution from the second component of $C(s)$ as

$$C_{p22}(s) = \frac{e^{-2Ts}}{1 - e^{-T(s+a)}} \frac{1}{\gamma - a} \left\{ \frac{1 - e^{-h_2(s+a)}}{1 - e^{-T(s+a)}} \frac{1}{s + a} - \frac{e^{-(h_1+\delta_1)(a-\gamma)}[1 - e^{-h_2(s+\gamma)}]}{1 - e^{-T(s+\gamma)}} \frac{1}{s+\gamma} \right\} \quad (9.106)$$

By adding the two components,

$$C_{p2}(s) = \frac{e^{-Ts}}{1 - e^{-T(s+a)}} \frac{1}{\gamma - a} \left[\frac{1 - e^{-h_2(s+a)}}{1 - e^{-T(s+a)}} \frac{1}{s+a} (e^{-Ta} + e^{-Ts}) - \frac{1 - e^{-h_2(s+\gamma)}}{1 - e^{-T(s+\gamma)}} \frac{1}{s+\gamma} (K_1 + K_2 e^{-Ts}) \right] \quad (9.107)$$

where

$$K_1 = e^{-T\gamma} e^{-\delta_1(a-\gamma)}$$

$$K_2 = e^{-(h_1+\delta_1)(a-\gamma)} \quad (9.108)$$

The final output $Q(s)$ can now be written as

$$Q(s) = C_{p2}(s)\, G_2(s) \quad (9.109)$$

The output time function $q(t)$ may be found by determining the inverse p-transform of equation (9.109), either by the ordinary Laplace inversion integral or by the modified z-transform method outlined in Chapter 2.

Note that if a third sampler were present, then $Q_p(s)$ could be found by the use of relation (9.89) and Tables 9.3 and 9.4.

9.10 Periodic Samplers with Different Periods

Systems with periodic samplers having different periods are investigated in this section. It is assumed that the samplers have uniform pulse widths. These need not be equal. The effect of samplers with operating delays may also be considered.

It was shown earlier that if the input to a synchronized periodic sampler with period T_1 is itself periodic, with a period equal to an integer multiple of sampler period, such that its Laplace transform can be written in the form of

$$C(s) = \frac{1}{1 - e^{-kT_1(s+a)}} F(s) \tag{9.110}$$

where k is an integer and $F(s)$ is a polynomial in s, then the output of the sampler can be written as

$$C_p(s) = \frac{1}{1 - e^{-kT_1(s+a)}} \underset{h,T_1}{\mathsf{P}} [F(s)] \tag{9.111}$$

That is, the term $1/[1 - e^{-kT_1(s+a)}]$ can be factored out directly whenever kT_1 is an integer multiple of the sampler period.

In systems having periodic samplers with different periods, inputs similar to $C(s)$ equation (9.110) arise, with the exception that T_1 does not usually equal T_2, the period of the sampler whose output is desired. This can greatly complicate the problem unless a way is found to express equation (9.100) as a function of T_2 only. Fortunately, this can be done readily once two integers b and q are found, such that

$$\frac{T_1}{T_2} = \frac{b}{q}, \qquad b, q = 1, 2, 3, \cdots \text{—positive integers} \tag{9.112}$$

It should be noted that for any given T_1 and T_2 a pair of integers b and q can always be found to satisfy relation (9.112) to any desired degree of accuracy. It is *preferable but not essential* that q be the lowest possible integer denominator.

To illustrate this, consider the function

$$C(s) = \frac{1}{1 - e^{-T_1(s+a)}} F(s) \tag{9.113}$$

This can be written as

$$C(s) = F(s) \sum_{i=0,1,2}^{\infty} e^{-T_1(s+a)} \tag{9.114}$$

Substituting equation (9.112) for T_1 in (9.114), we may write

$$C(s) = F(s) \sum_{i=0}^{\infty} e^{-(ib/q)T_2(s+a)} \tag{9.115}$$

Equation (9.115) can be expanded, factored, and written as

$$C(s) = F(s)[1 + (1 + e^{-bT_2(s+a)} + e^{-2bT_2(s+a)} + \cdots) \sum_{i=1}^{q} e^{-(ib/q)T_2(s+a)}] \tag{9.116}$$

which may also be written as

$$C(s) = \frac{F(s)[1 + \sum_{i=1}^{q-1} e^{-(ib/q)T_2(s+a)}]}{1 - e^{-bT_2(s+a)}} \tag{9.117}$$

Thus

$$C(s) = \frac{F(s)}{1 - e^{-T_1(s+a)}} = \frac{F(s)[1 + \sum_{i=1}^{q-1} e^{-(ib/q)T_2(s+a)}]}{1 - e^{-bT_2(s+a)}} \tag{9.118}$$

Similarly, it can be shown that

$$C(s) = \frac{F(s)}{[1 - e^{-T_1(s+a)}]^r} = \frac{F(s)[1 + \sum_{i=1}^{q-1} e^{-(ib/q)T_2(s+a)}]^r}{[1 - e^{-bT_2(s+a)}]^r} \tag{9.119}$$

where b, q, and r are positive integers and $T_1/T_2 = b/q$.

Relations (9.118) and (9.119) are very important in the solution of systems having periodic samplers with different periods. They can be used to express an input $C(s)$ in terms of T_2, the sampler period. Then Tables 9.3 and 9.4 can be used as in the previous case, to obtain the sampler output.

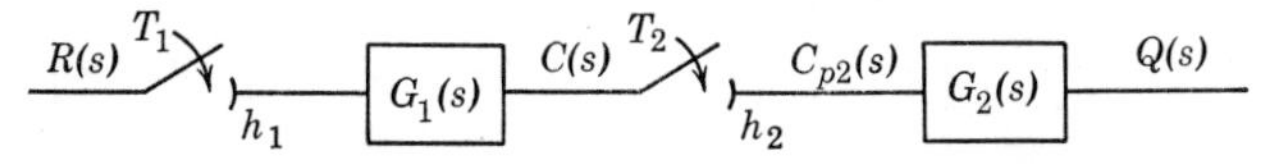

Figure 9.19 System with two samplers having different periods T_1, T_2 and pulse widths h_1, h_2

A simple example will best illustrate this procedure. Figure 9.19 shows a system with two samplers having different periods T_1 and T_2. Let

$$R(s) = \frac{1}{s} \qquad G_1(s) = \frac{1}{s+1} \tag{9.120}$$

and

$$h_1 = 0.6 \text{ second} \qquad T_1 = 1 \text{ second} \qquad h_2 = 0.2 \text{ second} \qquad T_2 = 0.4 \text{ second} \tag{9.121}$$

First, $R_{p1}(s)$ is obtained from relation 2 of Table 9.1 as

$$R_{p1}(s) = \frac{1 - e^{-h_1 s}}{1 - e^{-T_1 s}} \frac{1}{s} \tag{9.122}$$

Therefore

$$C(s) = \frac{1 - e^{-h_1 s}}{1 - e^{-T_1 s}} \frac{1}{s(s+1)} \tag{9.123}$$

Since $C(s)$ is the input to the second sampler having a period T_2 different from T_1, it is necessary to express equation (9.123) in terms of T_2 in order to be able to use Tables 9.3 and 9.4 and to simplify the results. From equation (9.121) it is apparent that

$$\frac{T_1}{T_2} = \frac{1}{0.4} = \frac{5}{2} \qquad \text{(i.e., } b = 5 \text{ and } q = 2) \tag{9.124}$$

By utilizing relation (4.118), $C(s)$ may be written as

$$C(s) = \frac{(1 - e^{-h_1 s})[1 + e^{-5/2 T_2 s}]}{1 - e^{-5T_2 s}} \frac{1}{s(s+1)} \tag{9.125}$$

By multiplying out the numerator and substituting the relation

$$h_1 = 0.6 = 1.5T_2 \tag{9.126}$$

for h_1, equation (9.125) becomes

$$C(s) = \frac{1}{1 - e^{-5T_2 s}} \left[\frac{1 - e^{-4T_2 s}}{s(s+1)} - \frac{(e^{-T_2 s} - e^{-2T_2 s})e^{-0.5T_2 s}}{s(s+1)} \right] \tag{9.127}$$

Now $C_{p2}(s)$, the output of the second sampler, can be written, using relations $3c$ and $3a$ of Table 9.3 respectively as

$$C_{p2}(s) = \frac{1}{1 - e^{-5T_2 s}} \left\{ (1 - e^{-4T_2 s}) \underset{h_2, T_2}{\mathbf{P}} \left[\frac{1}{s(s+1)} \right] \right.$$
$$\left. - e^{-2T_2 s}(1 - e^{-T_2 s}) \underset{h_2, T_2}{\mathbf{P}} \left[\frac{e^{+0.5T_2 s}}{s(s+1)} \right] \right\} \tag{9.128}$$

The p-transform of the functions in the square bracket can be obtained using relations 4 and 13 of Table 9.1. Equation (9.128) then reduces to

$$C_{p2}(s) = \frac{1}{1 - e^{-5T_2 s}} \left\{ (1 - e^{-2T_2 s} + e^{-3T_2 s} - e^{-4T_2 s}) \frac{1 - e^{-h_2 s}}{s(1 - e^{-T_2 s})} \right.$$
$$\left. - [1 - e^{-T_2(2s+0.5)}(1 - e^{-T_2 s}) - e^{-4T_2 s}] \frac{1 - e^{-h_2(s+1)}}{(s+1)[1 - e^{-T_2(s+1)}]} \right\}$$
$$\tag{9.129}$$

Therefore $Q(s)$, and hence $q(t)$, can be obtained from the relation

$$Q(s) = C_{p2}(s)\, G_2(s) \tag{9.130}$$

It is interesting to check the results obtained from the inverse of equations (9.123) and (9.129) for $c(t)$ and $c_{p2}(t)$ respectively, and to compare them with those physically expected.

Directly from relation 5 of Table 9.2 we obtain $c(t)$, the inverse of equation (9.123), and it may be written as

$$c(t) = [1 - d(-0.6)]\left\{n - \frac{1}{(e-1)}[e^{-(m-1)} - e^{-t}]\right\} \tag{9.131}$$

Table 9.5 is a sample calculation showing the procedure used for evaluating equation (9.131). Figure 9.20, curve a, is the plot of $c(t)$.

TABLE 9.5

Sample Calculation for Evaluating Equation (9.131)

				a	b		f	g	k	$c(t)$
t	n	mT_1	$(1-m)T_1$	$e^{(1-m)T_1}$	e^{-t}	$a-b$	$\frac{a-b}{1.72}$	$n-f$	$d(-0.6)g$	$(g-k)$
0	1	0	1	2.72	1	1.72	1	0	0	0
0.2	1	0.2	0.8	2.22	0.82	1.40	0.82	0.18	0	0.18
0.4	1	0.4	0.6	1.82	0.67	1.15	0.67	0.33	0	0.33
0.6	1	0.6	0.4	1.50	0.55	0.95	0.55	0.45	0	0.45
0.8	1	0.8	0.2	1.22	0.45	0.77	0.45	0.55	0.18	0.37
1	2	0	1	2.72	0.37	2.35	1.37	0.63	0.33	0.30
1.2	2	0.2	0.8	2.22	0.30	1.92	1.12	0.88	0.45	0.43

Similarly, $c_{p2}(t)$, the inverse of equation (9.129), can be evaluated either by the use of the modified z-transform or by the ordinary Laplace inversion integral. For the purpose of this comparison, however, it is sufficient to determine $c_{p2}(t)$ for a finite interval of time. Under this condition the ordinary Laplace inversion method is simpler and hence more advantageous.

Equation (9.129) can be expanded, simplified, and written as

$$C_{p2}(s) = \left[\frac{1 - e^{-h_2 s}}{s}(1 + e^{-T_2 s} + e^{-3T_2 s} + \cdots) - \frac{1 - e^{-h_2(s+1)}}{(s+1)}(1 + 0.67e^{-T_2 s} - 0.37e^{-2T_2 s} + 0.57e^{-3T_2 s} \cdots)\right] \tag{9.132}$$

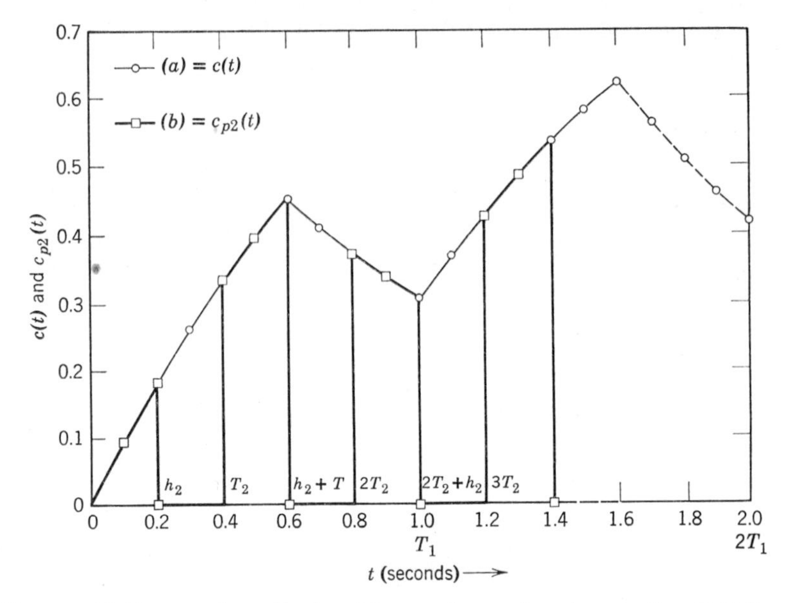

Figure 9.20 Curve a shows the input to sampler as given by equation (9.123) and expressed as a function of T_1; curve b shows corresponding sampler output given by equation (9.129) and expressed as a function of T_2

Thus for the finite interval of time $0 \leq t \leq 3T_2$, $c_{p2}(t)$, the inverse time function, can be written as

$$\begin{aligned} c_{p2}(t) = \{&[1 - d(-h_2)][1 + d(-T_2) + d(-3T_2)] \\ &-[1 - 0.82d(-h_2)][1 + 0.67d(-T_2) \\ &-0.37d(-2T_2) + 0.57d(-3T_2)]\, e^{-t}\} \end{aligned} \tag{9.133}$$

Hence $c_{p2}(t)$ can be determined from equation (9.133) for the finite time interval $0 \leq t \leq 3T_2$. Curve b, Fig. 9.20, shows the plot of $c_{p2}(t)$ so calculated. It is evident that the relation between $c(t)$ and $c_{p2}(t)$ satisfies those expected from physical considerations.

Referring to Fig. 9.19 we should note that if a third sampler is present, then relations (9.89), (9.118), and Table 9.3 can again be used to determine $Q_p(s)$. Also when the samplers have operating delays, corresponding relation of Table 9.4 can be used to find the correct solution.

9.11 Non-periodic Samplers

As mentioned previously, systems having non-periodic samplers must be treated term by term. However Tables 9.3 and 9.4 may still be usefully employed in cases where one or more of the samplers are periodic.

The term by term solution will now be illustrated by means of an example. Figure 9.21 shows a two-sampler system; for simplicity as-

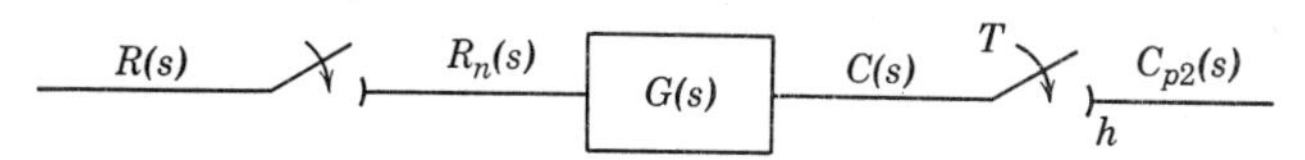

Figure 9.21 Finite pulsed system

sume that the first sampler is non-periodic but that the second is periodic with period T and uniform pulse width h. Let

$$R(s) = \frac{1}{s+a}$$
$$G(s) = \frac{1}{s+\gamma} \tag{9.134}$$

The output of the non-periodic sampler, $R_n(s)$, is given by equation (9.73) and relation 15 of Table 9.1 as

$$R_n(s) = \sum_{n=0}^{\infty} \frac{e^{-T_n(s+a)} - e^{-(T_n+h_{n+1})(s+a)}}{s+a} \tag{9.135}$$

where $T_0 = 0$, since no operating delay is assumed. Therefore $C(s)$ can be written as

$$C(s) = \sum_{n=0}^{\infty} [e^{-T_n(s+a)} - e^{-(T_n+h_{n+1})(s+a)}] \frac{1}{(s+a)(s+\gamma)} \tag{9.136}$$

which can be expanded as

$$C(s) = \frac{1}{(s+a)(s+\gamma)} - \frac{e^{-h_1(s+a)}}{(s+a)(s+\gamma)} + \frac{e^{-T_1(s+a)}}{(s+a)(s+\gamma)} - \frac{e^{-(T_1+h_2)(s+a)}}{(s+a)(s+\gamma)} + \cdots \tag{9.137}$$

Equation (9.137) shows that the input to the second sampler is composed of an infinite number of terms, each of which has a prescribed delay. Since it was assumed that the second sampler is periodic, relation 2 of Table 9.3 can be used to determine the sampler output corresponding to each of the input terms. For example, by assuming

$$h_1 < T$$
$$h_1 > h \tag{9.138}$$

the first two terms of the sampler output $C_{p2}(s)$ can be written as

$$C_{p2}(s) = \underset{h,T}{\mathsf{P}} \left[\frac{1}{(s+a)(s+\gamma)} \right] - e^{-Ts} \underset{h,T}{\mathsf{P}} \left[\frac{e^{(T-h_1)s}}{(s+a)(s+\gamma)} \right] + \cdots \tag{9.139}$$

If the second sampler had an operating delay, the corresponding relations of Table 9.4 could be used to find $C_{p2}(s)$.

The discussion given shows how systems with non-periodic samplers can be treated by a term by term procedure. However, it also illustrates that the equations become complicated if more than one non-periodic sampler is present, for then equation (9.73) must again be used to find $C_{p2}(s)$, leading to a double infinite series.

9.12 Limiting Cases in Multiple-Sampler Systems

Consider an open-loop system with a single periodic sampler. Let $R(s)$ be the input to this sampler. Then $C_p(s)$, the final output, can in general be written as

$$C_p(s) = R_p(s)\, G(s) \tag{9.140}$$

where

$$R_p(s) = \underset{h,T}{\mathsf{P}}\, R(s) \tag{9.141}$$

It is interesting to determine the limits of $C_p(s)$ as h is allowed to approach certain limiting values.

There are four possible limiting cases arising in such a system, as discussed earlier in the chapter. However, the two cases of interest here are

1. The limit as h approaches the sampler period T.
2. The limit as h becomes so small that the unit-pulse function (Fig. 9.16*c* can be replaced by a unit impulse function which has infinite amplitude, zero pulse width, and a unit area.

It was shown that in the first case the limit of $C_p(s)$ is

$$\lim_{h \to T} C_p(s) = C(s) = R(s)\, G(s) \tag{9.142}$$

which corresponds to the Laplace transform of the continuous output—a result which is to be expected from physical considerations. It was also demonstrated that in the second case,

$$\lim_{\substack{h\to 0\\ K\to\infty\\ hK\to 1}} R_p(s) = R^*(z)\big|_{z=e^{sT}} \tag{9.143}$$

where K is the amplitude of $u_p(t)$, and $R(z)$ is the z-transform of $R(s)$. Consequently, the limit of the output becomes

$$\lim_{\substack{h\to 0\\ K\to\infty\\ hK\to 1}} C_p(s) = R^*(z)\, G(s) \tag{9.144}$$

which is also a known result used in sampled-data systems in which the pulse width is considered to be extremely small.

In multiple-sampler systems these limiting cases are of course still valid. However, in such systems it is not always possible to derive the limiting conditions directly from the p-transform of the final output. For example, referring to Fig. 9.19, it cannot always be established that

$$\lim_{\substack{h_1\to T_1\\ h_2\to T_2}} C_{p2}(s)\, G_2(s) = R(s)\, G_1(s)\, G_2(s) \tag{9.145}$$

The reason for this is better appreciated when it is realized that the nature of $C_{p2}(s)$ depends on whether $h_1 \geq h_2$ or $h_1 \leq h_2$. Thus, having once determined $C_{p2}(s)$ on the assumption that $h_1 \geq h_2$, under no circumstances can h_1 be allowed to become less than h_2. However, it is possible that the initial values for a certain system are such that $h_1 > h_2$ but the limiting conditions demand that $h_1 < h_2$. Under these circumstances difficulties arise which do not allow the derivation of the limiting condition directly from the p-transform of the final output. In view of this, it is generally advisable and more convenient to derive the limiting conditions directly from the system after inserting the desired limits in the corresponding samples. To illustrate this procedure, the following limiting conditions will be derived from the system shown in Fig. 9.19.

1. The limit as $h_1 \to T_1$ and $h_2 \to T_2$.
2. The limit as h_1 † $\to 0$ and $h_2 \to T_2$.
3. The limit as h_1 † $\to 0$ and h_2 † $\to 0$.

a. Case 1

When $h_1 \to T_1$ and $h_2 \to T_2$, the samplers can be replaced by a line representing direct through transmission. It is readily seen from Fig.

† With the understanding that $u_p(t)$ then approaches the unit impulse function.

9.19 that under these conditions

$$Q(s) = R(s)\, G_1(s)\, G_2(s) \tag{9.146}$$

which is the Laplace transform of the continuous system.

b. *Case 2*

Under this condition the output becomes

$$Q(s) = R^*(z_{T1})\, G_1(s)\, G_2(s) \tag{9.147}$$

where $R^*(z_{T1})$ is the z-transform of $R(s)$ with $T = T_1$. The inverse time function $q(t)$ for such a system can be determined in closed form, and as a continuous function of time, by the use of the inverse p-transform tables or the modified z-transform tables.

c. *Case 3*

Under these conditions the output may be written as †

$$Q(s) = C^*(z_{T2})\, G_2(s) \tag{9.148}$$

and

$$C(s) = R^*(z_{T1})\, G_1(s) \tag{9.149}$$

where

$$C^*(z_{T2}) = \mathfrak{z}_{T2}\,[C(s)] = \mathfrak{z}_{T2}\,[R^*(z_{T1})\, G_1(s)] \tag{9.150}$$

$$R^*(z_{T1}) = \mathfrak{z}_{T1}\,[R(s)] \tag{9.151}$$

Since the periods T_1 and T_2 are not equal, relation (9.118) must be used to express equation (9.149) in terms of T_2 in order to be able to derive $C^*(z_{T2})$ and hence $Q(s)$. To show this, the correct solution for $Q(s)$ will be derived in terms of the system components given by equations (9.120) and (9.121). Since $R^*(z_{T1})$, the z_{T1}-transform of $R(s)$, can be obtained from equation (9.122) and is

$$R^*(z_{T1}) = \frac{1}{1 - e^{-T_1 s}} = \frac{z_{T1}}{z_{T1} - 1}\bigg|_{z_{T1} = e^{sT_1}} \tag{9.152}$$

therefore

$$C(s) = \frac{1}{1 - e^{-T_1 s}}\,\frac{1}{s + 1} \tag{9.153}$$

It is now necessary to determine $C^*(z_{T2})$ with period $T = T_2$. This can be achieved readily if equation (9.153) is expressed in terms of T_2.

† It should be noted that this case has been discussed in chapters 1 and 2, using the direct z-transform approach.

Equation (9.124) gives the ratio of T_1 to T_2 as

$$\frac{T_1}{T_2} = \frac{5}{2} \qquad \text{(i.e., } b = 5 \text{ and } q = 2\text{)} \tag{9.124}$$

By utilizing relation (9.118), $C(s)$ may be written as

$$C(s) = \frac{1 + e^{-(5/2)T_2 s}}{1 + e^{-5T_2 s}} \frac{1}{s+1} \tag{9.154}$$

The denominator can now be factored out, and hence $C^*(z_{T2})$ becomes

$$C^*(z_{T2}) = \frac{1}{1 - e^{-5T_2 s}} \left[\mathfrak{z}_{T2} \left(\frac{1}{s+1} \right) + e^{-3T_2 s} \mathfrak{z}_{T2} \left(\frac{e^{+0.5T_2 s}}{s+1} \right) \right] \tag{9.155}$$

The z-transforms of the terms in parentheses can be determined by taking the limits of relations 3 and 16 in Table 9.1; they are

$$\mathfrak{z}_{T_2} \left(\frac{1}{s+1} \right) = \lim_{\substack{h \to 0 \\ K \to \infty \\ hK \to 1}} \left[\frac{1 - e^{-h(s+1)}}{1 - e^{-T_2(s+1)}} \frac{K}{s+1} \right]$$

$$= \frac{1}{1 - e^{-T_2(s+1)}} = \frac{z_{T2}}{z_{T2} - e^{-T_2}} \bigg|_{z_{T_2} = e^{sT_2}} \tag{9.156}$$

and similarly

$$\mathfrak{z}_{T2} \left[\frac{e^{+0.5T_2 s}}{s+1} \right] = \frac{e^{-0.5T_2}}{1 - e^{-T_2(s+1)}} = \frac{e^{-0.5T_2} z_{T2}}{z_{T2} - e^{-T_2}} \bigg|_{z_{T_2} = e^{sT_2}} \tag{9.157}$$

By substituting equation (9.156) and (9.157) in relation (9.155), $C^*(z_{T2})$ becomes

$$C^*(z_{T2}) = \frac{z_{T2}^3 (z_{T2}^3 + e^{-0.5T_2})}{(z_{T2}^5 - 1)(z_{T2} - e^{-T_2})} \bigg|_{z_{T_2} = e^{sT_2}} \tag{9.158}$$

Therefore $Q(s)$, the continuous output, can be written as

$$Q(s) = \frac{z_{T2}^3 (z_{T2}^3 + e^{-0.5T_2})}{(z_{T2}^5 - 1)(z_{T2} - e^{-T_2})} G_2(s) \bigg|_{z_{T_2} = e^{sT_2}} \tag{9.159}$$

The sampled output z-transform for such a system would then be

$$Q^*(z_{T2}) = \frac{z_{T2}^3 (z_{T2}^3 + e^{-0.5T_2})}{(z_{T2}^5 - 1)(z_{T2} - e^{-T_2})} G_2^*(z_{T2}) \bigg|_{z_{T_2} = e^{sT_2}} \tag{9.160}$$

The inverse of equation (9.159) expresses $q(t)$ as a continuous function of time. This inverse can be found from the inverse p-transform tables or by the use of the modified z-transform as outlined in Chapter 2.

The inverse of equation (9.160) expresses the time function at instants $t = nT_2, (n = 0, 1, 2, \cdots)$. It can be found from the inverse z-transform tables or from the inverse integral in the z-domain.

9.13 Finite Pulsed Feedback Systems

The preceding discussion has been mainly concerned with the analysis of open-loop pulsed systems. However, pulsed feedback systems are being used increasingly in transmission of information and as means of compensating ordinary continuous systems by the pulsed-width modulation process. Thus the extension of the technique developed for the open-loop to feedback systems is important. This extension is discussed in the remainder of this chapter, and certain characteristics and stability phenomena of such systems are investigated.

9.14 Extension of p-Transform Technique to Feedback Systems

Figure 9.22*a* shows a finite pulsed feedback system. The object in analyzing such a system is to determine the output $c(t)$ for a specified input $r(t)$. Two general assumptions will be made regarding all feedback systems considered.

1. At $t = 0$ all initial conditions are zero.
2. Systems have a continuous step response. That is, the denominator of $KG(s)$ is one or more degrees higher than its numerator.

Assumption 1 is made so that the system under consideration can be represented by a transfer function $KG(s)$. Assumption 2 eliminates the discontinuities that would otherwise occur in the output owing to the step characteristics of the input pulses. This means that the output at the end of one period is the same as the output at the beginning of the next, a characteristic which is used in the following analysis. These assumptions may be modified wherever necessary. However, it is found that in general most systems satisfy these requirements.

In the following, the feedback system shown in Fig. 9.22*a* is studied. The principles applied to its analysis can be used with minor modifications for analysis of more general configurations.

Referring to Fig. 9.22*a*, let the sampler, not necessarily periodic, close at specified instants T_n, remain closed for duration h_{n+1} seconds, and then open at instants $T_n + h_{n+1}$. The pulse widths h_{n+1} and the sampling instants T_n may be dependent on any desired quantity. This does

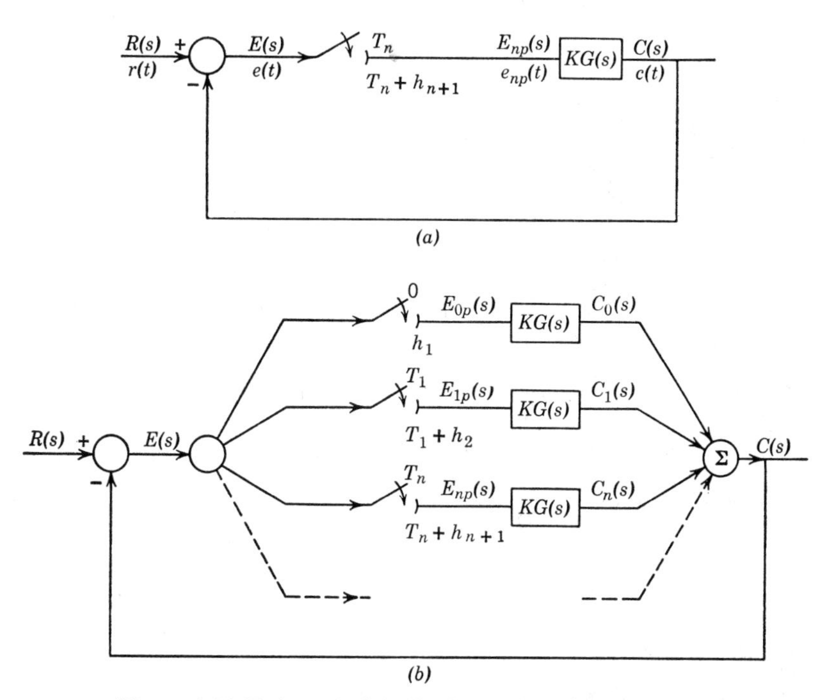

Figure 9.22 Finite pulsed feedback system and its equivalent

not affect the computations so long as the instants at which they occur are known or can be solved for.

Figure 9.22*a* can be replaced by its equivalent system shown in Fig. 9.22*b*. This consists of an infinite number of samplers operating in parallel, each sampler closing and opening only once and the *n*th sampler closing at instant T_n, opening at $T_n + h_{n+1}$ seconds, and remaining open thereafter. Consider the total output $C(s)$ during the interval $0 \leq t \leq T_1$ [the limit points $t = 0$ and $t = T_1$ can be included because of assumption 1]. With zero initial conditions the only component contributing to the total output in this interval is $C_0(s)$. This is because the other samplers have not yet closed and hence cannot contribute to the total output. Therefore,

$$C(s) = C_0(s) \qquad \text{for } 0 \leq t \leq T_1 \tag{9.161}$$

and the system of Fig. 9.22*b* can be represented by that shown in Fig. 9.23 for this duration.

Consider now the first input pulse $E_{0p}(s)$ and its component of output $C_0(s)$. By referring to Fig. 9.23 it is evident that while the sampler is closed,

$$e_{0p}(t) = e_0(t) \qquad 0 < t < h_1 \tag{9.162}$$

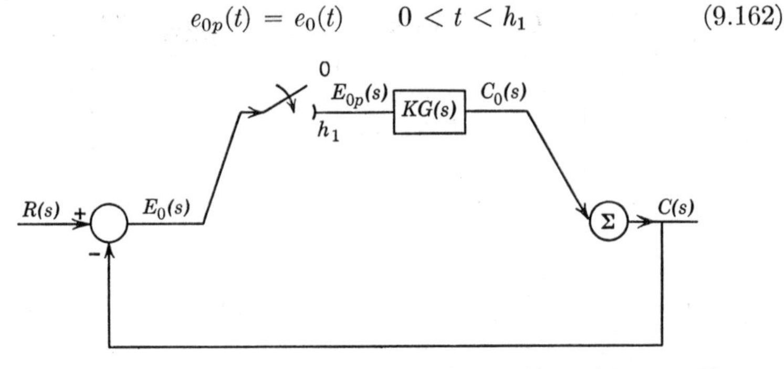

Figure 9.23 Equivalent system of Fig. 9.22 for the interval $0 \leq t \leq T_1$

During this interval the output and hence the error are also identical to the continuous system. Therefore

$$E_0(s) = \frac{R(s)}{1 + KG(s)} \qquad 0 < t < h_1 \tag{9.163}$$

At $t = h_1$ the sampler is opened and hence the input is zero for all t greater than h_1. Thus, the following equations can be written:

$$e_{0p}(t) = \begin{cases} e_0(t), & \text{for } 0 < t < h_1 \\ 0, & \text{for } t > h_1 \end{cases} \tag{9.164}$$

which may be expressed as

$$e_{0p}(t) = e_0(t)\, u_0^{h_1}(t), \qquad \text{for all } t > 0 \tag{9.165}$$

where in general u_x^y is a pulse of unit amplitude, stretching from $x < t < y$, and is zero elsewhere. The p-notation † can now be used to write the Laplace transform of equation (9.165) as

$$E_{0p}(s) = \mathsf{P}_0^{h_1}\left[\frac{R(s)}{1 + KG(s)}\right] \qquad \text{for all } t > 0 \tag{9.166}$$

The inverse of equation (9.166) satisfies all the conditions imposed on $e_{0p}(t)$ by equations (9.162) and (9.164). Therefore, $C_0(s)$, the component

† See equation (9.72) for evaluation of $E_{0p}(s)$.

of output from the first pulse becomes

$$C_0(s) = E_{0p}(s)KG(s) = \overset{h_1}{\underset{0}{\mathsf{P}}}\left[\frac{R(s)}{1 + KG(s)}\right]KG(s) \qquad (9.167)$$

Equation (9.167) describes $C_0(s)$ and hence its inverse $c_0(t)$ for all values of time. In view of this and relation (9.161), the total output for the duration $0 \leq t \leq T_1$ can be written as

$$C(s) = \overset{h_1}{\underset{0}{\mathsf{P}}}\left[\frac{R(s)}{1 + KG(s)}\right]KG(s), \qquad \text{for } 0 \leq t \leq T_1 \qquad (9.168)$$

Since both $R(s)$ and $KG(s)$ are known, the output $c(t)$ may be evaluated from the inverse of equation (9.168) for this interval.

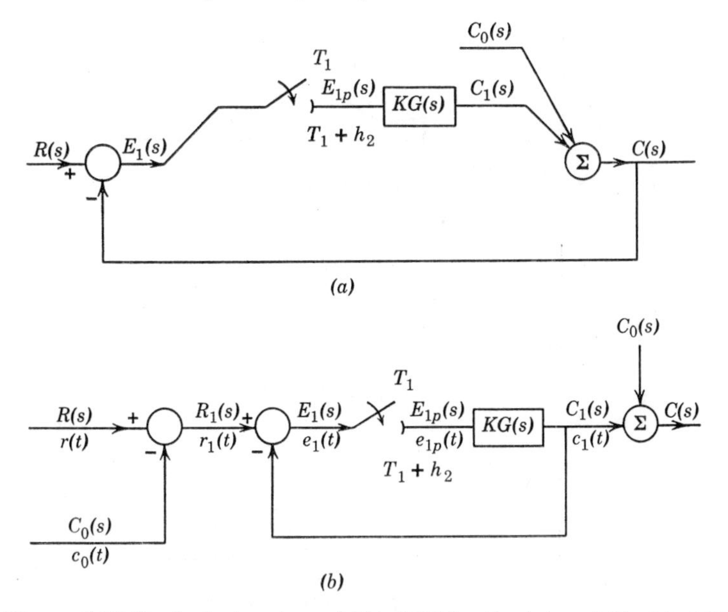

Figure 9.24 Equivalent system of Fig. 9.22 for the interval $T_1 \leq t \leq T_2$

Consider now the output for duration $T_1 \leq t \leq T_2$, that is, the next sampling interval. During this period the total output is equal to the sum of $C_0(s)$ and $C_1(s)$, all other components being zero. Figure 9.22*a* can therefore be represented by the equivalent system shown in Fig. 9.24*a*. This in turn may be simplified and reduced to that shown in Fig. 9.24*b*. The section of this figure to the left of the summator can now be treated as an independent unit with zero initial conditions. It contains a sampler which is open at all times except for the duration $T_1 < t < T_1 + h_2$ and has a known input $R_1(s)$ given by

$$R_1(s) = [R(s) - C_0(s)] \tag{9.169}$$

The output of this system, $C_1(s)$, may be evaluated in the following manner. Suppose that the input $r_1(t)$ is the time function shown in Fig. 9.25*a*. The value of this for the duration $0 < t < T_1$ has no effect

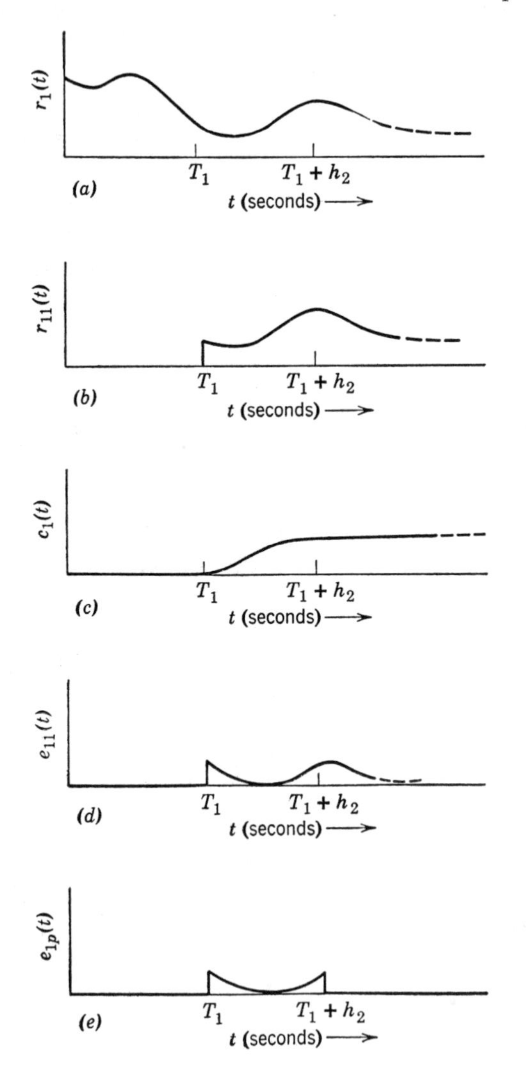

Figure 9.25 Relation between the input and output of the sampler shown in Fig. 9.24*b*

whatsoever on the output $c_1(t)$, because the sampler is open during this interval. It may therefore be assumed to be zero and can be conveniently replaced by a new function $r_{11}(t)$ as shown in Fig. 9.25*b*. Where

$$r_{11}(t) = \begin{cases} 0, & \text{for } 0 < t < T_1 \\ r_1(t), & \text{for } t > T_1 \end{cases} \tag{9.170}$$

equation (9.170) can also be written as

$$r_{11}(t) = r_1(t)\, u_{T1}{}^{\infty}(t) \tag{9.171}$$

By using the *p*-notation, the Laplace transform of this equation becomes

$$R_{11}(s) = \underset{T_1}{\overset{\infty}{\mathbf{P}}}\,[R_1(s)] = \underset{T_1}{\overset{\infty}{\mathbf{P}}}\,[R(s) - C_0(s)] \tag{9.172}$$

With zero initial conditions the output $c_1(t)$ will also be zero for the interval $0 < t < T_1$. This is illustrated graphically in Fig. 9.25*c*. The error is given by

$$e_1(t) = [r_1(t) - c_1(t)] \tag{9.173}$$

but this may be replaced by

$$e_{11}(t) = [r_{11}(t) - c_1(t)] \tag{9.174}$$

without affecting the actual output. Thus the effective error $e_{11}(t)$ can be considered to be zero for $0 < t < T_1$ as illustrated in Fig. 9.25*d*. The sampler closes at $t = T_1$, remaining closed for h_2 seconds, and is opened permanently at $t = T_1 + h_2$ seconds. The actual system input from this closure is the pulse $e_{1p}(t)$, as illustrated in Fig. 9.25*e*. The following procedures can be used to evaluate the Laplace transform of $e_{1p}(t)$ and hence the output $c_1(t)$. Let t_1 represent a new time axis such that

$$t_1 = t - T_1 \tag{9.175}$$

Now $r_{11}(t)$, $c_1(t)$, $e_{11}(t)$, and $e_{1p}(t)$ may be expressed in terms of t_1 as

$$\begin{aligned} r_{11}(t) &= d(-T_1)\, r_{11}(t_1) && (a) \\ c_1(t) &= d(-T_1)\, c_1(t_1) && (b) \\ e_{11}(t) &= d(-T_1)\, e_{11}(t_1) && (c) \\ e_{1p}(t) &= d(-T_1)\, e_{1p}(t_1) && (d) \end{aligned} \tag{9.176}$$

where the new functions $r_{11}(t_1)$, $c_1(t_1)$, $e_{11}(t_1)$, and $e_{1p}(t_1)$ are as shown in

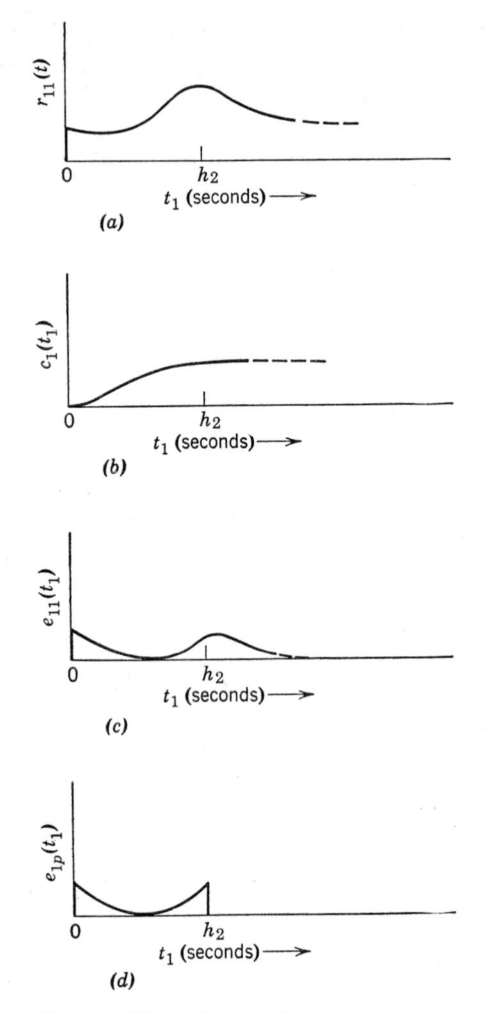

Figure 9.26 Showing Fig. 9.25 transformed to the new time axis t_1

Fig. 9.26*a*, *b*, *c*, *d* respectively, and $d(-T_1)$ is the notation used to express a delay of T_1 seconds along the time axis. The Laplace transform of equations (9.176) become

$$\begin{aligned} R_{11}(s) &= e^{-T_1 s}\,\mathcal{L}\,[r_{11}(t_1)] && (a) \\ C_1(s) &= e^{-T_1 s}\,\mathcal{L}\,[c_1(t_1)] && (b) \\ E_{11}(s) &= e^{-T_1 s}\,\mathcal{L}\,[e_{11}(t_1)] && (c) \\ E_{1p}(s) &= e^{-T_1 s}\,\mathcal{L}\,[e_{1p}(t_1)] && (d) \end{aligned} \quad (9.177)$$

The situation is now identical to that of the first pulse with respect to the time axis t_1. That is, an input $r_{11}(t_1)$ is sampled for duration $0 < t_1 < h_2$ and is fed to a system with zero initial conditions. By following the same procedure as before, the system equations with respect to time axis t_1 can be written as

$$\mathcal{L}\,[e_{11}(t_1)] = \frac{\mathcal{L}\,[r_{11}(t_1)]}{1 + KG(s)} \tag{9.178}$$

and therefore

$$\mathcal{L}\,[e_{1p}(t_1)) = \overset{h_2}{\underset{0}{\mathsf{P}}} \left[\frac{\mathcal{L}\,[r_{11}(t_1)]}{1 + KG(s)}\right] \qquad \text{for all } t_1 > 0 \tag{9.179}$$

The Laplace transform of the output may now be written as

$$\mathcal{L}\,[e_1(t_1)] = \overset{h_2}{\underset{0}{\mathsf{P}}} \left[\frac{\mathcal{L}\,[r_{11}(t_1)]}{1 + KG(s)}\right] KG(s) \tag{9.180}$$

In order to obtain the total output it is necessary to express this equation in terms of the original time axis t. This can be done by means of equation (9.177). By using relations (9.177a, b), equation (9.180) can be written as

$$e^{T_1 s}\, C_1(s) = \overset{h_2}{\underset{0}{\mathsf{P}}} \left[\frac{e^{T_1 s}\, R_{11}(s)}{1 + KG(s)}\right] KG(s) \tag{9.181}$$

By substituting equation (9.172) for $R_{11}(s)$ in equation (9.181), it becomes

$$C_1(s) = e^{-T_1 s} \overset{h_2}{\underset{0}{\mathsf{P}}} \left\{\frac{e^{T_1 s} \overset{\infty}{\underset{T_1}{\mathsf{P}}} [R(s) - C_0(s)]}{1 + KG(s)}\right\} KG(s) \tag{9.182}$$

Equation (9.182) expresses $C_1(s)$ and hence its inverse $c_1(t)$ for all values of time t greater than zero. The total output transform for the duration $T_1 \leq t \leq T_2$ can be written as

$$C(s) = C_0(s) + C_1(s) \tag{9.183}$$

which may be determined from equations (9.167) and (9.182). By proceeding in this manner, the total output may be evaluated at any instant of time. It is not difficult to generalize and show that $C_n(s)$, the component of output due to the $(n+1)$th pulse, is

$$C_n(s) = e^{-T_n s} \times \mathop{\mathsf{P}}_{0}^{h_{n+1}} \left\{ \frac{e^{T_n s} \mathop{\mathsf{P}}_{T_n}^{\infty} [R(s) - C_0(s) - C_1(s) - \cdots - C_{n-1}(s)]}{1 + KG(s)} \right\} KG(s) \tag{9.184}$$

from which the total output for the duration $T_n \leq t \leq T_{n+1}$ can be obtained using the relation

$$C(s) = \sum_{k=0}^{n} C_k(s) \tag{9.185}$$

In numerical calculations, equation (9.184) for $C_n(s)$ is simplified by the fact that at $t = T_n$ all the components $C_0(s)$, $C_1(s)$, $\cdots$, $C_{n-1}(s)$ must have the same poles as $KG(s)$. This is true because after the sampler is opened there is no feedback and the rise or decay of the system is dependent entirely on the poles of $KG(s)$. The sum of these components can therefore be expressed as a polynomial whose denominator is identical to that of $KG(s)$ and whose numerator is dependent on the value of T_n.

We have illustrated how the superposition principle, together with some properties of the p-transform, can be used in evaluating the output of a closed-loop finite pulsed system with a non-periodic sampler. The step by step analysis is necessary whenever the sampler operation is not governed by a repetitive pattern.

9.15 Error-Pulsed Feedback System with a Periodic Sampler

The general method developed in the previous section is now applied to the analysis of an error-pulsed feedback system with a periodic sampler. The periodic operation of the sampler leads to some simplification, but it also raises the question of stability. The stability criteria for such systems can be expressed in terms of a set of constant coefficients. These coefficients are referred to as the characteristic coefficients because they determine the system characteristic equation. The roots of this equation then determine the system stability.

Figure 9.27 shows an error-pulsed system with a periodic sampler having a period T and uniform pulse width h seconds. The transfer function can in general be expressed as the ratio of two polynomials in s.

For systems being considered this may be written as

$$KG(s) = \frac{a_{m-1}s^{m-1} + a_{m-2}s^{m-2} + \cdots + a_1 s + a_0}{s^m + b_{m-1}s^{m-1} + \cdots + b_1 s + b_0} = \frac{N(s)}{D(s)} \tag{9.186}$$

where m is the order of the system and the numerator is at least one degree lower than the denominator in accordance with assumption 2.

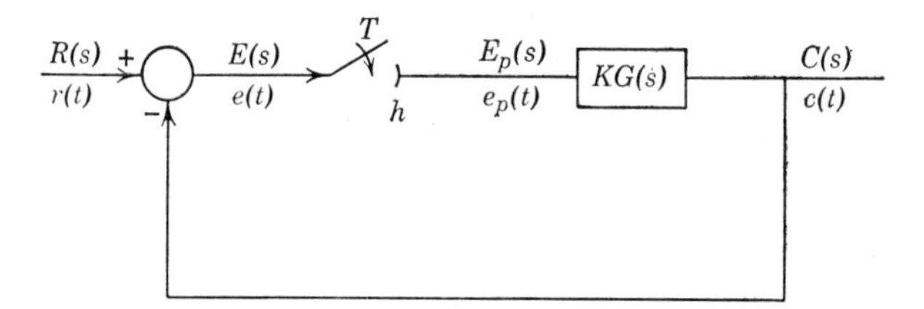

Figure 9.27 Error-pulsed feedback system with a periodic sampler

Consider the outputs for the $(n+1)$th sampling period, that is, for duration $nT \le t \le (n+1)T$. The total output for this interval can be written as

$$C(s) = \sum_{k=0}^{n} C_k(s) \tag{9.187}$$

where $n = 0, 1, 2, \cdots$, all positive integers. The component of output that results from the pulse stretching from $nT < t < nT + h$ can be obtained from equation (9.185) and is:

$$C_n(s) = e^{-nTs} \times \mathsf{P}_0^h \left\{ \frac{e^{nTs}\, \mathsf{P}_{nT}^{\infty} [R(s) - C_0(s) - C_1(s) - \cdots - C_{n-1}(s)]}{1 + KG(s)} \right\} KG(s) \tag{9.188}$$

Note that $c_n(t)$, the inverse of this, is a continuous function of time starting with zero amplitude. This is because $KG(s)$ is assumed to have a continuous step response. Therefore,

$$c_n(nT) = 0 \tag{9.189}$$

Equation (9.187) can be written as

$$C(s) = \mathsf{P}_{nT}^{\infty} \left[\sum_{k=0}^{n-1} C_k(s) \right] + C_n(s), \qquad nT < t \le (n+1)T \tag{9.190}$$

This merely reduces the first n components to zero for all time t less than nT but does not affect its value in the region of interest. The first term on the right-hand side of equation (9.190) can be expanded into

$$\overset{\infty}{\underset{nT}{\mathsf{P}}}\left[\sum_{k=0}^{n-1} C_k(s)\right] = \left\{\overset{\infty}{\underset{nT}{\mathsf{P}}}[C_0(s)] + \overset{\infty}{\underset{nT}{\mathsf{P}}}[C_1(s)] + \cdots + \overset{\infty}{\underset{nT}{\mathsf{P}}}[C_{n-1}(s)]\right\} \quad (9.191)$$

Some general characteristics of this term can now be determined from its individual components. For example, consider the first component

$$\overset{\infty}{\underset{nT}{\mathsf{P}}}[C_0(s)]$$

The general properties of this function may be summarized as follows:

1. Its inverse, $c_0(t)$, is zero for all $t < nT$. This is by virtue of the p-transformation and assures the presence of e^{-nTs} as a multiplier in the s-plane.
2. At $t = nT$, $c_0(nT)$ is finite in amplitude for all finite n.
3. For $t > h$, or $n \geq 1$, its denominator is identical to that of $KG(s)$. The reason for this has been pointed out previously.

From these three characteristics the general equation for this term can be written as (see Addendum, page 377)

$$\overset{\infty}{\underset{nT}{\mathsf{P}}}[C_0(s)] = e^{-nTs}\left[\frac{x_{m-1}^0 s^{m-1} + x_{m-2}^0 s^{m-2} + \cdots + x_1^0 s + x_0^0}{D(s)}\right] \quad (9.192)$$

where the x's are dependent on the system constants as well as on the value of nT, and $D(s)$ is the denominator of $KG(s)$ as in equation (9.186). Note that the numerator of equation (9.192) is at least one degree less than its denominator. This is because $c_0(t)$ is finite at $t = nT$. It is not difficult to verify the validity of this equation for any specified system. This reasoning can be extended to all other terms on the right-hand side of equation (9.191) to show that they all have e^{-nTs} as multiplier and $D(s)$ as denominator. Therefore, they can be placed on a common denominator and written as

$$\overset{\infty}{\underset{nT}{\mathsf{P}}}\left[\sum_{k=0}^{n-1} C_k(s)\right] = e^{-nTs}\left[\frac{\left\{\begin{array}{r} A_{m-1}(nT)\, s^{m-1} + A_{m-2}(nT)\, s^{m-2} \\ + \cdots + A_1(nT)\, s + A_0(nT) \end{array}\right\}}{D(s)}\right] \quad (9.193)$$

where

$$A_{m-1}(nT) = x_{m-1}^0 + x_{m-1}^1 + \cdots + x_{m-1}^{n-1}$$
$$\vdots \tag{9.194}$$
$$A_0\ (nT) = x_0^0 + x_0^1 + \cdots + x_0^{n-1}$$

By substituting equation (9.193) in (9.190), the total output becomes

$$C(s) = \left\{ e^{-nTs}\left[\frac{\left\{\begin{array}{l} A_{m-1}(nT)\, s^{m-1} + A_{m-2}(nT)\, s^{m-2} \\ \qquad + \cdots + A_0(nT) \end{array}\right\}}{D(s)}\right] + C_n(s) \right\} \tag{9.195}$$

for $nT < t \leq (n+1)T$

The initial-value theorem can be applied to this delayed function to show that

$$A_{m-1}(nT) = c(nT) \tag{9.196}$$

This is because $c_n(t)$, the component from the last term, is zero for all $0 < t < nT$ and at $t = nT$ as indicated by equation (9.189). A purely algebraic process can also be used to verify equation (9.196). In a similar way it can be shown that the other coefficients are related to the higher-order derivatives at $t = nT$. However, these are not of any interest in the present analysis but may be employed advantageously in a synthesis problem. The total output can now be written from equations (9.188), (9.193), (9.195), and (9.196) as

$$C(s) = e^{-nTs}\left[\frac{\left\{\begin{array}{l} c(nT)\, s^{m-1} + A_{m-2}(nT)\, s^{m-2} \\ \ + \cdots + A_1(nT)\, s + A_0(nT) \end{array}\right\}}{D(s)}\right.$$
$$\left. + \mathop{\mathsf{P}}_0^h \left[\frac{e^{nTs} \mathop{\mathsf{P}}_{nT}^{\infty} [R(s)] - \dfrac{\left\{\begin{array}{l} c(nT)\, s^{m-1} + A_{m-2}(nT)\, s^{m-2} \\ \ + \cdots + A_1(nT)\, s + A_0(nT) \end{array}\right\}}{D(s)}}{1 + KG(s)}\right] KG(s) \right\} \tag{9.197}$$

Equation (9.197) and its inverse describe the continuous output for duration $nT < t < (n+1)T$. It is possible to simplify this equation in the following manner: $C(s)$ can be divided into two components, $C_h(s)$ valid for $nT < t \leq nT + h$, that is, while the sampler is closed; and $C_T(s)$ valid for $nT + h < t \leq (n+1)T$, that is, while the sampler is open. The symbol $\overset{h}{\underset{0}{\mathsf{P}}}$ can be disregarded for $nT < t \leq nT + h$ because it signifies multiplication by unity during this interval. Therefore, the first component of output can be written as

$$C_h(s) = e^{-nTs}\left\{\frac{c(nT)\, s^{m-1} + A_{m-2}(nT)\, s^{m-2} + \cdots + A_0(nT)}{D(s)}\right.$$

$$\left.\times\left[1 - \frac{KG(s)}{1 + KG(s)}\right] + e^{nTs}\overset{\infty}{\underset{nT}{\mathsf{P}}}[R(s)]\frac{KG(s)}{1 + KG(s)}\right\},$$

$$\text{for } nT < t \leq nT + h \qquad (9.198)$$

which reduces to

$$C_h(s) = e^{-nTs}\left\{\frac{c(nT)\, s^{m-1} + A_{m-2}(nT)\, s^{m-2} + \cdots + A_0(nT)}{N(s) + D(s)}\right.$$

$$\left. + e^{nTs}\overset{\infty}{\underset{nT}{\mathsf{P}}}[R(s)]\frac{N(s)}{N(s) + D(s)}\right\} \qquad (9.199)$$

where $N(s)$ and $D(s)$ are the numerator and denominator of $KG(s)$ as given by equation (9.186). It is seen that during this interval the output has the same poles as $\dfrac{1}{1 + KG(s)}$.

The second component can be written as

$$C_T(s) = \overset{\infty}{\underset{nT+h}{\mathsf{P}}}[C(s)], \qquad nT + h < t \leq (n+1)T \qquad (9.200)$$

Because during this interval the sampler is open, $C_T(s)$ must have the same poles as $KG(s)$. In general, $C_T(s)$ can be shown to be in the form of

$$C_T(s) = e^{-(nT+h)s}\left\{\sum_{k=1}^{m}\left[(L_c^k\, c(nT) + L_{m-2}^k\, A_{m-2}(nT) + \cdots\right.\right.$$

$$\left.\left. + L_0^k\, A_0(nT) + L_{R_1}^k\, R_1(nT) + L_{R_2}^k\, R_2(nT) + \cdots)\frac{e^{-\rho_k h}}{s + \rho_k}\right]\right\} \qquad (9.201)$$

$$nT + h < t \leq (n+1)T$$

where $L_c^k, \cdots, L_0^k, L_R^k$ are constants, $R_1(nT)$, $R_2(nT)$, $\cdots$ are functions dependent on the type of input, and $\rho_1, \rho_2, \cdots, \rho_m$ are the m simple poles of $KG(s)$. $C_T(s)$ has a slightly different form if $KG(s)$ has multiple poles. The value of the preceding simplification is of importance in the evaluation of the total response.

Consider now the total output for the next sampling interval. This may be written as

$$\text{Total output} = \mathop{\mathsf{P}}_{(n+1)T}^{\infty} \left[\sum_{k=0}^{n} C_k(s) \right] + C_{n+1}(s) \tag{9.202}$$

$$(n+1)T < t \leq (n+2)T$$

The first term on the right-hand side can be expanded in accordance with equation (9.193) as

$$\mathop{\mathsf{P}}_{(n+1)T}^{\infty} \left[\sum_{k=0}^{n} C_k(s) \right]$$

$$= e^{-(n+1)Ts} \left[\frac{\left\{ \begin{array}{l} c(n+1)T\, s^{m-1} + A_{m-2}(n+1)T\, s^{m-2} \\ \quad + \cdots + A_1(n+1)T\, s + A_0(n+1)T \end{array} \right\}}{D(s)} \right] \tag{9.203}$$

It is evident from equations (9.190) and (9.197) that this equation can also be written as

$$\mathop{\mathsf{P}}_{(n+1)T}^{\infty} \left[\sum_{k=0}^{n} C_k(s) \right] = \mathop{\mathsf{P}}_{(n+1)T}^{\infty} [\text{equation (9.197)}] \tag{9.204}$$

For $t \geq (n+1)T$ the right-hand side of equation (9.204) can be shown to be

$$\mathop{\mathsf{P}}_{(n+1)T}^{\infty} [\text{equation (9.197)}]$$

$$= e^{-(n+1)Ts} \left[\frac{\left\{ \begin{array}{l} Q_{m-1}(n+1)T\, s^{m-1} + Q_{m-2}(n+1)T\, s^{m-2} \\ \quad + \cdots + Q_0(n+1)T \end{array} \right\}}{D(s)} \right] \tag{9.205}$$

where the Q's are functions of $c(nT)$, $A_{m-2}(nT) \cdots A_0(nT)$, as well as the pulse width h and the constants of transfer function. These can in general be written as

$$Q_{m-1}(n+1)T = K_c^c\, c(nT) + K_{m-2}^c\, A_{m-2}(nT) + \cdots + K_0^c\, A_0(nT)$$
$$+ K_{R1}^c\, R_1(nT) + K_{R2}^c\, R_2(nT) + \cdots$$
$$\vdots$$
$$Q_0 \quad (n+1)T = K_c^0\, c(nT) + K_{m-2}^0\, A_{m-2}(nT) + \cdots + K_0^0\, A_0(nT)$$
$$+ K_{R1}^0\, R_1(nT) + K_{R2}^0\, R_2(nT) + \cdots \qquad (9.206)$$

where the K_c, K_{m-2}, $\cdots$, K_1, K_0 are called the "characteristic coefficients" and are constants dependent only on the system parameters. The constants K_R, the functions $R_1(nT)$, $R_2(nT)$, $\cdots$, and the number of them is dependent on the type and order of the input function. Equating equations (9.203), (9.204), and (9.205), we obtain the following identities:

$$\left.\begin{aligned} Q_{m-1}(n+1)T &= c(n+1)T \\ Q_{m-2}(n+1)T &= A_{m-2}(n+1)T \\ Q_0(n+1)T &= A_0(n+1)T \end{aligned}\right\} \qquad (9.207)$$

By substituting these in equations (9.206), a relation between the nth and $(n+1)$th terms can be obtained. These are

$$c(n+1)T = K_c^c\, c(nT) + K_{m-2}^c\, A_{m-2}(nT) + \cdots + K_0^c\, A_0(nT)$$
$$+ K_{R1}^c\, R_1(nT) + K_{R2}^c\, R_2(nT) \cdots$$
$$\vdots$$
$$A_0(n+1)T = K_c^0\, c(nT) + K_{m-2}^0\, A_{m-2}(nT) + \cdots + K_0^0\, A_0(nT)$$
$$+ K_{R1}^0\, R_1(nT) + \cdots \qquad (9.208)$$

These equations provide m simultaneous first-order difference equations in m unknowns. They can be readily solved by the z-transform method in the following manner. The z-transform of $c(n+1)T$ may be written as

$$\mathfrak{z}\,[c(n+1)T] = z[C^*(z) - c(0)] \qquad (9.209)$$

where

$$C^*(z) = \mathfrak{z}\,[c(nT)] \qquad (9.210)$$

and

$$z = e^{sT} \tag{9.211}$$

Similarly,

$$\begin{aligned} \mathfrak{z}\,[A_{m-2}(n+1)T] &= z[A^*_{m-2}(z) - A_{m-2}(0)] \\ &\vdots \\ \mathfrak{z}\,[A_0(n+1)T] &= z[A_0{}^*(z) - A_0(0)] \end{aligned} \tag{9.212}$$

With zero initial conditions all the terms $c(0)$, $A_{m-2}(0) \cdots A_0(0)$ are zero. The z-transform of equations (9.208) can now be written with the aid of these equations as

$$\begin{aligned} &(z - K_c^c)\, C^*(z) - K^c_{m-2}\, A^*_{m-2}(z) \\ &\qquad - \cdots - K_0^c\, A_0^*(z) = K^c_{R1}\, R_1^*(z) + K^c_{R2}\, R_2^*(z) + \cdots \\ &-K_c^{m-2}\, C^*(z) + (z - K^{m-2}_{m-2})\, A^*_{m-2}(z) \\ &\qquad - \cdots - K_0^{m-2}\, A_0^*(z) = K^{m-2}_{R1}\, R_1^*(z) + K^{m-2}_{R2}\, R_2^*(z) + \cdots \\ &\vdots \\ &-K_c^0\, C^*(z) - K^0_{m-2}\, A^*_{m-2}(z) \\ &\qquad - \cdots - (z - K_0^0)\, A_0^*(z) = K^0_{R1}\, R_1^*(z) + K^0_{R2}\, R_2^*(z) + \cdots \end{aligned} \tag{9.213}$$

where the only unknowns are $C^*(z)$, $A^*_{m-2}(z) \cdots A_0^*(z)$. Equations (9.213) can be solved by the determinant method as follows. Let

$$\Delta(z) = \begin{vmatrix} (z - K_c^c) & -K^c_{m-2} & \cdots & -K_0^c \\ -K_c^{m-2} & (z - K^{m-2}_{m-2}) & \cdots & -K_0^{m-2} \\ \vdots & & & \\ -K_c^0 & -K^0_{m-2} & \cdots & -(z - K_0^0) \end{vmatrix} \tag{9.214}$$

Then $C^*(z)$, the z-transform of the output, can be written as

$$C^*(z) = \frac{\begin{vmatrix} K_{R1}^{c} R_1^*(z) + K_{R2}^{c} R_2^*(z) + \cdots - K_{m-2}^{c} & -K_{m-2}^{c} & \cdots & -K_0^{c} \\ \cdot & & & \\ \cdot & & & \\ \cdot & & & \\ K_{R1}^{0} R_1^*(z) + K_{R2}^{0} R_2^*(z) + \cdots - K_{m-2}^{0} & -K_{m-2}^{0} & \cdots & -(z - K_0^{0}) \end{vmatrix}}{\Delta(z)} \tag{9.215}$$

The inverse of equation (9.215) gives the values of the output at instants $t = nT$. The characteristic equation whose roots determine the stability is $\Delta(z)$. For a stable system these roots must be within the unit circle. For the mth-order system under consideration $\Delta(z)$ can be represented by an mth-order polynomial in z as

$$\Delta(z) = z^m + B_{m-1}z^{m-1} + \cdots + B_1 z + B_0 \tag{9.216}$$

The constant coefficients $B_{m-1} \cdots B_0$ can be expressed directly in terms of the characteristic coefficients, as is seen from relation (9.214). Note that they are independent of the input coefficients $K_{R1} \cdots$ etc. It is possible to develop the stability criteria in terms of the relation between the B coefficients. For example, it can be shown that for a second-order system

$$\Delta(z) = z^2 + B_1 z + B_0 \tag{9.217}$$

and for stability †

$$\left.\begin{aligned} \frac{1 - B_0}{1 + B_1 + B_0} &> 0 \\ \frac{1 - B_1 + B_0}{1 + B_1 + B_0} &> 0 \end{aligned}\right\} \tag{9.218}$$

The relations between the B's, the characteristic coefficients, and the system parameters, together with the stability conditions for a general second-order transfer function, are derived in the Appendix. Numerical substitutions in these general equations will immediately determine the stability of a given system. The same procedure can be used to derive the equations for a third- and higher-order configurations.

If only the stability and the output at $t = nT$ is desired, then equation (9.216) suffices to describe the system. In general, it is advisable to

† See Chapter 1.

determine the continuous output in order to examine its ripples. In this case it becomes necessary to solve for $A^*_{m-2}(z), \cdots A^*_0(z)$ as follows:

$$A^*_{m-2}(z) = \frac{\begin{vmatrix} (z - K^c_c) & K_{R1} R^*_1(z) + K^c_{R2} R^*_2(z) & \cdots & -K^c_{m-3} & \cdots & -K^c_0 \\ -K^{m-2}_c & K^{m-2}_{R1} R^*_1(z) + K^{m-2}_{R2} R^*_2(z) & \cdots & -K^{m-2}_{m-3} & \cdots & -K^{m-2}_0 \\ \cdot & & & & & \\ \cdot & & & & & \\ \cdot & & & & & \\ -K^0_c & K^0_{R1} R^*_1(z) + K^0_{R2} R^*_2(z) & \cdots & -K^0_{m-3} & \cdots & -(z - K^0_0) \end{vmatrix}}{\Delta(z)} \tag{9.218a}$$

$\cdot$

$\cdot$

$\cdot$

$$A^*_0(z) = \frac{\begin{vmatrix} z - K^c_c & -K^c_{m-2} & -K^c_{m-1} & \cdots & -K^c_1 & K^c_{R1} R^*_1(z) + K_{R2} R^*_2(z) \\ -K^{m-2}_c & (z - K^{m-2}_{m-2}) & & \cdots & & K^{m-2}_{R1} R^*_1(z) + K_{R2} R^*_2(z) \\ \cdot & & & & & \\ \cdot & & & & & \\ \cdot & & & & & \\ -K^0_c & -K^0_{m-2} & & \cdots & & K^0_{R1} R^*_1(z) + K^{m-2}_{R2} R^*_2(z) \end{vmatrix}}{\Delta(z)} \tag{9.219}$$

The steady-state ripple can usually be obtained directly from the equations for $C^*(z)$, $A^*_{m-2}(z) \cdots A^*_0(z)$. By assuming that the limits exist, the final-value theorem can be applied to these equations to determine the steady-state values of the corresponding coefficients. For example,

$$\lim_{n \to \infty} c(nT) = \lim_{z \to 1} \frac{z - 1}{z} C^*(z) \tag{9.220}$$

Substitution of these limits in equations (9.197) and (9.199) will give the steady-state continuous response. In the general case, however, equations (9.215) and (9.220) must be solved for the coefficients $c(nT)$, $A_{m-2}(nT) \cdots A_0(nT)$, which can then be substituted in equations (9.195) or (9.197) and (9.199) to find the continuous response for any desired interval $nT \leq t \leq (n + 1)T$. Note that all these coefficients have the same characteristic equation $\Delta(z)$. Thus, once the roots of $\Delta(z)$ have been determined, they can be used to evaluate all the other coefficients. This reduces the labor by a considerable amount. These techniques have been demonstrated by means of an example in the Appendix where the response of a second-order system to a step, ramp, and a sinusoidal input have been plotted for different values of the pulse width h.

a. Systems with Elements in Feedback Path

Figure 9.28*a* shows a system with elements in the feedback path. This may be redrawn as the unity feedback system shown in Fig. 9.28*b*.

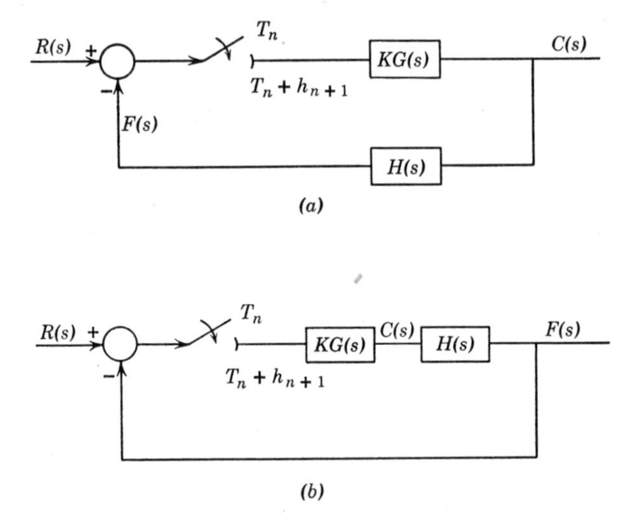

Figure 9.28 System with elements in the feedback path

Clearly the method described previously can now be used to find $F(s)$. When $F(s)$ has been obtained, $C(s)$ can be written as

$$C(s) = \sum_{n=0}^{\infty} \mathsf{P}_{T_n}^{T_n+h_{n+1}} [R(s) - F(s)]\, KG(s) \tag{9.221}$$

Since $R(s)$, $F(s)$, and $KG(s)$ are known, $C(s)$ and hence $c(t)$ can be determined.

9.16 Multiple-Sampler Feedback Systems

The method described in the preceding sections is based on the superposition principles, and the p-transform method which describes the relation between input and output of the sampler. Since these are independent of the location of the sampler, it is logical to assume that they can be extended to systems with one or more samplers, irrespective of where the samplers are located. To illustrate the procedure a system with two non-periodic samplers will be considered. The method of analysis can then be extended to more complicated configuration whenever desired.

Figure 9.29 shows a system with two non-periodic samplers. Let $u_1(t)$ and $u_2(t)$ shown in Fig. 9.30 represent the pattern of operation for the first and second sampler respectively. This indicates that the first

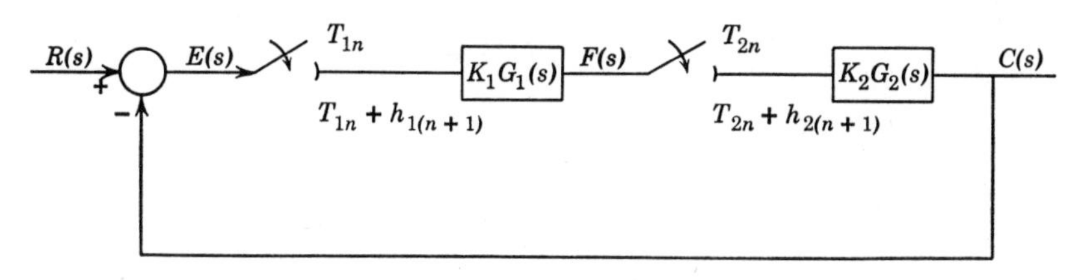

Figure 9.29 System with two non-periodic samplers

sampler closes at T_{10}, remains closed for duration h_{11} seconds, and then opens at $T_{10} + h_{11} \cdots$, etc. The knowledge of these patterns and their relative positions are essential for this analysis.

Consider the output for the duration $0 < t < T_{20}$. During this interval the second sampler is open and, assuming zero initial conditions,

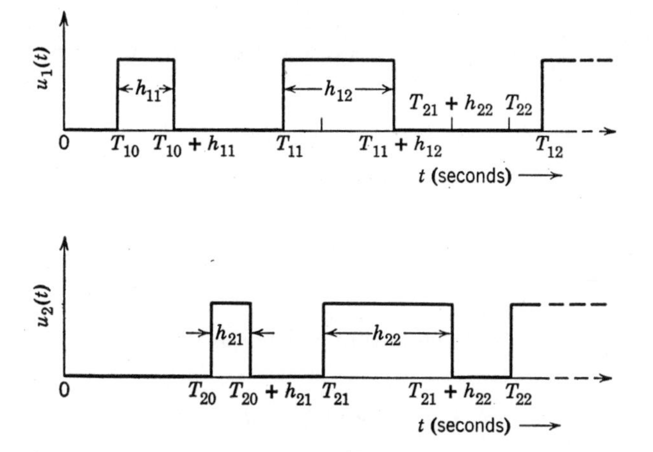

Figure 9.30 Pattern of operation for the samplers shown in Fig. 9.29

$C(s)$ is zero. The system can therefore be represented as an open-loop system shown in Fig. 9.31a. Since $T_{10} + h_{11}$ is less than T_{20}, $F_0(s)$ can be written as

$$F_0(s) = \overset{T_{10}+h_{11}}{\underset{T_{10}}{\mathsf{P}}} [R(s)]\, K_1G_1(s) \tag{9.222}$$

At $t = T_{20}$ the second sampler closes, remaining closed for h_{21} seconds, and then opens at $T_{20} + h_{21}$. During this period the first sampler is open and therefore the input to the second system is entirely due to $F_0(s)$. The system can therefore be represented as in Fig. 9.31*b* for dura-

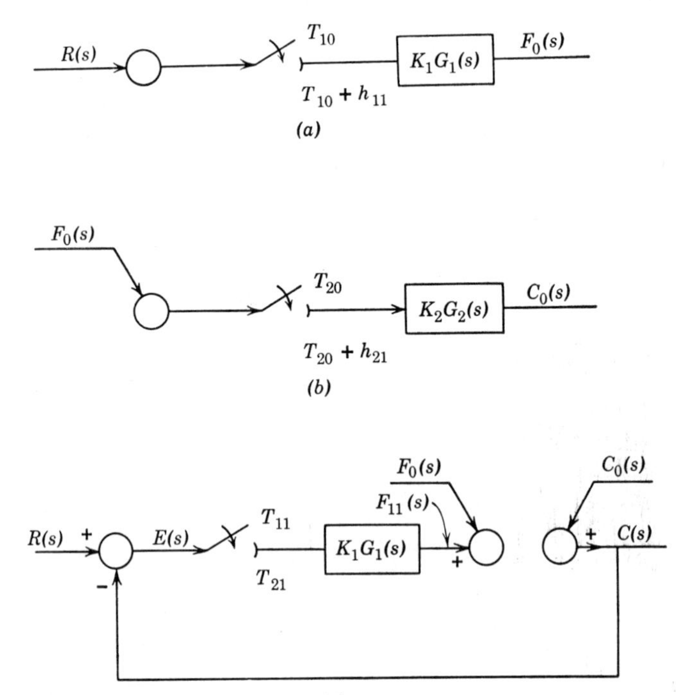

Figure 9.31 Equivalent systems of Fig. 9.29 at different intervals: (*a*) $0 < t < T_{20}$; (*b*) $T_{20} < t < T_{11}$; (*c*) $T_{11} < t < T_{21}$

tion $T_{20} < t < T_{11}$ and the output written as

$$C_0(s) = \underset{T_{20}}{\overset{T_{20}+h_{21}}{\mathsf{P}}} [F_0(s)]\, K_2G_2(s) \tag{9.223}$$

This may be calculated since $F_0(s)$ is known. Equations (9.222) and (9.223) define the components $F_0(s)$ and $C_0(s)$ for all values of time $t > 0$. At $t = T_{11}$ the first sampler closes again for the duration of h_{12} seconds. However, the second sampler also closes at $t = T_{21}$ for h_{22} seconds, which causes two overlapping pulses. Figure 9.30*a*, *b* shows that the interval $T_{11} < t < T_{21} + h_{22}$ can be conveniently divided into three regions:

(i) $T_{11} < t < T_{21}$ when only the first sampler is closed.
(ii) $T_{21} < t < T_{11} + h_{12}$ when both samplers are closed.
(iii) $T_{11} + h_{12} < t < T_{21} + h_{22}$ when only the second sampler is closed.

The equivalent system in region (i) is shown in Fig. 9.31*c*. In this region $E(s)$ can be written as

$$E(s) = R(s) - C_0(s) \tag{9.224}$$

from which $F_{11}(s)$ can be calculated as

$$F_{11}(s) = \mathop{\mathsf{P}}_{T_{11}}^{T_{21}} [R(s) - C_0(s)]\, K_1G_1(s) \tag{9.225}$$

The conditions for region (ii) are presented in Fig. 9.32. In this region the system can be considered to have two samplers which close simul-

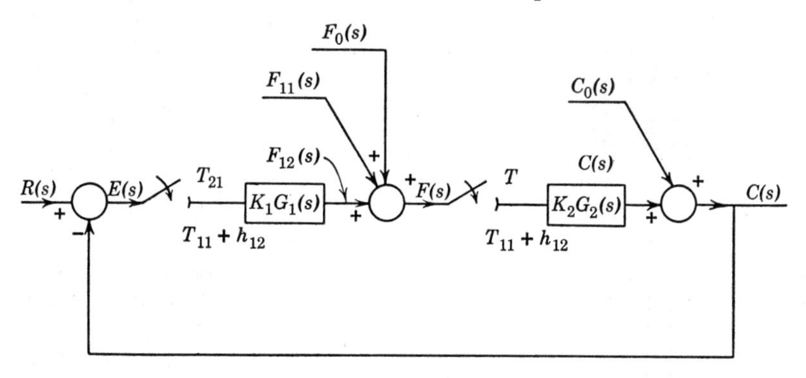

Figure 9.32 Conditions in region (ii) when both samplers are closed

taneously at $t = T_{21}$ and open at $t = T_{11} + h_{12}$; $F_{12}(s)$ and $C_{11}(s)$ are the components of output resulting from this closure. For the purpose of calculating $C(s)$, the total output, Fig. 9.32 may be replaced by Fig. 9.33. Where

$$R_1(s) = \mathop{\mathsf{P}}_{T_{21}}^{\infty} [R(s) - C_0(s)] - \mathop{\mathsf{P}}_{T_{21}}^{T_{21}+h_{22}} [F_0(s) + F_{11}(s)]\, K_2G_2(s) \tag{9.226}$$

The section between the points AB in this figure can now be treated as an independent system whose input is $R_1(s)$ and output $C_{11}(s)$. While both samplers are closed, $E(s)$ can be shown to be

$$E(s) = \frac{R_1(s)}{1 + K_1G_1(s)\, K_2G_2(s)}, \qquad T_{21} < t < T_{11} + h_{12} \tag{9.227}$$

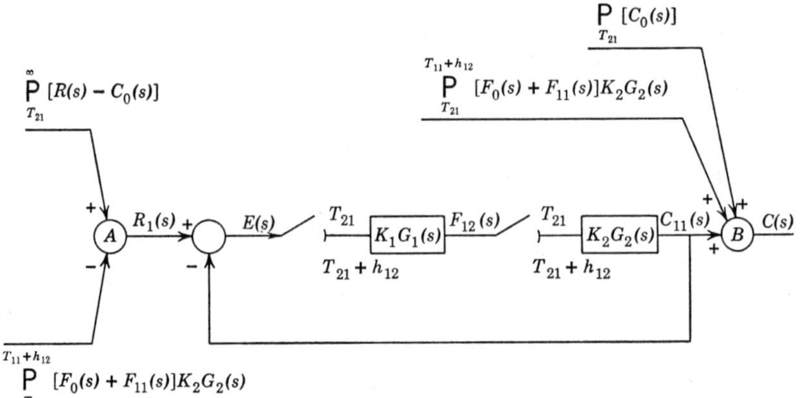

Figure 9.33 Equivalent system in region (ii) where both samplers are closed

Defining a new time axis

$$t_1 = (t - T_{21}) \tag{9.228}$$

and proceeding as in Figs. 9.25 and 9.26 and equations (9.176) and (9.177), we can show that

$$F_{12}(s) = e^{-T_{21}s} \left\{ \mathop{\mathsf{P}}_{0}^{T_{11}+h_{12}-T_{21}} \left[\frac{e^{T_{21}s} R_1(s)}{1 + K_1G_1(s)\, K_2G_2(s)} \right] K_1G_1(s) \right\} \tag{9.229}$$

and

$$C_{11}(s) = e^{-T_{21}s} \left[\mathop{\mathsf{P}}_{0}^{T_{11}+h_{12}-T_{21}} [F_{12}(s)]\, K_2G_2(s) \right] \tag{9.230}$$

The total output for $T_{21} < t < T_{11} + h_{12}$ can therefore be written as

$$C(s) = C_0(s) + C_{11}(s) + \mathop{\mathsf{P}}_{T_{21}}^{T_{11}+h_{12}} [F_0(s) + F_{11}(s)]\, K_2G_2(s) \tag{9.231}$$

which can be calculated from equations (9.223), (9.229), and (9.230). The conditions in region (iii) are presented in Fig. 9.34. The output of the first system is

$$F(s) = F_0(s) + F_{11}(s) + F_{12}(s) \tag{9.232}$$

This is fed to the second sampler which closes for $T_{11} + h_{12} < t < T_{21} + h_{22}$. The component of output due to this closure, $C_{12}(s)$, can be written as

$$C_{12}(s) = \mathop{\mathsf{P}}_{T_{11}+h_{12}}^{T_{21}+h_{22}} [F_0(s) + F_{11}(s) + F_{12}(s)]\, K_2G_2(s) \tag{9.233}$$

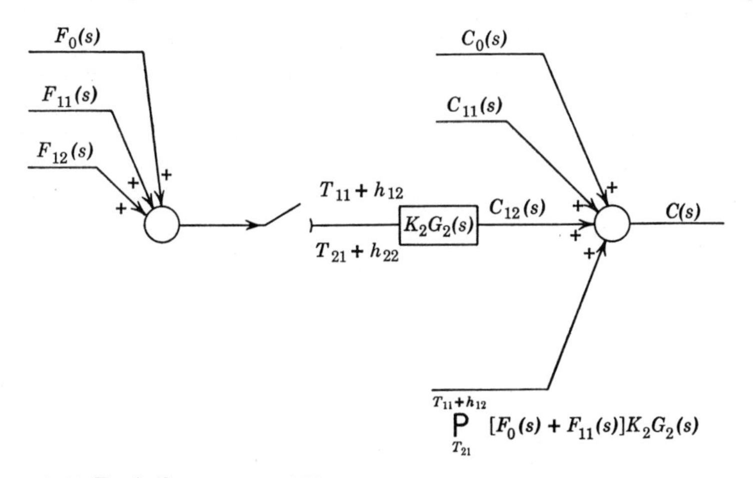

Figure 9.34 Equivalent system of Fig. 9.29 in region (iii) where $T_{11} + h_{12} < t < T_{22}$

Therefore the total output for $T_{11} + h_{12} < t < T_{22}$ becomes

$$C(s) = C_0(s) + C_{11}(s) + \overset{T_{21}+h_{22}}{\underset{T_{21}}{\mathsf{P}}} [F_0(s) + F_{11}(s)]\, K_2G_2(s) + \overset{T_{21}+h_{22}}{\underset{T_{11}+h_{12}}{\mathsf{P}}} [F_{12}(s)]\, K_2G_2(s) \quad (9.234)$$

By proceeding in this way, the output at any instant may be computed. It is clear that this technique can be applied to systems with any number of samplers operating in any desired sequence. It is reasonable to assume that with periodic samplers certain simplifications will result.† The equations for such systems may be derived in a way similar to that outlined for a single periodic sampler.‡

9.17 Conclusions

In this chapter a general method for the analysis of sampled-data systems with finite pulse width is presented. This method is based on the p-transform and the superposition principle. This method is exact and takes into account the actual pulse width and pulse shape as de-

† It should be noted that by effecting the limiting case $h \to 0$, the techniques above can be extended to the analysis of multirate sampled-data feedback systems or to sampled-data feedback systems having multiple samplers operating nonperiodically.

‡ See problems of this chapter.

termined by the operation of the sampler. The technique is applicable to open-loop and feedback systems and can be extended to systems with two or more periodic or non-periodic samplers.

When the samplers are periodic, general equations may be developed for the output. It is shown that for an error-pulsed feedback system with a periodic sampler these equations can be expressed in terms of a set of constant coefficients. These may be divided into two categories, (*a*) the characteristic coefficients and (*b*) the input coefficients as explained in detail. Stability can be established entirely in terms of the relations between the characteristic coefficients. The method can be easily extended to a system with a general linear transfer function.

The pulse width h can be varied from zero to the sampling period T. When $h = T$ is substituted in the equations, the output is identically that of the continuous system using the ordinary Laplace transform theory. Therefore, a continuous system may be looked upon as a pulsed system whose pulse width is equal to the sampler period. This point of view may be advantageously employed in a new approach to the synthesis of continuous feedback systems. In a similar way the stability conditions and the response of the equivalent sampled-data systems as discussed in the first two chapters are obtained if the pulse width is allowed to approach zero and the gain is increased inversely as h so that the product of h times the new gain is always equal to the fixed open-loop gain.

In concluding it is well to mention that the presence of the sampler is not an essential requirement for the application of this technique. Any linear system with finite pulse inputs at its various stages lends itself to analysis by this method, irrespective of how these pulses are generated.

References

1. G. Farmanfarma, "Analysis of Linear Sampled-Data Systems with Finite Pulse Width (Open Loop)," *Trans. A.I.E.E.*, Vol. 75, Pt. I, 1956, pp. 808–819.
2. G. Farmanfarma, "Analysis of Multiple Sampler Systems with Finite Pulse Width (Open Loop)," A.I.E.E. Transactions Paper No. CP56-1037, presented at Fall General Meeting, October 9, 1957.
3. G. Farmanfarma, "General Analysis of Stability Study of Finite Pulsed Feedback Systems," A.I.E.E. Transactions Paper No. 58-240, presented in New York, February 7, 1958.

ADDENDUM

It is not difficult to verify the validity of equation (9.192) for any specific system. For example, referring to Fig. 9.27, let

$$R(s) = 1/s \quad \text{unit step input} \tag{1}$$

and

$$KG(s) = \frac{6}{s(s+5)} \tag{2}$$

Then $C_0(s)$, the component of output from the first pulse, can be written from equation (9.167) as

$$C_0(s) = \mathsf{P}_0^h \left(\frac{s+5}{s^2+5s+6}\right) \frac{6}{s(s+5)} \tag{3}$$

Using relation 2 of Table II (Appendix, page 402) we obtain

$$C_0(s) = \left\{\frac{3[1 - e^{-h(s+2)}]}{s+2} - \frac{2[1 - e^{-h(s+3)}]}{s+3}\right\} \frac{6}{s(s+5)} \tag{4}$$

Assuming that $nT > h$, the term $\mathsf{P}_{nT}^{\infty} C_0(s)$ can be written, using relation 6 of Table I (Appendix, page 400), as

$$\begin{aligned} \mathsf{P}_{nT}^{\infty} [C_0(s)] = e^{-nTs} \Bigg\{ & \left[\frac{9(1 - e^{-2h})}{5} - \frac{12(1 - e^{-3h})}{15}\right] \frac{1}{s} \\ & + \left[\frac{18(1 - e^{3h})}{15} - \frac{6(1 - e^{2h})}{5}\right] \frac{e^{-5nT}}{s+5} \Bigg\} \end{aligned} \tag{5}$$

This can be placed on a common denominator and written as

$$\mathsf{P}_{nT}^{\infty} [C_0(s)] = e^{-nTs} \left[\frac{x_1{}^0(nT)s + x_0{}^0}{s(s+5)}\right] \tag{6}$$

where

$$x_1{}^0(nT) = [\tfrac{6}{5} e^{-5nT}(e^{2h} - e^{3h}) + (1 - \tfrac{9}{5} e^{-2h} + \tfrac{4}{5} e^{-3h})]$$

$$x_0{}^0 = (5 - 9e^{-2h} + 4e^{-3h})$$

The similarity of this to the more general equation of (9.192) is evident.

TABLE 9.1

p-Transform Pairs

No.	$F(s)$	$F_p(s)$ or $F_n(s)$
1	a_0	a_0
2	$\frac{a_0}{s}$	$\frac{a_0(1 - e^{-hs})}{s(1 - e^{-Ts})}$
3	$\frac{a_0}{s + \gamma}$	$\frac{a_0[1 - e^{-h(s+\gamma)}]}{(s + \gamma)[1 - e^{-T(s+\gamma)}]}$
4	$\frac{a_0}{s(s + \gamma)}$	$\frac{a_0}{\gamma}\left\{\frac{1 - e^{-hs}}{s(1 - e^{-Ts})} - \frac{1 - e^{-h(s+\gamma)}}{(s + \gamma)[1 - e^{-T(s+\gamma)}]}\right\}$
5	$\frac{a_1 s + a_0}{s(s + \gamma)}$	$\frac{1}{\gamma}\left\{\frac{a_0(1 - e^{-hs})}{s(1 - e^{-Ts})} - \frac{(a_0 - a_1\gamma)[1 - e^{-h(s+\gamma)}]}{(s + \gamma)[1 - e^{-T(s+\gamma)}]}\right\}$
6	$\frac{a_2 s^2 + a_1 s + a_0}{s(s + \alpha)(s + \gamma)}$	$\left\{\frac{a_0}{\alpha\gamma}\frac{1 - e^{-hs}}{s(1 - e^{-Ts})} + \frac{a_2\alpha^2 - a_1\alpha + a_0}{\alpha(\alpha - \gamma)}\frac{1 - e^{-h(s+\alpha)}}{(s + \alpha)[1 - e^{-T(s+\alpha)}]} - \frac{a_2\gamma^2 - a_1\gamma + a_0}{\gamma(\alpha - \gamma)}\frac{1 - e^{-h(s+\gamma)}}{(s + \gamma)[1 - e^{-T(s+\gamma)}]}\right\}$
7	$\frac{1}{s^2}$	$\left[\frac{Te^{-Ts}(1 - e^{-hs})}{s(1 - e^{-Ts})^2} + \frac{1 - e^{-hs}}{s^2(1 - e^{-Ts})} - \frac{he^{-hs}}{s(1 - e^{-Ts})}\right]$
8	$\frac{1}{s^N}$	$\frac{(-1)^{N-1}}{(N - 1)!}\frac{d^{N-1}}{ds^{N-1}}\left[\frac{1 - e^{-hs}}{s(1 - e^{-Ts})}\right]$

9	$\dfrac{1}{(s+\gamma)^2}$	$\left\{\dfrac{Te^{-T(s+\gamma)}[1-e^{-h(s+\gamma)}]}{(s+\gamma)[1-e^{-T(s+\gamma)}]^2}+\dfrac{1-e^{-h(s+\gamma)}}{(s+\gamma)^2[1-e^{-T(s+\gamma)}]}-\dfrac{he^{-h(s+\gamma)}}{(s+\gamma)[1-e^{-T(s+\gamma)}]}\right\}$
10	$\dfrac{1}{(s+\gamma)^N}$	$\dfrac{(-1)^{N-1}}{(N-1)!}\dfrac{d^{N-1}}{du^{N-1}}\left[\dfrac{1-e^{-hu}}{u(1-e^{-Tu})}\right], u = s+\gamma$
11	$\dfrac{a_1s+a_0}{s^2(s+\gamma)}$	$\left\{\dfrac{a_0-a_1\gamma}{\gamma^2}\dfrac{1-e^{-h(s+\gamma)}}{(s+\gamma)[1-e^{-T(s+\gamma)}]}+\dfrac{a_1\gamma-a_0}{\gamma^2}\dfrac{1-e^{-hs}}{s(1-e^{-Ts})}+\dfrac{a_0}{\gamma}\left[\dfrac{Te^{-Ts}(1-e^{-hs})}{s(1-e^{-Ts})^2}+\dfrac{1-e^{-hs}}{s^2(1-e^{-Ts})}-\dfrac{he^{-hs}}{s(1-e^{-Ts})}\right]\right\}$
12	$\dfrac{a_1s+a_0}{(s+\alpha)^2+\beta^2}$	$\dfrac{1}{2j\beta}\left\{\dfrac{[(a_0-a_1\alpha)+ja_1\beta][1-e^{-h(s+\alpha-j\beta)}]}{(s+\alpha-j\beta)[1-e^{-T(s+\alpha-j\beta)}]}-\dfrac{[(a_0-a_1\alpha)-ja_1\beta][1-e^{-h(s+\alpha+j\beta)}]}{(s+\alpha+j\beta)[1-e^{-T(s+\alpha+j\beta)}]}\right\}$
13	$\mathsf{P}_{h,T}\left[\dfrac{e^{\delta s}(a_1s+a_0)}{(s+\gamma)(s+\alpha)}\right]$	$\dfrac{1}{\alpha-\gamma}\left[\dfrac{(a_0-a_1\gamma)e^{-\delta\gamma}[1-e^{-h(s+\gamma)}]}{(s+\gamma)[1-e^{-T(s+\gamma)}]}-\dfrac{(a_0-a_1\alpha)e^{-\delta\alpha}[1-e^{-h(s+\alpha)}]}{(s+\alpha)[1-e^{-T(s+\alpha)}}\right]$
14	$\overset{T+h}{\underset{T}{\mathsf{P}}}\left(\dfrac{a_0}{s+\gamma}\right)$	$[1-e^{-h(s+\gamma)}]\dfrac{a_0e^{-T(s+\gamma)}}{s+\gamma}$
15	$\sum_{n=0}^{\infty}\overset{T_n+h_{n+1}}{\underset{T_n}{\mathsf{P}}}\left(\dfrac{a_0}{s+\gamma}\right)$	$\sum_{n=0}^{\infty} e^{-T_n(s+\gamma)}[1-e^{-h_{n+1}(s+\gamma)}]\dfrac{a_0}{s+\sim}$
16	$\mathsf{P}_{h,T}\left[\dfrac{a_0e^{\delta s}}{(s+\gamma)}\right]$	$\left[\dfrac{1-e^{-h(s+\gamma)}}{1-e^{-T(s+\gamma)}}\right]\dfrac{a_0e^{-\delta\gamma}}{s+\sim}$

TABLE 9.2

Inverse *p*-Transform Pairs

No.	$Fp(s)$	Condition	$f_p(t), \quad t = (n - 1 + m)\,T, \quad t \geqq 0$
1	$\dfrac{1 - ke^{-hs}}{1 - e^{-Ts}} \dfrac{a_0}{s}$		$[1 - k\,d(-h)]a_0 n$
2	$\dfrac{1 - ke^{-hs}}{1 - e^{-T(s+q)}} \dfrac{a_0}{s}$	$q \neq 0$	$[1 - k\,d(-h)] \dfrac{a_0(1 - e^{-nqT})}{(1 - e^{-qT})}$
3	$\dfrac{1 - ke^{-hs}}{1 - e^{-T(s+\gamma)}} \dfrac{a_0}{s + \gamma}$	$q = \gamma$	$[1 - k\,d(-h)]a_0 n e^{-\gamma t}$
4	$\dfrac{1 - ke^{-hs}}{1 - e^{-T(s+q)}} \dfrac{a_0}{s + \gamma}$	$q \neq \gamma$	$[1 - k\,d(-h)] \dfrac{a_0}{e^{-T(q-\gamma)} - 1} [e^{\gamma T} e^{-T(nq+m\gamma)} - e^{-\gamma t}]$
5	$\dfrac{1 - ke^{-hs}}{1 - e^{-Ts}} \dfrac{a_1 s + a_0}{s(s + \gamma)}$	$q = 0$	$[1 - k\,d(-h)] \left\{\dfrac{a_0 n}{\gamma} + \dfrac{a_1\gamma - a_0}{\gamma(e^{T\gamma} - 1)} [e^{-T\gamma(m-1)} - e^{-\gamma t}]\right\}$
6	$\dfrac{1 - ke^{-hs}}{1 - e^{-T(s+\gamma)}} \dfrac{a_1 s + a_0}{s(s + \gamma)}$		$[1 - k\,d(-h)] \left\{\dfrac{a_0(1 - e^{-n\gamma T})}{\gamma(1 - e^{-\gamma T})} + \dfrac{a_1\gamma - a_0}{\gamma} n e^{-\gamma t}\right\}$
7	$\dfrac{1 - ke^{-hs}}{1 - e^{-T(s+q)}} \dfrac{a_1 s + a_0}{s(s + \gamma)}$	$q \neq \gamma$ $q \neq 0$	$[1 - k\,d(-h)] \left\{\dfrac{a_0(1 - e^{-nqT})}{\gamma(1 - e^{-qT})} + \dfrac{a_1\gamma - a_0}{\gamma[e^{-T(q-\gamma)} - 1]} [e^{-T[nq+(m-1)\gamma]} - e^{-\gamma t}]\right\}$
8	$\dfrac{1 - ke^{-hs}}{1 - e^{-Ts}} \dfrac{a_1 s + a_0}{s^2}$		$[1 - k\,d(-h)] \left\{n \left[a_1 + \dfrac{a_0(mT + t)}{2}\right]\right\}$
9	$\dfrac{1 - ke^{-hs}}{1 - e^{-T(s+q)}} \dfrac{a_1 s + a_0}{s^2}$	$q \neq 0$	$[1 - k\,d(-h)] \left\{\dfrac{(a_1 + a_0 mT)e^{-nTq} - [a_1 + a_0(T + t)]}{e^{-Tq} - 1} + \dfrac{a_0 T(e^{-nTq} - 1)}{(e^{-Tq} - 1)^2}\right\}$

10	$\frac{1-ke^{-hs}}{1-e^{-T(s+\gamma)}}\frac{a_1s+a_0}{(s+\gamma)^2}$		$[1-k\,d(-h)]\left\{ne^{-\gamma t}\left[a_1+\frac{(a_0-a_1\gamma)(mT+t)}{2}\right]\right\}$
11	$\frac{1-ke^{-hs}}{1-e^{-T(s+q)}}\frac{a_1s+a_0}{(s+\gamma)^2}$	$q\neq\gamma$	$[1-k\,d(-h)]\left\{\frac{T(a_0-a_1\gamma)[e^{-T[nq+\gamma(m+1)]}-e^{-2T\gamma}e^{-\gamma t}]}{(e^{-Tq}-e^{-T\gamma})^2}+\frac{[a_1+mT(a_0-a_1\gamma)]e^{-T(nq+m\gamma)}-[a_1+(a_0-a_1\gamma)(T+t)]e^{-\gamma(T+t)}}{(e^{-Tq}-e^{-T\gamma})}\right.$
12	$\frac{1-ke^{-hs}}{[1-e^{-T(s+\gamma)}]^2}\frac{1}{(s+\gamma)}$		$[1-k\,d(-h)]\frac{n(n+1)}{2}e^{-\gamma t}$
13	$\frac{1-ke^{-hs}}{[1-e^{-T(s+q)}]^2}\frac{1}{(s+\gamma)}$	$q\neq\gamma$	$[1-k\,d(-h)]e^{-\gamma mT}\left[\frac{(n+1)e^{-nTq}}{e^{-Tq}-e^{-T\gamma}}-\frac{e^{-(n+1)Tq}-e^{-(n+1)T\gamma}}{(e^{-Tq}-e^{-T\gamma})^2}\right]$
14	$\frac{1-ke^{-hs}}{1-e^{-T(s+q)}}\frac{a_1s+a_0}{(s+\alpha)^2+\beta^2}$	$\beta\neq 0$	$[1-k\,d(-h)]\left\{\frac{[(a_1\alpha-a_0)^2+(a_1\beta)^2]^{1/2}}{\beta[1+e^{-2T(q-\alpha)}-2e^{-T(q-\alpha)}\cos\beta T]^{1/2}}\times[e^{-T[nq+(m-1)\alpha]}\sin(m\beta T+\theta+\phi)+e^{-\alpha t}\sin(\beta t+\theta+\psi)]\right\}$ where $\theta=\tan^{-1}\frac{a_1\beta}{a_0-a_1\alpha}$, $\phi=\tan^{-1}\frac{\sin\beta T}{e^{-T(q-\alpha)}-\cos\beta T}$, $\psi=\tan^{-1}\frac{-\sin\beta T}{e^{T(q-\alpha)}-\cos\beta T}$
15	$\frac{1-(k_1+jk_2)e^{-hs}}{1-e^{-T(s+\alpha+j\beta)}}\frac{1}{s+\gamma}$	$\beta\neq 0$ $\alpha\neq\gamma$	$[1-(k_1+jk_2)\,d(-h)]\left\{\frac{e^{-T[n\alpha+(m-1)\gamma]}e^{-jnT\beta}-e^{-\gamma t}}{e^{-T(\alpha-\gamma)}e^{-jT\beta}-1}\right\}$
16	$\frac{1-(k_1+jk_2)e^{-hs}}{[1-e^{-T(s+\rho+j\lambda)}]}\frac{1}{(s+\rho+j\lambda)}$		$[1-(k_1+jk_2)\,d(-h)]ne^{-\rho t}e^{-j\lambda t}$
17	$\frac{1-(k_1+jk_2)e^{-hs}}{1-e^{-T(s+\alpha+j\beta)}}\frac{1}{(s+\rho+j\lambda)}$	$\alpha+j\beta \neq \rho+j\lambda$	$[1-(k_1+jk_2)\,d(-h)]\left\{\frac{e^{-T[n\alpha+(m-1)\rho]}e^{-jT[n\beta+(m-1)\lambda]}-e^{-\rho t}e^{-j\lambda t}}{e^{-T(\alpha-\rho)}e^{-jT(\beta-\lambda)}-1}\right\}$

Note: By substituting $n = 1$, and $mT = t$ in any of these inverse pairs, the inverse time function $f_p(t)$ simplifies to the inverse Laplace transform for the continuous case.

TABLE 9.3

Input-Output Relations for Synchronized Periodic Sampler Period T and Pulse Width h Seconds

No.	Input $C(s)$	Conditions	Output $C_p(s)$
1	$F(s)$	$F(s)$ is a Polynomial in s	$\underset{h,T}{\mathsf{P}}[F(s)] = \frac{1}{2\pi j}\int_{\Gamma} F(v)\frac{1 - e^{-h(s-v)}}{[(s-v)1 - e^{-T(-v)}]}\,dv$
2	$e^{-(nT+\beta)s}F(s)$	$n = 0, 1, 2, \cdots$ $0 \leq \beta \leq T$	
	(a)	$h \leq \beta \leq T$	$e^{-(n+1)Ts}\underset{h,T}{\mathsf{P}}[F(s)\,e^{(T-\beta)s}]$
	(b)	$0 < \beta \leq h$	$\left\{e^{-(nT+\beta)s}\overset{h-\beta}{\underset{0}{\mathsf{P}}}[F(s)] + e^{-(n+1)Ts}\underset{h,T}{\mathsf{P}}[F(s)\,e^{(T-\beta)s}]\right\}$
	(c)	$\beta = 0$	$e^{-nTs}\underset{h,T}{\mathsf{P}}[F(s)]$
3	$\frac{e^{-(nT+\beta)s}}{1 - e^{-kT(s+\alpha)}}F(s)$	$n = 0, 1, 2, \cdots$ $k = 0, 1, 2, \cdots$ $0 \leq \beta \leq T$	
	(a)	$h \leq \beta \leq T$	$\frac{e^{-(n+1)Ts}}{1 - e^{-kT(s+\alpha)}}\underset{h,T}{\mathsf{P}}[F(s)\,e^{(T-\beta)s}]$
	(b)	$0 < \beta \leq h$	$\frac{1}{1 - e^{-kT(s+\alpha)}}\left\{e^{-(nT+\beta)s}\overset{h-\beta}{\underset{0}{\mathsf{P}}}[F(s)] + e^{-(n+1)Ts}\underset{h\,T}{\mathsf{P}}[F(s)\,e^{(T-\beta)s}]\right\}$
	(c)	$\beta = 0$	$\frac{e^{-nTs}}{1 - e^{-kT(s+\alpha)}}\underset{h\,T}{\mathsf{P}}[F(s)]$

TABLE 9.4

Input-Output Relations for a Delayed Periodic Sampler with Period T, Pulse Width h, and a Delay of δ Seconds

No.	Input $C(s)$	Conditions	Output $C_p(s)$
1	$F(s)$	$F(s)$ is a polynomial in s	$e^{-\delta s} \underset{h,T}{\mathsf{P}} [F(s)\, e^{\delta s}] = \dfrac{e^{-\delta s}}{2\pi j} \displaystyle\int_\Gamma F(\nu)\, e^{\delta \nu} \dfrac{1 - e^{-h(s-\nu)}}{(s-\nu)[1 - e^{-T(s-\nu)}]}\, d\nu$
2	$e^{-\sigma s} F(s)$	$\sigma \geq \delta$	
		$n = 0, 1, 2, \cdots$	
	Let $\sigma - \delta = nT + \beta$	$0 \leq \beta \leq T$	
	(*a*)	$h \leq \beta \leq T$	$e^{-[\delta + (n+1)T]s} \underset{h,T}{\mathsf{P}} [F(s)\, e^{(T-\beta)s}]$
	(*b*)	$0 < \beta \leq h$	$\left\{ e^{-\sigma s} \overset{h-\beta}{\underset{0}{\mathsf{P}}} [F(s)] + e^{-[\delta + (n+1)T]s} \underset{h,T}{\mathsf{P}} [F(s)\, e^{(T-\beta)s}] \right\}$

	(*c*)	$\beta = 0$	$e^{-\delta s} \underset{h,T}{\mathsf{P}} [F(s)]$
3	$e^{-\sigma s} F(s)$	$\sigma \leq \delta$	$e^{-\delta s} \underset{h\ T}{\mathsf{P}} [F(s)\ e^{(\delta-\sigma)s}$
4	$\dfrac{e^{-\sigma s}}{[1 - e^{-kT(s+\alpha)}]} F(s)$	$\sigma \geq \delta$ $k = 0, 1, 2, \cdots$ $n = 0, 1, 2, \cdots$	
	Let $(\sigma - \delta) = nT + \beta$	$0 \leq \beta \leq T$	
	(*a*)	$h \leq \beta \leq T$	$\dfrac{e^{-[\delta+(n+1)T]s}}{[1 - e^{-kT(s+\alpha)}]} \underset{h,T}{\mathsf{P}} [F(s)\ e^{(T-\beta)s}]$
	(*b*)	$0 < \beta \leq h$	$\dfrac{1}{[1 - e^{-kT(s+\alpha)}]} \left\{ e^{-\sigma s} \overset{h-\beta}{\underset{0}{\mathsf{P}}} [F(s)] + e^{-[\delta+(n+1)T]s} \underset{h,T}{\mathsf{P}} [F(s)\ e^{(T-\beta)s}] \right\}$
	(*c*)	$\beta = 0$	$\dfrac{e^{-\sigma s}}{[1 - e^{-kT(s+\alpha)}]} \underset{h,T}{\mathsf{P}} [F(s)]$

APPENDIX

In this appendix the procedures indicated earlier are applied to specific systems.

A general second-order transfer function may be represented by

$$KG(s) = \frac{a_1 s + a_0}{(s + \rho_1)(s + \rho_2)} \tag{1}$$

where it is assumed that $\rho_1 \neq \rho_2$. If $\rho_1 = \rho_2$, then the same procedure can be used except that the values of the residues are different. Consider the error-pulsed system shown in Fig. 9.27. This has a periodic sampler with period T and pulse width h. The stability of such a system is independent of the output; however, for the purpose of illustration a step input of magnitude R will be assumed. Therefore

$$R(s) = \frac{R}{s} \tag{2}$$

and

$$\frac{1}{1 + KG(s)} = \frac{(s + \rho_1)(s + \rho_2)}{s^2 + (\rho_1 + \rho_2 + a_1)s + (\rho_1\rho_2 + a_0)} = \frac{(s + \rho_1)(s + \rho_2)}{(s + \alpha_1)(s + \alpha_2)} \tag{3}$$

where α_1 and α_2 are the poles of $1/[1 + KG(s)]$ and can have complex values. Relation 1 of Table I (page 400) shows that

$$e^{nTs} \mathop{\mathsf{P}}_{nT}^{\infty} \left(\frac{R}{s}\right) = \frac{R}{s} \tag{4}$$

Hence the output for duration $nT < t \leq (n + 1)T$ can be obtained from equation (9.197) as

$$C(s) = e^{-nTs} \left\{ \frac{c(nT)\, s + A_0(nT)}{(s + \rho_1)(s + \rho_2)} + \mathop{\mathsf{P}}_{0}^{h} \left[\frac{\left\{ \begin{array}{l} [R - c(nT)]s^2 + [R(\rho_1 + \rho_2) \\ \qquad - A_0(nT)]s + R\rho_1\rho_2 \end{array} \right\}}{s(s + \alpha_1)(s + \alpha_2)} \right] \frac{a_1 s + a_0}{(s + \rho_1)(s + \rho_2)} \right\} \tag{5}$$

Relations 3 of Table II (page 400) may be used to write this as

$$C(s) = e^{-nTs}\left\{\frac{c(nT)\,s + A_0(nT)}{(s+\rho_1)(s+\rho_2)} + \left[\frac{R\rho_1\rho_2}{\alpha_1\alpha_2}\frac{1-e^{-hs}}{s}\right.\right.$$

$$+\frac{[R-c(nT)]\alpha_1^2 - [R(\rho_1+\rho_2) - A_0(nT)]\alpha_1 + R\rho_1\rho_2}{(-\alpha_1)(\alpha_2-\alpha_1)}\frac{1-e^{-h(s+\alpha_1)}}{s+\alpha_1}$$

$$+\left.\frac{[R-c(nT)]\alpha_2^2 - [R(\rho_1+\rho_2) - A_0(nT)]\alpha_2 + R\rho_1\rho_2}{(-\alpha_2)(\alpha_1-\alpha_2)}\frac{1-e^{-h(s+\alpha_2)}}{s+\alpha_2}\right]$$

$$\left.\times\frac{a_1 s + a_0}{(s+\rho_1)(s+\rho_2)}\right\} \tag{6}$$

The required difference equations can now be obtained from the following identity:

$$\underset{(n+1)T}{\overset{\infty}{\mathsf{P}}}\ [\text{equation (6)}] = e^{-(n+1)Ts}\left[\frac{c(n+1)T\,s + A_0(n+1)T}{(s+\rho_1)(s+\rho_2)}\right] \tag{7}$$

By utilizing relation 6 of Table I the left-hand side of this equation may be written as

$$\underset{(n+1)T}{\overset{\infty}{\mathsf{P}}}\ [\text{equation (6)}] = e^{-(n+1)Ts}\left\{[L_c^{\,1}c(nT) + L_0^{\,1}\,A(nT)\right.$$

$$\left.+ L_R^{\,1}R]\frac{e^{-\rho_1 T}}{s+\rho_1} + [L_c^{\,2}\,c(nT) + L_0^{\,2}\,A_0(nT) + L_R^{\,2}R]\frac{e^{-\rho_2 T}}{s+\rho_2}\right\} \tag{8}$$

where

$$L_c^{\,1} = \left\{\frac{-\rho_1}{\rho_2-\rho_1} + \frac{\alpha_1}{\alpha_2-\alpha_1}\frac{(a_0-a_1\rho_1)[1-e^{-h(\alpha_1-\rho_1)}]}{(\rho_2-\rho_1)(\alpha_1-\rho_1)}\right.$$

$$\left.+\frac{\alpha_2}{\alpha_1-\alpha_2}\frac{(a_0-a_1\rho_1)[1-e^{-h(\alpha_2-\rho_1)}]}{(\rho_2-\rho_1)(\alpha_2-\rho_1)}\right\}$$

$$L_0^{\,1} = \left\{\frac{1}{\rho_2-\rho_1} - \frac{1}{(\alpha_2-\alpha_1)}\frac{(a_0-a_1\rho_1)[1-e^{-h(\alpha_1-\rho_1)}]}{(\rho_2-\rho_1)(\alpha_1-\rho_1)}\right.$$

$$\left.-\frac{1}{\alpha_1-\alpha_2}\frac{(a_0-a_1\rho_1)[1-e^{-h(\alpha_2-\rho_1)}]}{(\rho_2-\rho_1)(\alpha_2-\rho_1)}\right\}$$

$$L_R{}^1 = \left\{\frac{\rho_1\rho_2}{\alpha_1\alpha_2}\frac{(a_0 - a_1\rho_1)(1 - e^{h\rho_1})}{(\rho_2 - \rho_1)(-\rho_1)} + \frac{\alpha_1{}^2 - \alpha_1(\rho_1 + \rho_2) + \rho_1\rho_2}{(-\alpha_1)(\alpha_2 - \alpha_1)}\right.$$

$$\times \frac{(a_0 - a_1\rho_1)[1 - e^{-h(\alpha_1-\rho_1)}]}{(\rho_2 - \rho_1)(\alpha_1 - \rho_1)} + \frac{\alpha_2{}^2 - \alpha_2(\rho_1 + \rho_2) + \rho_1\rho_2}{(-\alpha_2)(\alpha_1 - \alpha_2)}$$

$$\left.\times \frac{(a_0 - a_1\rho_2)[1 - e^{-h(\alpha_2-\rho_1)}]}{(\rho_2 - \rho_1)(\alpha_2 - \rho_1)}\right\}$$

$$L_c{}^2 = \left\{\frac{-\rho_2}{\rho_1 - \rho_2} + \frac{\alpha_1}{\alpha_2 - \alpha_1}\frac{(a_0 - a_1\rho_2)[1 - e^{-h(\alpha_1-\rho_2)}]}{(\rho_1 - \rho_2)(\alpha_1 - \rho_2)}\right.$$

$$\left.+ \frac{\alpha_2}{\alpha_1 - \alpha_2}\frac{(a_0 - a_1\rho_2)[1 - e^{-h(\alpha_2-\rho_2)}]}{(\rho_1 - \rho_2)(\alpha_2 - \rho_2)}\right\}$$

$$L_0{}^2 = \left\{\frac{1}{\rho_1 - \rho_2} - \frac{1}{\alpha_2 - \alpha_1}\frac{(a_0 - a_1\rho_2)[1 - e^{-h(\alpha_1-\rho_2)}]}{(\rho_1 - \rho_2)(\alpha_1 - \rho_2)}\right.$$

$$\left.- \frac{1}{\alpha_1 - \alpha_2}\frac{(a_0 - a_1\rho_2)[1 - e^{-h(\alpha_2-\rho_2)}]}{(\rho_1 - \rho_2)(\alpha_2 - \rho_2)}\right\}$$

$$L_R{}^2 = \left\{\frac{\rho_1\rho_2}{\alpha_1\alpha_2}\frac{(a_0 - a_1\rho_2)(1 - e^{h\rho_2})}{(\rho_1 - \rho_2)(-\rho_2)} + \frac{\alpha_1{}^2 - \alpha_1(\rho_1 + \rho_2) + \rho_1\rho_2}{(-\alpha_1)(\alpha_2 - \alpha_1)}\right.$$

$$\times \frac{(a_0 - a_1\rho_2)[1 - e^{-h(\alpha_1-\rho_2)}]}{(\rho_1 - \rho_2)(\alpha_1 - \rho_2)} + \frac{\alpha_2{}^2 - \alpha_2(\rho_1 + \rho_2) + \rho_1\rho_2}{(-\alpha_2)(\alpha_1 - \alpha_2)}$$

$$\left.\times \frac{(a_0 - a_1\rho_2)[1 - e^{-h(\alpha_2-\rho_2)}]}{(\rho_1 - \rho_2)(\alpha_2 - \rho_2)}\right\} \tag{9}$$

Equation (8) may be placed on a common denominator and written as

$$\underset{(n+1)T}{\overset{\infty}{\mathsf{P}}} [\text{equation (6)}] = e^{-(n+1)Ts}$$

$$\times \left[\frac{\left\{\begin{array}{l}[K_c{}^c\, c(nT) + K_0{}^c\, A_0(nT) + K_R{}^c R]s \\ \quad + [K_c{}^0\, c(nT) + K_0{}^0\, A_0(nT) + K_R{}^0 R]\end{array}\right\}}{(s + \rho_1)(s + \rho_2)}\right] \tag{10}$$

where

$$
\begin{aligned}
K_c{}^c &= L_c{}^1 e^{-\rho_1 T} + L_c{}^2 e^{-\rho_2 T} \\
K_0{}^c &= L_0{}^1 e^{-\rho_1 T} + L_0{}^2 e^{-\rho_2 T} \\
K_R{}^c &= L_R{}^1 e^{-\rho_1 T} + L_R{}^2 e^{-\rho_2 T} \\
K_c{}^0 &= \rho_2 L_c{}^1 e^{-\rho_1 T} + \rho_1 L_c{}^2 e^{-\rho_2 T} \\
K_0{}^0 &= \rho_2 L_0{}^1 e^{-\rho_1 T} + \rho_1 L_0{}^2 e^{-\rho_2 T} \\
K_R{}^0 &= \rho_2 L_R{}^1 e^{-\rho_1 T} + \rho_1 L_R{}^2 e^{-\rho_2 T}
\end{aligned}
\tag{11}
$$

Equating equations (7) and (10), we obtain the following difference equations:

$$
\begin{aligned}
c(n+1)T &= K_c{}^c\, c(nT) + K_0{}^c\, A_0(nT) + K_R{}^c R \\
A_0(n+1)T &= K_c{}^0\, c(nT) + K_0{}^0\, A_0(nT) + K_R{}^0 R
\end{aligned}
\tag{12}
$$

The constant coefficients $K_c{}^c$, $K_0{}^c$, $K_c{}^0$, and $K_0{}^0$ are called the characteristic coefficients. It is seen that they are independent of the input function. They are dependent only on the open-loop and closed-loop transfer functions, as well as the sampler characteristics. The constants $K_R{}^c$, $K_R{}^0$ are called the input coefficients. These are dependent on the type of input and the system parameters. The z-transforms of equations (12) are:

$$
\begin{aligned}
(z - K_c{}^c)\, C^*(z) - K_0{}^c\, A_0{}^*(z) &= K_R{}^c R \frac{z}{z-1} \\
-K_c{}^0\, C^*(z) + (z - K_0{}^0)\, A_0{}^*(z) &= K_R{}^0 R \frac{z}{z-1}
\end{aligned}
\tag{13}
$$

The characteristic equation is given by

$$
\Delta(z) = \begin{vmatrix} z - K_c{}^c & -K_0{}^c \\ -K_c{}^0 & z - K_0{}^0 \end{vmatrix} = (z^2 + B_1 z + B_0) \tag{14}
$$

where

$$
\begin{aligned}
B_1 &= -(K_c{}^c + K_0{}^0) \\
B_0 &= (K_c{}^c K_0{}^0 - K_0{}^c K_c{}^0)
\end{aligned}
\tag{15}
$$

The equations for $C^*(z)$ and $A_0^*(z)$ can also be written as

$$C^*(z) = \frac{\begin{vmatrix} K_R{}^c R \dfrac{z}{z-1} & -K_0{}^c \\ K_R{}^0 R \dfrac{z}{z-1} & z - K_0{}^0 \end{vmatrix}}{\Delta(z)}$$

$$= \frac{Rz[K_R{}^c z - (K_0{}^0 K_R{}^c - K_0{}^c K_R{}^0)]}{(z-1)(z^2 + B_1 z + B_0)} \tag{16}$$

and

$$A_0^*(z) = \frac{\begin{vmatrix} z - K_c{}^c & K_R{}^c R \dfrac{z}{z-1} \\ -K_c{}^0 & K_R{}^0 R \dfrac{z}{z-1} \end{vmatrix}}{\Delta(z)}$$

$$= \frac{Rz[K_R{}^0 z - (K_c{}^c K_R{}^0 - K_c{}^0 K_R{}^c)]}{(z-1)(z^2 + B_1 z + B_0)} \tag{17}$$

The inverse of equations (16) and (17) will give the values of $c(nT)$ and $A_0(nT)$. Note that the R appears as a multiplier indicating a direct proportionality between the input and output amplitudes. The continuous response can be evaluated in the following way: $C_h(s)$, the component of output valid for $nT < t \leq nT + h$, can be written in accordance with equation (9.199) as

$$C_h(s) = e^{-nTs}\left[\frac{c(nT)\, s + A_0(nT)}{(s+\alpha_1)(s+\alpha_2)} + \frac{R(a_1 s + a_0)}{s(s+\alpha_1)(s+\alpha_2)}\right] \tag{18}$$

The inverse Laplace of this equation describes the continuous output for the interval $nT < t \leq nT + h$, that is, while the sampler is closed. This can be calculated since $c(nT)$ and $A_0(nT)$ are known. The second component of output valid for $nT + h < t \leq (n+1)T$ can be derived from equation (8) and is

$$C_T(s) = e^{-(nT+h)s}\left\{[L_c{}^1\, c(nT) + L_0{}^1\, A_0(nT) + L_R{}^1 R]\frac{e^{-\rho_1 h}}{s+\rho_1} + [L_c{}^2\, c(nT) + L_0{}^2\, A_0(nT) + L_R{}^2 R]\frac{e^{-\rho_2 h}}{s+\rho_2}\right\} \tag{19}$$

where the coefficients L_c^1, L_0^1, $\cdots$, L_R^2 are already calculated and are given by equations (9). The inverse Laplace of this equation gives the continuous response while the sampler is open. Note the similarity between this and equation (9.201). Equations (18) and (19) must give the same numerical results at $t = nT + h$. This is because $KG(s)$ is assumed to have a continuous step response. The simplification which results from division of $C(s)$ into its two components $C_h(s)$ and $C_T(s)$ is evident from equations (18) and (19). It is seen that $c_T(t)$ can be computed rapidly since all the L coefficients are already known.

The stability of the system is determined by the roots of the characteristic equations. Let these be

$$\Delta(z) = z^2 + B_1 z + B_0 = (z - z_1)(z - z_2) \tag{20}$$

For a stable system, z_1 and z_2 must lie within the unit circle. It is convenient to transform the unit circle into the imaginary axis of the w-plane by means of the bilinear transformation,

$$z = \frac{w + 1}{w - 1} \tag{21}$$

This transforms the inside of the unit circle into the left half of the w-plane. Therefore, a stable system must have all its roots in this half of the w-plane. Routh's criteria can now be applied to the transformed $\Delta(z)$ to obtain the stability conditions in terms of the B coefficients. In this particular case $\Delta(z)$ transforms to

$$\left[\left(\frac{w+1}{w-1}\right)^2 + B_1\left(\frac{w+1}{w-1}\right) + B_0\right](w-1)^2$$
$$= (1 + B_1 + B_0)w^2 + 2(1 - B_0)w + (1 - B_1 + B_0) \tag{22}$$

and the stability conditions become

$$\frac{1 - B_0}{1 + B_1 + B_0} > 0$$
$$\frac{1 - B_1 + B_0}{1 + B_1 + B_0} > 0 \tag{23}$$

Thus, given a specific second-order system, the B coefficients can be calculated from equations (9), (11), and (15). These may then be substituted in conditions (23) to determine the stability of the system prior to calculating the system response.

The same method can be used to derive the equations for a third- and higher-order systems. Once these have been derived in terms of a general transfer function, they can be used repeatedly to evaluate the stability and response of specific systems.

Illustrative Example

So far the analysis has been carried out in a general form. This must now be applied to a specific example in order to illustrate some of the details. By referring to Fig. 9.27, let

$$R(s) = \frac{1}{s} \tag{24}$$

and

$$KG(s) = \frac{K}{s(s + \rho_2)} \tag{25}$$

Therefore,

$$\frac{1}{1 + KG(s)} \frac{s(s + \rho_2)}{s^2 + \rho_2 s + K} \frac{s(s + \rho_2)}{(s + \alpha_1)(s + \alpha_2)} \tag{26}$$

where

$$\alpha_1 = \frac{\rho_2}{2} + \beta$$

$$\alpha_2 = \frac{\rho_2}{2} - \beta \tag{27}$$

and

$$\beta = \sqrt{\left(\frac{\rho_2}{2}\right)^2 - K}$$

The equations for this system can be obtained directly from those given previously in this appendix by substitution of

$$\begin{aligned} a_1 &= 0 \\ a_0 &= K \\ \rho_1 &= 0 \\ R &= 1 \end{aligned} \tag{28}$$

The output for $nT < t \leq nT + h$ is obtained from equation (18) and is

$$C_h(s) = e^{-nTs}\left[\frac{c(nT)\, s + A_0(nT)}{(s + \alpha_1)(s + \alpha_2)} + \frac{K}{s(s + \alpha_1)(s + \alpha_2)}\right] \tag{29}$$

Similarly, the output for $nT + h < t \leq (n+1)T$ can be determined from equation (19) and is

$$C_T(s) = e^{-(nT+h)s}\left\{[L_c^{\,1}\,c(nT) + L_0^{\,1}\,A_0(nT) + L_R^{\,1}]\frac{1}{s} + [L_c^{\,2}\,c(nT) + L_0^{\,2}\,A_0(nT) + L_R^{\,2}]\frac{e^{-\rho_2 h}}{s+\rho_2}\right\} \tag{30}$$

where the L coefficients are given by equations (9). Relations (16) and (17) can be used to write $C^*(z)$ and $\overset{*}{A_0}(z)$ as

$$C^*(z) = \frac{z[K_R{}^c z - (K_R{}^c K_0{}^0 - K_0{}^c K_R{}^0)]}{(z-1)(z-z_1)(z-z_2)} \tag{31}$$

and

$$A_0{}^*(z) = \frac{z[K_R{}^0 z - (K_c{}^c K_R{}^0 - K_c{}^0 K_R{}^c)]}{(z-1)(z-z_1)(z-z_2)} \tag{32}$$

where the coefficients $K_R{}^0$, $K_c{}^c$, $\cdots$, etc. are given by equations (11) and z_1 and z_2 are the roots of the characteristic equations as given by

$$\Delta(z) = z^2 + B_1 z + B_0 = (z-z_1)(z-z_2) \tag{33}$$

In this example it can be seen that

$$B_1 = -e^{-(\rho_2 h/2)}\left\{[1 + e^{-\rho_2(T-h)}]\cosh\beta h + \left(\frac{\rho_2}{2} - \frac{K}{\rho_2}\right)[1 - e^{-\rho_2(T-h)}]\frac{\sinh\beta\text{h}}{\beta}\right\} \tag{34}$$

and

$$B_0 = e^{-\rho_2 T} \quad \text{(a constant independent of } h)$$

where β is given by equation (27). Note that when $K > \left(\frac{\rho_2}{2}\right)^2$, β is imaginary. In this case the cosh and sinh terms are replaced by cos and j sin, respectively. For the continuous system, $h = T$ and

$$B_1 = -2e^{-\rho_2 T/2}\cosh\beta T \tag{35}$$

when β is real and $K > 0$,

$$\cosh\beta T < \frac{e^{\rho_2 T/2} + e^{-\rho_2 T/2}}{2} \tag{36}$$

and

$$B_1 > -[1 + e^{-\rho_2 T}] \tag{37}$$

Therefore,

$$1 + B_1 + B_0 > 0 \tag{38}$$

and the stability conditions become

$$\left.\begin{aligned}(1 - e^{-\rho_2 T}) &> 0\\ 2(1 + e^{-\rho_2 T}) &> 0\end{aligned}\right\} \tag{39}$$

These are satisfied for all $\rho_2 > 0$. Similarly, when β is imaginary, B_1 becomes

$$B_1 = -2e^{-\rho_2 T/2} \cos \beta T \tag{40}$$

Substitution of this in equations (9.218) will show that the stability conditions are again satisfied for all $\rho_2 > 0$. This means that the equivalent continuous system is always stable if $\rho_2 > 0$, a result known from continuous servomechanism theory. Similar methods can be used to derive the stability conditions as $h \to 0$ and the gain K is replaced by K/h, which agrees with the conditions derived directly from the equivalent sampled-data system.

The values of the characteristic coefficients, together with that of the roots z_1 and z_2, are shown in Table III for various values of the pulse width h when

$$\begin{aligned}K &= 6\\ \rho_2 &= 5\\ T &= 1 \text{ second}\end{aligned} \tag{41}$$

TABLE III

Characteristic Coefficients for Second-Order System

Table of characteristic coefficients and the roots z_1 and z_2 for various values of the pulse width h for second-order system considered with $T = 1$ second, $\rho_2 = 5$, and $K = 6$.

h seconds	K_e^c	K_0^c	K_e^0	K_0^0	z_1	z_2
0.2	−0.1375	0.1815	−0.7290	0.9133	0.7671	0.0088
0.4	−0.1687	0.1491	−0.8888	0.7456	0.5650	0.0119
0.6	−0.1554	0.1175	−0.8153	0.5730	0.4008	0.0168
0.8	−0.1328	0.0945	−0.6670	0.4242	0.2662	0.0253
$h = T = 1$	−0.1213	0.0855	−0.5133	0.3064	0.1353	0.0498

Figure 9.35 shows the continuous response of this system to a unit step input as h is varied. Figure 9.36 shows the same except that the gain is increased from 6 to $K = 15.25$. This gives α_1 and α_2 a complex value.

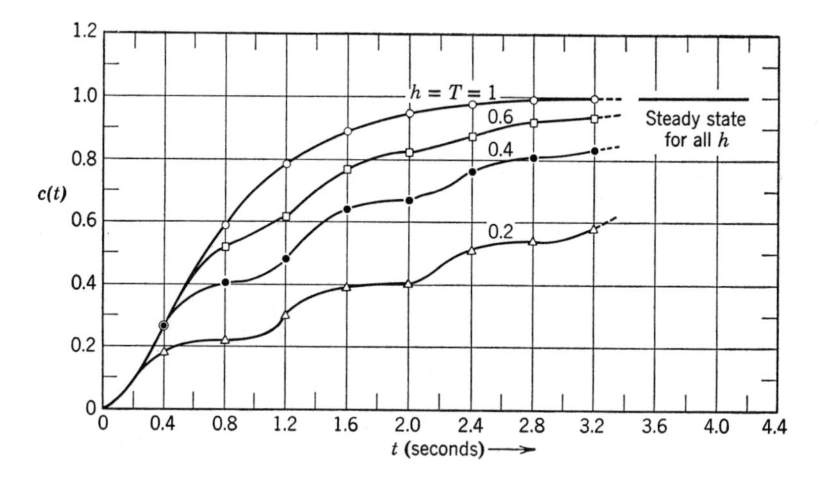

Figure 9.35 Response of the second-order system to a unit step input for various values of pulse width h

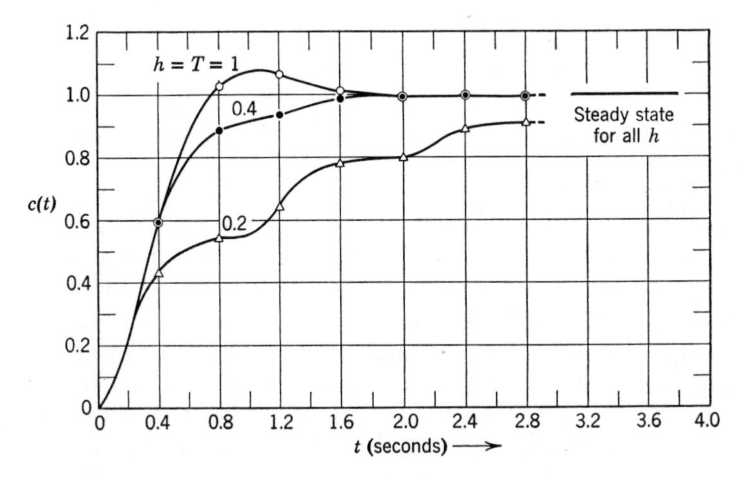

Figure 9.36 Response of the second-order system to a unit step input when $K = 15.25$ and the closed-loop poles are complex

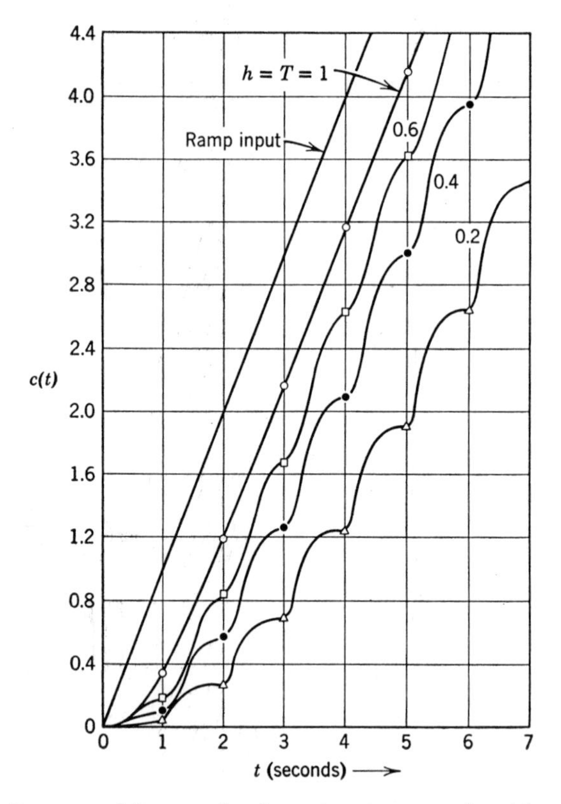

Figure 9.37 Response of the second-order system to a ramp input for various values of pulse width h

Note that for $h = 0.4$ second the system has the same rise time as the continuous case but no overshoot. Figures 9.37 and 9.38 show the response of the system defined by equation (41) to a ramp and a sinusoidal input respectively. It is seen that in each case as $h \to T$ the response approaches the equivalent continuous system output as calculated from its Laplace transform. Figure 9.39 shows the plot of z_1 and z_2 as h is varied. The product of these is a constant independent of h as required by equations (33) and (34). Figure 9.38 shows that the steady-state sinusoidal response is a distorted wave except for $h = T$. However, it can be shown analytically † that the steady-state output at all points separated by an integer multiple of the sampler period lies on a sinusoid of fixed amplitude and phase which has the same frequency as the input

† G. Farmanfarma, "General Analysis of Finite Pulsed Linear Systems," Doctor of Philosophy Thesis, University of California, Berkeley, 1957.

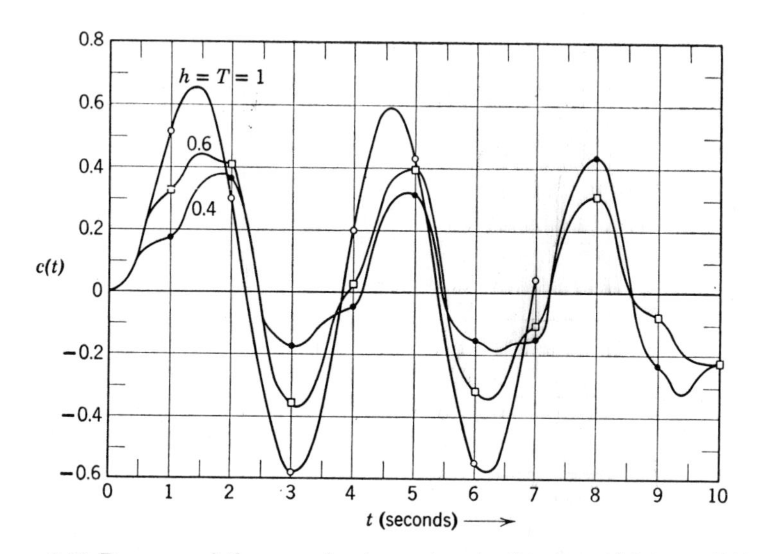

Figure 9.38 Response of the second-order system to the sinusoidal input $R(s) = 2/(s_2 + 4)$

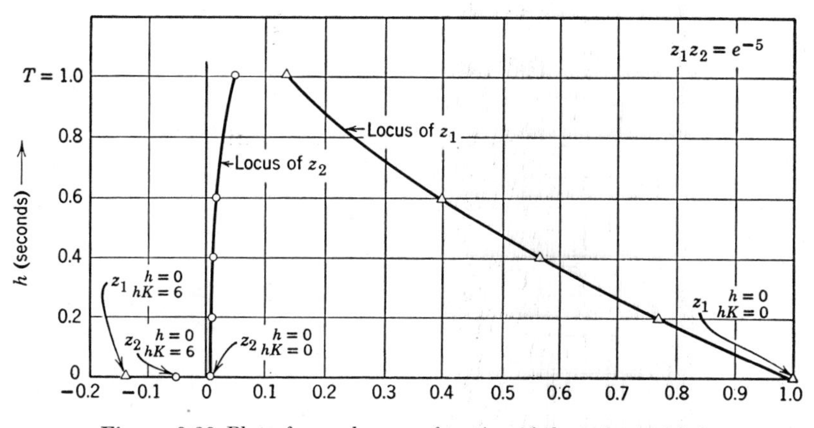

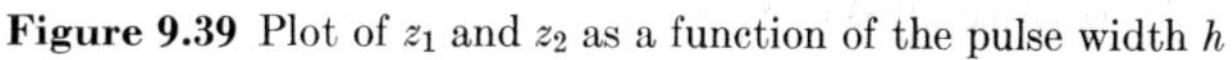
Figure 9.39 Plot of z_1 and z_2 as a function of the pulse width h

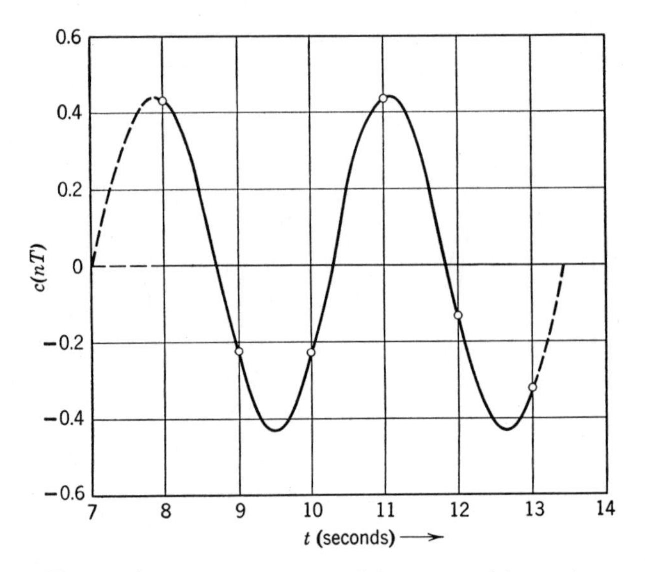

Figure 9.40 The steady-state response at points separated by an integer multiple of the sampling period lies on a sinusoid having the same frequency as the input sine wave

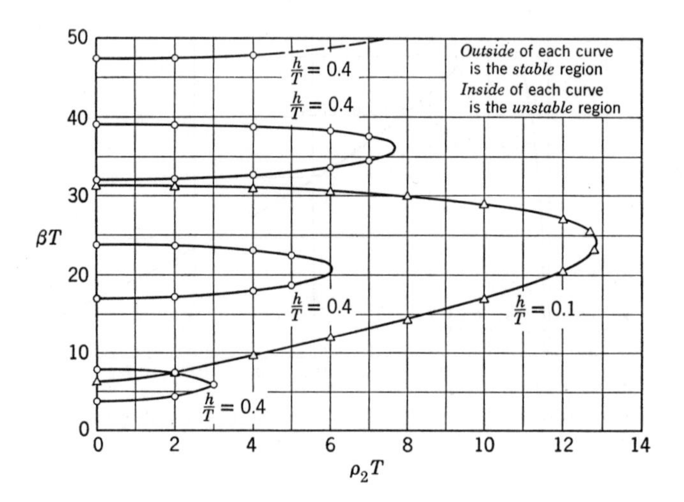

Figure 9.41 Part of a dimensionless plot of the stability boundaries for the second-order system

sine wave. This is shown graphically in Fig. 9.40 for the points $t = nT$, $n = (8, 9, 10, 11, 12, 13)$ when $h = .6$. The relative phase and amplitude of this wave differ for points not separated by an integer multiple of the sampler period. It also varies for different values of pulse width h.

Figure 9.41 shows part of a dimensionless plot of the stability boundaries for the second-order system considered. These are plotted in terms of the dimensionless quantities βT, $\rho_2 T$, and h/T. Equations (34) in conjunction with relations (23) are used to plot these curves.

TABLE I

p-Transforms x–∞

No.	Function	Condition	x to ∞
1	$\underset{x}{\overset{\infty}{\mathsf{P}}}\left(\frac{a_0}{s+\rho}\right)$	$x \geq 0$	$e^{-xs}\left(\frac{a_0 e^{-\rho x}}{s+\rho}\right)$
2	$\underset{x}{\overset{\infty}{\mathsf{P}}}\left(\frac{a_0}{s^2}\right)$	$x \geq 0$	$e^{-xs}\left(\frac{a_0}{s^2}+\frac{a_0 x}{s}\right)$
3	$\underset{x}{\overset{\infty}{\mathsf{P}}}\left[\frac{a_1 s + a_0}{(s+\rho_1)(s+\rho_2)}\right]$	$x \geq 0$	$e^{-xs}\left(\frac{a_0 - a_1\rho_1}{\rho_2-\rho_1}\frac{e^{-\rho_1 x}}{s+\rho_1}+\frac{a_0-a_1\rho_2}{\rho_1-\rho_2}\frac{e^{-\rho_2 x}}{s+\rho_2}\right)$
4	$\underset{x}{\overset{\infty}{\mathsf{P}}}\left(\frac{a_1 s + a_0}{s^2+\omega^2}\right)$	$x \geq 0$	$e^{-xs}\left[\frac{\left(a_1 \cos \omega x + \frac{a_0}{\omega}\sin \omega x\right) s + (a_0 \cos \omega x - a_1 \omega \sin \omega x)}{s^2+\omega^2}\right]$
5	$\underset{x}{\overset{\infty}{\mathsf{P}}}\left[\frac{1-e^{-h(s+\alpha)}}{s+\alpha}\frac{a_0}{s+\rho}\right]$	$x \geq h$	$a_0 e^{-xs}\left[\frac{e^{-\rho x}}{\alpha-\rho}\frac{1-e^{-h(\alpha-\rho)}}{s+\rho}\right]$
6	$\underset{x}{\overset{\infty}{\mathsf{P}}}\left[\frac{1-e^{-h(s+\alpha)}}{s+\alpha}\frac{a_1 s + a_0}{(s+\rho_1)(s+\rho_2)}\right]$	$x \geq h$	$e^{-xs}\left\{\frac{a_0-a_1\rho_1}{(\rho_2-\rho_1)(\alpha-\rho_1)}\frac{e^{-\rho_1 x}[1-e^{-h(\alpha-\rho_1)}]}{s+\rho_1} + \frac{a_0-a_1\rho_2}{(\rho_1-\rho_2)(\alpha-\rho_2)}\frac{e^{-\rho_2 x}[1-e^{-h(\alpha-\rho_2)}]}{s+\rho_2}\right\}$

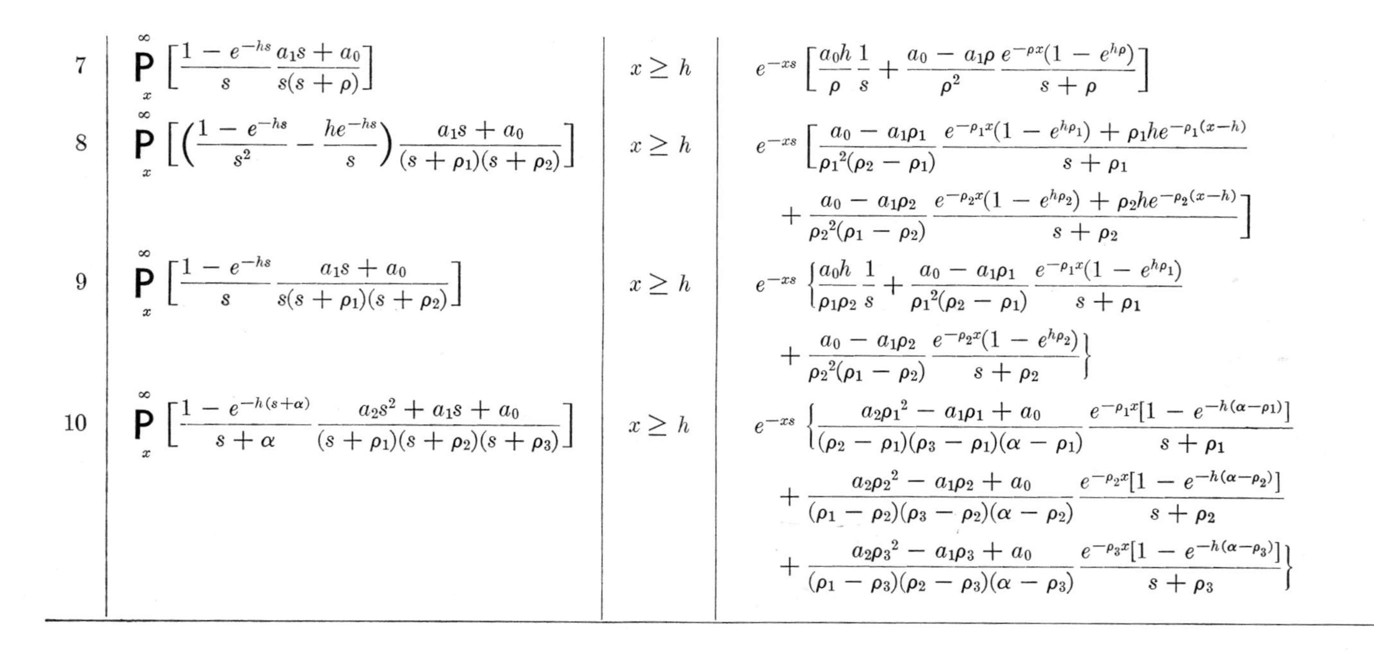

7	$\overset{\infty}{\underset{x}{\mathsf{P}}}\left[\frac{1-e^{-hs}}{s}\frac{a_1s+a_0}{s(s+\rho)}\right]$	$x \geq h$	$e^{-xs}\left[\frac{a_0h}{\rho}\frac{1}{s}+\frac{a_0-a_1\rho}{\rho^2}\frac{e^{-\rho x}(1-e^{h\rho})}{s+\rho}\right]$
8	$\overset{\infty}{\underset{x}{\mathsf{P}}}\left[\left(\frac{1-e^{-hs}}{s^2}-\frac{he^{-hs}}{s}\right)\frac{a_1s+a_0}{(s+\rho_1)(s+\rho_2)}\right]$	$x \geq h$	$e^{-xs}\left[\frac{a_0-a_1\rho_1}{\rho_1^2(\rho_2-\rho_1)}\frac{e^{-\rho_1x}(1-e^{h\rho_1})+\rho_1he^{-\rho_1(x-h)}}{s+\rho_1}\right.$ $\left.+\frac{a_0-a_1\rho_2}{\rho_2^2(\rho_1-\rho_2)}\frac{e^{-\rho_2x}(1-e^{h\rho_2})+\rho_2he^{-\rho_2(x-h)}}{s+\rho_2}\right]$
9	$\overset{\infty}{\underset{x}{\mathsf{P}}}\left[\frac{1-e^{-hs}}{s}\frac{a_1s+a_0}{s(s+\rho_1)(s+\rho_2)}\right]$	$x \geq h$	$e^{-xs}\left\{\frac{a_0h}{\rho_1\rho_2}\frac{1}{s}+\frac{a_0-a_1\rho_1}{\rho_1^2(\rho_2-\rho_1)}\frac{e^{-\rho_1x}(1-e^{h\rho_1})}{s+\rho_1}\right.$ $\left.+\frac{a_0-a_1\rho_2}{\rho_2^2(\rho_1-\rho_2)}\frac{e^{-\rho_2x}(1-e^{h\rho_2})}{s+\rho_2}\right\}$
10	$\overset{\infty}{\underset{x}{\mathsf{P}}}\left[\frac{1-e^{-h(s+\alpha)}}{s+\alpha}\frac{a_2s^2+a_1s+a_0}{(s+\rho_1)(s+\rho_2)(s+\rho_3)}\right]$	$x \geq h$	$e^{-xs}\left\{\frac{a_2\rho_1^2-a_1\rho_1+a_0}{(\rho_2-\rho_1)(\rho_3-\rho_1)(\alpha-\rho_1)}\frac{e^{-\rho_1x}[1-e^{-h(\alpha-\rho_1)}]}{s+\rho_1}\right.$ $+\frac{a_2\rho_2^2-a_1\rho_2+a_0}{(\rho_1-\rho_2)(\rho_3-\rho_2)(\alpha-\rho_2)}\frac{e^{-\rho_2x}[1-e^{-h(\alpha-\rho_2)}]}{s+\rho_2}$ $\left.+\frac{a_2\rho_3^2-a_1\rho_3+a_0}{(\rho_1-\rho_3)(\rho_2-\rho_3)(\alpha-\rho_3)}\frac{e^{-\rho_3x}[1-e^{-h(\alpha-\rho_3)}]}{s+\rho_3}\right\}$

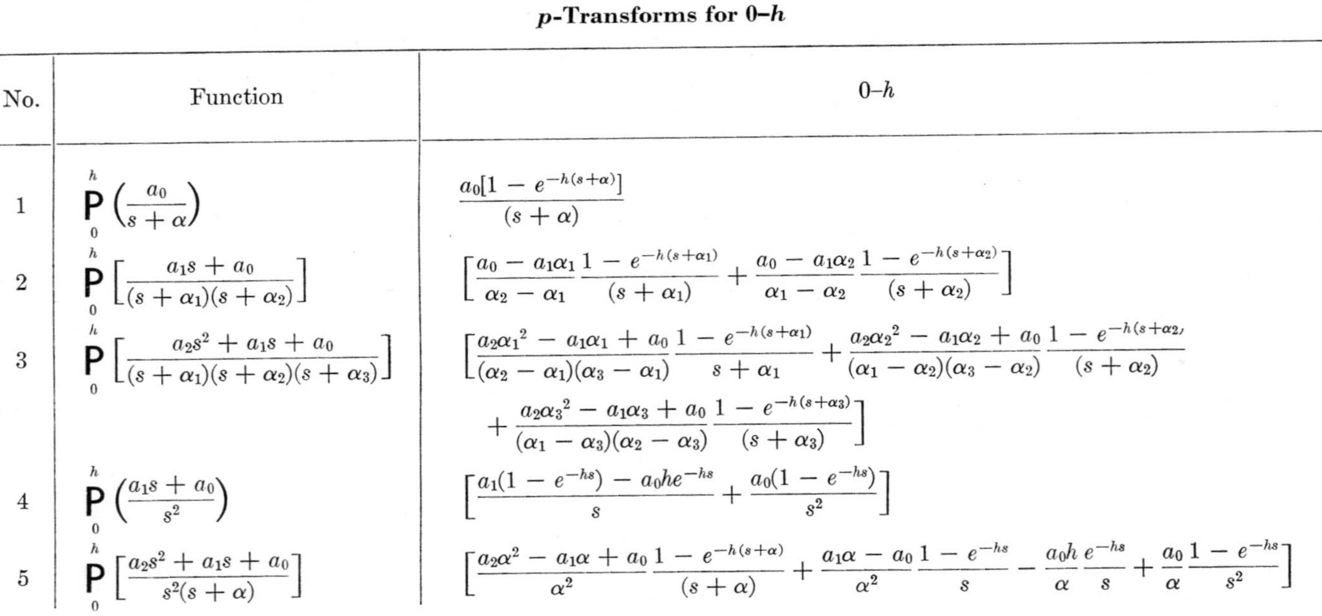

TABLE II

p-Transforms for 0–h

No.	Function	0–h
1	$\overset{h}{\underset{0}{\mathsf{P}}}\left(\frac{a_0}{s+\alpha}\right)$	$\frac{a_0[1-e^{-h(s+\alpha)}]}{(s+\alpha)}$
2	$\overset{h}{\underset{0}{\mathsf{P}}}\left[\frac{a_1s+a_0}{(s+\alpha_1)(s+\alpha_2)}\right]$	$\left[\frac{a_0-a_1\alpha_1}{\alpha_2-\alpha_1}\frac{1-e^{-h(s+\alpha_1)}}{(s+\alpha_1)}+\frac{a_0-a_1\alpha_2}{\alpha_1-\alpha_2}\frac{1-e^{-h(s+\alpha_2)}}{(s+\alpha_2)}\right]$
3	$\overset{h}{\underset{0}{\mathsf{P}}}\left[\frac{a_2s^2+a_1s+a_0}{(s+\alpha_1)(s+\alpha_2)(s+\alpha_3)}\right]$	$\left[\frac{a_2\alpha_1{}^2-a_1\alpha_1+a_0}{(\alpha_2-\alpha_1)(\alpha_3-\alpha_1)}\frac{1-e^{-h(s+\alpha_1)}}{s+\alpha_1}+\frac{a_2\alpha_2{}^2-a_1\alpha_2+a_0}{(\alpha_1-\alpha_2)(\alpha_3-\alpha_2)}\frac{1-e^{-h(s+\alpha_2)}}{(s+\alpha_2)}\right.$ $\left.+\frac{a_2\alpha_3{}^2-a_1\alpha_3+a_0}{(\alpha_1-\alpha_3)(\alpha_2-\alpha_3)}\frac{1-e^{-h(s+\alpha_3)}}{(s+\alpha_3)}\right]$
4	$\overset{h}{\underset{0}{\mathsf{P}}}\left(\frac{a_1s+a_0}{s^2}\right)$	$\left[\frac{a_1(1-e^{-hs})-a_0he^{-hs}}{s}+\frac{a_0(1-e^{-hs})}{s^2}\right]$
5	$\overset{h}{\underset{0}{\mathsf{P}}}\left[\frac{a_2s^2+a_1s+a_0}{s^2(s+\alpha)}\right]$	$\left[\frac{a_2\alpha^2-a_1\alpha+a_0}{\alpha^2}\frac{1-e^{-h(s+\alpha)}}{(s+\alpha)}+\frac{a_1\alpha-a_0}{\alpha^2}\frac{1-e^{-hs}}{s}-\frac{a_0h}{\alpha}\frac{e^{-hs}}{s}+\frac{a_0}{\alpha}\frac{1-e^{-hs}}{s^2}\right]$

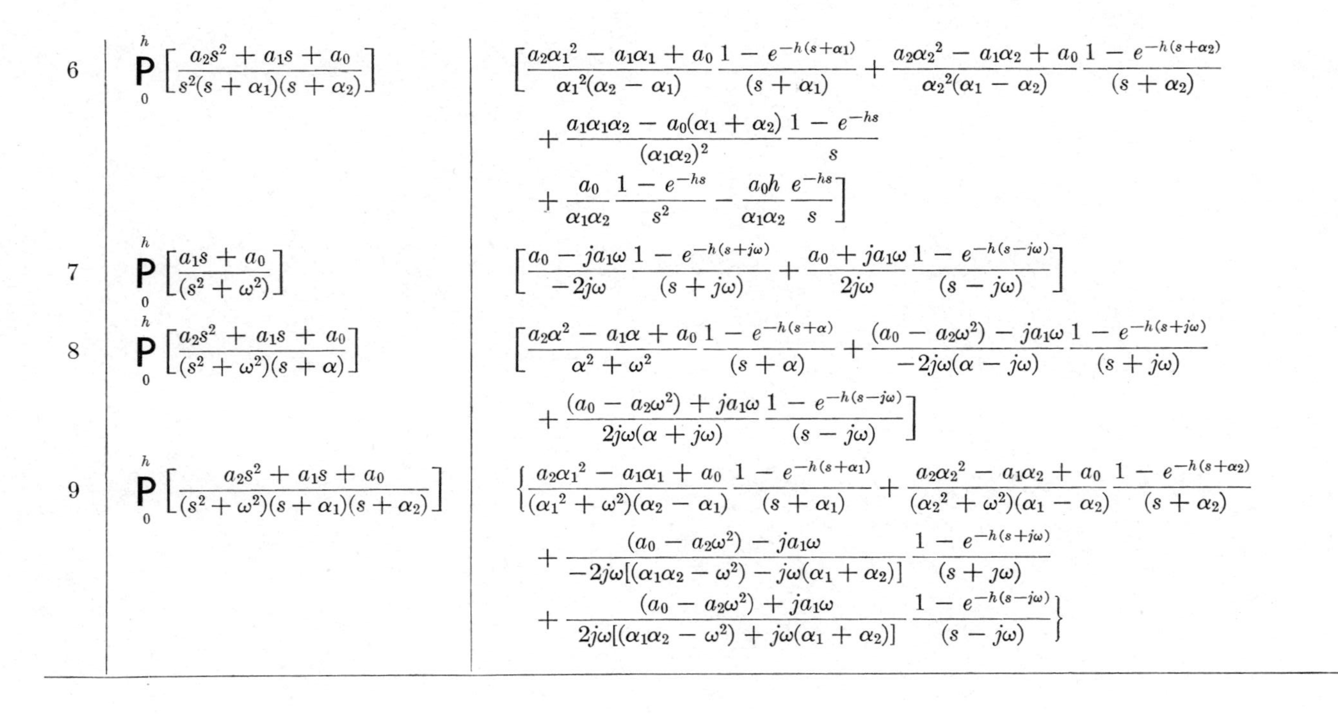

6	$\overset{h}{\underset{0}{\mathbf{P}}}\left[\dfrac{a_2s^2 + a_1s + a_0}{s^2(s+\alpha_1)(s+\alpha_2)}\right]$	$\left[\dfrac{a_2\alpha_1^2 - a_1\alpha_1 + a_0}{\alpha_1^2(\alpha_2 - \alpha_1)}\dfrac{1 - e^{-h(s+\alpha_1)}}{(s+\alpha_1)} + \dfrac{a_2\alpha_2^2 - a_1\alpha_2 + a_0}{\alpha_2^2(\alpha_1 - \alpha_2)}\dfrac{1 - e^{-h(s+\alpha_2)}}{(s+\alpha_2)} + \dfrac{a_1\alpha_1\alpha_2 - a_0(\alpha_1+\alpha_2)}{(\alpha_1\alpha_2)^2}\dfrac{1 - e^{-hs}}{s} + \dfrac{a_0}{\alpha_1\alpha_2}\dfrac{1 - e^{-hs}}{s^2} - \dfrac{a_0h}{\alpha_1\alpha_2}\dfrac{e^{-hs}}{s}\right]$
7	$\overset{h}{\underset{0}{\mathbf{P}}}\left[\dfrac{a_1s + a_0}{(s^2+\omega^2)}\right]$	$\left[\dfrac{a_0 - ja_1\omega}{-2j\omega}\dfrac{1 - e^{-h(s+j\omega)}}{(s+j\omega)} + \dfrac{a_0 + ja_1\omega}{2j\omega}\dfrac{1 - e^{-h(s-j\omega)}}{(s-j\omega)}\right]$
8	$\overset{h}{\underset{0}{\mathbf{P}}}\left[\dfrac{a_2s^2 + a_1s + a_0}{(s^2+\omega^2)(s+\alpha)}\right]$	$\left[\dfrac{a_2\alpha^2 - a_1\alpha + a_0}{\alpha^2+\omega^2}\dfrac{1 - e^{-h(s+\alpha)}}{(s+\alpha)} + \dfrac{(a_0 - a_2\omega^2) - ja_1\omega}{-2j\omega(\alpha - j\omega)}\dfrac{1 - e^{-h(s+j\omega)}}{(s+j\omega)} + \dfrac{(a_0 - a_2\omega^2) + ja_1\omega}{2j\omega(\alpha + j\omega)}\dfrac{1 - e^{-h(s-j\omega)}}{(s-j\omega)}\right]$
9	$\overset{h}{\underset{0}{\mathbf{P}}}\left[\dfrac{a_2s^2 + a_1s + a_0}{(s^2+\omega^2)(s+\alpha_1)(s+\alpha_2)}\right]$	$\left\{\dfrac{a_2\alpha_1^2 - a_1\alpha_1 + a_0}{(\alpha_1^2+\omega^2)(\alpha_2 - \alpha_1)}\dfrac{1 - e^{-h(s+\alpha_1)}}{(s+\alpha_1)} + \dfrac{a_2\alpha_2^2 - a_1\alpha_2 + a_0}{(\alpha_2^2+\omega^2)(\alpha_1 - \alpha_2)}\dfrac{1 - e^{-h(s+\alpha_2)}}{(s+\alpha_2)} + \dfrac{(a_0 - a_2\omega^2) - ja_1\omega}{-2j\omega[(\alpha_1\alpha_2 - \omega^2) - j\omega(\alpha_1+\alpha_2)]}\dfrac{1 - e^{-h(s+j\omega)}}{(s+j\omega)} + \dfrac{(a_0 - a_2\omega^2) + ja_1\omega}{2j\omega[(\alpha_1\alpha_2 - \omega^2) + j\omega(\alpha_1+\alpha_2)]}\dfrac{1 - e^{-h(s-j\omega)}}{(s-j\omega)}\right\}$

APPENDIX

A Method of Determining the Coefficients of the Modified z-Transform Expansion†

It has been shown in Chapter 2 that the modified z-transform $C^*(z, m)$ of the output of any sampled data configuration is of the form

$$C^*(z, m) = \sum_{k=1}^{N} A_k(z)\, B_k(z, m) \tag{1}$$

where $A_k(z)$ is in general the ratio of two polynomials in z, $B_k(z, m)$ is a polynomial in z, m is a variable whose range is from zero to one, and N is dependent on the number of continuous distinct transmission paths to the output.

Thus it can be seen that $C^*(z, m)$ can, by combination of the rational terms of equation (1), be expressed in general as the rational function

$$C^*(z, m) = \frac{P(z, m)}{Q(z)} \tag{2}$$

Note that the denominator polynomial is not a function of m. Also, as a

† E. I. Jury and F. W. Semelka, "A Method for Determining the Coefficients of the Modified z-Transform Expansion," Internal Memorandum No. 1, August 1956, Electronics Research Laboratory, University of California, Berkeley.

result of the definition of the modified z-transform, we can readily determine that the order of the numerator polynomial in z must always be at least one less (difference is greater than one when the feed-forward function contains pure delays greater than T or in most cases where the input function to the system is zero at the first sampling instant) than the order of the denominator polynomial in z.

When employing the z-transform for analysis, a simple and convenient means of finding the system response (division method) is through expansion of $C^*(z)$ in a Laurent series about the origin. This series expansion of $C^*(z)$ can be found by synthetic division of numerator and denominator polynomials. (Formulas shown later provide a more accurate means of determining the coefficients of the series than direct synthetic division.)

From physical realizability the impulsive response of any system for t less than zero is identically zero; thus we expect the system response to begin at t equals zero. Mathematically, this is expressed in the one-sided definition of the Laplace transform, and thus only the princ pal part and constant term of the Laurent series are present in the expansion of $C^*(z)$. Therefore, $C^*(z)$ expanded is of the form

$$C^*(z) = c_0 + c_1 z^{-1} + c_2 z^{-2} + c_3 z^{-3} + \cdots + c_n z^{-n} + \cdots \quad (3)$$

where the c_n are the nT^+ time sequence values (sampled values) of the output corresponding to the z^{-n} values of time.

When a similar Laurent expansion of $C^*(z, m)$ is made, only the principal part of the series is obtained (note the previous statement on the order of polynomials of the function). In order to get the same series when m approaches zero as is obtained by the expansion of the equivalent $C^*(z)$ (i.e., nT^+ values of the output time sequence), an expansion of $z\,C^*(z, m)$ is made instead, with a subsequent interpretation of the result. Thus the series expansion form is denoted by

$$z\,C^*(z, m) = c_0(m) + c_1(m)\,z^{-1} + c_2(m)\,z^{-2} + c_3(m)\,z^{-3} + \cdots + c_n(m)\,z^{-n} + \cdots \quad (4)$$

where the $c_n(m)$ are called the power series coefficients; this method of analysis is known as the power series expansion method. It is now understood that $c_0(m)$ traces the first interval of the response, $c_1(m)$ the second interval, etc; that is, the subscript notation does not agree with the interval that $c_n(m)$ describes. In other words, the function $c_n(m)$ describes the interval to the right of z^{-n} instead of to the left of z^{-n} as we would expect from examining the relation $t = (n - 1 + m)T$.

Whenever there is pure time delay in the feed-forward function or the input at the first sampling instant is zero, it is convenient to make an expansion of $z^k[z\,C^*(z, m)]$ where $k + 1$ is the difference in the order of numerator and denominator polynomials in z. Then k is interpreted as a delay of the response from t equals zero, that is, $c_0(m)$ describes the $k + 1$ interval response, etc.

The following describes some means for obtaining the power series coefficients in terms of the polynomial coefficients of $z^k[z\,C^*(z, m)]$. As was stated previously, $C^*(z, m)$ is given in general by

$$C^*(z, m) = \frac{P(z, m)}{Q(z)} \tag{5}$$

and

$$z^k[z\,C^*(z, m)] = \frac{z^{k+1}\,P(z, m)}{Q(z)} \tag{6}$$

where the order of the numerator is now equal to the order of the denominator. This can be expressed in general as a rational fraction in z^{-1} with the lead term of the denominator set equal to unity as follows:

$$z^k[z\,C^*(z, m)] = \frac{p_0(m) + p_1(m)\,z^{-1} + p_2(m)\,z^{-2} \cdots + p_n(m)\,z^{-n}}{1 + q_1 z^{-1} + q_2 z^{-2} + q_3 z^{-3} + \cdots + q_n z^{-n}} \tag{7}$$

which is to be equal to the series expansion

$$z^k[z\,C^*(z, m)] = c_0(m) + c_1(m)\,z^{-1} + c_2(m)\,z^{-2} + \cdots \tag{8}$$

Thus it can be easily verified that †

$$\begin{aligned} c_0(m) &= p_0(m) \\ c_1(m) &= p_1(m) - q_1\,c_0(m) \\ c_2(m) &= p_2(m) - q_1\,c_1(m) - q_2\,c_0(m) \\ c_3(m) &= p_3(m) - q_1\,c_2(m) - q_2\,c_1(m) - q_3\,c_0(m) \end{aligned} \tag{9}$$

and

$$\begin{aligned} c_n(m) = {} & p_n(m) - q_1\,c_{n-1}(m) - q_2\,c_{n-2}(m) - \cdots - q_{n-1}\,f_1(m) \\ & - q_n\,f_0(m) \end{aligned}$$

We would immediately consider that the recurrence relationship for the preceding formulas should be of considerable aid in computation of

† See Chapter 2 for verification of equation (9).

the response. This would be true except that, when we carry the process to any length, numerical errors from rounding off, etc., accumulate and serious inaccuracy easily results. Therefore a development of each of the power series coefficients in terms of the function coefficients (p_n, q_n) is presented. Continued use of the following formulas has proved them to be very valuable and time saving in determining system response over the first few intervals:

$$\begin{aligned}
c_0(m) &= p_0(m) \\
c_1(m) &= p_1(m) \\
&\quad - p_0(m)\, q_1 \\
c_2(m) &= p_2(m) \\
&\quad - p_1(m)\, q_1 \\
&\quad - p_0(m)\, [q_2 - q_1{}^2] \\
c_3(m) &= p_3(m) \\
&\quad - p_2(m)\, q_1 \\
&\quad - p_1(m)\, [q_2 - q_1{}^2] \\
&\quad - p_0(m)\, [q_3 - 2q_2q_1 + q_1{}^3] \\
c_4(m) &= p_4(m) \\
&\quad - p_3(m)\, q_1 \\
&\quad - p_2(m)\, [q_2 - q_1{}^2] \\
&\quad - p_1(m)\, [q_3 - 2q_2q_1 + q_1{}^3] \\
&\quad - p_0(m)\, [q_4 - 2q_3q_1 - q_2{}^2 + 3q_2q_1{}^2 - q_1{}^4] \qquad (10) \\
c_5(m) &= \cdots
\end{aligned}$$

It is convenient to adopt a matrix representation for the power series coefficients as follows:

$$c_n(m)\Big] = \begin{bmatrix} c_0(m) \\ c_1(m) \\ c_2(m) \\ \cdots \\ c_n(m) \end{bmatrix} \tag{11}$$

$$p_n(m)\Big] = \begin{bmatrix} p_0(m) \\ p_1(m) \\ p_2(m) \\ \cdots \\ p_n(m) \end{bmatrix} \tag{12}$$

$$[Q_n] = \begin{bmatrix} 1 & 0 & 0 & \cdots & 0 \\ -Q_1 & 1 & 0 & \cdots & 0 \\ -Q_2 & -Q_1 & 1 & \cdots & 0 \\ -Q_3 & -Q_2 & -Q_1 & \cdots & 0 \\ \cdots & \cdots & \cdots & \cdots & \cdots \\ -Q_n & -Q_{n-1} & -Q_{n-2} & \cdots & 1 \end{bmatrix} \tag{13}$$

where

$$c_n(m)] = [Q_n] \times p_n(m)] \tag{14}$$

Thus the nth power series coefficient is found by matrix multiplication, equation (14), of the nth row of $[Q_n]$ by the column matrix $p_n(m)]$. The first ten Q_n's are

$$Q_1 = q_1$$

$$Q_2 = q_2 - q_1^2$$

$$Q_3 = q_3 - 2q_2q_1 + q_1^3$$

$$Q_4 = q_4 - 2q_3q_1 - q_2^2 + 3q_2q_1^2 - q_1^4$$

$$Q_5 = q_5 - 2q_4q_1 - 2q_3q_2 + 3q_3q_1^2 + 3q_2^2q_1 - 4q_2q_1^3 + q_1^5$$

$$\begin{aligned} Q_6 = q_6 &- 2q_5q_1 - 2q_4q_2 + 3q_4q_1^2 - q_3^2 + 6q_3q_2q_1 - 4q_3q_1^3 - q_2^3 \\ &- 6q_2^2q_1^2 + 5q_2q_1^4 - q_1^6 \end{aligned}$$

$$\begin{aligned} Q_7 = q_7 &- 2q_6q_1 - 2q_5q_2 + 3q_5q_1^2 - 2q_4q_3 + 6q_4q_2q_1 - 4q_4q_1^3 \\ &+ 3q_3^2q_1 + 3q_3q_2^2 - 12q_3q_2q_1^2 + 5q_3q_1^4 - 4q_2^3q_1 + 10q_2^2q_1^3 \\ &- 6q_2q_1^5 + q_1^7 \end{aligned}$$

$$\begin{aligned} Q_8 = q_8 &- 2q_7q_1 - 2q_6q_2 + 3q_6q_1^2 - 2q_5q_3 + 6q_5q_2q_1 - 4q_5q_1^3 - q_4^2 \\ &+ 6q_4q_3q_1 + 3q_4q_2^2 - 12q_4q_2q_1^2 + 5q_4q_1^4 + 3q_3^2q_2 - 6q_3^2q_1^2 \\ &- 12q_3q_2^2q_1 + 20q_3q_2q_1^3 - 6q_3q_1^5 - q_2^4 + 10q_2^3q_1^2 \\ &- 15q_2^2q_1^4 + 7q_2^2q_1^6 - q_1^8 \end{aligned}$$

$$\begin{aligned} Q_9 = q_9 &- 2q_8q_1 - 2q_7q_2 + 3q_7q_1^2 - 2q_6q_3 + 6q_6q_2q_1 - 4q_6q_1^3 \\ &- 2q_5q_4 + 6q_5q_3q_1 + 3q_5q_2^2 - 12q_5q_2q_1^2 + 5q_5q_1^4 + 3q_4^2q_1 \\ &+ 6q_4q_3q_2 - 12q_4q_3q_1^2 - 12q_4q_2^2q_1 + 20q_4q_2q_1^3 - 6q_4q_1^5 + q_3^3 \\ &- 12q_3^2q_2q_1 + 10q_3^2q_1^3 - 4q_3q_2^3 + 30q_3q_2^2q_1^2 - 30q_3q_2q_1^4 \\ &+ 7q_3q_1^6 + 5q_2^4q_1 - 20q_2^3q_1^3 + 21q_2^2q_1^5 - 8q_2q_1^7 + q_1^9 \end{aligned}$$

$$
\begin{aligned}
Q_{10} = {} & q_{10} - 2q_9q_1 - 2q_8q_2 + 3q_8q_1^2 - 2q_7q_3 + 6q_7q_2q_1 - 4q_7q_1^3 - 2q_6q_4 \\
& + 6q_6q_3q_1 + 3q_6q_2^2 - 12q_6q_2q_1^2 + 5q_6q_1^4 - q_5^2 + 6q_5q_4q_1 \\
& - 12q_5q_3q_1^2 + 6q_5q_3q_2 - 12q_5q_2^2q_1 + 20q_5q_2q_1^3 - 6q_5q_1^5 \\
& + 3q_4^2q_2 - 6q_4^2q_1^2 + 3q_4q_3^2 - 24q_4q_3q_2q_1 + 20q_4q_3q_1^3 \\
& - 4q_4q_2^3 + 30q_4q_2^2q_1^2 - 30q_4q_2q_1^4 + 7q_4q_1^6 - 4q_3^3q_1 \\
& - 6q_3^2q_2^2 + 30q_3^2q_2q_1^2 - 15q_3^2q_1^4 + 20q_3q_2^3q_1 - 60q_3q_2^2q_1^3 \\
& + 42q_3q_2q_1^5 - 8q_3q_1^7 + q_2^5 - 15q_2^4q_1^2 + 35q_2^3q_1^4 - 28q_2^2q_1^6 \\
& + 9q_2q_1^8 - q_1^{10} \qquad (15)
\end{aligned}
$$

Q_n for $n > 10$ can be found from equation (16).

Thus, the formulas together with the matrix representation have systematically reduced this portion of the analysis problem to numerical processes which can be handled conveniently on a desk calculator.

The following is a rule for obtaining the Q_n which are the coefficients (arrangement of q_n) of the p_n terms of the power series coefficients.

As seen from equation (15), Q_n is formed by the addition of all possible distinct arrangements of all possible combinations of q_1 through q_n such that the sum of the subscripts of any combination is equal to n. After collection of like terms, the sign of each resultant term is found by adding the exponents of that term, those having an odd sum being positive and those having an even sum being negative.

Or alternately, this rule can be stated as

$$
Q_n = A \sum_{\substack{a,b,c,d,\cdots,h \\ \alpha,\beta,\gamma,\delta,\cdots,\lambda}} q_a^{\alpha} q_b^{\beta} q_c^{\gamma} q_d^{\delta} \cdots q_h^{\lambda} \qquad (16)
$$

where

1. $a, b, c, d, \cdots, h,$
   $\alpha, \beta, \gamma, \delta, \cdots, \lambda$
   are integers $(1, 2, 3, 4, \cdots)$.

2. $a \neq b \neq c \neq d \neq \cdots \neq h$, i.e.,
   exclude all duplicate combinations.

3. $(a\alpha + b\beta + c\gamma + d\delta + \cdots + h\lambda) = n$
   are fulfilled as follows:

   a. $a\alpha = n,\ 1 \leq \alpha \leq n$
   b. $a\alpha + b\beta = n$ where a and b are determined,
      (1) for $\beta = 1$, α equals $1, 2, 3, \cdots$
      (2) for $\beta = 2$, α equals $1, 2, 3, \cdots$
      (3) for $\beta = 3$, α equals $1, 2, 3, \cdots$
      etc.

c. $a\alpha + b\beta + c\gamma = n$, where a, b, and c are determined,

(1) for $\gamma = 1$

(a) $\beta = 2$, α equals 1, 2, 3, $\cdots$

(b) $\beta = 2$, α equals 1, 2, 3, $\cdots$

(c) $\beta = 3$, α equals 1, 2, 3, $\cdots$

etc.

(2) for $\gamma = 2$

(a) $\beta = 1$, α equals 1, 2, 3, $\cdots$

(b) $\beta = 2$, α equals 1, 2, 3, $\cdots$

(3) etc.

Note the maximum number of different q's in any term of the coefficient is determined by n.
When $\alpha = \beta = \gamma = \delta = \cdots = 1$,
then $(a + b + c + \cdots) = n$
and $a \neq b \neq c \neq d \neq \cdots$;
therefore $1 + 2 + 3 + \cdots \leq n$.

The number of terms in this last sum determines the maximum number of different q's in any term of the coefficients.

The maximum number of different q's determines the extent of the process in a, b, c, d, etc., above. For example, when n equals 6, the maximum number of q's is three; therefore the process is only a to c inclusive.

(4) Signs of each term are determined by:

$$\alpha + \beta + \gamma + \delta + \cdots + \lambda = \text{even, term is positive}$$
$$\alpha + \beta + \gamma + \delta + \cdots + \lambda = \text{odd, term is negative}$$

(5) A is the function that assigns to each term its coefficient. The value of A at each term is given by the number of all possible distinct arrangements of the members of that term. A is given by

$$A = \prod_{i=1}^{N} \begin{bmatrix} B - \sum_{j=1}^{i} u_{j-1} \\ u_i \end{bmatrix} \tag{17}$$

where

$$B = \sum_{i=1}^{N} u_i$$

N is the number of distinct q_k's in the term
u_i is the exponent of the ith q_k
u_0 is defined as zero

and $\binom{n}{r} = \dfrac{n!}{r!(n-r)!}$

Example: Find $A(q_1{}^3q_2{}^2q_3{}^2)$

$$B = 3 + 2 + 2 = 7$$

i	u_i	$\sum_{j=1}^{i} u_{j-1}$	$B - \sum_{j=1}^{i} u_{j-1}$
1	3	0	7
2	2	3	4
3	2	5	2

$$A = \binom{7}{3} \times \binom{4}{2} \times \binom{2}{2} = 35 \times 6 \times 1 = 210$$

The following are some helpful suggestions in using the preceding formulas in computation of response:

1. Make tables of p_n for desired values of m [gives set of matrices for equation (12)].
2. Set up a table of the Q_n necessary to obtain the response to the desired interval [gives matrix in equation (13)].
3. If the impulsive response of the feed-forward function is continuous, then $p_{n+1}(0)$ equals $p_n(1)$ which is a useful check to detect numerical errors at the beginning of the computation.
4. Similarly, if the impulsive response is continuous, the relation $c_{n+1}(0)$ equals $c_n(1)$ serves as a valuable check in the solution.

Since the z-transform of the output can be readily obtained by letting m go to zero in the expressions for $z\,C^*(z, m)$, the power series coefficients formulas are thus completely applicable for z-transform analysis (response at sampling instants only).

Some prominent features and advantages of the power series expansion method and the formulas presented are:

1. They provide a simple and accurate means of obtaining the complete system response during the first few intervals. (The method is particularly useful if the system is known to be stable.)
2. The response at the sampling instants can be found accurately and without recourse to synthetic division (division method of z-transform analysis).

3. The response of any interval can be determined independently, that is, without dependence on previous interval response; furthermore, the response of intervals prior to the one calculated can be easily obtained.

4. Equation (9) in conjunction with the results of equation (14) can be effectively used to extend the region over which a response can be easily calculated, still retaining sufficient accuracy.

5. This series expansion method leads to a transmission matrix representation which makes it possible to portray linear plant characteristics for impulsive inputs at sampling instants with or *without* a knowledge of the transfer function; all that is required is an experimental graph of the plant's impulsive response on an accurate time scale from which a set of transmission matrices can be written by inspection.

6. Finally, this analysis method has a readily apparent application to synthesis of sampled-data systems or continuous control systems employing discrete compensation, as discussed in Chapter 5.

BIBLIOGRAPHY

Ba Hli, F., "A General Method for Time Domain Network Synthesis," *I.R.E. Transactions on Circuit Theory*, Vol. CT-1, No. 3, September 1954, pp. 21–28.

Barker, R. H., "The Pulse Transfer Function and Its Application to Sampling Servo Systems," *Proceedings of the I.E.E. (London)*, Vol. 99, Part IV, 1952, pp. 302–317.

Barker, R. H., "A Servo System for Digital Data Transmission," *Proceedings of the I.E.E. (London)*, Vol. 103, Part B, 1956, pp. 52–64.

Barker, R. H., *The Theory of Pulse Monitored Servomechanisms and Their Use for Prediction*, Ministry of Supply, Signals Research and Development Establishment, Christchurch, Hants, England, Report No. 1046, November 1950.

Bennett, W. R., "Spectra of Quantized Signals," *Bell System Technical Journal*, Vol. 27, July 1948, pp. 446–472.

Bergen, A. R., and J. R. Ragazzini, "Sampled-Data Processing Techniques for Feedback Control Systems," *Transactions of the A.I.E.E.*, Vol. 73, Part II, 1954, pp. 236–247.

Bertram, J. E., "Factors in the Design of Digital Controllers for Sampled-Data Feedback Control Systems," *Transactions of the A.I.E.E.*, Vol. 75, Part II, 1956, pp. 151–159.

Bharucha, B. H., "Analysis of Integral-Square Error in Sampled-Data Control Systems, Electronics Research Laboratory Report, Series 60, Issue 206, June 1958, University of California, Berkeley.

Boxer, R., "Analysis of Sampled-Data Systems and Digital Computers in the Frequency Domain," *I.R.E. Convention Record*, Part 10, 1955, pp. 78–85.

Boxer, R., "A Note on Numerical Transform Calculus," *Proceedings of the I.R.E.*, Vol. 45, October 1957, pp. 1401–1406.

Boxer, R., and S. Thaler, "A Simplified Method of Solving Linear and Non-linear Systems," *Proceedings of the I.R.E.*, Vol. 44, No. 1, 1956, pp. 89–101.

Brown, B. M., "Application of Finite Difference Operators to Linear Systems," in *Automatic and Manual Control*, edited by A. Tustin, *Proceedings of the Cranfield Conference, 1951*, Butterworth Scientific Publications, London, 1952, pp. 490–518.

Brown, R. G., and G. J. Murphy, "An Approximate Transfer Function for the Analysis and Design of Pulsed Servos," *Transactions of the A.I.E.E.*, Vol. 41, Part II, 1952, pp. 435–440.

Chestnut, H., and R. W. Mayer, *Servomechanisms and Regulating System Design*, John Wiley and Sons, Inc., New York, Vol. 1, 1951.

Chu, Yaohan, "Feedback Control Systems with Dead-time Lag or Distributed Lag by Root-Locus Method," *Transactions of the A.I.E.E.*, Vol. 71, Part II, 1952, pp. 291–296.

Chu, Yaohan, "Synthesis of Feedback Control Systems by Phase-Angle Loci," *Transactions of the A.I.E.E.*, Vol. 71, Part II, 1952, pp. 330–339.

Cruickshank, A. J. O., "A Note on Time Series and the Use of Jump Functions in Approximate Analysis," *Proceedings of the I.E.E. (London)*, Vol. 102, Part C, 1955, pp. 81–87.

Cypkin, J. Z., "Automatic Control Systems Containing Digital Computers," *Avtomatika i Telemekhanika (Moscow)*, Vol. 17, No. 8, 1956, pp. 665–679.

Cypkin, J. Z., *Differenzengleichungen Der Impulse-Und Regeltechnik*, Veb Verlag Technie, Berlin, 1956.

Cypkin, J. Z., "Frequency Analysis of Pulsed Systems," in *Frequency Response*, edited by R. Oldenbourg, Macmillan Company, New York, 1956.

Cypkin, J. Z., "Frequency Method of Analyzing Intermittent Regulating Systems," *Avtomatika i Telemekhanika (Moscow)*, Vol. 14, No. 1, 1953, pp. 11–33.

Cypkin, J. Z., "Investigation of Steady-State Processes in Pulse Servo Systems," *Avtomatika i Telemekhanika (Moscow)*, Vol. 17, No. 12, 1956, pp. 1057–1069.

Cypkin, J. Z., "Theory of Intermittent Regulations," *Avtomatika i Telemekhanika (Moscow)*, Vol. 10, No. 3, 1949, pp. 189–224.

Cypkin, J. Z., "Uber die Synthese von Impulssystemen der Automatischen Regelung und Steurerung," *Fachtagung Regelungstechnik*, Heidelberg, Germany, 1956, Beitrag Nr. 95 Unkorrigierter Vordruck mil-18 Biedern.

Farmanfarma, G., "Analysis of Linear Sampled-Data Systems with Finite Pulse Width (Open Loop)," *Transactions of the A.I.E.E.*, Vol. 75, Part I, 1956, pp. 808–819.

Farmanfarma, G., "Analysis of Multiple-Sampler Systems with Finite Pulse Width (Open Loop)," *Transactions of the A.I.E.E.*, Vol. 77, Part II, 1958, pp. 20–28.

Farmanfarma, G., "General Analysis and Stability Study of Finite Pulsed Feedback Systems," *A.I.E.E. Applications and Industry*, July 1958, pp. 148–162.

Fort, T., "Linear Difference Equations of the Dirichlet Series Transform," *American Mathematical Monthly*, November 1955, p. 641.

Franklin, G., "The Optimum Synthesis of Sampled-Data Systems," Dissertation, Electronics Research Laboratory, Technical Report T-6/B, May 2, 1955, Columbia University, New York.

Freeman, H., "Multipole Sampled-Data Control Systems," Electronics Research Laboratory, Technical Report T-12/B, September 1955, Columbia University, New York.

Freeman, H., and O. Lowenschuss, "Bibliography of Sampled-Data Control Systems and z-Transform Applications," *I.R.E. Transactions on Automatic Control* (PGAC), March 1958, pp. 28–30.

Friedland, B., "A Technique for the Analysis of Time-Varying Sampled-Data Systems," *Transactions of the A.I.E.E.*, Vol. 75, Part II, 1956, pp. 407–414.

Gardner, M. F., and J. L. Barnes, *Transients in Linear Systems*, Vol. 1, John Wiley and Sons, New York, 1942.

Helm, H. A., "The Analysis of Digital Control Systems," A.I.E.E. Special Publication T-101, Conference on Computers in Control Systems, May 1958, p. 67.

Huggins, W. H., "A Low-Pass Transformation for z-Transforms," *I.R.E. Transactions on Circuit Theory*, Vol. 1, September 1954, pp. 69–70.

Hurewicz, W., "Filters and Servo Systems with Pulsed Data," Chapter 5 in *Theory of Servomechanisms*, edited by H. James, N. Nichols, and R. Phillips, M.I.T. Radiation Laboratory Series, Vol. 25, McGraw-Hill Book Company, Inc., New York, 1947.

Johnson, G. W., and D. P. Lindorff, "Transient Analysis of Sampled-Data Control Systems," *Transactions of the A.I.E.E.*, Vol. 73, Part II, 1954, pp. 147–153.

Johnson, G. W., D. P. Lindorff, and C. G. A. Nordling, "Extension of Continuous-Data System Design Techniques to Sampled-Data Control Systems," *Transactions of the A.I.E.E.*, Vol. 74, Part II, 1955, pp. 252–263.

Jury, E. I., "Analysis and Synthesis of Sampled-Data Control Systems," *Transactions of the A.I.E.E.*, Vol. 73, Part I, 1954, pp. 332–346.

Jury, E. I., "Analysis and Synthesis of Sampled-Data Control Systems," Doctorate of Engineering Science Thesis, Columbia University, New York, April 1953.

Jury, E. I., "Correlation between Root-Locus and Transient Response of Sampled-Data Control Systems," *Transactions of the A.I.E.E.*, Vol. 74, Part II, 1955, pp. 427–435.

Jury, E. I., "The Effect of Pole and Zero Locations on the Transient Response of Sampled-Data Systems," *Transactions of the A.I.E.E.*, Vol. 74, Part II, 1955, pp. 41–48.

Jury, E. I., "Hidden Oscillations in Sampled-Data Control Systems," *Transactions of the A.I.E.E.*, Vol. 75, Part II, 1956, pp. 391–395.

Jury, E. I., "Sampled-Data Control Systems," Air Force Office of Scientific Research Briefs, No. 57/6, November-December 1957 Issue, Directorate of Research Communications, Washington 25, D. C.

Jury, E. I., "Synthesis and Critical Study of Sampled-Data Control Systems," *Transactions of the A.I.E.E.*, Vol. 75, Part II, 1956, pp. 141–151.

Jury, E. I., and G. Farmanfarma, "Table of z-Transform and Modified z-Transform of Various Sampled-Data Systems Configurations," Electronics Research Laboratory Report, Series 60, Issue 136, 1955, University of California, Berkeley.

Jury, E. I., and F. J. Mullin, "The Analysis of Sampled-Data Control Systems with a Periodically Time-Varying Sampling Rate," Electronics Research Laboratory Report, Series 60, Issue 207, June 1958, University of California, Berkeley.

Jury, E. I., and F. J. Mullin, "A Note on the Operational Solution of Difference Equations," Electronics Research Laboratory Report, Series 60, Issue 198, January 1958, University of California, Berkeley.

Jury, E. I., and W. Schroeder, "Discrete Compensation of Sampled-Data and Continuous Control Systems," *Transactions of the A.I.E.E.*, Vol. 75, Part II, 1956, pp. 317–325.

Jury, E. I., and F. W. Semelka, "A Method for Determining the Coefficients of the Modified z-Transform Expansion," Internal Memorandum No. 1, August 1956, Electronics Research Laboratory, University of California, Berkeley.

Kalman, R. E., and J. E. Bertram, "General Synthesis Procedure for Computer Control of Single and Multiloop Linear Systems," A.I.E.E. Special Publication T-101, Conference on Computers in Control Systems, May 1958, pp. 130–137.

Katt, D. R., "Conditional Feedback Systems Applied to Stabilizing a Missile in Pitch Attitude," *I.R.E. Wescon Convention Record,* Part IV, August 21, 1957, p. 171.

Kautz, W. K., "Transient Synthesis in the Time Domain," *Transactions of the I.R.E.*, P.G.G.T., CT-1, September 1954.

Kranc, G. M., "Compensation of an Error-Sampled System by a Multi-rate Controller," *Transactions of the A.I.E.E.*, Vol. 76, Part II, 1957, pp. 149–159.

Kukel, J., "Sampling in Linear and Nonlinear Feedback Systems," *I.R.E. Convention Record,* Part IV, 1957, pp. 43–56.

Lago, G. V., "Additions to z-Transformation Theory for Sampled-Data Systems," *Transactions of the A.I.E.E.*, Vol. 74, Part II, 1955, pp. 403–408.

Lago, G. V., and J. G. Truxal, "The Design of Sampled-Data Feedback Systems," *Transactions of the A.I.E.E.*, Vol. 73, Part II, 1954, pp. 247–253.

Lawden, D. F., "A General Theory of Sampling Servo Systems," *Proceedings of the I.E.E. (London)*, Vol. 98, Part IV, 1951, pp. 31–36.

Linvill, W. K., "Sampled-Data Control Systems Studied Through Comparison of Sampling with Amplitude Modulation," *Transactions of the A.I.E.E.*, Vol. 70, Part II, 1951, pp. 1779–1788.

Linvill, W. K., and J. M. Salzer, "Analysis of Control Systems Involving Digital Computers," *Proceedings of the I.R.E.*, Vol. 41, No. 7, 1953, pp. 901–906.

Linvill, W. K., and R. W. Sittler, "Design of Sampled-Data Systems by Extension of Conventional Techniques," Report No. R-222, M.I.T., July 1953.

Linvill, W. K., and R. W. Sittler, "Extension of Conventional Techniques to the Design of Sampled-Data Systems," *I.R.E. Convention Record*, New York, Part I, 1953, pp. 99–104.

MacColl, L. A., *Fundamental Theory of Servomechanisms*, D. Van Nostrand Company, Inc., Princeton, N. J., 1945.

Maitra, K. K., and P. E. Sarachik, "Digital Compensation of Continuous-Data Feedback Control Systems," *Transactions of the A.I.E.E.*, Vol. 75, Part II, 1956, pp. 107–116.

Marden, M., *The Geometry of the Zeros of a Polynomial in a Complex Variable*, American Mathematical Society, New York, 1949.

Metzger, I. W., "Experimental Study of a Sampled-Feedback System with Finite Pulse Width," Master of Science Thesis, University of California, Berkeley, May 1957.

Miller, K. S., and R. J. Schwarz, "Analysis of a Sampling Servomechanism," *Journal of Applied Physics*, Vol. 21, April 1950, pp. 290–294.

Mori, Masahiro, "Root-Locus Method of Pulse Transfer Function for Sampled-Data Control Systems," *I.R.E. Transactions on Automatic Control*, PGAC-3, November 1957, pp. 13–20.

Mori, Masahiro, "Statistical Treatment of Sampled-Data Control Systems for Actual Random Inputs," *Transactions of the A.S.M.E.*, February 1958, pp. 444–456.

Murphy, G. J., and R. D. Ormsby, "A Survey of Techniques for the Analysis of Sampled-Data Control Systems," *I.R.E. Transactions on Automatic Control*, Vol. 2, February 1957, pp. 79–90.

Nease, R. F., "Analysis and Design of Non-linear Sampled-Data Control Systems," W.A.D.C. Technical Note 57-162, M.I.T., June 1957.

Neufeld, J., "On the Operational Solution of Linear Mixed Difference Differential Equations," *Proc. Cambridge Philosophical Society*, Vol. 30, 1934, p. 289.

Noor, Billawalla, "Experimental Study of Pulse Width Modulated Feedback Control Systems," Master of Science Thesis, University of California, Berkeley, January 1958.

Oldenbourg, R. C., and H. Sartorius, *The Dynamics of Automatic Controls*, translated by H. L. Mason, American Society of Mechanical Engineers, New York, 1948.

Pantazelos, P. G., "Sampled-Data Analysis of a Drift-Stabilization System," A.I.E.E. Conference Paper No. CP 56-961, presented in Chicago, Ill., October 1956.

Porter, A., F. W. Stoneman, and D. F. Lawden, "A New Approach to the Design of Pulse-Monitored Servo Systems," *Proceedings of the I.E.E. (London)*, Vol. 97, Part II, 1950, pp. 597–610.

Ragazzini, J. R., "Digital Computers in Feedback Systems," *I.R.E. Convention Record*, Part IV, 1957, pp. 33–42.

Ragazzini, J. R., and A. R. Bergen, "A Mathematical Technique for the Analysis of Linear Systems," *Proceedings of the I.R.E.*, Vol. 42, November 1954, pp. 1645–1651.

Ragazzini, J. R., and L. A. Zadeh, "Analysis of Sampled-Data Systems," *Transactions of the A.I.E.E.*, Vol. 71, Part II, 1952, pp. 225–232.

Raymond, F. H., "Analysis of Discontinuous Servomechanisms," *Annales de Telecommunications (Paris)*, Vol. 4, 1949, pp. 250–256, 307–314, 347–357.

Rogers, W. I., "Data Desampling Techniques in Digital Computer Control Systems," Master of Science Thesis, University of California, Los Angeles, June 1954.

Salzer, J. M., "Frequency Analysis of Digital Computers Operating in Real Time" *Proceedings of the I.R.E.*, Vol. 42, No. 2, 1954, pp. 457–466.

Salzer, J. M., "Signal Flow Techniques for Digital Compensation," presented at Conference on Computers in Control Systems, Atlantic City, N. J., October 16–18, 1957. Proceedings to be published by A.I.E.E.

Schroeder, W. I., "Analysis and Synthesis of Sampled-Data and Continuous Control Systems with Pure Time Delays," Electronics Research Laboratory Report, Series 60, Issue 156, June 8, 1956, University of California, Berkeley.

Semelka, F. W., *Time Domain Synthesis of Sampled-Data Control Systems*, Electronics Research Laboratory Report, Series 60, Issue 175, January 18, 1957, University of California, Berkeley.

Shannon, C. E., "Communication in the Presence of Noise," *Proceedings of the I.R.E.*, Vol. 37, No. 1, 1949.

Sklansky, J., "Network Compensation of Error-Sampled Feedback Control Systems," Electronics Research Laboratory, Technical Report T-7/B, April 1955, Columbia University, New York.

Sklansky, J., "Optimizing the Dynamic Parameters of a Track-While-Scan System," *R.C.A. Review*, Vol. 18, No. 2, 1957, pp. 163–185.

Sklansky, J., and J. R. Ragazzini, "Analysis of Errors in Sampled-Data Feedback Systems," *Transactions of the A.I.E.E.*, Vol. 74, Part II, 1955, pp. 65–71.

Sklansky, J., "Pulsed RC Networks for Sampled-Data Systems," *I.R.E. Convention Record*, Part II, 1956, pp. 81–99.

Smith, C. H., D. F. Lawden, and A. E. Bailey, "Characteristics of Sampling Servo Systems," in *Automatic and Manual Control*, edited by A. Tustin, Butterworth Scientific Publications, London, 1952, pp. 377–409.

Stone, W. M., "A List of Generalized Laplace Transforms," *Iowa State College Journal of Science*, Vol. 22, April 1948, pp. 215–225.

Teichmann, T., "Closed-Loop Control Systems Containing a Digital Computer," *I.R.E. Transactions on Electronic Computers*, September 1955, pp. 106–117.

Thaler, S., and R. Boxer, "An Operational Calculus for Numerical Analysis," *I.R.E. Convention Record*, Part II, 1956, pp. 100–105.

Thomson, W. E., "On Two-Sided *z*-Transforms," *I.R.E. Transactions on Circuit Theory*, Vol. 3, June 1956, p. 156.

Tou, J., "Analysis of Sampled-Data Control Systems with Finite Sampling Duration," *Proceedings of the National Electronics Conference*, Vol. 13, 1957.

Tou, J., "Digital Compensation for Control and Simulation," *Proceedings of the I.R.E.*, Vol. 45, September 1957, pp. 1243–1248.

Truxal, J. G., *Automatic Feedback Control System Synthesis*, McGraw-Hill Book Co., Inc., New York, 1955.

Truxal, J. G., "Numerical Analysis for Network Design," *I.R.E. Transactions on Circuit Theory*, Vol. 1, September 1954, pp. 49–60.

Tustin, A., "A Method of Analyzing the Behavior of Linear Systems in Terms of Time Series," *Journal of the I.E.E. (London)*, Vol. 94, Part IIA, 1947, pp. 130–142.

Vassian, H. J., "Application of Discrete Variable Servo Theory to Inventory Control," *Journal of the Operations Research Society of America*, Vol. 3, No. 3, August 1955, pp. 272–282.

Widder, D. V., *The Laplace Transform*, Princeton University Press, Princeton, N. J. 1941.

Zadeh, L. A., "Frequency Analysis of Variable Networks," *Proceedings of the I.R.E.*, Vol. 38, 1950.

PROBLEMS

CHAPTER 1

Problem 1.1 (*a*) Show that the complex Fourier series representation of $\delta_T(t)$ is the following:

$$\delta_T(t) = \frac{1}{T} \sum_{k=-\infty}^{k=\infty} e^{jk\omega_r t}, \qquad \omega_r = \frac{2\pi}{T}$$

(*b*) Using complex translation show that, in general,

$$\mathcal{L}\,[e(t)\,\delta_T(t)] = \frac{1}{T} \sum_{k=-\infty}^{k=\infty} E(s + jk\omega_r) + \frac{1}{2}\,e(0^+)$$

where $E(s) = \mathcal{L}\,[e(t)]$.

Problem 1.2 (*a*) Obtain the *z*-transform of the following functions:

$$\frac{1}{s^5}, \qquad \frac{1}{s^2(s^2 + a^2)}, \qquad \frac{1}{(s + a)^2(s^2 + b^2)}$$

(*b*) Show that

$$z\text{-transform of } F(s + a) = F^*(e^{aT}z)$$

Problem 1.3 Show that the *z*-transform of $1/s^n$ is

$$\mathfrak{z}\,[1/s^n] = \frac{Tz}{n - 1}\,\frac{(n - 1)\,N_{n-1}(z) - (z - 1)\,N'_{n-1}(z)}{(z - 1)^n}, \qquad \text{for all } n > 1$$

where

$$\mathfrak{z}\left[\frac{1}{s^{n-1}}\right] = \bar{F}_{n-1}(z) = \frac{N_{n-1}(z)}{D_{n-1}(z)}$$

$$N'_{n-1}(z) = \frac{d\,N_{n-1}(z)}{dz}$$

Problem 1.4 (*a*) Show that by using the Laplace-Stieltjes transform † given below, the transform of the sampled function $c^*(t)$ is

$$\mathcal{L}\,[c^*(t)] = \sum_{n=0}^{\infty} c(nT)\,e^{-nTs}$$

where

$$\mathcal{L}\,[c^*(t)] = \int_0^{\infty} c(t)\,s^{-st}\,d\alpha(t)$$

† Widder, D. V., *The Laplace Transform*, Princeton University Press, Princeton, 1941.

and $\alpha(t)$ is the unit staircase function shown in Fig. 1.4.

(*b*) As with (*a*), show that

$$\mathcal{L}\,[c^*(t - \Delta T)] = e^{-sT} \sum_{n=0}^{\infty} c(n,m)T\, e^{-nTs}$$

where

$$\Delta = (1 - m) \quad \text{and} \quad c(t) = 0, \qquad \text{for } t < 0$$

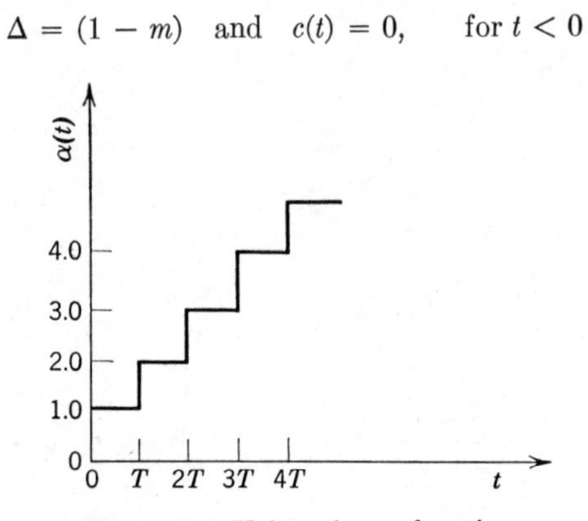

Figure 1.4 Unit staircase function

Problem 1.5 Find the inverse function of the following z-transform functions.

(*a*) $C^*(z) = \dfrac{z}{(z-\gamma)^2(z-1)^3}$

(*b*) $C^*(z) = \dfrac{z(z+a_0)}{(z-\gamma)^2(z-1)^2}$

(*c*) $C^*(z) = \dfrac{z(z^2+a_0z+b_0)}{(z-\gamma)^3(z-1)^2[(z-\alpha)^2+\beta^2]}$

Problem 1.6 Show that:

(*a*) $\mathfrak{Z}\left[\dfrac{\partial}{\partial a} f(nT, a)\right] = \dfrac{\partial}{\partial a}[F^*(z, a)]$

where $F^*(z, a) = \mathfrak{Z}\,[f(nT, a)]$

(*b*) Present an example to verify the theorem in part *a*.

Problem 1.7 If

$$f(t) \to f(t/a), \qquad \text{is a real number}$$

$$T \to aT$$

Show that

$$F^*(s)\Big|_{z=e^{sT}} \equiv F^*(z)\Big|_{z=e^{(aT)s}}$$

where

$$F^*(z) = \mathfrak{Z}\,[f(t)]$$

Example: Let $f(t) = t,\ a = 2,\ T = 1.$ Verify this theorem.

Problem 1.8 (*a*) Obtain the output $c(t)$ of a linear sampled-data system with finite pulse width, shown in Fig. 1.8, when subjected to a step input.

$$G(s) = \frac{1}{s+a}$$

$$a = 1, \qquad T = 0.5 \text{ second}$$

$$h = 0.2 \text{ second}$$

(*b*) Plot the response $c(t)$ for the given values.
(*c*) Plot the response at sampling instants using the z-transform approximation.

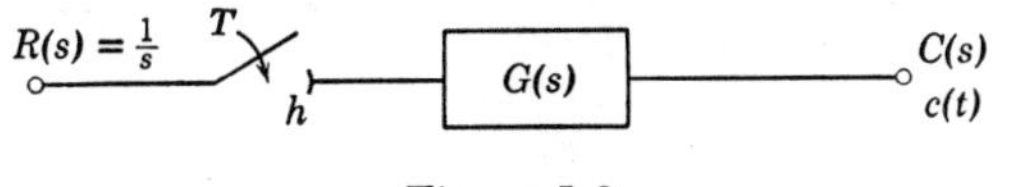

Figure 1.8

Problem 1.9 If $F^*(z)$ is the z-transform of $f(t)$, show that (*a*) the z-transform of $f(t + T)$ is

$$z\,[F^*(z) - f(0)], \qquad f(0) = \lim_{t\to 0} f(t)$$

(*b*) Show that the z-transform of $f(t - T)$ is

$$z^{-1}\,F^*(z), \qquad \text{if } f(t) = 0 \text{ for } n < 0$$

Problem 1.10 If $F^*(z)$ is the z-transform of $f(t)$ and k is a non-negative integer, show that

$$\mathfrak{z}\,[f(t + kT)] = e^{kTs}[F^*(z) - \sum_{k=0}^{k-1} f(kT)\,z^{-k}]$$

Problem 1.11 If $F^*(z)$ is the z-transform of $f(t)$, show that

$$\frac{1}{T}\int_z^\infty F^*(z)\,dz = \mathfrak{z}\left(\frac{f(t+T)}{t+T}\right)$$

Problem 1.12 If $F^*(z)$ is the z-transform of $f(t)$, show that

$$-T\frac{d\,F^*(z)}{dz} = \mathfrak{z}\,[(t - T)\,f(t - T)]$$

Problem 1.13 Show that if $F^*(z)$ is the z-transform of $f(t)$, then

$$\frac{z}{z-1}F^*(z) = \mathfrak{z}\left[\sum_{k=0}^{k} f(kT)\right]$$

Problem 1.14 An error-sampled-data control system shown in Fig. 1.14 has an open-loop transfer function $G(s)$ as follows:

$$G(s) = \frac{K}{s(s+10)}$$

$$hK = 13.4$$

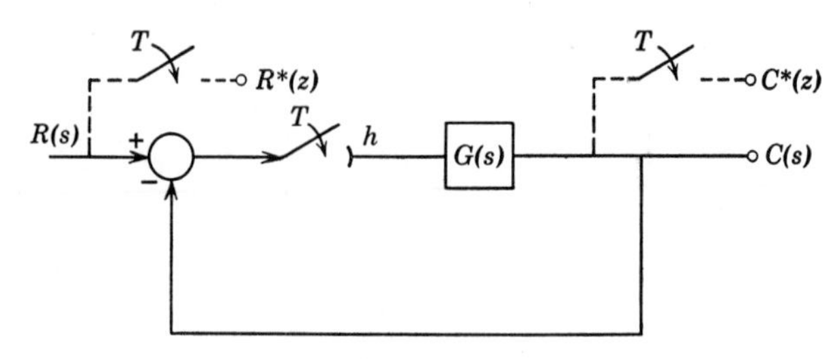

Figure 1.14

Assuming the sampling period $T = 0.1$ second, calculate the following:

(*a*) The z-transform of the open-loop transfer function, $G^*(z)$.

(*b*) The z-transform of the output $C^*(z)$.

(*c*) Find the initial and final value of the response if a unit step function is applied to the input.

(*d*) Calculate the total response $c(nT)$, using (1) the inversion formula and (2) the division method. Plot.

(*e*) Find the maximum overshoot and peak time by finding the zeros of the first difference. Check with the computed response.

(*f*) Plot the Nyquist diagram of the z-transform of the open-loop transfer function in the $G^*(z)$-plane.

(*g*) Find the maximum-frequency overshoot and the value of the resonant frequency.

(*h*) Tabulate the correlation between frequency response quantities and the transient overshoot and peak time.

(*i*) Determine the stability condition using (1) the Shur-Cohn criterion and (2) the Hurwitz criterion.

(*j*) Determine the value of hK to make the system unstable.

Problem 1.15 If the input to a sampled-error feedback system shown in Fig. 1.15 is a sinusoidal function, then

$$r(t) = A \sin \omega t$$

Obtain the steady-state value of the output at the sampling instants.

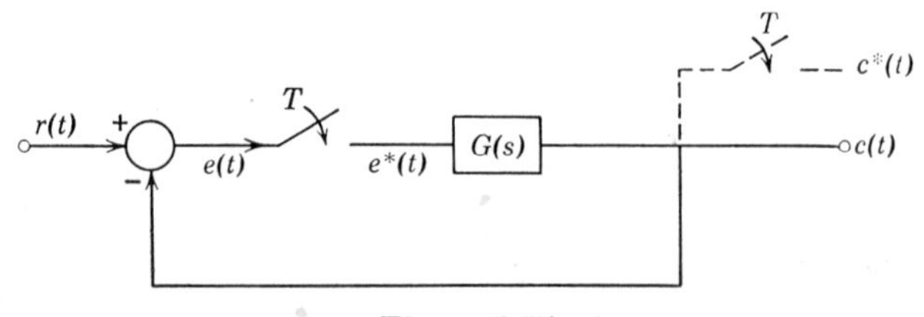

Figure 1.15

Problem 1.16 For a sampled-data system shown in Fig. 1.15, the following is given:

$$G(s) = \frac{s^2 + (\pi + 2\alpha)s + \pi(\pi + \gamma) + \alpha^2}{(s + \gamma)[(s + \alpha)^2 + \pi^2]}$$

$$T = 1, \quad e^{-\alpha} = 0.98, \quad \gamma = 1$$

(*a*) Obtain the z-transform of the output for unit step input, that is, $C^*(z)$.
(*b*) Obtain the initial and final value of the response.
(*c*) Obtain the output at the sampling instants.

Problem 1.17 If z describes the unit circle, show that the bilinear transformation given in equation (1.7) also describes a circle for all values of a, b, c, and d, real or complex.

$$G^*(z) = \frac{az + b}{cz + d} \tag{1.7}$$

Problem 1.18 Show that when z is replaced by its conjugate in the expression of $G^*(z)$, then

$$G^*(\bar{z}) = G_c^*(z)$$

where $G_c^*(z)$ represents the conjugate of $G^*(z)$
$\bar{z}$ represents the conjugate of z

Problem 1.19 Show that if the input to the system shown in Fig. 1.15 is a sinusoidal sequence whose envelope is the continuous sinusoidal function, the output is also a sinusoidal sequence of the same frequency with magnitude equal to the magnitude of the input times $\left|\frac{G^*(z)}{1 + G^*(z)}\right|_{z=e^{j\omega T}}$ and phase equal to the phase of $\angle \frac{G^*(z)}{1 + G^*(z)}\Big|_{z=e^{j\omega T}}$.

Thus the overall transfer locus $\frac{G^*(z)}{1 + G^*(z)}$, when z describes the unit circle, represents the steady-state response relationship between the sinusoidal envelopes of the output to that of the input.

Problem 1.20 Describe an electric circuit which produces a zero-order hold.

Problem 1.21 Draw a schematic circuit diagram of a generalized first-order hold circuit (linear extrapolation-type desampler).

Problem 1.22 Obtain an approximate linear network which has an approximate impulsive response as a generalized first-order hold.

CHAPTER 2

Problem 2.1 Find the response at half the sampling instants in problem 1.14 using:
(*a*) Submultiple method.
(*b*) Impulsive-response method.
(*c*) z-Transform and impulsive-response methods.

Problem 2.2 (*a*) Obtain the modified z-transform of the following functions:

$$\frac{1}{s^4}, \quad \frac{1}{s^2(s^2 + a^2)}, \quad \frac{1}{(s + a)^2(s^2 + b^2)}$$

(*b*) Check with the z-transform of the last two functions obtained in problem 1.2*a* by letting $m = 1$.

Problem 2.3 For the system shown in Fig. 2.3:

(*a*) Find the actual response for a step input for value of gain $K = 2.4$ and $T = 1$ second. Use the modified z-transform method.

(*b*) Find the initial and final value as well as the maximum of the output and the peak time. Check with the computed response.

(*c*) What is the maximum gain that tends to make the system become unstable?

(*d*) Find the response at the sampling instants and check with the actual response.

(*e*) Find the response at half-points between the sampling instants using the submultiple method.

(*f*) Plot the Nyquist diagram of the open-loop z-transform function in the $HG^*(z)$-plane.

(*g*) Find the maximum-frequency overshoot and the frequency at which it occurs.

(*h*) Tabulate the correlation between the frequency response and time response quantities.

(*i*) Plot the steady-state output for sinusoidal input.

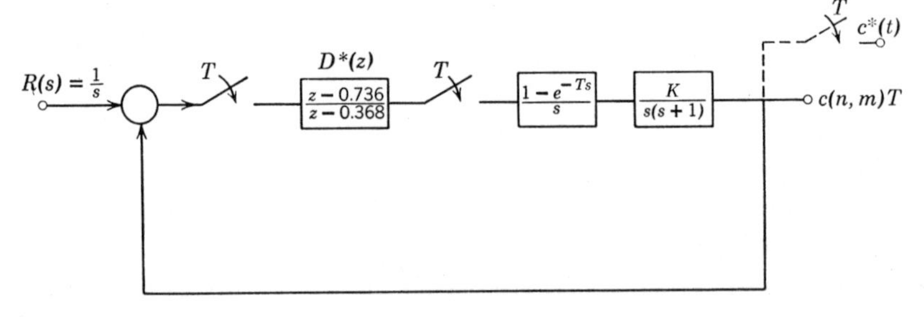

Figure 2.3

Problem 2.4 Obtain the modified z-transform output of the system shown in Fig. 2.4.

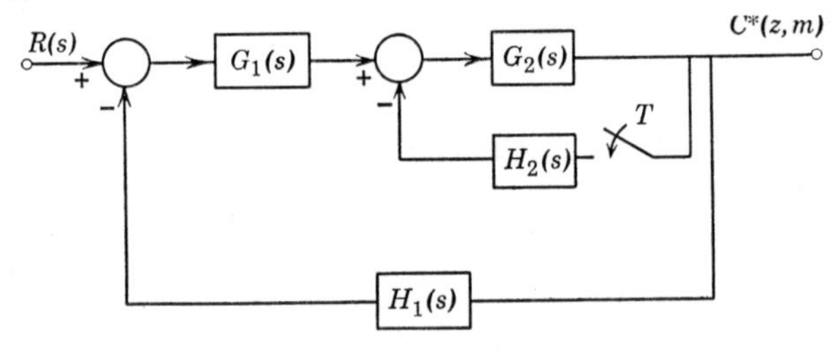

Figure 2.4

Problem 2.5 The equivalent sampled-data feedback system of a track-while-scan system is shown in Fig. 2.5, where α = position-smoothing constant and β = velocity-smoothing constant:

(*a*) Obtain the modified z-transform of the output $C^*(z, m)$.

(*b*) What conditions should be satisfied for the system to be stable?

(*c*) Obtain the relationship between α and β for (1) underdamped response,

(2) critically damped response, and
(3) overdamped response.

Note: Sampling at the discontinuity of $g(t)$, that is, $\mathcal{L}^{-1}\left[\frac{\alpha}{s}\right]$, occurs at an instant just preceding the discontinuity, which is zero in this case.

(*d*) How is $G(s)$ related to the first-order hold circuit.

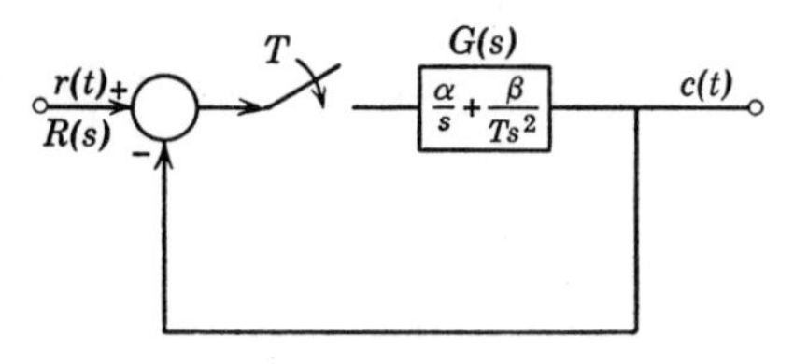

Figure 2.5

Problem 2.6 (*a*) Obtain the modified z-transform of the output for a system configuration shown in Fig. 2.6.

(*b*) Write an expression whereby the actual output can be found.

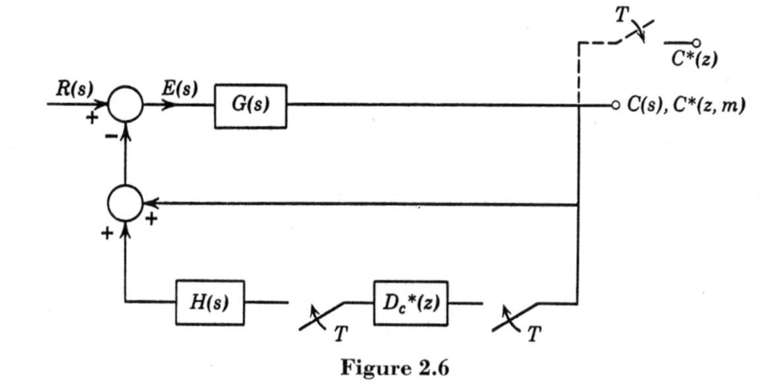

Figure 2.6

Problem 2.7 If the input to the system shown in Fig. 2.7 is a unit ramp, given:

$$D_c{}^*(z) = \frac{2}{0.632}\,\frac{(z - 0.368)(z - 0.2)}{(z - 1)^2}$$

(*a*) Obtain the actual output.
(*b*) Obtain the steady-state error.
(*c*) Plot the output response.

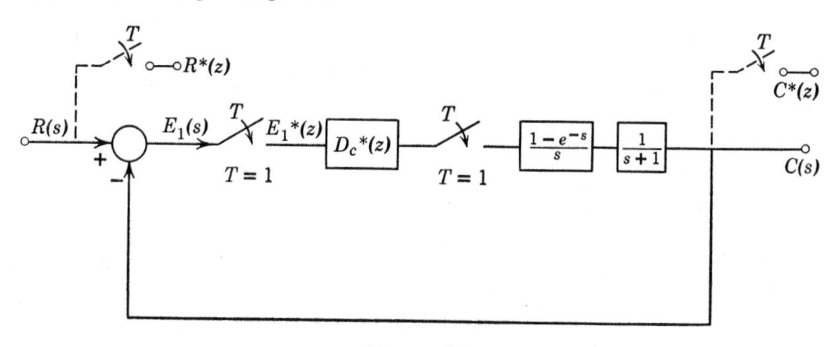

Figure 2.7

Problem 2.8 For a sampled-data control system shown in Fig. 2.8, given

$$G(s) = \frac{s^2 + (\pi + 2\alpha)s + \pi(\pi + \alpha) + \alpha^2}{(s + \gamma)[(s + \alpha)^2 + \pi^2]}$$

$$T = 1, \quad e^{-\alpha} = 0.98, \quad \gamma = 1$$

(*a*) Obtain the modified z-transform of the output for a step input.
(*b*) Obtain the initial value and the response for the first sampling period.
(*c*) Obtain the final value.
(*d*) Obtain the response for all of time.

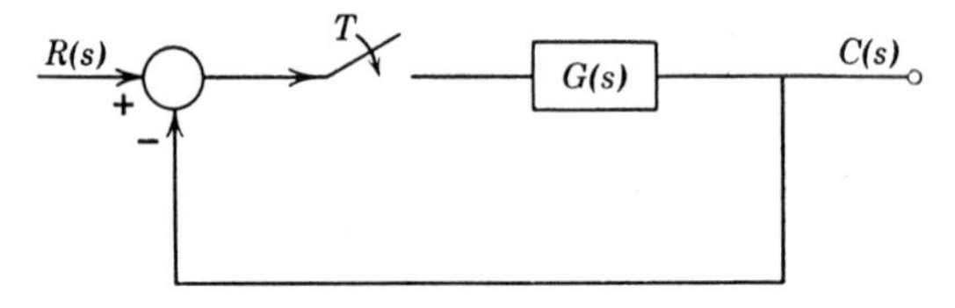

Figure 2.8

Problem 2.9 Obtain the following for a sampled-data control system shown in Fig. 2.9:

$$G(s) = \frac{1}{s + 1} e^{-1.35sT}$$

$$H(s) = \frac{1}{s + 2} e^{-2.85sT}$$

$$T = 1, \quad R(s) = 1/s$$

(*a*) Obtain $C^*(z, m)$
(*b*) Find the actual response.
(*c*) Indicate how you obtain the response at the sampling instants from part *b*.

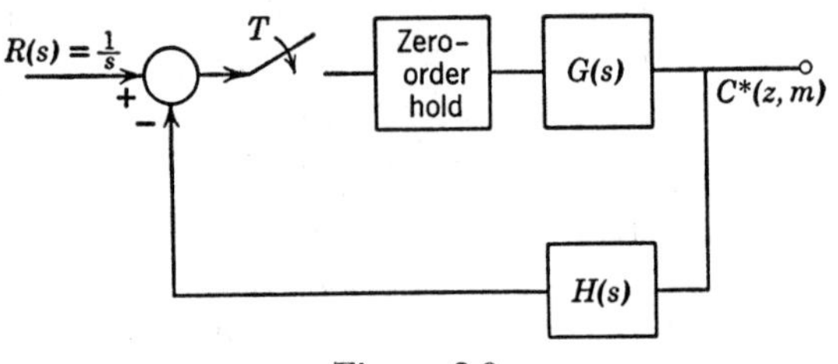

Figure 2.9

Problem 2.10 For the system shown in Fig. 2.10, given:

$$G_2(s) = 10$$

$$G_1(s) = \frac{1}{s(s + 0.5)}$$

$$G_0(s) = \text{zero-order hold}$$

$$T = 1 \text{ second}$$

$$D_c^*(z) = \frac{0.0384z^2 + 0.17z + 0.108z}{(1.786z + 1.378)(z - 1)}$$

do the following.

(*a*) Obtain the response to a step input for the uncompensated system, that is, $D_c^*(z)$ = unity.

(*b*) Obtain the response to a step input for the compensated system.

(*c*) Plot the results.

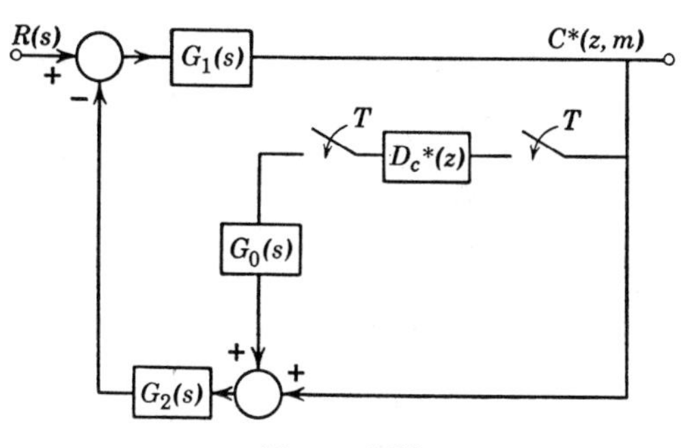

Figure 2.10

Problem 2.11 Obtain and plot the ramp and step responses of the system shown in Fig. 2.11, given:

$$D_c^*(z) = \frac{(z - 0.368)^2(0.81z - 0.51)}{(z - 1)(z + 0.162)(z + 1.19)}$$

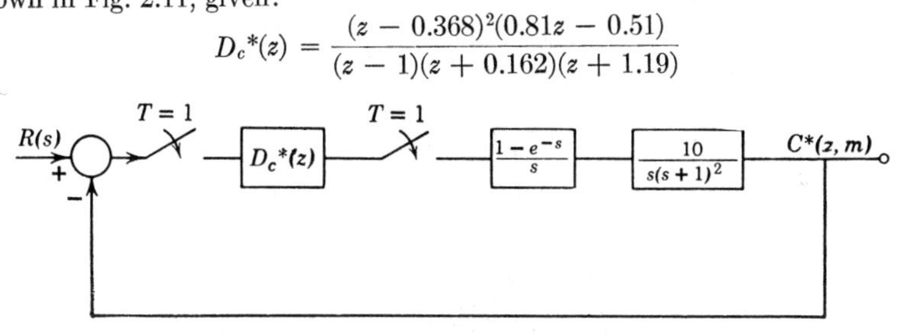

Figure 2.11

Problem 2.12 A second-order error-sampled system shown in Fig. 2.12 has the following constants:

$$G_2(s) = \frac{K}{s(s + a)}$$

$$G_0(s) = \frac{1 - e^{-Ts}}{s}$$

$$K = 1, \quad a = 1, \quad T = 1$$

$$r(t) = \sin 8t$$

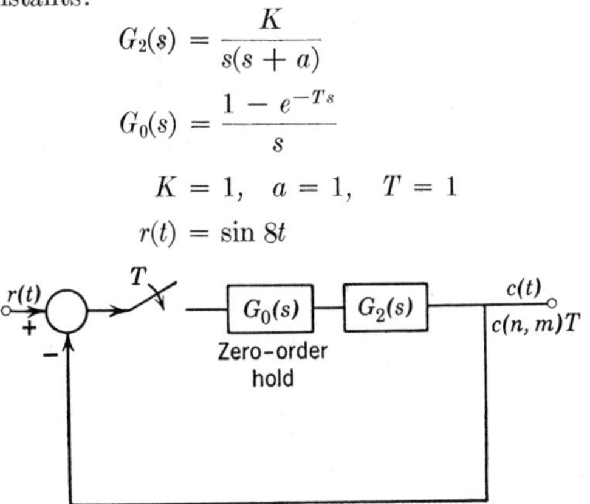

Figure 2.12

(*a*) Obtain the transient solution for $c(t)$ or $c(n, m)T$.

(*b*) Obtain the steady-state solution of the output for the given sinusoidal input.

(*c*) Plot the total response.

(*d*) Show that for the steady-state solution we can replace z by $e^{j\omega T}$ in the system transfer function, to obtain the magnitude and the phase of the steady-state solution.

CHAPTER 3

Problem 3.1 Sketch the root-locus of the following functions in the z-plane:

(*a*) $G^*(z) = \dfrac{1}{(z - b)(z - 1)}, \qquad 0 < b < 1$

(*b*) $G^*(z) = \dfrac{1}{z^2 + p^2}$

(*c*) $G^*(z) = \dfrac{1}{z^3}$, find the roots of $(1 + z^3) = 0$ from the root-locus of part *c*.

Problem 3.2 For a sampled-data system, given the following:

$$G^*(z) = \frac{1}{(z - b)(z - 1)^2}, \qquad 0 < b < 1$$

(*a*) Sketch the root-locus in the z-plane.

(*b*) What should be the form of the compensator to *insure* stabilization of this system for certain values of gain?

(*c*) Sketch the shaped root-locus.

Problem 3.3 For an error-sampled system shown in Fig. 3.3 ($T = 1$ second):

(*a*) Plot the root-locus in the z-plane.

(*b*) Determine the actual location of the roots.

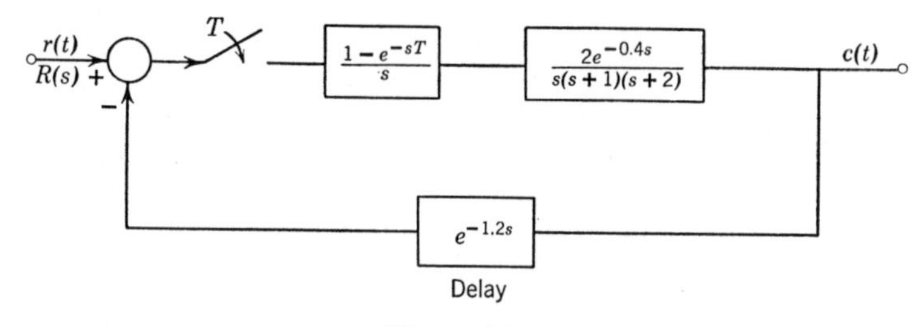

Figure 3.3

Problem 3.4 The transfer function of a sampled-data feedback system is given by

$$\frac{C^*(z)}{R^*(z)} = \frac{z[(z-0.6)^2+1]}{[(z-0.5)^2+0.8^2][(z-0.1)^2+0.3^2]}$$

(*a*) Obtain the normalized time sequence response for a step input and plot.

(*b*) Obtain the value of n which yields the maximum of the time sequence response and the value of the overshoot.

(*c*) Obtain the ranges of n for which dominance does not hold and for which dominance holds.

(*d*) Obtain the frequency response graphically from the pole zero locations in the z-plane.

Problem 3.5 Plot the inverse root-locus of the following function:

$$\frac{C^*(z)}{R^*(z)} = K_c \frac{z+27.5}{[(z+12.5)^2+20^2](z+20)(z+57.7)}$$

Problem 3.6 A sampled-data feedback system, shown in Fig. 3.6, has the following constants:

$$T = 15 \text{ seconds}, \qquad \delta = 10 \text{ seconds}, \qquad \tau = 60 \text{ seconds}$$

(*a*) Plot the root-locus in the z-plane.

(*b*) Plot the constant ζ – curve (see Fig. 1.30*a* in Chapter 1) which equals 0.2 in the z-plane (logarithmic spiral); $\zeta = \sin \alpha$.

(*c*) Obtain the value of K by finding the intersection between root-locus and constant $\zeta = 0.2$ curve in the z-plane.

(*d*) Plot the step response for the value of gain obtained in part *c*.

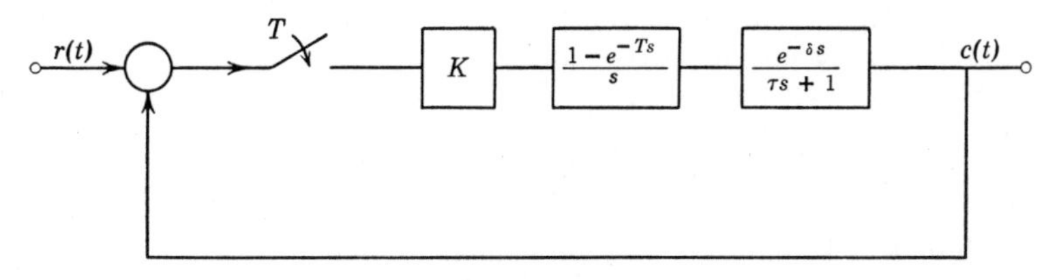

Figure 3.6

Problem 3.7 For a sampled-data feedback system shown in Fig. 3.7*a*:

(*a*) Plot the root-locus as a function of KT.

(*b*) Obtain the discrete compensating network as shown in Fig. 3.7*b* to yield a zero overshoot for a step input.

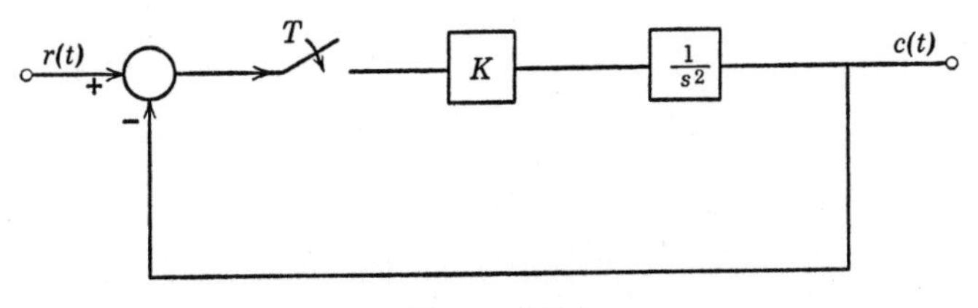

Figure 3.7*a*

(*c*) Plot the root-locus of the compensated system.
(*d*) Plot the step response for $KT = 1$.

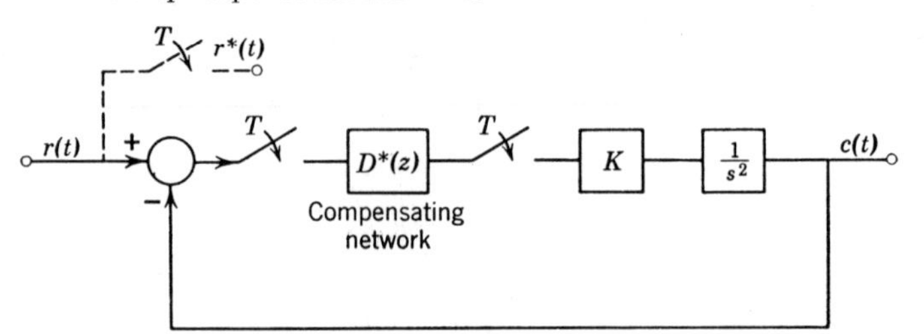

Figure 3.7*b*

CHAPTER 4

Problem 4.1 (*a*) Evaluate:

$$\mathfrak{L}^{-1}\left[\frac{1}{T}\sum_{k=-\infty}^{k=\infty}\frac{1}{(s+a+jk\omega_r)}\right]\times\frac{1}{s+b}$$

for $0 < t < T$. Let $T = 1$, $b = 2$, and $a = 4$.
(*b*) Evaluate:

$$\mathfrak{L}^{-1}\left[\frac{1}{1-e^{-T(s+a)}}\times\frac{1}{s+b}\right]$$

for $0 < t < T$ and for the same constants.
(*c*) Plot the responses for parts *a* and *b*.
(*d*) Show the following:

$$\frac{1}{1-e^{-T(s+a)}}\frac{1}{s+b} = \left[\frac{1}{T}\sum_{k=-\infty}^{\infty}\frac{1}{s+jk\omega_r}+\frac{1}{2}\right]\frac{1}{s+b}$$

Problem 4.2 Using block diagram reductions, obtain the equivalent output to input disturbance of the system in Fig. 4.2.

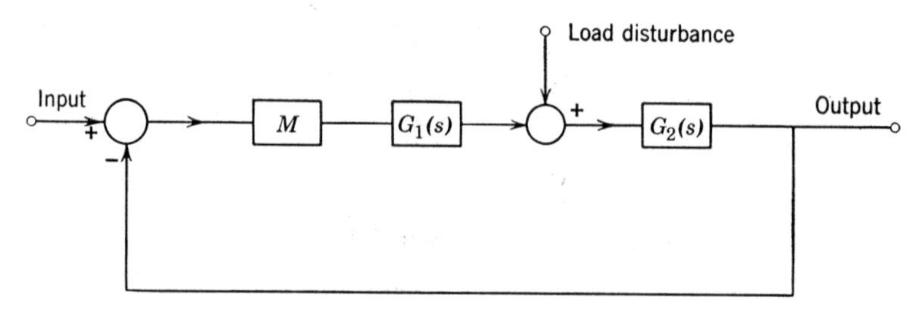

Figure 4.2

Problem 4.3 Using block diagram reduction, show the equivalence of the systems in Figs. 4.3*a* and *b*.

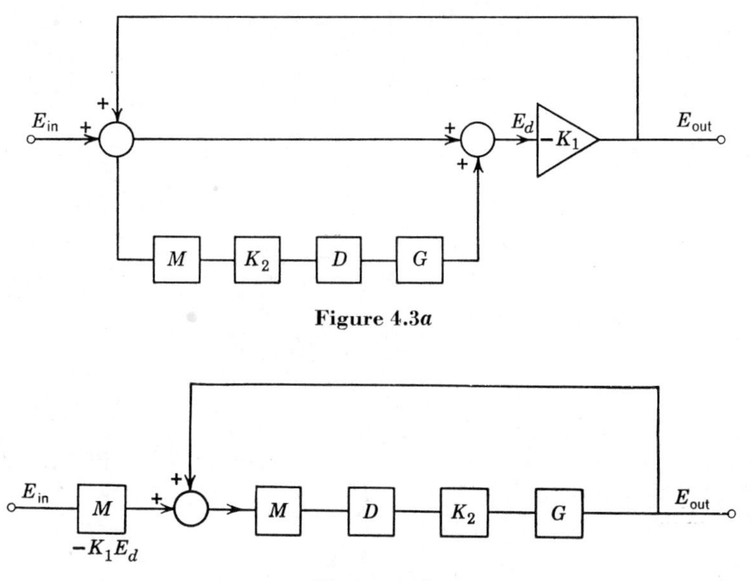

Figure 4.3a

Figure 4.3b

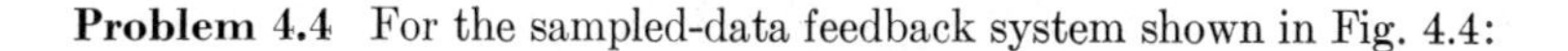

Problem 4.4 For the sampled-data feedback system shown in Fig. 4.4:

$$G_1(s) = \frac{K_u}{s + \alpha}$$

$$G_2(s) = \frac{1 - e^{-Ts}}{s^2}$$

$$T = \alpha = 1$$

(*a*) Plot $G_1G_2^*(w)$ in the w-plane, using logarithmic plots.
(*b*) Plot the phase of $G_1G_2^*(w)$ as a function of dimensionless frequency v.
(*c*) Obtain the gain K_u for a 45°-degree phase margin.
(*d*) For the same phase margin obtain M_m, ω_m (bandwidth).
Note: Assume the input to be a unit step.

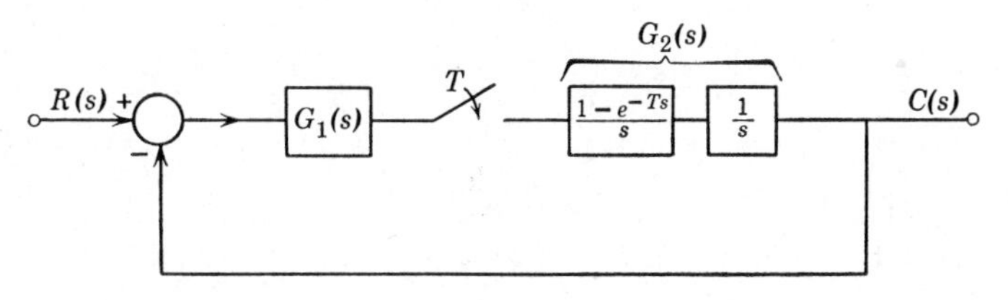

Figure 4.4

Problem 4.5 Repeat problem 4.4, for the compensated system shown in Fig. 4.5. Given

$$D^*(z) = 0.104 \frac{z - 0.91}{z - 0.99}$$

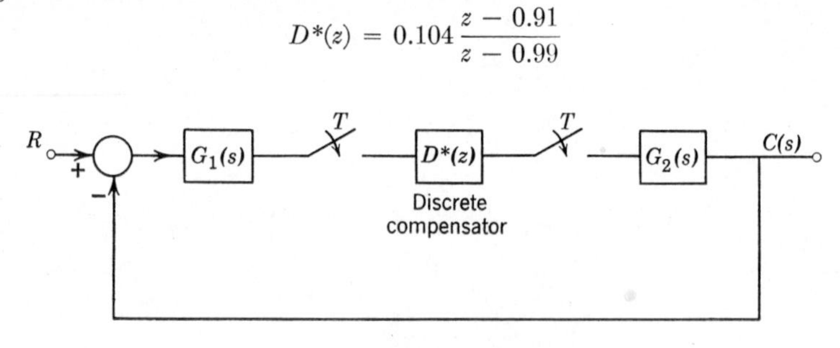

Figure 4.5

Problem 4.6 A conditional feedback sampled-data system used in missile control systems is shown in Fig. 4.6. The advantages of this conditional system is the minimization of the effects of angle-of-attack perturbation on the airframe and of misalignment errors.

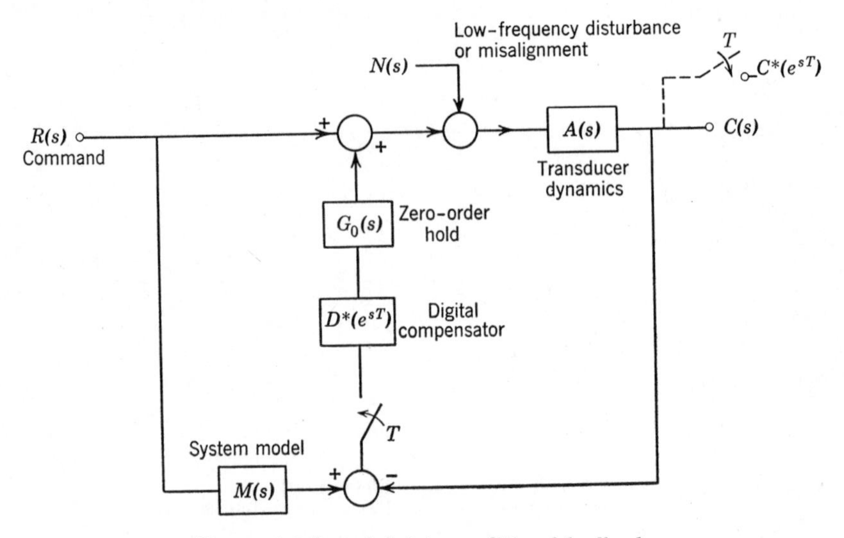

Figure 4.6 Sampled-data conditional feedback

(*a*) Obtain the Laplace transform of the output $C(s)$ for input command only.
(*b*) If in (*a*) $M(s) = A(s)$, obtain the transfer function $C(s)/R(s)$.
(*c*) Obtain the Laplace transform of the output for a disturbance input.
(*d*) Obtain the transform of the sampled output.

Reference: D. R. Katt, "Conditional Feedback Systems Applied to Stabilizing a Missile in Pitch Attitude," *I.R.E. Wescon Convention Record*, Pt. IV, August 21, 1957, p. 171.

CHAPTER 5

Problem 5.1 Obtain the output matrix representation $c_n(m)$ of the sampled-data feedback system shown in Fig. 5.1.
Note: See Appendix of Chapter 5.

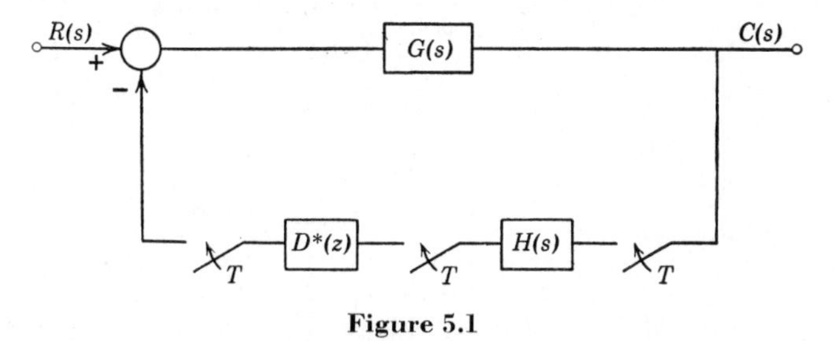

Figure 5.1

Problem 5.2 For the sampled-data control system shown in Fig. 5.2:
(*a*) Obtain $D_c^*(z)$ for a dead-beat ramp response:

$$R(s) = 1/s^2$$

$$t_r = 1 \text{ second} = \text{rise time}$$

(*b*) Plot the ramp response of the compensated system.
(*c*) Plot the step response of the compensated system.

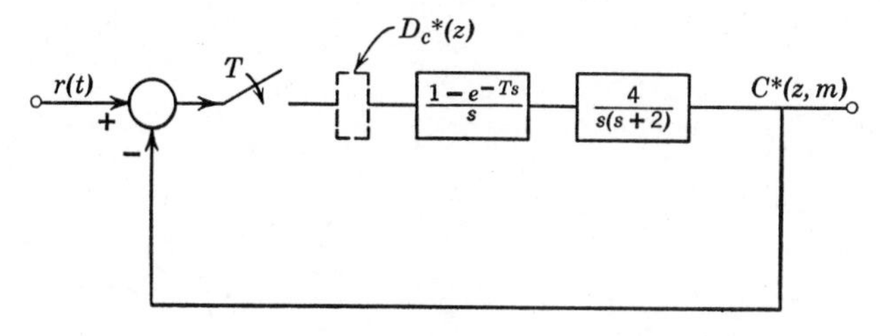

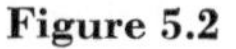
Figure 5.2

Problem 5.3 For a sampled-data feedback system shown in Fig. 5.3, given

$$\Delta = \text{pure delay of one sampling period}, \quad G(s) = \frac{K}{s^3}, \quad T = 1$$

(*a*) Determine the simplest form of $D_c^*(z)$ and the value of K to satisfy the following conditions: (1) the steady-state error for step input is zero, (2) the system characteristic equation is $z^3 = 0$, and (3) the discrete compensator $D_c^*(z)$ is physically realizable.

(*b*) Obtain $C^*(z)/R^*(z)$ and the output at the sampling instants for a step input.

(*c*) Obtain the actual output $c(n, m)$.

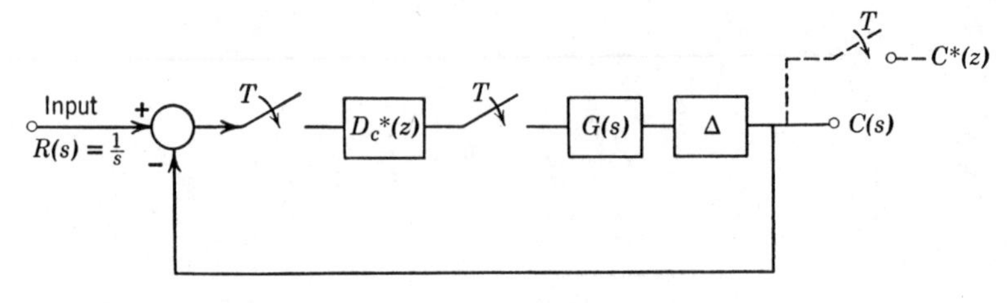

Figure 5.3

Problem 5.4 For an error-sampled-data system shown in Fig. 5.4 ($T = 2$):

(*a*) Obtain the parameters of the discrete compensators that give $\omega_s T = 75°$ for the same $M_{\max}$ of the uncompensated system,† using first the Nyquist plot and then the logarithmic plot.

(*b*) Plot the compensated response of step and ramp inputs.

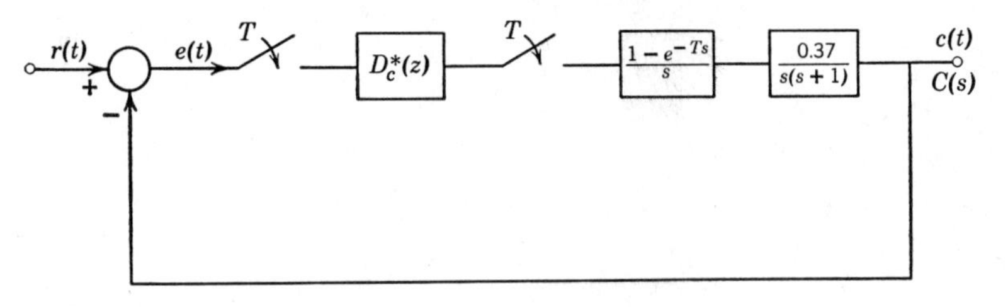

Figure 5.4

Problem 5.5 Given an error-sampled system with the pure delay as shown in Fig. 5.5 ($T = 1$):

(*a*) Find the discrete-compensator transfer function $D_c{}^*(z)$ to obtain a dead-beat step response.

(*b*) Plot the compensated and uncompensated systems.

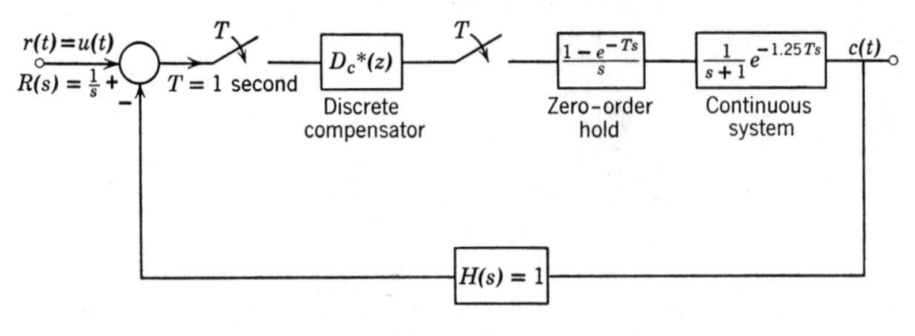

Figure 5.5

† The uncompensated system is the system without the discrete compensator.

Problem 5.6 A sampled-error feedback system shown in Fig. 5.6 has the following constants:

$$T = \tfrac{1}{3}$$

$$K = a = 1$$

(*a*) Obtain the compensator transfer function $D_c^*(z)$ to yield a deadbeat ramp response with a rise time of 1 second.

(*b*) Plot the step response of the compensated system.

(*c*) Explain a method whereby the step response overshoot can be reduced.

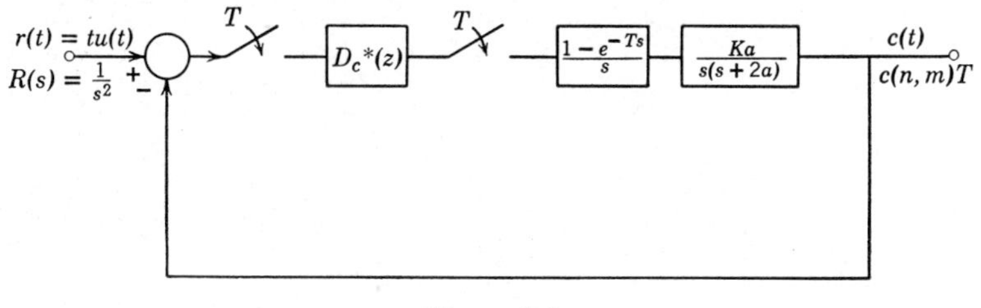

Figure 5.6

Problem 5.7 For the system shown in Fig. 5.7 (*a*) design the discrete compensator $D_c^*(z)$ to yield the following response:

1. Final value $\lim_{n\to\infty} c(n,m)T = 1.0, \quad 0 \leq m \leq 1$

2. Peak time $t_p = 1.375$ seconds,

$$\frac{d}{dm} c_2(m) \bigg|_{m=0.75} = 0, \quad c''_2(m) \,|_{m=0.75} < 0$$

3. Overshoot $M_p = 20\%, \quad c_2(0.75) = 1.2$

4. Settling time Minimum for three open-loop compensator variables, that is,

$$D_s^*(z) = \frac{z^3 + d_1 z^2 + d_2 + d_3}{s^3} F_{ss}^*(z)$$

(*b*) Plot the compensated and uncompensated response.

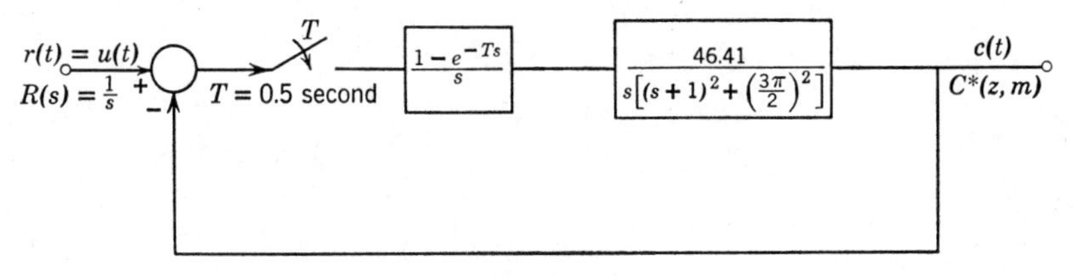

Figure 5.7

Problem 5.8 For a sampled-data control system shown in Fig. 5.8:
(*a*) Obtain the step response.
(*b*) Obtain the discrete-compensator transfer function $D_c^*(z)$ to fulfill the following design requirements:

1. Final value $\quad c(n, m)T_{n \to 0} = 1.0, \qquad 0 \leq m \leq 1$

2. Peak time $\quad t_p = 1.25$ seconds $\quad \left.\dfrac{d}{dm} c_2(m)\right|_{m=0.5} = 0,$

   $c''_2(m) \,|_{m=0.5} < 0$

3. Overshoot $\quad M_p = 20\%. \qquad c_2(0.5) = 1.2$

4. Settling time $\quad (t_s) \cdots |e(n,m)T| < 3\%$ of final value for

   $t > t_s = 3.0$ seconds

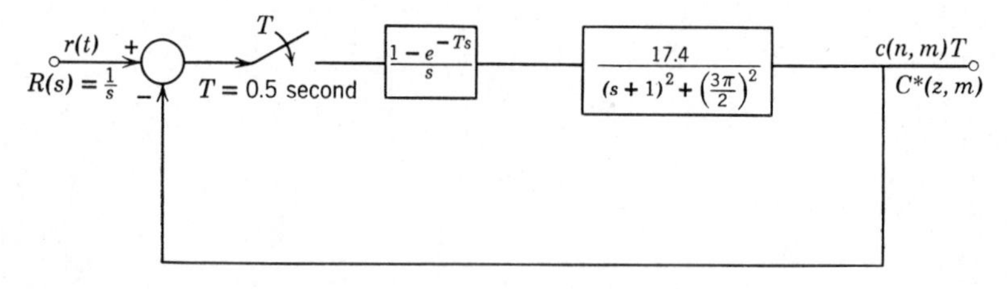

Figure 5.8 Uncompensated system

Problem 5.9 Repeat part (*b*) of 5.8 except for the following alternate t_p and M_p and settling time.

$$t_p = 1.125 \text{ seconds}, \quad \left.\frac{d}{dm} c_2(m)\right|_{m=0.25} = 0$$

$$M_p = 20\%, \quad c_2(0.25) = 1.2$$

$$t_s \cdots \left|e(n, m)\right| = 0 \qquad \text{for } t > t_s = 2 \text{ seconds}$$

Note: Use equation (5.32) for finite settling time and limit A_j to A_1 and A_2.

Problem 5.10 For a continuous-data control system using the digital compensator shown in Fig. 5.10 the following is given:

$$G(s) = \frac{1}{s(s + 0.5)}$$

$$G_0(s) = \frac{1 - e^{-sT}}{s}$$

$$T = 1.5 \text{ seconds}, \quad R(s) = 1/s$$

(*a*) Obtain the digital unit transfer function $D^*(z)$ designed so that the output will follow the input without error after two sampling periods.
(*b*) Plot the ramp response of the compensated system.

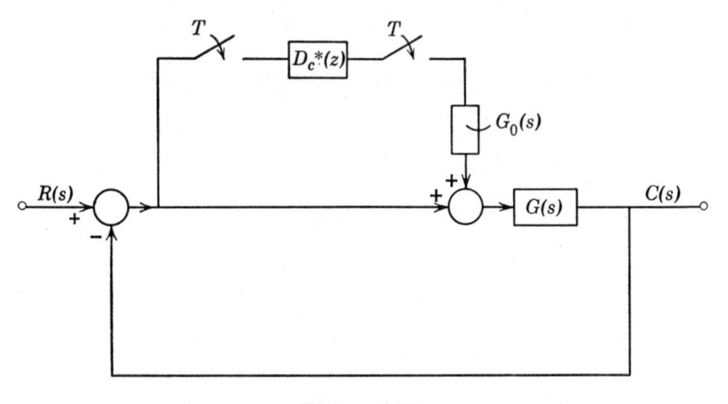

Figure 5.10

CHAPTER 6

Problem 6.1 For an error-sampled-data feedback system shown in Fig. 6.1, given $T = 2$, $K = 0.695$.

(a) Determine $\omega_s T$ for the uncompensated system whose locus is tangent to $M_{\max} = 1.4$.

(b) To improve the performance, $\omega_s T$ is required to be 70° and the type of $N(s)$ must be

$$N(s) = \frac{1}{\tau s + 1}$$

Determine the value of τ, using the exact z-transform locus.

(c) Plot the compensated and uncompensated responses to step input.

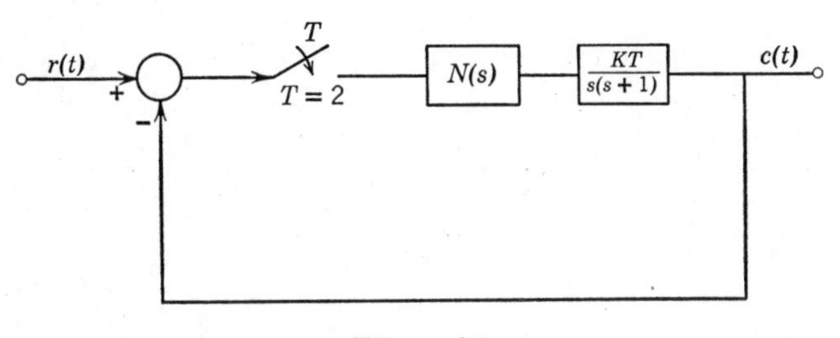

Figure 6.1

Problem 6.2 Repeat 6.1b using the z–s approximation for $n = 2$.

Problem 6.3 Use the constants (area of moments) for the impulsive response of a discrete compensator plus hold as given in equation (6.102). Obtain the fifth-order network approximation using the first ten equations of 6.101 (q_0 can be normalized to unity).

Problem 6.4 (*a*) Using Table 6.2 obtain

$$N^*(z) \text{ for } N(s) = \frac{\alpha\tau s + 1}{\tau s + 1}.$$

(*b*) Using the bilinear transformation $z = w + 1/w - 1$ discussed in Chapter 4, obtain $N^*(jv)$. Write $N^*(jv)$ in the following form:

$$N^*(jv) = \frac{jv(\alpha_1 + \tau_1) + 1}{jv\tau_2 + 1}$$

(*c*) Obtain $\alpha_{\text{effective}} = \dfrac{\alpha_1\tau_1}{2}$

(*d*) Assuming $\alpha = 10$, calculate and plot $\alpha_{\text{eff.}}$ as a function τ/T. Use a range of τ/T from $0.1 - 10$.

Problem 6.5 (*a*) Using Table 6.2 obtain $N(s)$ from the specification:

$$[H(s)\,N(s)]^* = \frac{\frac{9}{4}(z - \frac{1}{3})^2}{(z-1)^2(z - \frac{1}{4})}$$

given

$$H(s) = \left[\frac{1 - e^{-sT}}{s^2(0.721s + 1)}\right]$$

(*b*) Use exact method for obtaining $N(s)$.

Problem 6.6 Given $G(s)$ as follows:

$$G(s) = \frac{1}{s^2 + \omega_r^{\,2}}, \qquad \omega_r = \frac{2\pi}{T}$$

(*a*) Obtain $G^*(s)$.
(*b*) Obtain $G^{**}(s)$.

Problem 6.7 Given the discrete-compensator transfer function $D^*(e^{Ts})$ as follows:

$$D^*(e^{Ts}) = \frac{\frac{2}{3}\,e^{-sT}(1 + e^{-sT})}{(1 - e^{-sT})^3} + \frac{\frac{14}{9}\,e^{-sT}}{(1 - e^{-sT})^2} + \frac{\frac{1}{27}}{1 - e^{-sT}} - \frac{\frac{1}{27}}{1 - e^{-sT/4}}$$

obtain the corresponding continuous network which when sampled yields this equation.

Problem 6.8 Figure 6.8*a* represents a block diagram of a distance-measuring device which indicates both distance and velocity as continuous quantities.

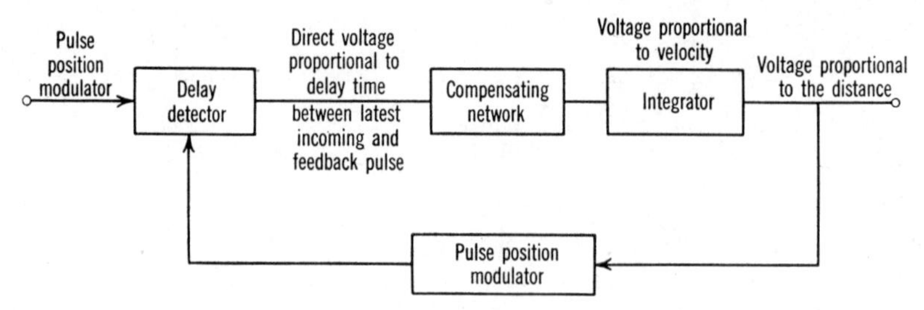

Figure 6.8*a*

The distance of the object is provided by a pulse position modulated signal with a repetition frequency of one pulse per second.

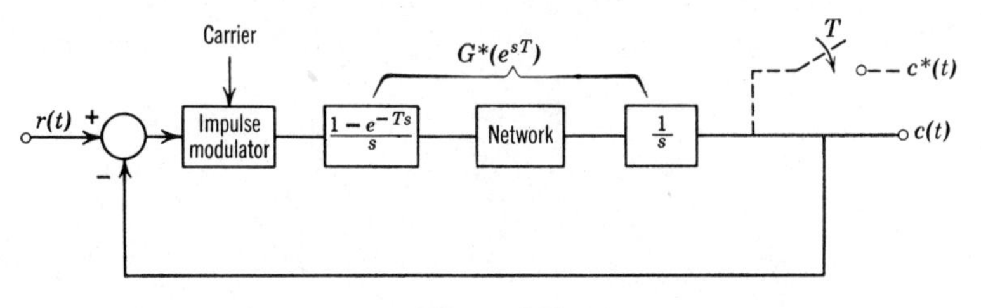

Figure 6.8b

The equivalent diagram for equipment is shown in Fig. 6.8b. The pulsed transfer function of the forward transfer function is designed to give

$$G^*(e^{sT}) = 2\frac{e^{-sT}(1 - \frac{2}{3}e^{-sT})}{(1 - e^{-sT})^2}$$

(a) Obtain the transfer function of the continuous compensating network.
(b) Plot the continuous output for a unit ramp input.
(c) Plot the step response of the compensated system.
(d) What can be done to reduce the step overshoot?

Reference: W. K. Linvill and R. W. Sittler, "Design of Sampled-Data Systems by Extension of Conventional Techniques," Report No. R-222, M.I.T., July 1953.

CHAPTER 7

Problem 7.1 For the system shown in Fig. 7.1, the discrete-compensator transfer function is given

$$D^*(z) = \frac{z - 0.135}{z + 0.523}$$

(a) Realize this function with a basic feedback *R-C* network.
(b) Plot the step response of the system.

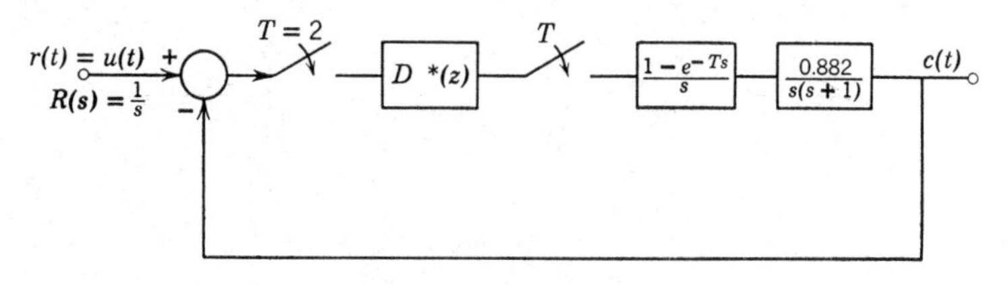

Figure 7.1

Problem 7.2 The transfer function of a pulsed simulator is given by

$$D^*(z) = \frac{0.944z^{-1}(1 - 1.502z^{-1} + 0.698z^{-2})}{(1 - 0.435z^{-1})(1 - 1.504z^{-1} + 0.831z^{-2})}$$

To realize $D^*(z)$ as a pulsed R-C network:
(*a*) Use cascade realization.
(*b*) Use feedback realization.
(*c*) Use parallel realization.

Problem 7.3 Obtain the operational-instruction controller for the following discrete transfer function:

$$D^*(z) = \frac{z}{z^2 + A_1 z + A_2}, \qquad \text{when } A_1 \text{ and } A_2 \text{ are positive constants}$$

Problem 7.4 Obtain the operational-instruction controller for the following discrete transfer function:

$$D^*(z) = \frac{z(z + A_3)}{(z^2 + A_1 z + A_2)(z - 1)}, \qquad A_1, A_2, A_3 \text{ are positive constants}$$

CHAPTER 8

Problem 8.1 Given a feedback system shown in Fig. 8.1*a* in which

$$R(s) = \frac{1}{s^2}$$

$$G_1(s) = G(s)\,e^{-\Delta s} = \frac{s + 0.3}{s^2} \times e^{-0.8s}$$

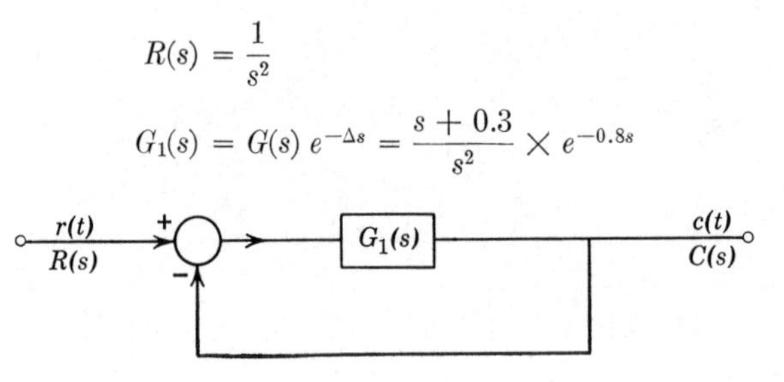

Figure 8.1*a*

(*a*) Obtain as many significant roots as possible of the characteristic equation.
(*b*) Plot the response $c(t)$ for ramp input.

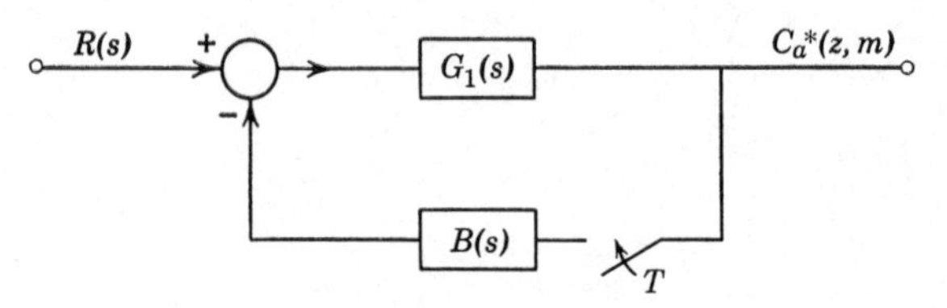

Figure 8.1*b*

This system is to be approximated by a sampled-data control system shown in Fig. 8.1*b*. $B(s)$ is a fictitious hold having low-pass filter characteristics and is represented by the following transfer function:

$$B(s) = \frac{(1 - e^{-sT})^2\, e^{sT}}{Ts^2}$$

Choose $T = 0.5$ second:

(*c*) Obtain $C_a^*(z,m)$, the modified z-transform of the output.

(*d*) Obtain the actual output by creeping method (division method); plot at least up to ten sampling periods.

(*e*) Compare the actual output with the approximated output, and plot the error.

Problem 8.2 Given a continuous feedback system as shown in Fig. 8.2:

(*a*) Obtain the approximate response at all times, using the modified z-forms method. Choose $T = 0.5$ second.

(*b*) Using the fictitious-hold approximation and the same value of T, obtain the response at all times and at the sampling instants.

(*c*) Compare with the exact response.

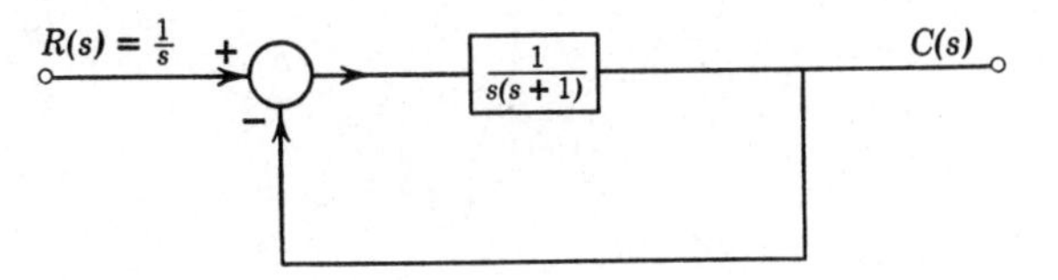

Figure 8.2

Problem 8.3 Find the inverse Laplace transform of the following function for all time:

$$F(s) = \frac{1}{s^3 + s}$$

(*a*) Use the modified z-forms, choosing $T = 0.5$ second.

(*b*) Use the inverse integral formula and compare results for t between 0 and 5 seconds.

Problem 8.4 Show that the z-transform of the second difference of $c(nT)$ is

$$\mathfrak{Z}\,[\Delta^2 c(nT)] = (z - 1)^2\, C^*(z) - z(z - 1)\, c(0) - z\, \Delta c(0)$$

where $\Delta c(0) = c(1T) - c(0)$.

Problem 8.5 Obtain the z-transform, $C^*(z)$, of the following difference equation.†

$$a_0\, c(nT + T) + a_1\, c(nT) + a_2\, c(nT - T) = r(nT)$$

where a_0, a_1, and a_2 are constants.

† Note that $c(nT)$ can also be written as c_n.

Problem 8.6 For $y_n = 2.0$ for all $n > 0$, find x_n which is a solution of

$$x_{n+2} - x_{n+1} + 0.632x_n = 0.368y_{n+1} + 0.264y_n$$

(*a*) Neglect all initial conditions.
(*b*) Assume that $x_0 = 1.0$ and $x_1 = 0.0$.

Problem 8.7 Find x_n which is a solution of

$$x_{n+2} - 1.5x_{n+1} + x_n = (-0.5)^n$$

Problem 8.8 Find the continuous function $x(t)$ which satisfies the following equation:

$$x(t) = x_{n+1}(2.582 - 1.582e^{-m} - m) - x_n(1 - e^{-m}) + y_{n+1}(m - 1 + e^{-m}) + 0.418y_n(1 - e^{-m})$$

with $y_n = 1.0$ for all n, and $(n + 1) \leq t \leq (n + 2)$.

CHAPTER 9

Problem 9.1 Derive the general equation for $I(s)$, the Laplace transform of the current in the R-L circuit shown in Fig. 9.1*a* when $e(t)$, the applied voltage, is the periodic saw-toothed voltage shown in Fig. 9.1*b*. Plot the transient values of this current for the first 2 seconds and its steady-state wave shape when

$$R = 1 \text{ ohm}$$
$$L = 2 \text{ henries}$$
$$h = 0.4 \text{ second}$$
$$T = 1 \text{ second}$$
$$K = 1$$

Assume zero initial conditions.

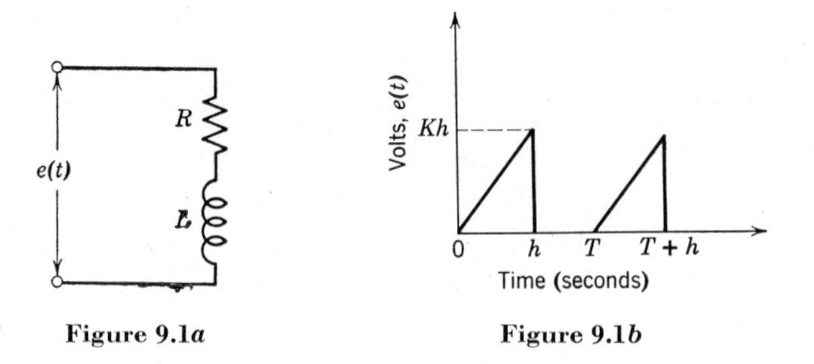

Figure 9.1*a* Figure 9.1*b*

Problem 9.2 A 60 cycles per second sinusoidal voltage with a peak of 100 volts is rectified by a full-wave rectifier. The resulting voltage wave, shown in

Fig. 9.2a, is then applied to the L-section filter shown in Fig. 9.2b. Plot the open-circuit output voltage, $e_o(t)$, appearing at the terminals C and D.

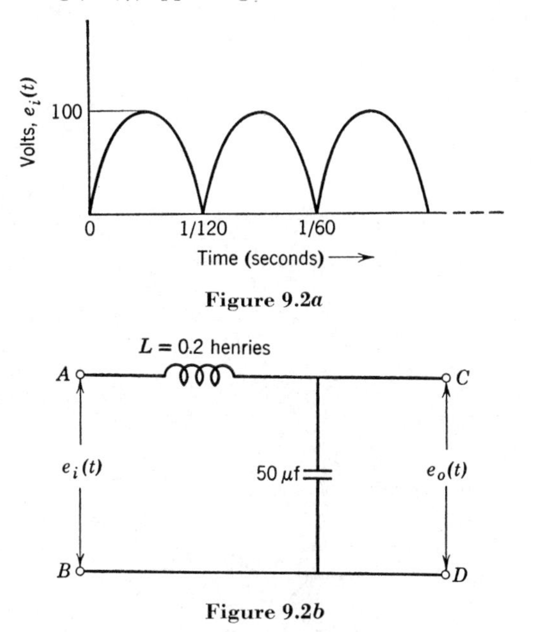

Figure 9.2a

Figure 9.2b

Problem 9.3 Figure 9.3 shows a multiple-sampler open-loop system with periodic samplers having different periods. Compute $Q(s)$ and hence $q(t)$ when the input is a unit step and $T_1 = 0.6$ second and $h_1 = 0.2$ second; $Q(s)$ is fed to a second sampler with a delay of $\delta_2 = 0.8$ second, period $T_2 = 0.4$ second, and $h_2 = 0.2$ second.

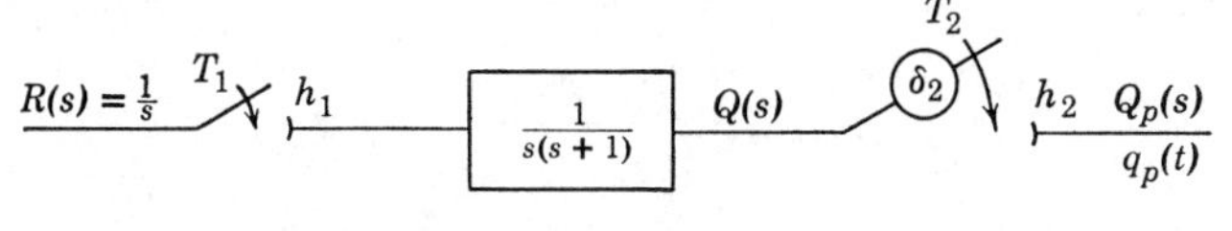

Figure 9.3

Compute $Q_p(s)$ and $q_p(t)$, the output of the second sampler. Plot and compare the functions $q(t)$ and $q_p(t)$.

Problem 9.4 Derive $C^*(z_{T2})$, the z-transform of the output for the sampled-data system shown in Fig. 9.4, when $z_{T2} = e^{sT_2}$, and $T_1 = 0.5$ second, $\delta_2 = 0.8$ second, $T_2 = 0.3$ second, and $R(s) = 1/s$.

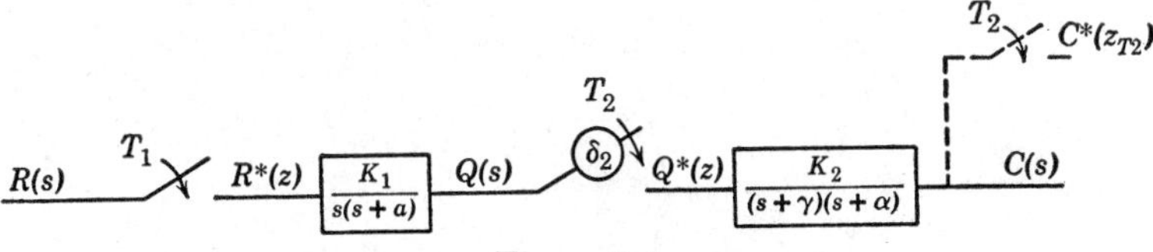

Figure 9.4

Problem 9.5 Figure 9.5 shows a general error-pulsed third-order system. Derive the stability conditions and the equations for the characteristic coefficients in terms of the given system coefficients. Assume simple poles, and designate the poles of the closed-loop transfer function by α_1, α_2, α_3.

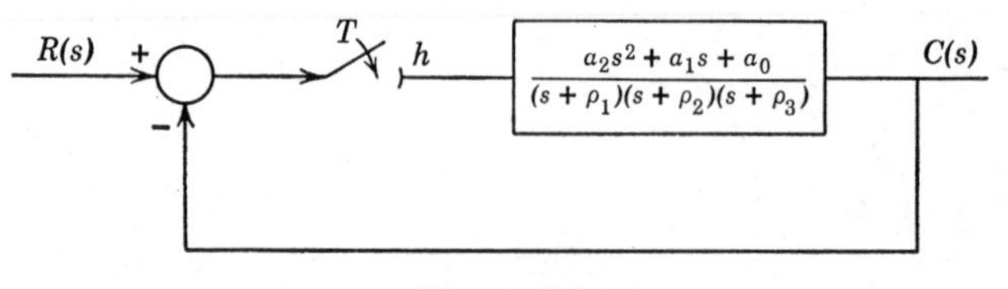

Figure 9.5

Problem 9.6 Calculate the output $c(t)$ for the system shown in Fig. 9.6 when $h = 0.4$ second, $T = 1$ second.

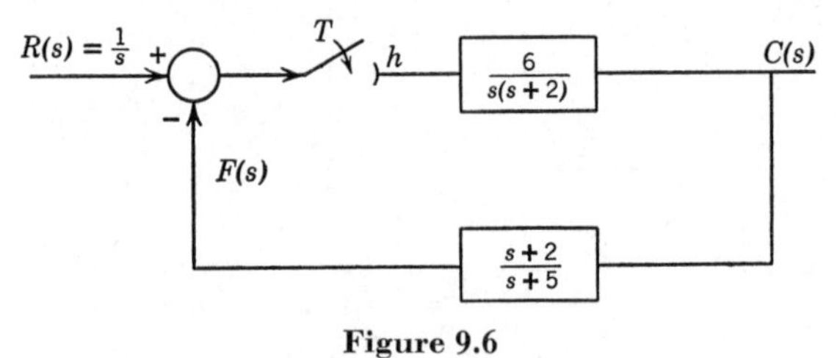

Figure 9.6

Problem 9.7 Calculate $c(t)$, the output of the system shown in Fig. 9.7, when $T = 1$ second and $h = 0.5$ second.

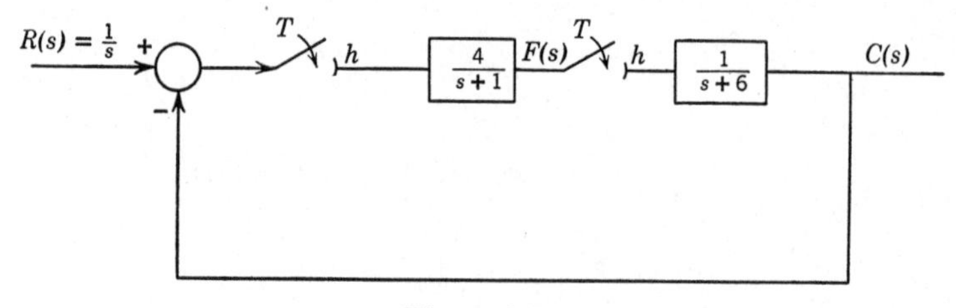

Figure 9.7

Problem 9.8 Calculate $c(t)$, the output of the system shown in Fig. 9.8a, when $T = 1$ second and $h = 0.5$ second.

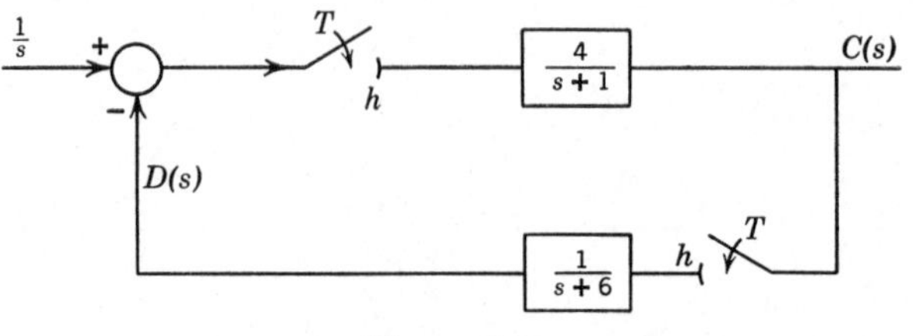

Figure 9.8a

Hint: This problem is identical to problem 9.7 because it can be redrawn as Fig. 9.8*b*, which can be solved for either $D(s)$ or $C(s)$.

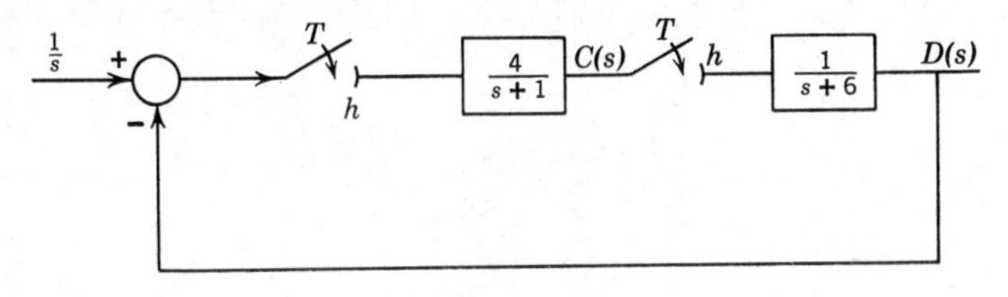

Figure 9.8*b*

Problem 9.9 Calculate the output of the system shown in Fig. 9.7, problem 9.7, if the time closure of the first sampler is $h_1 = 0.5$, $T = 1$ for both samplers and $h_2 = 0.2$ second. Plot the results.

Problem 9.10 Repeat problem 9.9 for the sampling period of the first sampler $T_1 = 1$ second, $h = 0.5$ for both samplers, and $T_2 = 2.5$ seconds.

Problem 9.11 Repeat problem 9.10 for the following constants:

$$T_1 = 1 \text{ second}$$

$$h_1 = 0.5 \text{ second}$$

$$T_2 = 2.5 \text{ seconds}$$

$$h_2 = 0.2 \text{ second}$$

Problem 9.12 In problem 9.7 let,

$$h = 1 \text{ second} = T$$

Show that the solution in this limiting case is equivalent to the continuous system.

INDEX